DISEASES OF COCOA

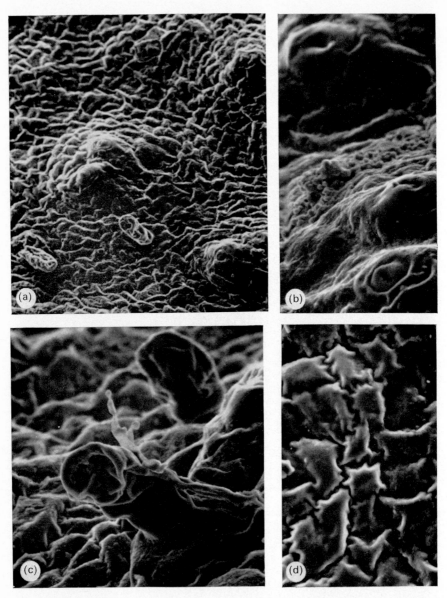

Scanning electron microscopy of the surface of a mature cocoa fruit (pod), showing (a) general features, × 300, (b) stomata on mounds, × 1000, (c) two hairs, one with a fungal hypha, × 1000, (d) outlines of epidermal cells, × 1000 (these magnifications are approximations). For further details, see text (page 49).

DISEASES OF
COCOA

BY

C. A. THOROLD

CLARENDON PRESS · OXFORD

1975

Oxford University Press, Ely House, London W. 1

GLASGOW NEW YORK TORONTO MELBOURNE WELLINGTON
CAPE TOWN IBADAN NAIROBI DAR ES SALAAM LUSAKA ADDIS ABABA
DELHI BOMBAY CALCUTTA MADRAS KARACHI LAHORE DACCA
KUALA LUMPUR SINGAPORE HONG KONG TOKYO

ISBN 0 19 854507 X

© OXFORD UNIVERSITY PRESS 1975

PRINTED IN GREAT BRITAIN
BY COX & WYMAN LTD
LONDON, FAKENHAM AND READING

FOREWORD

BY

PROFESSOR A. F. POSNETTE, ScD, AICTA, FRS

THE most recent book devoted entirely to diseases of the cocoa tree was published in 1934. The need for a new book on the subject would be obvious even if the past 40 years had not witnessed a spate of research into the causes of ill health in the crop and into the biology and control of the disease agents.

Throughout the nineteenth and twentieth centuries the history of cocoa production has followed a similar pattern of expansion and decline in country after country to which the crop has been introduced. In recent years some countries, of which Ghana is an example, have achieved a resurgence in production by extensive new planting and at least partial control of the pests and diseases responsible for the decline. In other countries, notably in South America and the West Indies, diseases sometimes aided by unrelated economic factors continue to constrain production despite man's efforts to expand it. On a world scale no crop seems so prone to diseases of serious consequences, partly, no doubt, because it thrives only in the wet, humid tropics where the climate favours the fungi and mitigates against their control by conventional chemical means.

Mr. Thorold has undertaken a formidable labour in consulting with superb thoroughness the extensive and dispersed literature on cocoa diseases of all kinds, and in then writing this compendium, which must surely remain the definitive work for very many years. He is well qualified for the task as he served for many years as a plant pathologist in countries where cocoa is grown under different systems—the large, long-established estates of Trinidad, with traditions reaching back more than two centuries, and the small farms of Ghana and Nigeria, mostly established in the last 60 years. It was typical of his ingenuity that he adopted calcium carbide imported into Nigeria (for acetylene lamps) as a substitute in Bordeaux mixture for lime, which was unobtainable there during the 1939–45 War. Encouraged by the long experience of spraying cocoa in Fernando Po and ably supported by his colleagues, Thorold used this novel mixture in Nigeria to institute large-scale spraying which proved very effective against black pod disease.

The publication of this book is timely. Production of cocoa has never for long, except in war years, exceeded world demand; the current shortage has resulted in a price attractive to the producing countries. Since rainfall cannot be regulated, increased yields must depend largely on disease control whilst the application of control measures depends in turn on a cocoa price adequate to pay for them. Interest in cocoa diseases is therefore intense wherever the crop is grown. Those concerned with this fascinating crop, be they research or extension workers, advisers, planters, or government administrators, should all find at least some parts of this book valuable reading if they wish to claim to have done their homework.

A.F.P.

East Malling Research Station,
Maidstone, Kent

PREFACE

'Savoir pour prévoir, afin de pourvoir'
Comte (1852)

THIS book considers the possibilities of increased production of cocoa per unit area through disease control, with or without using higher-yielding selections. In its widest sense as employed here, 'disease' implies deprivation, possibly leading to death. Greater productivity through better nutrition requires removal or amelioration of conditions prejudicial to optimum nutrient uptake, thereby implicating biotic and/or chemical and physical factors of the environment.

Injuries due directly to insect attack are excluded, but certain virulent disorders which cannot be accounted for entirely by insect damage are considered. In the practice of plant pathology, there may be no clear distinction between a morbid state being considered as a 'disease' or as due to the activity of a 'pest'. Chemicals used to control either 'disease' or 'pests' are now referred to comprehensively as 'pesticides' (Martin 1971).

In addition to interest deriving from localized economic importance of particular cocoa diseases, they give scope for speculation and investigation in connection with their geographical distributions.

Cocoa exemplifies topics arising from the theme of evolution through 'pest pressure' propounded by Gillett (1962, 1963). With cocoa, as with coffee (*Coffea arabica*), and rubber (*Hevea brasiliensis*), there has been 'escape' from pests and diseases in their homelands through major cultivations in alien continents (Purseglove 1968a). Great success attended the introduction of cocoa to West Africa, but pest pressure has operated there in the forms of insect-transmitted virus (Chapter 7), and of attack by mirids (Chapter 9). Recently extended cultivation of cocoa in New Guinea now has a new pathogen, belonging to a new genus (p. 164).

It is important to forestall possible pressure from pest and disease; there is no longer a 'new' continent to which cocoa can be taken to escape from them. As an aid to precognition, detailed consideration is given to the geography of reported occurrences of organisms associated with cocoa.

There is much information on cocoa diseases, which this book attempts to convert into useful knowledge. The pathology of cocoa involves many disciplines treated in a wide range of publications. A present aim is to aid the search for knowledge of particular aspects of diseases emanating from previous investigations, which the seeker may otherwise miss or repeat unprofitably. As has been stated for sociology, 'research is a relatively cheap commodity until it is ignored and then it becomes very expensive' (Bannister 1972).

The results of published work are cited according to the 'Harvard system' (Callow, Klyne, and Kurti 1965). References to unpublished work are cited by giving the author's name with initials, and date of correspondence (abbreviated indication as: *in litt*(eris)).

Twickenham   C. A. THOROLD
August 1973

ACKNOWLEDGMENTS

In the course of preparing this book over a period of more than a decade, many have helped me in various ways. It is difficult now to apportion my indebtedness, and some past assistance may be inadvertently overlooked in this ultimate expression of gratitude.

I have received much help in the preparation of the manuscript, and in other ways from the following: Mr. P. K. C. Austwick, Mr. G. Ayerst, Dr. J. Bolton, Dr. C. Booth, Mr. A. A. Brunt, Dr. E. E. Cheesman, Dr. G. W. Cooke, Mr. D. J. B. Copp, Mr. D. C. M. Corbet, Dr. R. K. Cunningham, Dr. D. F. Cutler, Mr. M. J. F. Duncan, Mr. P. F. Entwistle, Dr. S. D. Garrett, Mr. D. R. Glendinning, Dr. P. H. Gregory, Professor F. Hardy, Mr. P. Holliday, Dr. L. M. Hutchins, Dr. E. F. Iton, Dr. C. G. Johnson, Dr. F. G. W. Jones, Dr. R. H. Le Pelley, Mr. D. B. Murray, Dr. R. Nichols, Dr. A. F. Posnette, Professor J. W. Purseglove, Dr. J. Rishbeth, Mr. A. H. Strickland, Dr. J. M. Thresh, Dr. T. W. Tinsley, Mr. J. M. Todd, Mr. P. P. Watkins, Mr. A. L. Wharton, Dr. A. G. Whitehead, Dr. D. J. Williams, and Mr. G. A. R. Wood.

For advice on nomenclature and taxonomy of various groups, I am indebted to the directors and staffs of the Commonwealth Institute of Entomology, the Commonwealth Institute of Helminthology, the Commonwealth Mycological Institute, and the Royal Botanic Gardens, Kew, the keepers and staffs of the British Museum (Natural History), Departments of Botany, Entomology and Zoology including the Sub-Department of Ornithology, Tring. For other scientific and technical information and advice, I am indebted to the directors and staffs of the Commonwealth Bureau of Horticulture and Plantation Crops, the Tropical Products Institute, and the Tropical Stored Products Centre.

I am much indebted to Professor J. Heslop-Harrison, Mr. J. P. M. Brenan, and Dr. D. F. Cutler, Royal Botanic Gardens, Kew, for the provision of cocoa fruits, and for the study of them in the Jodrell Laboratory by scanning electron microscopy, on my behalf.

I thank Mr. and Mrs. J. R. G. Hadland, and Mr. A. Johnston, for help with translations, Mrs. M. A. Verity for drawing and lettering Maps 1 to 14, and Fig. 3, Miss V. Goaman for drawing Figs. 2, 4, 8(a) and 8(b), Mrs. J. Diment for typing preliminary and final versions of the manuscript, and my wife for library research and help with the preparation of the manuscript. I wish to record my grateful appreciation of the helpfulness of the Clarendon Press, Oxford, in facilitating the publication of this book.

I gratefully acknowledge permission to reproduce or adapt illustrations and photographs, from the Milwaukee Public Museum, Wisconsin, U.S.A. (Fig. 1); Arqgo. José García Payón, Jalapa, Mexico (Fig. 2); Professor S. H. Crowdy, University of Southampton, England (Figs. 5(a) and (b) and 6(a) and (b)); the Regents of the University of California, U.S.A. (Fig. 7); Major H. A. Dade, Mornington, Victoria, Australia (Fig. 8(a); the Royal Tropical Institute (Archives of the Koninklijk Instituut voor de Tropen), Amsterdam, the Netherlands (photograph was by Professor G. Stahel) (Fig. 8(b)); Dr. P. H. B. Talbot, the University of Adelaide, Waite Agricultural Research Institute, South Australia, Mr. P. J. Keane, the University of Papua and New Guinea, Boroko, Port Moresby, and Mr. B. J. Walby, editor-in-chief, the Commonwealth Scientific and Industrial Research Organization, East Melbourne, Victoria, Australia (Fig. 9). The photographs used for the frontispiece are subject to Crown Copyright, they are reproduced with the permission of the Controller of Her Majesty's Stationery Office and of the Director, Royal Botanic Gardens, Kew.

CONTENTS

CONVERSION TO S.I. UNITS

acre	...	0·405 hectare
ton (2240 pound)	...	1016 kilogram (1·016 metric ton (tonne))
pound	...	0·454 kilogram
ounce	...	28·4 gram
pound per acre	...	1·121 kilogram per hectare
gallon	...	4·55 litre
mile	...	1·609 kilometre
foot	...	0·305 metre
inch	...	2·54 centimetre

I

HISTORY AND GEOGRAPHY
OF COCOA

Introduction

Cocoa illustrates various facets of man's struggle against man and man's struggle against nature. The ancient use of cocoa in Central America both for consumption (Popenoe 1919) and for currency (Prescott 1855) was ominous. The impact of cocoa on the Old World must be accredited to the Spanish Conquistadores, and its subsequent history has been stormy. Widlake (1963) referred to it as 'the bean of contention', and commented that 'cocoa is substantially different from almost any other commodity. The path to a coloured chocolate wrapper and Cadbury's Milk Tray is strewn with blight, rains, drought, a spot of smuggling and all the problems that go with a peasant industry'. The incitement of civil disturbance may be added to these horrors (p. 103).

In contrast to the nefariousness of cocoa, it is important to note its positive cultural influence (Thompson 1956). It stimulated trade and the accompanying spread of ideas throughout Central America. The single 'bean' (seed) was a unit of reckoning, and one outcome was the ability of the Maya to handle large numbers. Another attribute was their framework of time which apparently developed earlier in the lowland cocoa areas than in the highlands. Cocoa-bean currency was confined to Central America, with the implication of restricted availability, which would probably be associated with the product of an introduced plant, rather than with the product of an indigenous one. Consequently, money did grow on trees there, as noted by Martyr (1612).

Nomenclature

The word 'cacao', with variations in pronunciation and spelling, occurs in Maya dialects. Thompson (1956) considered that the Náhuatl (Aztec) term 'cacauatl' derives from the Maya 'cacau' rather than the reverse. He depicted and discussed the cacau glyph (Thomas 1888; Thompson 1962, 1972a, b), which may have been pronounced as a disyllable (Thompson, J. E. S. 1972 in litt.). However, the possible phoneticism of Maya glyphs is controversial (Weaver 1972). In this book I adopt the English word 'cocoa' for both the plant and the product. Some writers prefer 'cacao' as the trivial name which consequently appears as an alternative in some quotations and literature citations.

Plants of the assemblage here termed cocoa are all potentially interfertile and referable to a single species (*Theobroma cacao* L.). Cuatrecasas (1964) subdivided *T. cacao* botanically into subspecies and forms, based mainly on plants currently in cultivation and partly on plants that may be relicts of ancient cultivation which are here referred to as 'feral' cocoa. Cocoa with a 'vine-like' habit, reported by Miranda (1962) from Caribal Lacanja, Zona Lacandones, Chiapas, Mexico, was described by Cuatrecasas (1964) as *T. cacao* subspecies *cacao* forma *lacandonense* (Table 1.1). It is interesting to note the pre-Columbian (A.D. 527 ± 136) representation of a vine-like cocoa plant on 'Monument 21' at Bilbao (Santa Lucia Cotzumalhuapa), in the adjacent area of southern Guatemala (Thompson 1948; Parsons 1969), shown in Fig. 1. Near Yoxihá, in the same region, Blom and La Farge (1926) found cocoa trees which they considered might

FIG. 1.   Cocoa plant shown in bas-relief on Monument 21 (Parsons 1969), measuring *ca.* 4×4 m. at Bilbao, Cotzumalhuapa, Guatemala.

FIG. 2. Cocoa tree shown in bas-relief on the tablet measuring about 1·3 × 1·3 m. from El Tajín, now at Instituto Nacional de Antropologia e Historia, Jalapa, Veracruz, Mexico (García Payón 1936).

be remnants of a Maya 'plantation'. Fig. 2 shows a cocoa tree with more conventional habit, which is shown on the tablet from the Late Classic Period (A.D. 600–900) site at El Tajín, Veracruz, Mexico (García Payón 1936; Marquina 1964; Weaver 1972), now at Jalapa, Mexico (Kampen 1972).

In this book, it is convenient to use the simpler primary subdivision of cocoa into two main groups (termed 'criollo' and 'forastero') based on fruit and bean characters as originally suggested by Morris (1887), and subsequently adopted by Cheesman (1932a, 1938, 1944c), and by Cuatrecasas

(1964) with the addition of another grouping (termed 'Trinitario') having uncertain status. No literal significance attaches now to the translations of the three terms used here for both cultivated and feral cocoa, namely criollo and forastero as 'native' and 'foreign' respectively (Cheesman 1944*c*), and Trinitario as 'native of Trinidad' (Purseglove 1968*b*). It is believed that a different cocoa population was introduced into Trinidad about 30 years after the predominantly criollo plantings there were affected by the so-called 'blast' in about 1727 (see pp. 60, 114). Pound (1932*a*) believed that variability was enhanced by crossing with criollo remnants. Subsequently, Trinitario cocoa was conventionally regarded as the outcome of inter-breeding between criollo and forastero (Cheesman 1944*c*; Cuatrecasas 1964; Purseglove 1968*b*). An alternative suggestion is that Trinitario populations have derived naturally from the segregating *T. cacao* populations which presumably existed before man inhabited the Continent of America.

Perez Arbelaez (1937) referred to 'trinitario (de Venezuela)', and stated that 'forastero' was brought from Trinidad in 1825 to Venezuela. It has been assumed that this was a re-introduction, on the supposition that Trinidad cocoa may have come originally from Venezuela (Shephard 1932*a*). Cuatrecasas (1964) suggested that Trinitario cocoa probably originated in the Venezuelan Orinoco basin, whence it was brought to Trinidad. It is not known whether early interchanges of cocoa were by seed or by seedlings. Since the viability of cocoa seeds is conserved with diffi-culty (Purseglove 1968*b*), it is likely that early introductions were by plants. Therefore it is interesting to note that a single plant may provide a diverse progeny. In Ceylon (now Sri Lanka), van Buuren (1928) studied the pro-geny of a single tree, which had originated in Trinidad (Wright 1903; Lock 1904, 1911). He classified this sibling progeny of 609 bearing trees into groups according to the pod-form nomenclature of van Hall (1914). There was a full range of criollo (e.g. angoleta and cundeamor), and forastero (e.g. amelonado and calabacillo) pod and bean characters. A single-tree progeny studied in Trinidad, was similar qualitatively (Pound 1933*b*). Such single-tree progenies constitute Trinitario mixtures.

In botanical taxonomy, the terms 'variety' (*varietas*), 'form' (*forma*), and 'type' (*typus*) have stringent applicabilities, therefore they should be avoided when needed for less exacting purposes, as commonly in agri-culture, horticulture, and sylviculture. The terms 'clone' and 'selection' are used here for cocoa at subspecific level. Clone accords with the defini-tions of the International Code of Nomenclature for Cultivated Plants (Gilmour, Horne, Little, Stafleu, and Richens 1969), in which the 'cultivar' (from *culti*vated *vari*ety) is the lowest category under which names are recognized. Cultivars differ in their modes of reproduction which for present purposes may be either a 'clone' derived by asexual (vegetative) propagation, or similar lines of normally self-fertilizing, or cross-fertilizing individuals, or an assemblage of individuals reconstituted on each occasion by crossing (single-crosses, double-crosses, three-way crosses, top-crosses) as discussed by Glendinning (1967), and by Bartley (1971). The term 'selection' is used in the ordinary etymological sense (i.e. to pick out as best or most suitable), for a single individual, or imprecisely for its uncontrolled seedling progeny.

Countries are here referred to by names current since 1957, when the Gold Coast became the Republic of Ghana. Accordingly, the name Ghana is used even when referring to work done there before 1957. The name Gold Coast appears only in quotations and for citing publications. Some other changes to be noted are as follows, with earlier name and date (year) of change in brackets: Malawi (Nyasaland, 1964); Guyana (British Guiana, 1966); Sri Lanka (Ceylon, 1972); Belize (British Honduras, 1973).

For the United Republic of Cameroon (1972), it is convenient to indicate the regions corresponding with the former British (Cameroon (S.W.)), and French (Cameroon (S.E.)) United Nations Trust Territories, which constituted the Federal Republic of Cameroon (1961).

The name 'Congo' is retained as a geographical entity because many early records do not indicate localization in either the Republic of Zaire (formerly Democratic Republic of Congo (Kinshasa)), or in the Peoples' Republic of the Congo (Brazzaville).

To show the geographical distributions of organisms associated with cocoa, the following global divisions are used, with countries listed alphabetically:*

AFRICA: without subdivision into central, eastern, or western areas (Maps 9–13).

CENTRAL AMERICA: for convenience includes Mexico (Maps 1 and 2).

NORTH AMERICA: United States (U.S.A.); Mexico excluded.

SOUTH AMERICA: (Maps 3–6).

WEST INDIES: (Maps 7 and 8).

EUROPE: includes the Soviet Union (U.S.S.R.).

ASIA and AUSTRALASIA: (Map 14).

The subdivision of the eastern hemisphere accords with 'Wallace's Line' (Beddall 1969). This imaginary line starts from about longitude 128°E. and about latitude 10°N., and runs south-westwards, thereby allotting the Philippine Islands and the territories of Kalimantan, Sabah, and Sarawak to Asia, and the Territory of Papua and New Guinea, with West Irian, to Australasia. The course of the line between the other islands of the archipelago need not be considered now because organisms associated with cocoa have not been reported there.

* Maps 1–14 are on pp. 361–371.

Origin of cultivated cocoa

Prehistory

The western coast of South America may have been inhabited by man about 10000 B.C. (Martin 1973), but several millennia may have elapsed before the interior was inhabited and farmed (Sanders and Marino 1970). Cocoa plantings were seen about A.D. 1526 on the coast of Colombia near the present border of Ecuador (Prescott 1862), but cocoa was not considered to have been within the agricultural complex of pre-Columbian Peru (Willey 1971). There, common and lima beans (*Phaseolus* spp.) were grown in the 'oasis' valleys of the generally arid coast, as at Callejón de Huaylas, in the Department of Ancash, Peru, about 6000 B.C. (Kaplan, Lynch, and Smith 1973). Such a 'seed-culture' system would have been inappropriate for cocoa, which was probably established then as now in association with tropical 'vegeculture' (Harris 1972), based on cassava *Manihot* spp.), in the wetter interior regions. The latter system was practised in South America about 1000 B.C. (Sanders and Marino 1970), as indicated by the occurrence (dated *ca.* 700 B.C.) of 'budares' (ceramic griddles) at Momíl in north-western Colombia (Reichel-Dolmatoff 1957), and contemporaneously at Rancho Peludo in north-western Venezuela (Rouse and Cruxent 1963). These two sites are interesting in connection with the possibility that cocoa was taken, from a hypothetical gene centre somewhere in the Colombian-Venezuelan marches, to Central America to escape from witches' broom and Monilia diseases (Chapters 2 and 3).

Culturally associated with Momíl (Sinú area) was the Mompós area in northern Colombia (Willey 1971), with pre-Columbian agricultural ridged-fields at the confluence of the Cauca, Magdalena, and San Jorge rivers (Parsons and Denevan 1967). The Momíl and Mompós sites are about 200 miles from the Panama isthmus, so it seems likely that there was trade from this food-producing area to Central America, by sea or overland. Rancho Peludo at the base of Guajira Peninsula, close to the border with Colombia, was nearer to the hypothetical cocoa gene-centre (p. 8). Proximity to the Gulf of Venezuela and Lake Maracaibo may have favoured trade with Central America, because ability to navigate may have been acquired in these sheltered waters (Rouse and Cruxent 1963). However, there is little direct evidence to support the supposition of pre-Columbian trading between the north of South America and Central America. We do not know either the origin or destination of the cargo of cocoa beans encountered off the coast of Honduras (*ca.* A.D. 1502) during the fourth voyage of Columbus (Lothrop 1927; Strong 1935). There is some archaeological evidence for pre-Columbian transport from Colombia to Mexico (Lothrop 1952), which is supported by cultural affinities between these two regions (Reichel-Dolmatoff 1965). There is more evidence regarding trade within Central America, between Maya and Aztec civilizations (Chapman

1957). The success of the supposed pre-Columbian introduction of cocoa to Central America is indicated by the accounts of tribute to Tenochtitlan (Mexico City), and by an estimated average (pre-Columbian) yield of 1·9 lb. cocoa per tree in the present-day state of Guerrero, Mexico (King 1971), with presumptive absence of witches' broom and Monilia diseases then, as now.

Present occurrence of Theobroma and Herrania species

There is no evidence that any species of the genus *Theobroma* was growing in the Old World until after the discovery of the New World (Purseglove 1968*a*). For consideration of the botanical relationships of *Theobroma*, it is unnecessary to review all the genera of its family (Sterculiaceae). Within the limits of present knowledge, it is indisputable that there was no genus in the Old World with as close affinity to *Theobroma* as that of *Herrania*, which was also confined to the New World until members of both genera were dispersed by man in post-Columbian times. Schultes (1958) upheld the status of *Herrania* as a genus distinct from *Theobroma*, but he noted that it had previously been treated as a section or subgenus of *Theobroma*.

Cope (1953*a*) and Baker, Cope, Holliday, Bartley, and Taylor (1954) reported difficulty in finding ripe seeds of *Theobroma* and *Herrania* species in Colombia, due to the depredations of pods by monkeys and other animals (Chapter 5). These losses were comparable to the destruction of

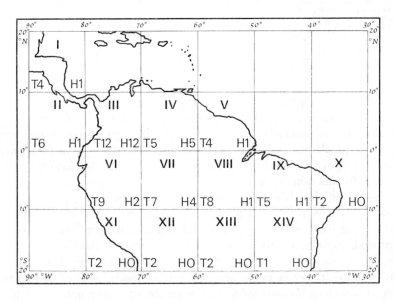

FIG. 3. Outline map of parts of Central and South America, divided into 10° latitude × 10° longitude 'squares' (I–XIV), to show sympatric occurrences of *Theobroma* (T), and *Herrania* (H) species (see Tables 1.1 and 1.2).

TABLE 1.1

Occurrences of Theobroma *species in 10° latitude × 10° longitude areas (squares I–XIV) of Central and South America, as shown in Fig. 3*

Area	I	II	III	IV	V	VI	VII	VIII	IX	X	XI	XII	XIII	XIV	Total
Theobroma species															
T. angustifolium Moçiño and Sessé	+	+													2
T. bernouillii Pittier (a)		+	+			+									3
T. bicolor Humb. and Bonpl.*	+	+	+	+	+	+	+	+	+	+					10
T. cacao L. (b)*	+	+	+	+	+	+	+	+	+	+	+	+	+	+	14
T. canumanense Pires and Froés								+							1
T. chocoense Cuatr.			+												1
T. cirmolinae Cuatr.			+												1
T. gileri Cuatr.			+												1
T. glaucum Karst			+	+		+									3
T. grandiflorum (Willd. ex Spreng.) Schum.								+	+						2
T. hylaeum Cuatr.			+												1
T. mammosum Cuatr. and León		+													1
T. microcarpum Mart.					+	+	+						+		4
T. nemorale Cuatr.			+												1
T. obovatum Klotzsch ex Bernoulli			+	+		+	+								4
T. simiarum Donn. Smith	+	+													2
T. sinuosum Pavón ex Huber						+									1
T. speciosum Willd.						+	+	+	+		+	+			6
T. stipulatum Cuatr.			+												1
T. subincanum Mart.			+	+	+	+	+	+	+						7
T. sylvestre Mart.							+	+							2
T. velutinum Benoist								+							1
Total	4	6	12	5	4	9	7	8	5	2	2	2	2	1	69

* Occurrences of *T. bicolor* and *T. cacao* are, to an unknown extent, due to human dispersal.
(a) *Theobroma bernouillii* Pittier, here includes the following subspecies (Cuatrecasas 1964)
    subspecies *asclepiadiflorum* (Schery) Cuatr.
    subspecies *bernouillii*
    subspecies *capilliferum* (Cuatr.) Cuatr.
(b) *Theobroma cacao* L., here includes the following subspecies and forms (Cuatrecasas 1964)
    subspecies *cacao*
    subspecies *cacao* forma *lacandonense* Cuatr.
    subspecies *cacao* forma *leiocarpum* (Bernoulli) Ducke
    subspecies *cacao* forma *pentagonum* (Bernoulli) Cuatr.
    subspecies *cacao* forma *sphaerocarpum* (Chevalier) Cuatr.

seeds of another plant in East Africa, due to an ovule-eating insect, reported by Gillett (1962) to exemplify the action of 'pest pressure', inducing the phenomenon of numerous species represented by few scattered individuals in tropical forests. The single hectare area of forest near Belém, Pará, Brazil, studied by Pires and Humberto M. Koury (1959), carried 539 individuals, representing fifty different species. There were twenty-six individuals of *T. cacao* and six individuals of *T. subincanum*. Another consequence of pest pressure discussed by Gillett (1962) was the tendency for pests to be more numerous and diversified where the species originated, compared with farther out in its range. In the north of South America, cocoa and related plants are uniquely affected by two diseases which destroy the seeds and/or seriously reduce yields (witches' broom and Monilia diseases). Accordingly, pest pressure will have operated within the affected area, which may contain the primary region of diversity, for which the term 'gene centre' was used (Leppik 1970).

TABLE 1.2

Occurrences of Herrania *species in 10° latitude × 10° longitude areas (squares I–IX) of Central and South America (no occurrences reported in areas X–XIV), as shown in Fig. 3*

Area	I	II	III	IV	V	VI	VII	VIII	IX	Total
Herrania species										
H. albiflora Goudot (a)			+							1
H. balaënsis Preuss			+							1
H. breviligulata R. E. Schultes			+							1
H. camargoana R. E. Schultes				+						1
H. cuatrecasana García-Barriga			+							1
H. dugandii García-Barriga			+				+			2
H. kanukuensis R. E. Schultes			+	+						2
H. kofanorum R. E. Schultes			+	+						2
H. laciniifolia Goudot ex Tr. and Planch.			+							1
H. lemniscata (Schomb.) R. E. Schultes			+	+						2
H. mariae (Mart.) Decaisne ex Goudot (b)							+	+	+	3
H. nitida (Poepp.) R. E. Schultes (c)					+	+	+			3
H. nycterodendron R. E. Schultes						+	+			2
H. pulcherrima Goudot (d)				+						1
H. purpurea (Pitt.) R. E. Schultes	+	+	+							3
H. tomentella R. E. Schultes			+							1
H. umbratica R. E. Schultes			+							1
Total	1	1	12	5	1	2	4	1	1	28

(a) *Herrania albiflora* Goudot, here includes the following form (Schultes 1958) forma *titanica* R. E. Schultes.

(b) *Herrania mariae* (Mart.) Decaisne ex Goudot, here includes the following variety (Schultes 1958) variety *putumayonis* R. E. Schultes.

(c) *Herrania nitida* (Poepp.) R. E. Schultes, here includes the following form (Schultes 1958) forma *sphenophylla* R. E. Schultes.

(d) *Herrania pulcherrima* Goudot, here includes the following variety (Schultes 1958) variety *pacifica* R. E. Schultes.

To consider the natural distribution of *Theobroma* and *Herrania* species, it is convenient to divide the northern part of South America and the whole of Central America diagrammatically into fourteen 'squares' (each 10° longitude × 10° latitude) as shown in Fig. 3, but for convenient presentation truncated at the north-west extremity, with indication of the number of species of *Theobroma* (T1–T12), and the number of species of *Herrania* (H0–H12) occurring within each area (square). The details of species and occurrences are shown in Tables 1.1 and 1.2, using the nomenclature and other information given by Schultes (1958) and by Cuatrecasas (1964).

It is important to note that sympatric occurrences of *Theobroma* and *Herrania* species in particular squares do not necessarily indicate a sharing of the same site, because their habitats may differ. Baker *et al.* (1954) and

Schultes (1958) explained that the ecological requirements of most *Herrania* species seem to be less exacting than those of *T. cacao*, and possibly of some other *Theobroma* species. It is interesting to note that the exploitation of different habitats by *Herrania* and *Theobroma* species is associated with different seed sizes, which are smaller for *Herrania* species (*ca.* 1 cm. long) than for *Theobroma* species (> 1 cm. long). Harper, Lovell, and Moore (1970) commented that 'in pairs of related species occupying open and closed communities it is normal to find the larger-seeded species in the more closed community'.

Fig. 3 shows the greatest frequency of *Theobroma* and *Herrania* species in square III, followed by square VI for *Theobroma* species. However, the diversity of species in the region composing squares III and VI, which comprises parts of Colombia, Ecuador, Panama, Peru, and Venezuela, may reflect the disproportionately greater amount of botanical work done there (Pound 1943*a*, *b*; Baker *et al.* 1954), compared with square IV (Cuatrecasas 1964; Dennis 1970).

The finding of populations with diverse pod characters by Pound (1938) in the area of the upper headwaters of the Amazon (Rios Caqueta, Napo, and Putumayo) had suggested that the hypothetical gene centre of cocoa might be there (i.e. between the southern part of square III and the northern part of square VI). Further exploration brought disillusion because the criollo group was poorly represented (Baker 1953*b*; Cheesman 1953). The predominance of forastero-group characteristics in the Amazon basin was confirmed by subsequent expeditions (Soria 1970).

In the parts of Ecuador and Colombia which contain the northern tributaries of the Amazon, and the southern tributaries of the Orinoco, the pods of trees characterized as criollo were generally unpigmented (Baker 1953*b*; Baker *et al.* 1954). In the parts of eastern Colombia and western Venezuela which contain the northern tributaries of the Orinoco (between squares III and IV), the range of criollo characters was much greater (Perez Arbelaez 1937; Bartley 1964*b*). Even if the location of the gene centre of *T. cacao* is not demonstrable there, it seems likely that 'Upper Orinoco' selections may in the future provide material for plant breeders of value comparable with that of Upper Amazon selections today.

2

WITCHES' BROOM DISEASE

Introduction

Over-development (hyperplasia) is a common traumatic response shown by plant parts, including those of cocoa. Hypertrophied and proliferated growths that give rise to the term 'witches' brooms' are in the case of cocoa uniquely due to attack by a member of the Agaricaceae (Holliday 1971). This pathogen (*Crinipellis perniciosa*, formerly *Marasmius perniciosus*) fructifies on dead tissues (Fig. 4A(*b*)). The characteristic 'mushrooms', here termed 'basidiocarps' (Ainsworth 1971), may or may not be evident at the start of an epiphytotic.

There are general accounts of witches' broom disease by Nowell (1923), Briton-Jones (1934), Baker and Holliday (1957), Desrosiers (1960), Burle (1961), Braudeau (1969), and Holliday (1952, 1970a, 1971).

Geographical distribution

C.M.I. Distribution Map No. 37 (2nd ed. 1965) shows that witches' broom disease is confined to part of the New World cocoa-area. It is widespread in lowland tropical South America (Bolivia, Brazil, Colombia, Ecuador, Guyana, Peru, Surinam, and Venezuela) and it occurs in the West Indies (Grenada, Tobago, and Trinidad). Relevant literature references are given in Chapter 12 (p. 180).

Economic importance

Surinam was seriously affected by witches' broom disease. Production there increased from 1870 until 1895 when the disease was reported (Stahel 1945). From 1905 to 1912, some cocoa fields were cleared for other crops (e.g. banana and Liberica coffee). The downward trend from 1895 may not have been due entirely to witches' broom disease (Reyne 1921). The industry's prospects have since improved through new plantings and rehabilitation of old ones (Krug and Quartey-Papafio 1964). Guyana's cocoa exports ceased from 1923 to 1930 through debilitation of trees and reduced acreage associated with spread of the disease (Altson 1926a; Dash 1931). There have been attempts to revive production (Kitching 1954). Witches' broom was reported in the Balao region of Ecuador about 1921 and by 1926 this disease had spread to all producing areas (Stell 1933; Fowler and López 1949). However, there are no data for differentiating

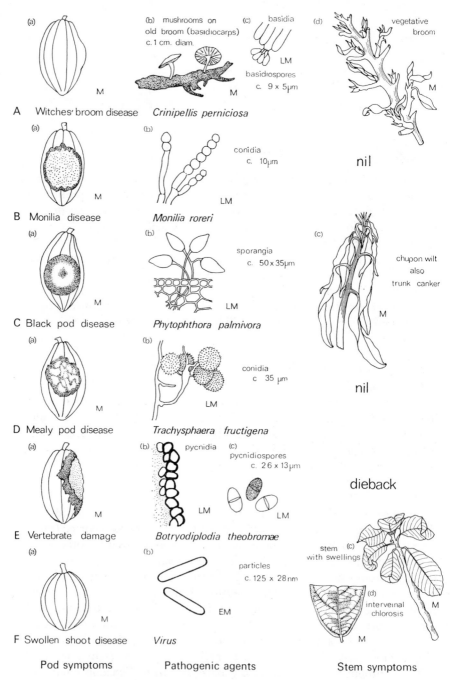

A Witches' broom disease · *Crinipellis perniciosa*

(a) M · (b) mushrooms on old broom (basidiocarps) c. 1 cm. diam. M · (c) basidia LM · basidiospores c. 9 × 5μm · (d) vegetative broom M

B Monilia disease · *Monilia roreri*

(a) M · (b) conidia c. 10μm LM · nil

C Black pod disease · *Phytophthora palmivora*

(a) M · (b) sporangia c. 50 × 35μm LM · (c) chupon wilt also trunk canker M

D Mealy pod disease · *Trachysphaera fructigena*

(a) M · (b) conidia c 35 μm LM · nil

E Vertebrate damage · *Botryodiplodia theobromae*

(a) M · (b) pycnidia LM · (c) pycnidiospores c. 26 × 13μm LM · dieback · (c) stem with swellings M · (d) interveinal chlorosis M

F Swollen shoot disease · *Virus*

(a) M · (b) particles c. 125 × 28nm EM

Pod symptoms Pathogenic agents Stem symptoms

FIG. 4. Diagram showing macroscopic (M), microscopic (light microscope (LM), and electron microscope (EM)) features characterizing six cocoa diseases (A–F).

between the damage done by witches' broom and Monilia diseases (see Chapter 3). Two areas comprising several hundred acres were already affected when witches' broom disease was recognized in Trinidad in 1928 (Stell 1928). This disease may then have been present there for some years. The cocoa planters' difficulties were already considerable when the incidence of witches' broom caused further financial losses (Shephard 1932c). This disease was initially severe in the eastern side of Trinidad where the Department of Agriculture in July 1929 acquired a cocoa property, named Marper Estate (from *Marasmius perniciosus*), for witches' broom investigations (Shephard 1937b). The disease spread westwards and in the period 1930 to 1938 reached the Diego Martin valley near Port of Spain and became common at River Estate, where witches' broom investigations started in 1939. Subsequently this Estate was closed (Murray 1967) and part of Las Hermanas Estate was developed as a Cocoa Research Scheme substation (Murray 1959). Losses at Marper Estate increased from 1 per cent in 1932–3 to 10–12 per cent in 1939–40 (Baker and McKee 1943). Losses were greater (75 per cent infection) in certain fields at River Estate (Baker and Dale 1944a, b, c). Improved production in Trinidad was anticipated through subsidized replanting (de Verteuil and Moll 1960). Padwick (1956) commented that losses were difficult to assess because some decline in production was associated with rapid spread of the disease, but part was due to poor prices and war conditions.

Host range

C. *perniciosa* attacks species of the genus *Herrania* (*H. albiflora, H. nitida*, and *H. purpurea*) in Trinidad (Bartley and Iton 1959), and *H.* sp. (Pound 1938) in Colombia. Baker and Holliday (1957) discussed the symptomatology of *Theobroma* species affected in South America (*T. bicolor* (Stahel 1919, 1932; Holliday 1955), *T. glaucum* (Baker, Cope, Holliday, Bartley, and Taylor 1954), *T. grandiflorum* (Pound 1938), *T. microcarpum* (Baker *et al.* 1954), *T. obovatum* (Baker *et al.* 1954), *T. speciosum* (Stahel 1915), *T. subincanum* (Baker *et al.* 1954; Holliday 1955)). These seven species are not all certainly alternative hosts for witches' broom disease of cultivated cocoa, because comprehensive cross-inoculations were not attempted. Through pathogenic specialization of *C. perniciosa* (p. 18), host species may be affected differentially.

C. *perniciosa* basidiocarps occur on woody tissues of other plants when in contact with fructifying brooms (Baker and Holliday 1957). Desrosiers and von Buchwald (1949) saw basidiocarps which appeared to be those of *C. perniciosa* on dead lianes, bamboo, and unidentified wood, near Coca, upper River Napo, Ecuador.

Symptoms

Vegetative tissue

The kind of broom produced depends on the age and nature of the tissue attacked. In this connection, it is necessary to note the dimorphic branching habit of cocoa (Pyke 1934*b*). There are 'fan' branches with leaves arranged in two ranks, and 'chupons' which have a spiral phyllotaxis. A vegetative broom results from infection of a bud, the development of which is referred to as a 'flush' and provides the first sign of infection. Instead of growing normally, such a bursting bud develops into a dense, generally somewhat curved growth, through excessive development of lateral shoots and

(a)   (b)

FIG. 5.   Vegetative brooms. (a) shows a 'grown-through' broom; (b) shows a very small lateral fan-broom (arrowed) (Baker and Crowdy 1943).

shortening of the internodes (Fig. 4A(*d*)). The lamina of a leaf may not appear to be abnormal except for thickening of the leaf-stalk, and the pulvinus is often swollen. Frequently though, leaves remain small, particularly the apical ones. Stipules are generally larger than normal and persistent. Vigorous shoots may grow away from the infection and then a 'grown-through' broom results (Fig. 5(a)). This expression was used by Stahel (1915), as a translation of the original term *doorgroeide*, or *durchgewachsenen*. On fan branches, brooms may be either grown-through, terminal (leading bud infected), or lateral (axillary bud infected). On chupons, brooms may be either grown-through, or terminal.

Large brooms are produced at the beginning of a flush, but hypertrophy is less marked when older tissues are attacked. Some brooms are inconspicuous, as when an infected bud dies (Fig. 5(b)). Occasionally, infections are not associated with buds, then there is a roughening and swelling of the twig, with internal discoloration, later developing into a canker (Baker and Crowdy 1943).

Cortex, phloem, and xylem may all exceed normal thickness. There is

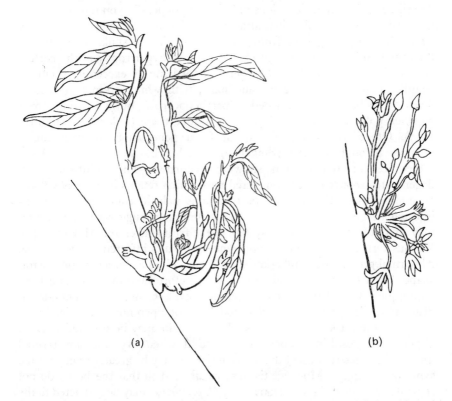

(a)   (b)

FIG. 6. Cushion brooms. (a) mainly with vegetative shoots, (b) with mainly 'star blooms' (Baker and Crowdy 1943).

generally proliferation of parenchyma cells which remain undifferentiated. Fibres tend to disappear and cork is rarely formed (Went 1904).

Inflorescence tissues

The reduced flowering shoots known as 'cushions' (Dade 1929b; Lent 1966) are infected, sometimes leading to the production of leafy brooms similar in character to vegetative brooms (Fig. 6(a)), but with less proliferation of axillary buds than on fans. At other times, cushion infection results in production of abnormal flowers (Fig. 6(b)) known as 'star blooms' (Stahel 1919). Infected flowers may be abnormally large, with thickened stalks, so that these flowers stand out from the cushion, instead of hanging limply as normally. Infected flowers persist, unlike normal ones which absciss after 3 days (Baker and McKee 1943).

Fruits

Stahel (1919) differentiated between 'direct infection' (by spores) and 'indirect infection' (by mycelium). Dale (1946) inoculated fruits and described various manifestations of infection, depending on mode of infection and on age of fruit when attacked. Fruits may be infected indirectly by hyphae entering them from the cushion via the stalk. The latter is thickened and no ovules are produced. Due to hypertrophy of the cortex, such fruits are rounded or strawberry-shaped, rarely exceeding 6 cm. in length, finally becoming black and hard, with white internal mycelium. These fruits have been described as 'parthenocarpic', but it was not known whether pollination was required to produce them (Baker and Holliday 1957). Other fruit symptoms result from penetration by germ-tubes, possibly through stomata (Stahel 1919). Cherelles (see Chapter 6) are sometimes infected without showing distortion. The uninfected part degenerates sooner than the infected part which retains its normal colour. In cross-section, the infected part remains pale in colour after the uninfected tissue has turned brown. This difference suggests that infection may affect the normal oxidase system of the fruit (Baker and McKee 1943). Various terms were given to appearances of fruits infected at later stages. Abnormal growth after infection at ca. 1 cm., gives a characteristic 'carrot' shape. Such fruits may attain 12–15 cm., before becoming dry and hard with liquefaction of the beans. Infection at ca. 2–5 cm., causes a one-sided distortion (Fig. 4A(a)). 'Distorted pods' do not ripen normally. The beans adhere to the husk and are useless. Larger fruits may be infected without hypertrophy resulting. They become hard when dry and are termed 'indurated'. Destruction of the internal tissues may be greater than external symptoms suggest. Mucilage tissues are affected so that the beans do not separate as in normal pods. Damage by *C. perniciosa* may be restricted to the husk, causing a black necrotic speckling with slight browning of the beans, but if the pod is picked promptly no beans are lost.

The cause of a pod disease may be uncertain through the simultaneous presence of two or more pod-rotting fungi. Sectioning and staining with cotton blue-lactophenol may reveal the characteristic mycelium of *C. perniciosa* ramifying in the mucilage canals of the infected area.

Causal fungus

Abnormal growths were seen in Surinam before 1895 (Stell 1928), and there were subsequent attempts to identify the pathogen. Ritzema Bos (1900*a*) in the Netherlands examined dry brooms from Surinam and, on the basis of a few asci on two leaves, he gave the name *Exoascus theobromae* to this fungus, which he believed had caused the brooms. Howard (1901*a*) found *Fusarium* on preserved brooms from Surinam and stated that neither J. H. Hart nor G. Massee found the *Exoascus* reported by Ritzema Bos. Went (1904) examined fresh brooms and found intercellular mycelium, but his inoculations were unsuccessful. Van Hall, C. J. J. and Drost (1907, 1909) found a fungus associated with brooms and indurated pods, which they described as *Colletotrichum luxificum*. Despite negative results from inoculations, they claimed that it caused witches' brooms. Rorer (1913) examined Surinam material and found the fungus with clamp-connections (Ainsworth 1971), which Stahel (1915) described as *Marasmius perniciosus*, causing vegetative brooms. Subsequently, Stahel (1919) showed that an identical fungus caused cushion brooms and indurated pods. Singer (1942) transferred the species to the genus *Crinipellis*, and this was upheld by Dennis (1951) and Holliday (1970*a*).

In addition to the diagnosis of *Crinipellis perniciosa* (Stahel) Singer (1942), there are descriptions by Holliday (1970*a*) and by Dennis (1951). The latter illustrated *C. perniciosa* in colour and likewise saprobic species of *Marasmius* with which it may be confused. The saprobes have dark- or light-coloured stalks. The stalk of *C. perniciosa* is white at first, darkening later.

Culture

Baker and Holliday (1957) summarized observations of *C. perniciosa* in pure culture on various media. Slow and irregular growth produced a felt of white or pinkish mycelium. Neither basidiocarps nor any resting form occurred in cultures. Clamp-connections appeared, including cultures started from single spores, showing that the fungus is homothallic. Presumably, every infection is potentially capable of producing basidiocarps.

Biochemistry

C. perniciosa formed an extra-cellular catecholase when grown on nutrient solutions (Lindeberg 1948*a,b*). Cellulose and lignin were decomposed readily, but the nutritional requirements of the witches' broom fungus did not differ essentially from those of saprobic *Marasmius* species (Lindeberg and Molin 1949).

A pathogen may induce excessive and abnormal branching through disturbance of auxin balance (Brian 1957), but relevant studies by Nichols (1959*a*) and Dudman and Nichols (1959) were inconclusive for *C. perniciosa*. Krupasagar and Sequeira (1969) showed that certain pathogenic effects of *C. perniciosa* may be associated with production of auxin-inactivating systems.

Pathogenic specialization

It is uncertain whether or not *T. cacao* is susceptible to some *C. perniciosa* isolates which infect other species of *Theobroma*. Pound (1938) observed abundant vegetative brooms on *T. grandiflorum* at Belém, Brazil, but only some of the intermixed cocoa trees were affected. Cross-inoculations there showed that *C. perniciosa* infected both *T. cacao* and *T. grandiflorum* (Gonçalves 1965). However, in Trinidad, *T. grandiflorum* trees were not infected by *C. perniciosa* (Murray 1964*a*).

At La Pedrera, both *T. cacao* and *T. subincanum* trees had witches' brooms, but elsewhere in Colombia the cultivated cocoa was without brooms when the other species was affected (Baker 1953*b*; Cope 1953*a*).

Variation

Dark red basidiocarps produced on brooms from Ecuador were considered by Stahel (1923) to justify a new variety. His *Marasmius perniciosus* var. *ecuadoriensis* was insufficiently described for validity, and remains unsubstantiated by later workers.

C. perniciosa isolates in Ecuador, and Trinidad differ in pathogenicity (Bartley and Chalmers 1970; Chalmers 1972*b*), but varietal separation seems unjustifiable (Baker and Holliday 1957; Bartley 1964*a*; Chalmers 1969, 1970*a, b*).

Infection

Basidiocarp production

For studies in Trinidad of circumstances associated with production of basidiocarps (formerly termed 'sporophores'), Baker and Crowdy (1943, 1944) used the expression 'sporophore index' (number of basidiocarps per week per 100 brooms). Size of broom, stage of necrosis, rainfall, and humidity were important factors. Brooms normally became 'dry' 5–6 weeks after formation, a dormant period followed before basidiocarp production started at about 20–25 weeks. Basidiocarp production continued as long as brooms were retained on the tree. Fallen brooms seldom produced basidiocarps, either through being overgrown by saprobes or because conditions on the ground were too wet. Under suitable conditions, dry brooms will produce basidiocarps after removal from the tree, even young green ones will eventually do so. Basidiocarps will form on dry pods, but not when the tissue remains turgid. Extremes of wetness or dryness inhibit basidiocarp growth, but resumption may soon follow return of favourable conditions. Many brooms persisted on trees for more than a year, but few survived for more than 2 years.

Spore production

In Surinam, basidiocarps produced spores (Fig. 4A(c)) when the pileus was only 2–3 mm. diameter, and continued to do so after it was fully expanded (Stahel 1919). In Trinidad (Baker and Crowdy 1943), spores were shed from mature basidiocarps when temperature ranged from about 14 °C. (57 °F.) to 29 °C. (85 °F.), if there was sufficient moisture to keep the pileus turgid and fully expanded. Basidiocarps recovered from desiccation and deposited spores again when moistened. Spore deposition started between 5 p.m. and 8 p.m. and continued throughout the night and early morning, until the temperature was too high after sunrise. Under controlled conditions, the length of time during which a basidiocarp would deposit its spores varied with the temperature, ranging from about 4 hours at 28 °C. (83 °F.) to a maximum of 24 hours at 15·5 °C. (60 °F.).

Spore germination

C. perniciosa spores germinated readily in water or in a saturated atmosphere, but a short exposure to a low humidity was considered fatal (Stahel 1915; Baker and Crowdy 1943). Germination may start 2 hours after deposition and be almost complete 4 hours later. If a spore does not cause an infection on the night it is shed, it is likely to be killed the next day. Good germination (30–54 per cent) resulted from young basidiocarps, but germination of spores from old basidiocarps was impeded, probably through bacterial contamination. Spores from artificially cooled basidiocarps germinated poorly (Baker and McKee 1943).

Host penetration

Stahel (1919) observed the entrance of germ-tubes into stomata of leaves and fruits within a few hours. He did not find evidence for penetration of the ovary cuticle and he presumed that infection occurred after fertilization when the first stomata were formed. Studies by Holliday (1955) indicated that intact cuticle might be penetrated, if sufficiently embryonic tissue was present.

Natural infection

C. perniciosa spores are small and light, so they may be airborne, but will soon lose their viability if the air is below saturation (Baker, Crowdy, and Thorold 1941). An infection gradient was evident at River Estate, where

Field 7 was planted with ICS clones (Cheesman 1941*a,b*), and was severely attacked from the adjoining Field 6 where the trees were infested with brooms producing basidiocarps. The effect of this source was serious for about 100 yards (90 m.) in the direction of the prevailing wind. Dispersal followed the pattern of infection shown by other airborne fungus diseases in the great importance of dissemination over short distances (Baker and Holliday 1957). Long-distance dispersal is presumed but unsubstantiated (Stahel 1935; Pound 1938; Holliday 1962; Baker 1966).

Artificial inoculation

The stage at which the developing shoot or fruit is infected markedly influences the symptoms produced (Baker and Holliday 1957). Details were given of procedures for inoculating vegetative tissues (Baker and Crowdy 1943), and for cushions and fruits (Baker and McKee 1943; Dale 1946).

Possible dispersal by human agency

There was an unpublished report that witches' broom occurred in Java (Hubert 1957). Ostendorf, F. W. (1963 *in litt.*) explained that cocoa fruits which had been treated with paraffin wax were introduced into Java about 1932–3. This material was destroyed when live mycelium with clamp-connections was found under the layer of wax. This suspected introduction of *C. perniciosa* would not have been an immediate hazard to healthy cocoa since attempts to induce its mycelium to cause infection were unsuccessful (Stahel 1919). Witches' broom disease was not reported in the upper Cauca valley of Colombia, despite introductions of cocoa from the Pacific coast region where the disease occurred (Pound 1938; Baker and Holliday 1957).

Predisposing factors

Basidiocarp incidence

The supply of spores was important even in heavily infested areas. There was a highly significant positive correlation between sporophore index (p. 18) and number of brooms produced 5 weeks later, which suggested that the brooms developed with one flush were initiated during the previous one. Intervals between flushes varied from 35–100 days. Infection at time of flowering was followed shortly by cushion broom production, without having to await the next flush, as for vegetative brooms (Baker and Crowdy 1944).

Temperature

The minimum temperature for *C. perniciosa* corresponds with the 'cold limit' for commercial cocoa-production (15 °C. (60 °F.)), as discussed by Hardy (1958). At low elevations in tropical countries, there are generally nightly temperature regimes with periods of at least the 4 hours required for spore germination, above this minimum and below the maximum (29 °C. (85 °F.)), which latter will be commonly exceeded during the day.

Humidity

In Trinidad at night, the humidity was generally suitable for spore germination, since it ranged from near saturation to about 90 per cent R.H. (Baker and Crowdy 1943). In the River Guayas area of Ecuador, spread of witches' broom disease was favoured through humidity provided by the 'garúa' tending to be higher in the 'dry' season than in the 'wet' season (Erneholm 1948).

Rainfall

Rain influences basidiocarp production, but in Trinidad the correlation between sporophore index and rainfall was positive but not significant (Baker and Crowdy 1943). There is generally optimum development of witches' broom disease with evenly distributed annual rainfall in the range 60–90 in. (1,524–2,286 mm.) (Baker and Holliday 1957). Erneholm (1948) stated that witches' broom 'has now spread to almost every part of tropical South America in which the cultivation of cacao is possible without irrigation'. He noted that witches' broom was not present in the dry parts of Manabi Province, Ecuador, where cocoa must be irrigated. Inland from the Pacific coast, rainfall increased two-fold from 39 in. (991 mm.), to over 79 in. (2,007 mm.), in about 62 miles (100 km.). Near Chiclayo, Lambayique Province, Peru, witches' broom did not occur (Alvim, P. de T. 1962 *in litt.*) in cocoa grown with irrigation, because rainfall averaged about 4 in. (102 mm.), per year (Alvim 1960).

There is conflicting evidence concerning the possible effect of much rain on the incidence of witches' broom disease. In Trinidad, sporophore index values diminished in the course of three consecutive weeks with 9–14 in. (229–356 mm.), rain per week (Baker and Crowdy 1943). Baker and Holliday (1957) suggested that very damp atmospheres in the higher parts of Trinidad Northern Range valleys might account for the disease not being serious there, through rainfalls in the range 120–80 in. (3,048–4,572 mm.), per year. On the other hand, witches' broom disease was reported in the Tingo Maria region of the Andes foothills at 2,000 ft. (610 m.), altitude, with rainfall about 120 in. (3,048 mm.), per year (Pound 1943a).

Flushing and flowering

Seasonal periodicities in the manifestation of witches' broom disease are associated with flushing and flowering, in relation to basidiocarp production. Inoculation experiments demonstrated the importance of shoot immaturity for infection (Baker and Crowdy 1943). Successful inoculations (40 per cent) were achieved when developing buds were used. When some flush leaves were 1·5 in. (38·1 mm.) long, 13 per cent of the inoculations were successful. When some leaves had reached full size, 7 per cent of the inoculations were successful. When leaves had hardened and a dormant bud had formed, inoculations were unsuccessful

Age of host

Symptom expression by particular clones and selections has varied inexplicably over a period of time in Trinidad (Baker 1943a, 1953a; Pound 1943a) and in Ecuador (Desrosiers, Bolaños, and Vargas 1955).

Host nutrition

Bartley (1959) showed that uniformly optimum greenhouse conditions were desirable for satisfactory expression of symptoms in connection with testing the resistance of cocoa seedlings to *C. perniciosa* (Holliday 1955). Varying reactions were attributable to unbalanced fertilizer applications to different batches of potting soil. Increased mortality was associated with extra nitrogen (Bartley and Amponsah 1967).

Tollenaar (1966) discussed leached volcanic-ash soils in the riverine area of Ecuador. The clone S.C.A. 6 (Enriquez and Soria 1967) was normally resistant to witches' broom disease, but had many vegetative brooms there when in an advanced stage of boron deficiency (Tollenaar 1967). Foliar applications of copper improve the appearance of the cocoa canopy (Tollenaar 1958), but this 'tonic effect' is not properly understood (Nichols 1961c). Nichols (1963) considered that yield increases associated with cuprous oxide applications were due to lessening of pathogenic infections, including those of *C. perniciosa*, rather than to a possible nutritional effect of copper on cocoa.

Unexplained 'disease escape'

Apparent absence of witches' broom disease in French Guiana may have been due to the cocoa being planted on high ground (Jacquet 1929), or to isolation of the small plantations (Meiffren and Braudeau 1963), or to certain 'drought' conditions (Fougerouze 1966). Myers (1934) did not find witches' brooms in the Kanuku mountains area, Rupununi district of Guyana. This absence may have been due to isolation, although the disease occurred in the interior of Surinam and along the River Kutari, near the border with Brazil (Stahel 1935). Chalmers (1970c) drew attention to enigmatic factors controlling 'disease escape', whereby some cocoa trees were without brooms when neighbouring trees were severely infected in Ecuador, and likewise in Venezuela (Posnette and Palma 1944).

Control

Sanitary methods

Ritzema Bos (1900a) recommended removal and burning of brooms. Removal of brooms is still advised, but recommendations regarding the severity and frequency of pruning have varied. Stahel (1915) emphasized the special attention necessary when removing grown-through brooms which were sometimes difficult to recognize. He advised cutting these brooms with a piece of the attached stem about 4 in. (10 cm.) long, to prevent possible development of further brooms from diseased tissue. Briton-Jones and Cheesman (1931) deplored the practice of cutting brooms at such a distance below the affected area, because it encouraged new shoots which frequently became infected. Briton-Jones (1934) explained the degree of pruning required in relation to amount of growth.

To avoid the possibility of leaving infected tissue, van Hall, C. J. J. and Drost (1909) had proposed 'pollarding' (removing the leafy parts entirely). This procedure was not generally adopted in Surinam because most estates could not afford the cost of treatment and the loss of crop involved. This procedure was further discredited when many pollarded trees died during the 1911–12 drought (Stahel 1915). Briton-Jones and Cheesman (1931) suggested 'semi-pollarding' (removing all growths up to 1 in., diameter), but this suggestion was not adopted in Trinidad. When no pruning was done in Surinam, there were large numbers of brooms with many fructifications (Wardlaw 1929). Severe incidence of the disease in Tobago in 1951 probably resulted from relaxation of control measures (Baker and Holliday 1957). Legislation for compulsory control was unenforceable (Thorold 1943a).

To minimize the cost of removing brooms whilst aiming at efficient control, Baker et al. (1941) advocated two clearances during the year in Trinidad, one in April–May, and another in October–November. This procedure was based on the experience that large numbers of brooms developed from January to March during the dry season when conditions were unsuitable for basidiocarp development. It was important to remove all brooms before the wet season started in May or June. Subsequent infections might occur and brooms might develop from July onwards, but they would not be sufficiently mature to produce basidiocarps until November, therefore a second removal in October was recommended. Brooms produced subsequently would not produce basidiocarps until after the next removal, due to be done in April. Two experimental clearances in accord with this procedure in 1941–3 were not effective in controlling the disease at either of the two estates which represented areas of moderate and severe incidence (Thorold 1943a,b). A possible reason for this lack of success was the likelihood that some inconspicuous brooms were overlooked in the high interlacing canopies of old trees under estate conditions. A large number of small brooms spread over a wide area may constitute a serious source of infection. Successful control through removal of brooms at least twice yearly, was considered to depend on the use of plant material of low susceptibility and on high standards of cultivation (Holliday 1970a).

Chemical methods

Protection against infection. Some spraying with Bordeaux mixture against witches' broom disease was done intermittently in Surinam but was unrewarding (van Hall, C. J. J. and Drost 1909; Stahel 1915, 1919). Experiments in Trinidad with copper and sulphur fungicides, applied either as sprays or as dusts from 1932 to 1939, were inconclusive. Further trials in Trinidad (Thorold 1943*c*, 1953*a*; Holliday 1954*b*,*c*, 1960) showed that applications of copper fungicides at 1-, 2-, or 4-weekly intervals may significantly reduce the number of vegetative brooms and lessen the number of fruit infections. At best, control was partial and not economic.

Prevention of spore production. Experimental spraying of brooms with certain chemicals significantly suppressed basidiocarps (Desrosiers and Bolaños 1955). Dinitro-o-cresol (1·5 per cent) was effective in this way and was less phytotoxic than sodium pentachlorophenate (0·2 per cent), but this procedure was not tried commercially (Desrosiers 1960).

Resistance

Stahel (1915) found only degrees of susceptibility within the genetically uniform cocoa population of Surinam. Resistance was sought within the Trinitario population of Trinidad where 150,000 cocoa trees were observed in badly affected areas in 1934 (Pound 1938; Williams 1943). Trees which showed susceptibility were eliminated in the course of this survey. In 1936, twelve selections remained which were propagated and established at Marper Estate, but in 1943 none remained completely free from brooms. Since the discovery of immunity to witches' broom disease seemed as unlikely in Trinidad as it had been in Surinam, an immediate alternative aim was to select for yielding ability, with the hope that extra productivity might compensate for the cost of removing brooms. One hundred Imperial College Selections (I.C.S.) which were considered to have sufficiently large pods (Pound 1933*c*; Cheesman 1933, 1934; Cheesman and Pound 1934), were described by Pound (1934, 1935*a*, 1936), and clonal material was recorded for yield (Cheesman 1941*a*,*b*, 1944*a*,*b* 1945, 1946) and witches' broom susceptibility (Baker 1943*b*; Baker and Crowdy 1942). Although immunity was not sought, there was nevertheless a bias against selection for resistance to witches' broom disease by aiming at yielding ability (through large pods) and quality (heavy beans). Trees with high 'pod value' (weight of beans per pod), which was the selection criterion, also had the high mean weight of bean that was an important component of quality for the manufacturer (Pound 1933*c*). Because pod size tends to be negatively correlated with number of pods produced (Glendinning 1963*a*), the selection procedure excluded some heavy-bearing trees having small pods. However, three selections (I.C.S. 91, 95, and 98) had relatively low pod values and were resistant to witches' broom disease (Holliday 1954*a*, 1957*a*). One of these clones (I.C.S. 95) was included in a study of seed size inheritance (Bartley 1965*a*). Table 2.1 shows a range of seed sizes and the associated gradation from susceptibility to resistance.

TABLE 2.1
Four cocoa clones

Clone	Witches' broom disease expression	Single bean dry weight range (g.)
I.C.S. 40	very susceptible	1·5–2·3
I.C.S. 1	susceptible	1·2–1·9
I.C.S. 95	resistant	1·0–1·1

I.C.S. 95 was recommended for commercial planting (Holliday and Baker 1953). It was distributed to growers in Trinidad (Montserin 1966), and in Surinam (Lems 1965). I.C.S. 98 was used for breeding work in Surinam (Lems 1967).

The clones started from single trees within the Trinidad Trinitario population were not immune, whilst resistance was associated with the commercially unsatisfactory character of small bean size. Immune or resistant trees were sought in South America (Pound 1938, 1943*a,b*). Precautions were taken to prevent accidental introduction of diseases from there to Trinidad. At first, seeds from open-pollinated trees were suitably treated and grown firstly in Barbados, which was not a cocoa-growing country, whence budwood from the seedlings was taken to Trinidad for propagation and establishment at Marper Estate. Later, it was decided that budwood for propagation, instead of seed, should be taken from selected trees in South America. This was achieved by initial propagation in Peru, using seedling stocks in Iquitos to receive buds which ultimately provided material for propagation in Trinidad.

Three clones derived from Pound's introductions have been especially valuable in attempts to overcome losses from witches' broom disease. Two trees from 'Scavina' as stated by Bartley (1957), but actually from 'Sabina' plantation in Ecuador (Hardy 1960*b*), gave clones designated S.C.A. Both S.C.A. 6 and S.C.A. 12 were without vegetative brooms at first, but later had infected cushions and diseased pods (Baker 1953*a*; Baker and Holliday 1957; Bartley 1970). With little or no infection, S.C.A. 6 and S.C.A. 12 progenies gave similar yields, but when crosses with S.C.A. 12 developed more brooms, they yielded less than crosses with S.C.A. 6 (Bartley 1970). The other potentially valuable clone is I.M.C. 67, from Iquitos (see Chapter 7, p. 111), its beans are heavier than those of both S.C.A. 6 and S.C.A. 12 (Enriquez and Soria 1967). It is worth noting that some Trinidad selections had small, round pods containing large beans (Bartley 1970). I.M.C. 67 rooted easily, was more resistant to witches' broom than any

I.C.S. clone, and showed resistance to black pod and wilt diseases (de Verteuil 1959).

There have been attempts to improve the size of beans by hybridizing with Trinidad selections (Bartley 1957, 1968, 1971). Freeman (1967) described the progenies resulting from such breeding work. A noteworthy clone was T.S.H. 991 ((I.M.C. 67 × S.C.A. 6) × (S.C.A. 6 × I.C.S. 1)), which combined disease resistance with satisfactory bean weight (1·2 g.) and yield (4·0 lb. dry cocoa per tree, or about 1,550 lb. per acre). Analysis of segregation among Trinitario × Scavina hybrids indicated that the small seed size of S.C.A. 6 was dominant (Bartley 1966). It appeared that the genes for resistance to witches' broom in S.C.A. 6 and S.C.A. 12 were dominant (Bartley and Amponsah 1967). A selection from the cross I.C.S. 1 × I.C.S. 6 (Pound 1934) referred to as I.C.S. 111 (Chalmers 1972a) had good combining ability for yield. Table 2.2 summarizes some of the results

TABLE 2.2

Mean yield of I.C.S. 95 and of S.C.A. 6 × I.C.S. 111 (1962–71 period) and mean yield of I.C.S. 111 (1964–71 period), and witches' broom incidences (mean 1969–71 period)

Selection	Mean yield (lb dry cocoa per acre)	Mean percentage trees with witches' broom (%)
I.C.S. 95	539	96
I.C.S. 111	552	67
S.C.A. 6 × I.C.S. 111	1,353	27

from a progeny trial at Las Hermanas, planted in 1958 (Chalmers 1972a, Table 2), to show mean yields and incidence of witches' broom disease for I.C.S. 95 (Pound 1936), I.C.S. 111, and S.C.A. 6 × I.C.S. 111. S.C.A. 6 × I.C.S. 111 yielded best and had least witches' broom disease; this cross was recommended for commercial planting (average bean weight *ca.* 1 g.) (Chalmers 1972a).

Material collected by Desrosiers and von Buchwald (1949) was used for breeding work at the Pichilingue Tropical Experimental Station (I.N.I.A.P.), in Ecuador. Two of their selections (S.I.L.1 and S.I.L. 5) from Silecia Estate, Archidona, in River Napo area, Ecuador (Enriquez and Soria 1967) had fewer brooms and larger beans than S.C.A. 6 and S.C.A. 12 (Ampuero and Desrosiers 1960). The observation by Bartley (1965b) that resistance of S.I.L. 1 and S.I.L. 5 appeared to be recessive, was subject to confirmation. Chalmers (1972b) reported that Scavina (S.C.A.) selections, which showed some resistance to *C. perniciosa* in Trinidad (Chalmers 1972a), appeared to have no resistance to the supposedly different strain of the pathogen in Ecuador.

3

MONILIA DISEASE

Introduction

Rorer (1918a) found a fungus of the genus *Monilia* damaging cocoa pods in Ecuador. Since then, 'Monilia' has been commonly used as part of the trivial name, and it seems desirable to retain it. Holliday (1970b, 1971) employed the descriptive name 'watery pod rot' (*podredumbre acuosa*) because fungal invasion converted the pod contents into a wet and rotten mass. Affected pods were said to be heavier and more difficult to open than healthy ones of similar age. These features, and the white fungal 'frosting' on the exterior, presumably account for another descriptive term (*helada*, 'frozen'), according to Ciferri and Parodi (1933). They studied affected material from Ecuador. The causal fungus was described, and named *Monilia roreri* Ciferri apud Ciferri and Parodi (1933), in honour of J. B. Rorer, with mention that it occurred also in Colombia.

There are general accounts of Monilia disease by Desrosiers (1960), Burle (1961), Urquhart (1961), and Moreno, Zuleta, and Laurent (1968).

Geographical distribution

C.M.I. Distribution Map No. 13 (2nd ed. 1952) shows that Monilia disease is confined to the north-west of South America and the adjacent part of Central America. It is widespread in the main cocoa area of Ecuador, where it was first observed in about 1914 near Quevedo (Fowler and López 1949). It is not known when *M. roreri* first attacked cocoa in Colombia, but there may have been an outbreak in the nineteenth century (Baker *et al.* 1954; Holliday 1957b, 1971). Large-scale plantings in about 1830 around Antioquia and Sopetrán were devastated in 1851 onwards. Affected pods were covered by a velvet-like fungus which dried to an 'impalpable dust', but leaves were unaffected, as reported by Parsons (1949, 1968). He cited a relevant article by José M. Martinez Pardo of Antioquia City (in 'Los Ecos del Ruiz' (Manizales) of 5 December 1880), which was not available (Parsons, J. J. 1962 *in litt.*). Recent occurrences in Colombia were climatically diverse; in the Pacific coastal plain, in the high, and rather dry, valleys of the Cauca and Magdalena rivers (Baker *et al.* 1954), but also at Villa Arteaga, Department of Antioquia (Holliday, P. 1969 *in litt.*), where Para rubber (*Hevea brasiliensis* (Willd. ex Adr. de Juss.) Müll. Arg.) was grown (Parsons 1968). In Peru, Monilia disease occurred near Jaén, Cajamarca, at

Tingo Maria, Huanuco, and in the Convención Valley, Cuzco (McLaughlin 1950b; Hunter 1958). The disease occurred in eastern Panama, in Comarea de San Blas, and near Rio Paya, Darien Province (Orellana 1956b). In Venezuela, Monilia disease occurred near Rio Catatumba, Zulia (Müller 1941), and possibly elsewhere in the occidente region (Hernandez 1968).

Economic importance

Ecuador was worst affected by this disease. Peak production there of nearly 50,000 tons in 1915–16 declined rapidly to about 30,000 tons in 1922–3 when Monilia disease became widespread, and fell further to about 20,000 tons in 1925 with the onset of witches' broom disease (Rorer 1925; Wood 1959). Unfavourable prices associated with competitive production in West Africa also affected the industry adversely. Ecuador ceased to be the major cocoa-producing country, but since 1933 there has been an upward trend in production (Viton 1955). It is uncertain why the economic impact of Monilia disease was less severe in Colombia than in Ecuador. This difference may have been due to the generally lower rainfall and humidity in Colombia (Wood 1959), but it is worth noting that cocoa areas were isolated and smaller in Colombia than in Ecuador (Krug and Quartey-Papafio 1964, cf. their Maps 3 and 4). Monilia disease was probably relatively unimportant in western Venezuela where output was less than 2 per cent of the country's total production (Wood 1959). Monilia disease appears to be economically unimportant in Panama and Peru (Krug and Quartey-Papafio 1964).

Symptoms

Fruit infection by *M. roreri* is not immediately evident externally, because fungal invasion proceeds internally at first, but soon affects some or all of the beans. Sometimes there appears to be uneven ripening, with surface spots having the colour of the mature pod when the remainder of the surface is still green. Consequently, affected pods are likely to be harvested earlier than healthy ones of similar age (Desrosiers, von Buchwald, and Bolaños 1955). When an immature affected pod is cut longitudinally, disorganization of the vascular system is revealed by brown, black, or greyish stripes. These internal necrotic areas produced conidia within a few hours, thereby characterizing infection at an early stage (Holliday 1970b, 1971). Later external sporulation begins on black necrotic areas which become covered with a mealy, powdery, dirty white, or orange to pale brown mass of conidia (Fig. 4B(a,b)).

Monilia, witches' broom, and black pod diseases are sympatric in the north of South America. Their symptoms may be confused, particularly with respect to black pod and Monilia diseases (McLaughlin 1950a). However, there are characteristic features. *M. roreri* conidia are produced as typically 'dry' spores which scatter on touching, whilst the encrusted sporangia of *Phytophthora palmivora* are less readily dislodged from the pod surface. Pods attacked by *M. roreri* sometimes have swellings which resemble the malformations of pods affected by *Crinipellis perniciosa*. Unharvested Monilia pods shrivel when dry (Wood 1959), thereby differing from the 'normal' shape of old black pods and witches' broom pods, which more nearly resemble over-ripe attached pods in shape.

M. roreri infects pods but not other parts of the plant, and differs in this respect from *Botryodiplodia theobromae, C. perniciosa*, and *P. palmivora* which infect vegetative parts and fruits.

Host range

M. roreri attacks only species of the genera *Herrania* and *Theobroma*. Fruits of *H. balaënsis* and of *T. bicolor* were attacked in Ecuador (Rorer 1918a). Infection of *T. gileri* may have aided ingress of Monilia disease from western Colombia to eastern Panama (Baker *et al.* 1954).

Causal fungus

Descriptions of *M. roreri* were given by Ciferri and Parodi (1933) and by Holliday (1970b). It is sufficient for present purposes to note that the conidiophores are not differentiated from the mycelial hyphae. They are more or less upright, loosely tufted, or occasionally isolated, and erect, sometimes simple but generally bifid, or trifidly branched, hyaline, pluriseptate, constricted at the septa, 9–50 μm. long. Conidia vary in shape from spherical, sub-cylindrical, to elliptical, hyaline 8–10·5 μm. × 9–14 μm.

Culture of fungus

López (1954) isolated *M. roreri* by surface sterilization (2·5 per cent sodium hypochlorite for 1 min.), followed by washing in sterile water and transfer to potato dextrose agar. Mycelial growth resulted in 48 hours. Nutritional requirements of *M. roreri* in culture were not reported.

Dispersal

It is not known how *M. roreri* is spread naturally; conidia are probably airborne, and insects may carry them.

Germination

Germination percentages of conidia from cultures ranged from 0–15 per cent (within 4–22 hours), and from affected fruits the range was 8–53 per cent (within 4–12 hours) (López 1954). Conidia germinated in water or in moist air (*ca.* 81 per cent R.H.). Ability to germinate declined with age, from a maximum at 1 or 2 days. Germination was better at 22 °C. (72 °F.) than at 32 °C. (90 °F.).

Invasion

Insect punctures may facilitate entry of germ tubes (Rorer 1918*a*; Naundorf 1954). Uncontrolled experiments suggested that *Antiteuchus tripterus* (Fabr.) (*Mecistorhinus tripterus*, Pentatomidae) transmitted *M. roreri* (Sepúlveda 1955).

Infection may occur via the flower (Holliday 1970*b*), but infection at time of pollination has not been demonstrated (Addoh 1971). Inoculation experiments indicated that infection by *M. roreri* occurred at an early stage of fruit development, since attempts to inoculate mature, or nearly mature pods failed (Desrosiers *et al.* 1955).

Predisposing factors

Harvesting of 147 recorded trees at Pichilingue, Ecuador, substantiated infection at an early stage. Monthly percentages of pods infected by *M. roreri* were positively correlated with amount of rain in the fourth preceding month. Disease incidence and amount of rain in the month of harvesting were not associated. Since about 5 months elapsed between pollination and harvesting, infection seemingly depended on rainfall at flowering, or shortly after (Desrosiers *et al.* 1955).

Simultaneous incidences of Monilia and witches' broom diseases vitiated attempts to relate the influence of Monilia disease alone on yields, to amounts of sunlight and/or rainfall in Ecuador plantations (Fowler, Desrosiers, and Hopp 1956). Within the surveyed area, altitudes ranged from 5 m. (16 ft.) at Vinces to about 100 m. (328 ft.) at Quevedo. *M. roreri* occurred at higher altitudes in Colombia (*ca.* 400 m. (1,312 ft.)), where *C. perniciosa* infection was apparently absent (Baker *et al.*, 1954). *M. roreri* seemed to tolerate a wider rainfall range (35–400 in. (890–10,000 mm.) per year) than *C. perniciosa* (> 80 in. (2,000 mm.) per year) (Holliday 1953).

Control

Cultural methods

Removal of affected pods seemed to be beneficial in Colombia, but its efficacy was not satisfactorily established (Garcia and Naundorf 1952). Bartley (1967) reported some control from burning trash and suggested trying this in combination with chemicals.

Chemical methods

Attempts to prevent infection by chemical applications are empirical because the dispersal of *M. roreri* conidia and the penetration of fruits are not understood.

Wood (1959), Desrosiers (1960), and Ampuero (1967) reviewed chemical methods in Ecuador. Control with increased yield was claimed for wettable sulphur (15 lb. per 100 gall. water). Cuprous oxide and different organo-metallic fungicides (Brestan, Fermate, Maneb, and Zineb) were tried experimentally with some success. There was little or no spraying by farmers in Ecuador (Lass 1970). Recommendations for Colombia included fungicide combined with an insecticide (Avila 1966) or fungicide alone (Moreno *et al.* 1968).

Resistance

Delgado, Ampuero, and Doak (1960) observed fifty-two clones for 3 years at Pichilingue, Ecuador, and reported a wide range of apparent susceptibility to *M. roreri* infection. This comparison and another in Colombia (Naundorf 1954) probably had uncertain validities through irregular dispersion of conidia and the likelihood that cropping periodicity affected the number of fruits 'at risk' (Vernon 1971). An inoculation technique developed at Pichilingue helped testing for resistance to *M. roreri* (Ampuero 1967).

4

BLACK POD DISEASE

Introduction

The cocoa pod-rot pathogen was referred to by Ashby (1929a) as '. . . an omnivorous tropical species of wide distribution, existing as a number of morphologically, and in some instances pathologically distinguishable strains . . .'. Previously, Butler (1920) stated that 'this fungus will rank as one of the most destructive known'. At first, the fungus associated with black pod disease was incorrectly referred to as *Phytophthora omnivora* de Bary by Massee (1899). This epithet was an invalid synonym of *P. cactorum* (Lebert and Cohn) Schroeter, according to Waterhouse (1970). The name *P. theobromae* (Coleman 1910a) was soon withdrawn (Coleman 1910b) because it was antedated. This pathogen had already received two different names through its affecting various hosts in diverse climates. Butler (1907, 1910) described *Pythium palmivorum* from palms (*Areca, Borassus,* and *Cocos* species), in the monsoonal climate (December to April, less than 1·0 in. (25 mm.) rain per month) of Godavery District, India. Damage to cocoa was initially studied in equatorial climates (January to December, more than 1·0 in. (25 mm.) rain per month) of Cameroon (von Faber 1907) and Trinidad (Rorer 1910a), where the pathogen was currently referred to as *P. faberi* Maublanc (1909), based on material and data provided by von Faber. Reinking (1919) showed that *P. faberi* isolated from cocoa produced a bud rot of coconut seedlings and of mature palms, whilst the fungus causing coconut bud rot was identical with the pathogen causing cocoa pod rot. After studying Reinking's figures and descriptions of *P. faberi*, Butler (1925) confirmed that this fungus was morphologically identical with *P. palmivora*, which was the proper name.

P. palmivora infections were considered in books on cocoa and its diseases (van Hall 1914; Nowell 1923; Briton-Jones 1934; Nosti 1953; Burle 1961; Urquhart 1961; Braudeau 1969). Investigations were reviewed by Thorold (1967).

Geographical distribution

P. palmivora is a cosmo-tropical fungus, which has been reported as a cocoa pathogen in fifty-nine countries (Chapter 12, p. 197–8).

Economic importance

The cocoa industry in Cameroon (S.W.) declined because black pod disease affected one-fifth to four-fifths of the pods produced (West and Voelcker 1942). There were severe losses in Nigeria (Thorold 1955*b*), and elsewhere in West Africa (Viton 1955). Braudeau (1969) mentioned 25–50 per cent crop losses in Central and South America. Seasonal losses ranged from 2–50 per cent in the British Solomon Islands Protectorate (Friend and Brown 1971).

Padwick (1956) considered that losses due to black pod disease amounted to at least 10 per cent of world production. Pod rot was a main disease in most (83 per cent) of the forty-two cocoa-growing countries which received questionnaires in 1958 and 1963 (Krug and Quartey-Papafio 1964).

The economic importance of black pod disease can be objectively estimated from observed losses of pods, but there is no such basis for assessing economic damage sustained through infection by *P. palmivora* of cocoa roots (Turner and Asomaning 1962), leaves and young stems (Turner and Wharton 1960), and older stems (Chapter 12).

Because losses through black pod disease vary annually and spatially, such variability is one of the factors influencing cocoa prices, which fluctuate in response to shortfall or surplus in estimated production, as noted by Gregory (1972).

Host range

P. palmivora has been reported as attacking species belonging to forty-one families of flowering plants (Chee 1969*c*). This assessment may underestimate the host range because infection of some plants lacking economic importance may have been overlooked (Turner 1961*b*).

Since banana plants (*Musa* sp.) are commonly interspersed in West African cocoa farms, infection of banana flowers and fruits by *P. palmivora* may initiate outbreaks of black pod disease (Esenam 1971).

Symptoms

Fruits at all stages of development may be attacked by *P. palmivora*. The first indication of infection is the appearance of a circular brown spot (Fig. 4C(a), p. 12) which enlarges concentrically and evenly to involve the whole pod surface. Ultimately the colour of the affected pod is dark brown or black. The name 'brown pod' was applied in some countries to the disease caused by *P. palmivora* (Miranda and da Cruz 1953), but sometimes to the rot associated with *Botryodiplodia theobromae* (Chapter 5). To avoid such confusion, the term 'brown pod' is rejected here. Discoloration spreads internally with rotting of the beans in immature pods. The beans in a mature pod may remain partly or wholly unaffected because the pathogen may not traverse the gap between the mass of beans and the internal wall of the husk. In Nigeria, sporangia were first formed during the night following the second day of visible symptoms (Thorold 1953*b*). Sporangial production gives a dingy white bloom to the fruit surface, with or without some superficial white mycelium (Fig. 4C(b), p. 12). Variations in symptoms may be inherent characters. Inoculation of detached pods with various isolates of *P. palmivora* showed differences in colour, outline, and rate of growth of the lesion, either discrete or confluent masses of sporangia, and varying amounts of aerial mycelium (Turner 1960*a,b*, 1961*a*).

Causal fungi

Taxonomy

For a general appreciation of some mycological features of the black pod pathogens, it is useful to consider their classification. The family Pythiaceae (Oomycetes, Peronosporales) comprises the genera *Phytophthora*, *Pythiogeton*, and *Pythium*. Blackwell (1949) explained their separation and relevant terminology; the place of sporulation differentiates these genera. For present purposes, it suffices to note that 'in *Phytophthora* the protoplasm of the sporangium is segmented into zoospores within a sporangium wall', in contrast to the emission of an unsegmented mass of protoplasm in genera *Pythiogeton* and *Pythium*. Butler (1907) described *Pythium palmivorum*, which was transferred to *Phytophthora* as *P. palmivora* (Butler) Butler (Waterhouse 1956, 1968). The validity of some *Phytophthora* species is uncertain, and the black pod pathogens present taxonomic difficulties (Tucker 1931; Savage, Clayton, Hunter, Brenneman, Laviola, and Gallegly 1968). Waterhouse (1963) recognized the need to test the validity of 'species' which were close together, and she stated that 'there is still much information needed concerning many of the species, in particular chromosome numbers and mating type relationships, and it would be wise to defer further name changes until more is known'. Ashby (1922) discussed the separability of *P. palmivora* and *P. nicotianae* var. *parasitica* (Dastur) Waterhouse (as *P. parasitica* Dastur), and Holliday and Mowat (1963) commented that many tropical isolates could probably be placed in either species. No type cultures are available (Waterhouse 1963). Tucker (1931) considered that *P. meadii* McRae should be merged with *P. palmivora*. *P. heveae* Thompson (1929) also rots pods naturally, but produces a lighter brown lesion than *P. palmivora* (Turner 1968*a*). Chee (1969*a*) found that *P. palmivora* was a variable species, and he described another species (*P. botryosa*) which could infect a wounded cocoa pod. Gallegly (1970) suggested that taxonomic difficulties might be attributed to variation through interspecific sexual recombination, since there was opportunity for hybridization through simultaneous infections of the same host by two or more species of *Phytophthora*. There was apparently support for this possibility from the observation by Ashby (1922) that cospores were formed when a *P. palmivora* isolate from cocoa was grown in mixed culture with an isolate of *P. nicotianae* var. *parasitica* (as *P. parasitica*) from *Ricinus communis* L.

Physiologic specialization

Ainsworth (1971) defined 'physiologic race' as 'one of a group of forms like in morphology but unlike in certain cultural, physiological, biochemical, pathological, or other characters'. Ashby (1922) studied such behaviour exhibited by *P. palmivora* isolates. Oospores were absent in pure cultures of this species from different hosts. Vigorous isolates from coconut (*Cocos nucifera* L.) and cotton (*Gossypium* sp.) did not produce oospores when grown together in mixed culture but oospores were formed when either of them was grown in mixed culture with a more weakly growing isolate from cocoa. On the basis of confirmatory observations, Gadd (1924) designated a 'cacao group' of 'strains' (comprising isolates from cocoa and from papaw (*Carica papaya* L.) which produced oospores when grown in mixed culture with a 'rubber group' of 'strains' (comprising isolates from rubber (*Hevea brasiliensis*) breadfruit (*Artocarpus* sp.), *Dendrobium* sp., and *Odontadenia* sp.). In the absence of constant morphological differences between the two groups, there was no justification for delimiting the groups specifically. Tucker (1931) also confirmed oospore production in mixed cultures of *P. palmivora*, but he considered that heterothallism was unproved. Although the amphigynous antheridia developed on separate hyphae from the oogonia, he was unable to trace them to different thalli. Orellana (1959a) considered that differences warranted varietal status and he proposed that isolates from cocoa should be designated *P. palmivora* var. *theobromae*, and that isolates from rubber should be designated *P. palmivora* var. *heveae*. This proposal was not adopted by other workers. On the basis of his study of 225 isolates from cocoa and ten from rubber, Turner (1961a) stated that 'survey of a large number of isolates has shown that "cacao" group isolates are found on rubber, and vice versa; in fact, the dominant pathogen in a large part of West Africa is of the "rubber" group'. The wide range of hosts (p. 33) seemed to preclude subdivision of *P. palmivora* on a basis of host specialization. However, there seemed to be some such specialization of isolates attacking pepper plants (*Piper* spp.). In Indonesia, *P. nigrum* L. was attacked preferentially, but cocoa was also infected by a fungus designated *P. palmivora* var. *piperis* Muller (1936), but invalidly (Waterhouse 1970). Isolates of *P. palmivora* from *P. betle* L. and from *P. nigrum* were considered to be atypical (Turner 1969). Atypical isolates did not form oospores in any combination with other isolates (Turner 1960b, 1961a,b). On the basis of pairings with *Phytophthora infestans* Montagne, and other heterothallic species, Savage *et al.* (1968) referred the original 'rubber' (plus) group of isolates to A[1] compatibility (mating) 'type' and the original 'cacao' (minus) group of isolates to A[2] compatibility (mating) 'type'. Within a collection of *P. palmivora* isolates studied at Riverside, California, both A[1] and A[2] mating 'types' were found on cocoa, but the A[2] 'type' predominated (Chee 1969b). In Malaysia, all isolates from cocoa (pods, bark, and seedlings) belonged to the cacao group, but isolates from Hevea rubber belonged to rubber and to cacao groups (Chee 1969b, 1971). Chee (1971) obtained laboratory germination of *P. palmivora* oospores, the products of which infected cocoa and rubber tissues differentially and in a manner suggesting that under field conditions, a cocoa host might be affected preferentially by cacao group 'strains', whilst a rubber host might be affected by both 'strains'. Zentmyer and Mitchell (1971) discussed the hosts and geographical range of *P. palmivora* mating types.

A volatile chemical substance may break down the self-sterility (Sansome 1970) of heterothallic *Phytophthora* species (Brasier 1971, 1972). Brasier (1971) found that A² but not A¹ isolates of *Phytophthora* species, including *P. palmivora*, formed selfed oospores in the presence of *Trichoderma viride* Pers. ex S. F. Gray. This fungus has been isolated from cocoa (Chapter 12, p. 205).

Desjardins, Zentmyer, and Reynolds (1969) described the morphology of flagella of *P. palmivora* zoospores. Some of these zoospores were quadri-flagellated and binucleate (Desjardins *et al.* 1970).

The mating behaviour of *P. palmivora* cannot at present be interpreted satisfactorily because the nuclear situation (haploidy *versus* diploidy) of species of the genus *Phytophthora* is controversial (Laviola 1972).

Sansome (1966) discussed evidence that the oomycete fungi are diploid, with meiosis occurring just before gamete formation. This belief was supported by a cytological examination of *Phytophthora infestans* antheridia and oogonia. Sansome and Brasier (1973) stated that 'the nuclear behaviour in the material we have examined shows that meiosis occurs in the game-tangia, indicating that *P. infestans*, in common with other Oomycetes, is diploid in the vegetative state'.

Spread of black pod disease

Short-distance dispersal of fungus from diseased fruits to healthy ones on the same tree

The fruits on a cocoa tree tend to be clustered because several may be borne on a single cushion or on near-by cushions (Dade 1929b). Spread of infection from a diseased fruit to a healthy one in contact with it was noted by Jenman and Harrison (1897) in Guyana and by Bunting and Dade (1924) in Ghana. The sporangia of *P. palmivora* fall from their sporangiophores when mature. When an infected pod with abundant sporangia was placed in a closed container and supported over a microscope slide which was about 1 cm. below it, the number of sporangia that landed on the slide in a period of 24 hours ranged from 0·4 sporangia per cm.² to 3·4 sporangia per cm.² (Thorold 1955b). Similar numbers (2–5 sporangia per cm.² in a 12-hour period) were 'trapped' near attached pods in 'dry' air (Medeiros 1965). Larger numbers (*ca.* 20 sporangia per cm.²) were trapped during periods when rain fell, suggesting that rain-splash take-off had occurred (Thorold 1955b). Take-off from the near-by source in 'dry' air was confirmed when *P. palmivora* was 'labelled' by spraying an aqueous solution of 'Primuline' on to the sporangia-bearing surface of an infected pod. The treated sporangia showed greenish-yellow fluorescence when examined under the microscope with an illumination source rich in ultraviolet light. During periods without rain, sporangia showing the characteristic primuline fluorescence were observed on 'vaselined' disks of 'Cellophane', mounted on pins above the sporangia-bearing surface (Thorold 1954). Non-fluorescent sporangia were also observed that may have come from the air spora, or they were possibly sporangia from the primuline-treated fruit which had escaped treatment. The treatment did not apparently impair the capacity of sporangia to infect because healthy pods near to the treated pods became infected. The majority (74 per cent) of these infected pods showed fluorescence associated with the infected areas. The remainder (26 per cent), on which fluorescence was not detected, may have been infected from an unknown source. Such 'extraneous infection' or 'background contamination' (Gregory 1968) seems to be important in black pod disease epidemiology.

Circumstantial evidence suggested that there was vertical dispersal of *P. palmivora* (sporangia or zoospores) from two likely sources. A healthy pod might apparently become infected from a diseased pod several feet below it. Fruits near to, or in contact with, the soil commonly became infected (Thorold 1955b). There is confirmatory evidence that a black pod epiphytotic may start through infection from the soil (Okaisabor 1965, 1969a,b).

Long-distance dispersal of fungus to healthy pods, from another tree or from an unknown source

To compare possible sources of infection, black pod dispersion gradients were observed in Nigeria, and the results are summarized in Table 4.1 (Thorold 1955b).

TABLE 4.1

Numbers of total (healthy plus diseased) pods (T.P.), and numbers of black pods (B.P.) expressed as percentages of total pods and grouped according to distance from the source, when the source was either a single inoculated pod, or a heap of black pods, or the soil in the vicinity

Distance from source	0–39 in. (0–1 m.)		40–79 in. (1–2 m.)		80 in. and over (over 2 m.)	
	T.P. (No.)	B.P. (%)	T.P. (No.)	B.P. (%)	T.P. (No.)	B.P. (%)
Source						
Inoculated pod	89	56·2	67	11·9	80	3·8
Soil	57	56·2	154	33·1	176	7·4
Heap of black pods	46	45·7	65	21·5	165	6·7

Table 4.1 shows similar dispersion gradients for each of the three sources considered. It was important to know whether the consequences of sporangial dispersal could be detected as a general phenomenon and over distances greater than about 2 m., in cocoa plantings affected by black pod disease. For this purpose, it was convenient to describe a tree as 'diseased' when it carried one or more affected pods, as opposed to a 'healthy' tree carrying only healthy pods. Black pod disease distribution in a Nigeria cocoa field was examined on two occasions by observing the number of doublets (pairs of diseased trees) in sequences of trees, according to the procedure described by van der Plank (1947). The numbers of doublets observed slightly exceeded the numbers to be expected if the diseased trees were randomly distributed, but these differences were not statistically significant. Spread of infection between neighbouring trees may have occurred but was not certainly detected, probably because of extraneous infection from the soil or from other trees. There was similar uncertainty when attempts were made to observe a possible infection gradient in an area of 10 acres at Agodi, near Ibadan, Nigeria, which comprised over 4,000 cocoa trees recorded for numbers of black pods and healthy pods, in two seasons. In the first season (1952–3) black pods were removed from the trees and heaped at the base of a central tree which served as the source of infection. In the second season (1953–4) the heap of old black pods remained but all new black pods were removed from the area. In both seasons, all trees were inspected every other day, to record and remove black pods in the earliest symptom stage (before the start of sporangia production). Accordingly, there was no opportunity for secondary spread from the observed trees. The results obtained have already been discussed (Thorold 1955*b*), and they are summarized here (Table 4.2) for the distances nearest to (0–10 m.) and farthest from (171–80 m.) the infection source.

TABLE 4.2

Incidence of black pod disease at distances from a central source, at Agodi, Nigeria, in two seasons

| Distance from source (m.) | Season 1952–3 | | Season 1953–4 | |
	Number of diseased trees, as percentage of total trees (%)	Number of diseased pods per tree	Number of diseased trees, as percentage of total trees (%)	Number of diseased pods per tree
0–10	77·2	2·3	52·7	1·4
171–80	17·4	0·3	8·7	0·1
Mean 50·9		1·4 (observed)	33·1	0·9 (observed)
		0·8 (expected)		0·4 (expected)

Table 4.2 shows that near the source the percentage of diseased trees (77·2 per cent, 52·7 per cent) and the number of diseased pods per tree (2·3, 1·4) were greater than farther from the source (17·4 per cent, 8·7 per

cent), in both seasons. At intermediate distances, there were irregularities in these values, which indicated the phenomenon of 'over dispersion' (Gregory 1948). There was a tendency for the 'observed' number of diseased pods per tree (mean 1·4, 0·9) to exceed the 'expected' number (mean 0·8, 0·4). This 'background contamination' might have arisen in either or both of two different ways. Some extraneous infection may have come from non-experimental (untreated) trees near the periphery of the experimental area, but was probably mainly from the soil. Such random infection would probably have been similar in both seasons. There is evidence that some of the observed infections, at least in the first season, were due to airborne sporangia and/or zoospores dispersed from the source, which was more potent in the first season (fresh black pods) than in the second season (old black pods). The percentage of diseased trees and the number of diseased pods per tree were greater in the first season (50·9 per cent and 1·4) than in the second season (33·1 per cent and 0·9). There was confirmatory evidence for probable aerial dispersal of *P. palmivora* sporangia or zoospores, from observed leaf lesions on *Piper* spp. throughout a range of distances (0·6–3·3 m.) from the soil (Turner 1969).

Spread by invertebrates

Animals may carry sporangia, either externally or internally. Ingestion and subsequent defecation of viable sporangia have been demonstrated (Dade 1927b). Dade (1928b) and Evans (1971) noted that ants (*Crematogaster* spp.) removed epidermis from cocoa fruits for 'carton' construction. Healthy fruits may become infected when damaged and contaminated by epidermis from infected fruits, or through *Odontomachus* sp. (Formicidae) carrying infected soil particles up from the ground (Evans and Leston 1971). In Nigeria, Gorenz (1970) found that uninfected pods about 4 ft. (1·3 m.) above the ground on two infested trees (having ant-attended scale-insects on pod stalks) developed black pod disease 2 weeks after placing infected pods, with litter cover, at the bases of these trees. Three near-by trees without ant-scale infestation had pods at similar height which remained healthy. Deliberate wounding favours infection of healthy pods by *P. palmivora* (Thorold 1955b), but the extent to which wounding by invertebrates may promote infection is uncertain. Capsid (Miridae) punctures occur commonly on pod surfaces, but they are seldom, if ever, subsequently infected by *P. palmivora* (Anon. 1951).

Induced radioactivity of black pods, and of their insect visitors in Ghana, indicated that two species in particular were important vectors of *P. palmivora* (Evans 1973). *Brachypeplus depressus* Erichson (Coleoptera, Nitidulidae) and *Chaetonerius latifemur* Enderlein (Diptera, Neriidae) fed regularly on black pods, carried *P. palmivora* sporangia internally and/or externally, and visited wounded but otherwise healthy pods. Both these insects were seen in Cameroon and Nigeria where they may also participate in horizontal and vertical spread of *P. palmivora*.

The 'giant African snail' (*Achatina fulica* Bowdich) damages young cocoa plants, but apparently without inducing infection of leaves, stems, or roots by *P. palmivora* (Edward 1961; Greathead, Lionnet, Lodos, and Whellan 1971), although it may function as a vector of the 'foot rot' affecting *Piper nigrum* in Sarawak (Turner 1964).

Spread by vertebrates

Squirrels (see Chapter 5) may have spread *P. palmivora* in Nigeria (Gorenz 1970, 1972*a*).

Predisposing factors

Climate

Black pod disease occurs wherever climatic conditions are suitable for satisfactory growth and cropping of cocoa. Using controlled-environment growth rooms, Sale (1968, 1969*a,b* 1970) showed that cocoa functioned satisfactorily with high humidity (80–95 per cent R.H.) at *ca*. 27 °C. (80 °F.). These are also suitable conditions for *P. palmivora* (Thorold 1955*b*), that should persist for a period of 2–4 hours which may suffice for infection by zoospores (Tarjot 1965). In Nigeria, little or no black pod occurred in dry-season months (January–April) with R. H. less than 80 per cent for over 12 hours, compared with wet-season months (May–December) when most black pod occurred. August represented typical wet-season conditions (R.H. greater than 85 per cent and R.H. greater than 95 per cent for over 12 hours), but in December humidity conditions were intermediate, with R.H. less than 80 per cent for 6 hours (Thorold 1955*b*). Although high humidity induced black pod incidence, much rain was not invariably an overwhelming factor. In Cameroon (S.W.), with annual rainfall greater than 100 in. (2,550 mm.), the number of total (healthy and diseased) pods and black pod percentage were small (Thorold 1952, 1953*b*). In Grenada, with fairly large and well-distributed rainfall (80 in. (2,000 mm.) per year, mostly in 10 months), black pod caused a small (*ca*. 2 per cent) annual loss (Cruickshank 1970). It is possible that disease incidence is restricted by one or more factors associated with shaded or sheltered plantings (Krug and Quartey-Papafio 1964; Cruickshank 1970). The significance of humidity in black pod epidemiology is probably complex. It may operate partly through influencing the moisture content of the husk pericarp (Tarjot 1971*a*), whilst the role of insolation, as influenced by overhead shade, may be important (Tarjot 1971*b*).

Periodically enhanced severity of black pod disease in association with low minimum temperature was reported in Bahia, Brazil (Lellis 1952; Miranda and da Cruz 1953; Hardy 1958) and in Sri Lanka (Orellana and Som 1957). The significance of this 'cold effect' is uncertain. There does not appear to be either an altitudinal or latitudinal factor which makes the pod more susceptible, through departure from a typical low-altitude equatorial temperature regime. In Cameroon, at high altitudes (2,500–3,000 ft. (762–914 m.)), incidence of black pod disease was not enhanced in comparison with lower altitudes (Thorold 1952). Black pod disease was economically unimportant at about latitude 20°S. in the State of Espírito Santo, Brazil, along the River Doce near Linhares (Medeiros and de Mello 1969).

There is reason to believe that a black pod association with low temperature reported by Park (1953) related to Sri Lanka and not to West Africa as stated by Hislop and Park (1962c). With generally high absolute humidity in the West African cocoa belt (Anon. 1949), and probably in cocoa areas elsewhere, dew point is commonly reached at night. Therefore there seems no need to invoke extra deposition of water on the pod surface as the factor of major importance in connection with the black pod cold effect. Such enhancement of infection is not in accord with the optimum temperature range for *P. palmivora*, which Waterhouse (1963) gave as $27 \cdot 5$ °C. ($81 \cdot 5$ °F.) to 32 °C. ($89 \cdot 6$ °F.). A possible explanation for the cold effect is offered in Chapter 12 (p. 161).

Various factors affect the relationship between temperature and germination of *P. palmivora* sporangia. In Ghana, throughout a wide range of controlled temperatures (10–34 °C. (50–93 °F.)), sporangia in water germinated indirectly (by zoospores) within 6 hours. At the higher temperatures (30–34 °C. (86–93 °F.)), there was also some direct germination (by germ tubes). The greatest percentage germination of sporangia (97 per cent) was at 22 °C. (72 °F.) (Clerk 1972). In distilled water, zoospore motility was retained longest at 17 °C. (62 °F.) (84 hours), but motility was retained for 24 hours, or longer, in the range 21–7 °C. (70–81 °F.). However, cessation of motility and encystment of zoospores were induced by chemicals (organic and inorganic), by contact with obstacles, and when zoospores were overcrowded. Encysted zoospores germinated readily, but disintegrated at pH $2 \cdot 2$–$5 \cdot 0$ (Bimpong and Clerk 1970).

Amount and timing of fruit production

A survey of cocoa plantings in Nigeria and Cameroon (S.W.) gave estimates of yields in relation to black pod disease incidence, in a variety of eco-climates where annual rainfall ranged from about 40 in. (1,020 mm.) to about 400 in. (10,200 mm.) (Thorold 1952). There was interaction between rainfall, cropping performance, and disease. Black pod incidence was directly proportional to total pods and to rainfall, but total pods were in inverse proportion to rainfall. Gregory (1971) noted general acceptance of the postulate 'that as yields per acre increased so, other things being equal, does the absolute amount of black pod', but the extent of such increase is controversial. In Nigeria, percentage loss increased at higher yields (Thorold 1953*b*, 1956). In Ivory Coast, percentage loss decreased at higher yields (Renaud 1953). In Ghana, percentage loss remained constant as yield increased (Blencoe and Wharton 1961). This inconsistency may be associated with the skew distribution of cocoa yields, whether based on individual trees (Ivory Coast and Nigeria) or on plots (Ghana), as discussed by Williams (1964). A typical example was a population of 4,936 cocoa trees in Nigeria, among which the highest yield for a single tree was 172 pods. The arithmetic mean was 14·8 pods per tree. The greater proportion of the trees (62 per cent) occurred in the range 0–14 pods per tree. The remainder (38 per cent) yielded in the range 15–172 pods per tree, but only twelve trees (0·2 per cent) gave more than 100 pods per tree. Consequently, there is a tendency for information on black pod incidence at high yields to be limited and liable to sampling errors (Yates 1949).

The yield of a single tree, or of a number of trees comprising an experiment plot, is conventionally considered in terms of total production during a 12-month period. Such procedure obscures cropping periodicity. The proportion of the total crop at risk (Vernon 1971) affects black pod incidence directly. Attention has been given to the possibility that the loss of fruits through disease, or their removal in the normal course of harvesting, may affect black pod incidence indirectly. In Ghana, the total number of pods and the total weight of beans reaped from plots harvested at weekly intervals exceeded the total number and weight from plots harvested at monthly intervals (Wharton 1955). Confirmatory observations showed significant increases in the numbers of pods per tree associated with decreasing intervals between pickings (Wickens 1955). It seemed that frequency of black pod removal might also affect total fruit production directly and black pod incidence indirectly. Black pod losses were greater in 'peak' periods which preceded the harvesting peaks, because immature fruits were prone to infection (Blencowe and Wharton 1961). A measure of 'earliness' E was devised for studies in Nigeria of this factor in relation to frequent (every other day), or infrequent (monthly interval) removal of black pods. With frequent removal, the value of the correlation coefficient between earliness E and number of total pods was positive and significant (Thorold 1956). This relationship indicated that black pod occurrence early in the season was associated with greater total number of fruits, which might induce greater black pod loss subsequently. Observations in Nigeria of nine clones, during 3 years, showed that 'seasonal yield periodicity' influenced black pod disease incidence (Weststeijn 1966*a*). Lockwood (1971) studied a wider range of cultivars (amelonado, Trinitario, and Upper Amazon) in Ghana, and he stated that 'late-maturing clones, in which most of the crop was harvested after mid-October, showed a lower incidence of black pod (*Phytophthora palmivora*) than those in which harvesting took place during the black pod epidemic period, June to mid-October'.

A statistical procedure is needed for studying a multi-harvest crop such as cocoa. Cropping patterns tend to be bi-modal or multi-modal, and Vernon (1969) showed that such distributions might be treated as two or more overlapping normal distributions. These procedures require electronic computation.

Interaction between frequency of black pod removal and productivity

In Nigeria, black pod percentage was dependent on total fruit number when black pods were removed frequently, because secondary infection was prevented. When black pods were removed infrequently, there was secondary spread which produced a uniform disease incidence so that black pod percentage was independent of total fruit number (Thorold 1956). In Ghana, the proportion of diseased pods did not alter as levels of yield increased because the plots were harvested at monthly intervals, consequently black pods were removed infrequently (Blencowe and Wharton 1961). Gregory (1971) noted that *P. palmivora* infections were not all at random. He suggested that black pods on a tree might comprise the results of two kinds of infection: primary infection arriving at random and secondary infection through local spread from primary infection. This hypothesis served to explain observations in Nigeria. When there are few pods per tree they tend to escape primary infection and little or no secondary infection occurs. In these circumstances, the number of trees with no black pods was greater than the expected number. When larger numbers of pods were present, there was greater opportunity for secondary spread of infection from pods infected primarily. In these circumstances, the number of affected trees and the number of black pods per tree exceeded expectation (Thorold 1953*b*).

Tree spacing

Cocoa trees in West African farms are generally spaced irregularly. At Agodi, near Ibadan, Nigeria, a 10-acre block of cocoa comprised fifteen holdings, some planted by different farmers, others by the same farmer at different times (Pearce and Thom 1951). Densities ranged from 322 trees per acre (*ca.* 3·8 m. × 3·8 m. spacing) to 1,351 trees per acre (*ca.* 1·7 m. × 1·9 m. spacing). Such differences affect black pod incidence. The number of pods per tree was least with closely spaced trees and greatest with widely spaced trees. The number of trees without black pods tended to be greater when yields were small (seven or eight pods per tree). Such trees generally had few branches and fruited on the trunks. Consequently, *P. palmivora* did not readily spread from tree to tree. At wide spacings there were low branches which bore pods. In mature trees at wide spacings, the branches of adjacent trees may intermingle, so that pods on neighbouring trees may be close together, thereby facilitating spread of *P. palmivora* from tree to tree (Thorold 1953*b*). These observations were supported experimentally, despite agronomic difficulties which beset comparisons between plots at different spacings. There were fewest healthy pods per acre at the widest spacing tested (4·6 m × 4·6 m.), and most at close spacing (1·9 m. × 1·9 m.), but slightly fewer at 1·5 m. × 1·5 m. (Russell 1953).

Cushion infection

Black pod disease epidemiology has been considered so far in relation to spread by sporangia or zoospores. There is some evidence that mycelial hyphae may participate (Gregory 1969). Nevertheless, it has been difficult to establish the sequence of putative processes which may occur within periods of one, two, or more seasons; spread of hyphae from an infected fruit via the stalk (adaxially) to the cushion, persistence of viable mycelium in the cushion, and passage of hyphae via the stalk (abaxially) into a healthy fruit to infect it.

Observations on the development of infection within a pod and its stalk showed that cushion infection was likely to occur if an infected pod remained on the tree for about 2 weeks after the first appearance of the characteristic brown spot. An infected cushion may subsequently bear fruits which can become infected systemically (Thorold 1955b).

From observations on over 5,000 pods in Ghana, Dade (1927b) stated that 'a certain proportion of the incidence of black pod disease is caused by infected cushions, which are also probably responsible in a large degree for carrying over infection from one season to another'. He noted that 'pod infection due to diseased cushions cannot be readily diagnosed by inspection' (Dade 1928a). He described the procedure by which a 'cushion canker' developed and pod infection might follow, but in the succeeding season most of these cushions bore no fruit, a few bore fruits which were either diseased or sound (Dade 1929a, 1930). In Nigeria, there was no evidence that infrequent removal of infected pods was associated with much cushion infection and systemic infection of fruits, in contradistinction to the earlier experience in Ghana (Thorold 1955b).

Control

Chemical methods

For over 60 years, cocoa fruits have been sprayed with fungicides to minimize losses from black pod disease, but not always economically (Thorold 1967). These control procedures have been reviewed (Newhall 1969; Gregory 1969). Because better fungicidal control of P. palmivora is needed, some problems and their possible remedies are considered.

Leaching of deposits. A laboratory estimate of the threshold deposit for protection against P. palmivora zoospores (1 μg Cu per cm.^{2}) was applicable under field conditions (Hislop and Park 1962a). Weathering of deposits on attached pods was compared with reduction of deposits on detached pods by 'artificial rain' (Hislop and Park 1962b). In contrast to the tenacity of deposits when adequately dried after application of fungicide, the deposit might be rapidly reduced when high humidity and frequent rain did not allow full drying. Ideally, spraying should be confined to sunny periods, with R.H. 80 per cent or less for at least 2 hours. Laboratory tests indicated possible achievement of better retention through rapid drying associated with low-volume spraying (Hislop 1963a). This expectation was not substantiated when cuprous oxide was applied by mist-blower. Disease control was not improved and the cost was greater than with high-volume application by pneumatic knapsack sprayer (Hislop 1963b).

In Costa Rica (*ca.* 100 in. (2,550 mm.) rain per year), a spraying schedule was based on totals of daily rainfall amounts. The aim was fungicide application when about 8 in. (200 mm.) rain had fallen, after the previous application. Newhall, Paredes, and Salazar (1968) concluded that 'making frequent fungicide applications for two or three months before the harvest peak, brings the greatest returns'.

Fungicide choice. Although high tenacity was associated with satisfactory control, as exemplified by forms of Bordeaux mixture, copper oxychloride formulations were tenacious but gave unsatisfactory control. Captan deposits on pods were readily removed by artificial rain, and this low tenacity was associated with ineffectiveness for black pod control. The tenacity of fentin acetate (triphenyltin acetate) on pods was apparently inadequate for black pod control when there was much rain. With less rain, fentin acetate applications were about as effective as Bordeaux mixture (Hislop and Park 1962a,b,c; Hislop 1963a). Kocide (cupric hydroxide) was claimed to be a convenient alternative to Bordeaux mixture in Costa Rica (Newhall *et al.* 1968), and in Trinidad (Jones 1971). Muller and Njomou (1970) found that two organic fungicides (Orthodifolatan (Captafol) and triphenyltin hydroxide (Du-Ter)) were superior to a copper formulation (Viricuivre) (Martin 1971).

Forms of Bordeaux mixture have consistently given some control of black pod disease in trials (Hislop 1963a) and commercially (Thorold 1957a; Swarbrick, Toxopeus, and Hislop 1964). Since copper is essential for cocoa (Chapters 6 and 14), there may be some 'tonic effect' in addition to the benefit from the fungitoxic action of this element. However, in Cameroon, Hasselo and Price (1961) attributed increased yields of cocoa from mist-blown copper fungicide to control of black pod rather than to a nutritional effect.

There has been regular spraying of cocoa trees in Fernando Po for at least 30 years (Swarbrick *et al.* 1964). The necessary copper sulphate and lime were imported at the rate of 4,000–5,000 tons of each per year. Since application rates were commonly in the range 100–200 gal. per acre, there were opportunities for uptake of copper from parts of the cocoa tree, or

from the soil, as apparently indicated by some chemical analyses. Determinations provided by Wood, G. A. R. (1971 *in litt.*) showed that copper
content of shell (testa) of prepared beans from Fernando Po (108 p.p.m.
Cu) was greater than the amounts in shells of prepared beans from the
following five countries where the trees were not sprayed regularly with a
copper fungicide: Sarawak (30 p.p.m. Cu), Sierra Leone (32 p.p.m. Cu),
Ivory Coast (35 p.p.m. Cu), Ghana (37 p.p.m. Cu), and Trinidad (40
p.p.m. Cu). The amount in the nib (cotyledons) of Fernando Po beans
(31 p.p.m. Cu) exceeded the amounts in nibs of beans from the other
countries (range 10–21 p.p.m. Cu).

Growth of pod. The surface area of a cocoa fruit at different stages of growth
was estimated from measurements of the length and diameter, in Ghana
(Waters and Hunter 1929) and in Nigeria, where Hislop and Park (1962b)
stated that 'at the maximum rate of growth the area doubles in 10 days and
at least a fivefold increase occurs during 2 months. Even if a fungicide film
were to expand uniformly with the increasing surface area of the pod, and
without developing cracks, growth alone would reduce the deposit to
marginal or ineffective levels in about a month. The effects of weathering
will be superimposed upon this attenuation by growth'. Under field conditions, it is generally convenient to spray at regular intervals. Through
vagaries of weather, such fixed intervals between 'rounds' may be either too
long or too short for maximum efficiency. An interval of 3 weeks between
fungicide applications was adopted somewhat arbitrarily (Thorold 1953a,
1959).

Efficiency of fungicide application. To study the effects of some of the factors
influencing deposits of fungicides in the field, a colorimetric procedure was
sufficiently accurate and more convenient than chemical determination of
copper (Hislop and Park 1962a).

   For large-scale control of black pod disease in Nigeria, it was considered
important to teach farmers how to mix and apply fungicide. Increased
production of cocoa apparently followed instructing 1,000 farmers in 1954,
and over 10,000 farmers for the following season (Hadland and Reeves
1955; Hadland 1957). Subsequently, Hislop (1963b) reported that 184,065
farmers had received instruction.

   The prevention of infection through fruit surfaces by fungicide applications would be vitiated by systemic infection (cushion infection is discussed
on p. 44). Attempts were made to assess the incidence of cushion infection
in Ghana by observing the possible effects of weekly applications of Perenox
paste to all accessible fruits, but the results from this 'pod-painting'
experiment were inconclusive (Wharton 1957, 1958).

   As a possible adjunct to the reduction of infection of fruits by fungicide
applications to their surfaces, the reduction of infection from the soil was
tried. Chemicals which effectively reduced or apparently eliminated *P.*

palmivora in a period of 4 weeks after application to the soil were as follows (Okaisabor 1970): Dexon at 10 per cent a.i. concentration, Plantvax at 10 per cent a.i. concentration, and Tillex (received as 3·3 per cent a.i. solution) was effective at 2–3 per cent concentration (Martin 1971).

Sanitary and cultural methods

There was apparently little or no response in Ghana to recommendations for the elimination of the black pod pathogen (Bunting and Dade 1924). Ameliorative pruning of trees and breeding work to select for disease avoidance were advised instead (Dade 1927b). The presence of old black pods and husk heaps in farms was considered to be unimportant (Dade 1927b; West 1936), and their possible significance in black pod epidemiology is still controversial. There was evidence that *P. palmivora* survived longer in pods on the ground than when remaining attached (Waite and Díaz 1969; Onesirosan 1971). Weststeijn (1969b) disputed that infections of pods near the ground, commonly occurring early in the season, were evidence that the soil was a primary source of infection. Few early infections in the canopy region, in contrast to the greater number nearer the ground, might be accounted for by higher humidity there. Another possibility was that pods near the ground became infected from sources in the canopy. Pending further investigations, sanitary control measures are somewhat empirical.

Whilst the importance of old infections is uncertain, there has been consensus of opinion that avoidance of recently infected material was important. Accordingly, frequent harvesting was recommended for black pod disease control in Nigeria (West 1936) and in Ghana (Owen 1951; Wharton 1962). Further observations in Nigeria indicated that inspection of trees every other day for removal of black pods in the earliest symptom stage, should be recommended as a control measure only for low-yielding trees (< 12 pods per tree), or in an area where black pod disease was not severe (Thorold 1953b). Hislop (1964) noted possible advantages from frequent harvesting and explained that there was reluctance to examine trees in small farms often enough for this method of disease control to be effective, whilst it was unlikely to be practicable for most large farms.

Close spacing of trees was recommended because it was likely to give more healthy pods per acre (p. 43) than wider spacing of trees (Thorold 1959).

Biological control

In mixed culture of *P. palmivora* with *Botryodiplodia theobromae* in wounded pods and on culture medium, *P. palmivora* was suppressed (Okaisabor 1968). There may be opportunities for exploiting the possibility of impeding *P. palmivora* on pod surfaces by weaker pathogens (e.g. *B. theobromae*) or other organisms (p. 160).

Resistance

Black pod disease incidences vary both in time and place. At a site where this disease was generally severe, a small percentage (2 per cent) of the amelonado trees had no black pods in 2 successive years. At a site where the disease was less severe, a larger percentage (26 per cent) of the amelonado trees did not have black pods in 2 successive years (Thorold 1959). I.C.S. 1 was resistant in Jamaica (Rocha and Madeiros 1968) but susceptible in Trinidad (Rocha 1965). Lafi 7 clone had no black pods in Western Samoa, few black pods in Ghana, but was considered susceptible in Cameroon and Malaya (Thorold 1967).

In view of these uncertainties, there were attempts to find a possible chemical basis for apparent resistance to *P. palmivora*. Since increased activity of host polyphenoloxidase is commonly associated with infection by micro-organisms, such a change may be involved in the mechanism of resistance (Maraite 1972). Turner (1965*b*) considered that polyphenol-oxidase activity was not an important factor in conferring resistance to *P. palmivora*. Contrariwise, Rocha and Jiménez (1966*b*) found that resistance of cocoa to *P. palmivora* depended primarily on phenolic substances in the husk, which were fungitoxic. Further studies by Akinrefon (1968*a,b*, 1969) were inconclusive.

It was difficult to devise a test for possible resistance of cocoa to *P. palmivora* without knowing the factor(s) which may determine the success or failure of sporangia or zoospores to infect. The methods tried were reviewed (Rocha 1965, 1966; Rocha and Jiménez 1966*a*; Rocha and Medeiros 1968; Weststeijn 1969*a*).

When detached immature pods were inoculated with *P. palmivora*, significantly fewer sporangia were produced on selections considered to be highly resistant, than on selections which were less resistant or susceptible (Turner 1965*c*). However, tests with detached pods may be unreliable for assessing resistance or susceptibility. Resistance was lessened, or suscepti-bility increased with maturity, and there was breakdown of resistance with inoculation accompanied by wounding (Prendergast and Spence 1965). The inoculation of unwounded attached pods was claimed to give more reliable results in testing for resistance or susceptibility (Adebayo 1971). A fundamental difficulty when testing attached pods, and even more so when they are deliberately removed from the tree (detached pods), is to avoid the presence of at least minor injuries. Limited observations by the writer indicated that the surfaces of detached fruits, even when handled carefully, may differ from the surfaces of intact fruits. It seems that one effect of severing a fruit from the tree is to alter its surface tension properties, either by blemishing and/or through loss of normal turgidity. Casual observations indicated that cocoa fruits were likely to suffer a variety of major or minor injuries in the course of their development.

The frontispiece to this book shows the results of an attempt to demonstrate magnification of the natural surface of a live cocoa fruit, by the use of scanning electron microscopy (Hearle, Sparrow, and Cross 1972). For this purpose, a portion was excised from a 'furrow' of a mature cocoa fruit grown at the Royal Botanic Gardens, Kew, and studied directly at the Jodrell Laboratory, without fixing, dehydrating, or coating. Features shown are stomata on mounds, trichomes (probably glandular), and the outlines of epidermal cells. Tarjot (1972) studied the epidermis of cocoa fruits in connection with penetration by *P. palmivora*. He concluded that the structure of the epidermis, including the numbers of stomata and hairs, was not related to susceptibility to infection. His surface-replication technique seemingly did not reveal whether the stomata were on mounds.

In Trinidad, a 'tissue block method' devised by Prendergast (1965) served to distinguish a number of genotypes but there were some anomalous reactions (Spence and Bartley 1966). In Nigeria, the 'Prendergast method' gave negative results (Weststeijn 1969*a*). Bartley (1969) considered that whole pods were preferable to blocks of pod tissue for testing.

Complications associated with the use of fruits to test for possible resistance to *P. palmivora* prompted trials with young seedlings, notably at Riverside, California, where it was difficult to test pods (Gregory 1969). Four clones tested there for resistance to *P. palmivora*, included 'Catongo' (Medeiros 1965). Vertical cuts, about 5 mm. long were made in the cortex of seedling stems. These cuts were inoculated with disks (3 mm. diameter) from an agar culture of *P. palmivora*. The mean length of the cankers which followed inoculation of the Catongo seedlings was significantly shorter than the mean lengths of stem cankers in the other clones, and some of these seedlings were killed (Zentmyer, Mircetich, and Mitchell 1968). This finding conformed with the resistance to infection shown by fruits of Catongo populations in Bahia, Brazil (Medeiros 1965). In Ghana, amelonado seedlings had stunted roots 8 weeks after adding a sporangial suspension of *P. palmivora* to sand plus nutrients in which they were grown. This fungus was recovered from the affected roots, as described by Turner and Asomaning (1962). They suggested that different responses of roots to similar inoculations might serve to indicate resistance to *P. palmivora*. Asomaning (1964*a,b*) grew and inoculated in sand culture, a range of clones considered to be either resistant or susceptible to black pod disease in Ghana. There were significant dry-weight differences between resistant selections and the susceptible amelonado standard. It was claimed that resistance or susceptibility was a general property of the plant tissues and not a property of the pods alone. Zentmyer *et al.* (1968) made similar experiments but found that root inoculation did not discriminate so satisfactorily between four selections as did the stem inoculation procedure considered above.

The outcome of attempts to develop a satisfactory testing procedure cannot be foreseen. It may suffice for local needs to test a number of cocoa selections for response to indigenous isolates of *P. palmivora*. Nevertheless, scientific interest may require the testing of selections for response to a wider range of isolates. Such comprehensive testing may have to be done either with rigorous phytosanitary precautions, to avoid possible hazards to the local cocoa industry, or with the provision of controlled environments in a country where there will never be commercial cocoa production. In the meantime, there is need to develop field tests, with the realization that apparent resistance may be a manifestation of 'disease avoidance'. For example, the selection referred to as 'ACu85' was considered to be resistant to black pod disease in Ghana (Turner 1962, 1963). It was one of the clones, with low over-all loss of diseased pods which produced most of their crop outside the main epidemic period (Lockwood 1971). It is not yet established satisfactorily that there is consistent resistance to, as well as avoidance of, infection of fruits by *P. palmivora*.

5
POD ROT ASSOCIATED WITH DAMAGE BY VERTEBRATES

Introduction

This chapter considers two important consequences of vertebrate attack on cocoa pods, the contents of which may be either infected *in situ* by fungi or scattered to give volunteer seedlings developing at random. Such animal dispersal probably extended the range of *Theobroma cacao* before this plant was spread by man. There is evidence of bird damage in pre-Columbian times. Thompson (1972*b*) discussed the depiction in the Madrid Codex (Cortés 36; Tro-Cortés 70) of a quetzal (*Pharomacrus mocino* (Pablo de la Llave) (Trogonidae)) attacking a cocoa pod, as illustrated by Seler (1909). This species is now localized through severe exploitation (Stuart 1964). Vertebrate damage is probably a universal cocoa-problem because the pulp surrounding the beans is attractive to ubiquitous animal-groups (e.g. fruit-eating birds, rats and squirrels). Such depredations may have suggested to man the comestible potentiality of cocoa beans.

Economic importance

As the cause of 'brown rot' and under the name *Diplodia cacaoicola*, Bancroft (1910) referred to *Botryodiplodia theobromae* as 'the most serious fungus pest of cacao in the West Indies'. Nowell (1923) explained that its ubiquity had belied its importance. The term 'brown pod rot' is not adopted here, to avoid confusion through its having been used as an alternative name for black pod disease (Miranda and da Cruz 1953).

Inoculation experiments in Surinam showed that *B. theobromae* did not infect healthy pods unless they were wounded, or after removal from the tree (van Hall, A. E. and Drost 1909).

B. theobromae affects over fifty different species of plants (MacFarlane 1968), and occurs in as many different cocoa-growing countries (Chapter 12, pp. 174–5).

Damage to cocoa by vertebrates was considered in general terms by Chalot and Luc (1906). Johnson (1912) referred to considerable damage by squirrels in Ceylon (now Sri Lanka) in 1907. Van Hall (1914) discussed vertebrate damage and noted much damage by rats in S. Tomé. Damage to cocoa by vertebrates has been reported for Nigeria (Everard 1968) and for Sabah (Conway 1971). Entwistle (1972) reviewed the vertebrate pests of cocoa.

None of the vertebrate pests feeds solely on cocoa and depredation varies from year to year. They generally seek the external pulp for food and not whole beans, which are unattractive to rodents (Anon. 1969). Through removal and/or breaching of pods, beans may be deposited at a distance from the parent tree. In Bahia, Silva (1944) reported 'natural establishment of plantations in forest' through seed scattered by the kinkajou (*Potos flavus*) which is a non-carnivorous member of the Carnivora (p. 57). In the course of eliminating cocoa from a part of Trinidad for phytosanitary reasons (Thorold 1945*a*, 1948), some 'self-sown' cocoa seedlings were found in a neglected area where they had probably originated from vertebrate dispersal. Such volunteer cocoa seedlings might have become virus-infected and a potential virus source in an area intended to be free from virus infection (see also Chapter 7, p. 104).

Expenditure on pest and disease control in Trinidad was in the range 1–3 per cent of total annual expenditure on cultivation when witches' broom disease was absent (Shephard 1936). The level of economic loss sustained there through vertebrate damage to cocoa pods was not given.

In Ghana (Taylor 1961; Wharton 1962), percentages of rodent-damaged pods were generally in the range 1–11 per cent and, exceptionally, much greater (20–7 per cent). In Nigeria (Everard 1964) annual losses mostly ranged similarly (1–15 per cent). At Keravat, New Britain, 'flying foxes' (Chiroptera, Pteropodidae) and birds (unspecified) destroyed between 8 and 9 per cent of pods (Hicks 1967). In Sabah, losses through vertebrates were estimated to be in the range 3–6 per cent (Conway 1971). The Sierra Leone cocoa crop suffered severely (*ca,* 25 per cent loss) from damage by monkeys (Mackenzie 1952).

Appearance of damaged pods

The cocoa pod is an indehiscent fruit with a firm and thick (5–15 mm.) pericarp (husk) enclosing the seeds (beans) which are surrounded by pulp (von Bernegg 1934; Cuatrecasas 1964). The intact pod is resistant to invasion by fungi but, when the pericarp is damaged, to expose either the fleshy part within the epidermis or this and the pulp surrounding the beans, then a suitable substrate is provided for fungal infection.

When a pod is infected by *B. theobromae*, the earliest external symptom is a brown discoloration which darkens later. The surface becomes rough through the projections of the pycnidia formed below the epidermis of the pod (Fig. 4E(a,b)).

In Sabah, *B. theobromae* occasionally infected pods through lesions caused by *Glomerella cingulata* (Chapter 12, p. 163). This 'anthracnose fungus' produced raised, shiny, brown, oval blisters which dried and became sunken (Berwick 1964). In Ghana, injured pods were often infected by *Trachysphaera fructigena,* through small rodent-wounds (Wharton 1962).

Taylor (1961) distinguished three kinds of damage to pods by rodents. Mature pods were attacked preferentially and the beans rejected after consumption of the mucilage. In the absence of mature pods, immature fruits might be attacked and then the undeveloped beans were sometimes eaten.

The main pathogen (*Botryodiplodia theobromae* Patouillard)

The brief description of *B. theobromae,* as *Diplodia cacaoicola* Hennings (1895) from cocoa in Cameroon, accords with accounts of an isolate of this species from yam (*Dioscorea* sp.) in Nigeria (Ekundayo and Haskins 1969*a,b*; Ekundayo 1970). Light was required for the production of pycnidia, which measured 135–230 μm. × 95–155 μm. Pycnidiospores were light brown and aseptate at first, but when released were dark brown with a single septum, which was continuous with the secondary spore wall. Pycnidiospores (Fig. 4E(c)) oozed through the ostiolar pore as a white to light brown sticky mass. They measured 24–30 μm. × 11·5–13·5 μm. Germination began after about 2 hours, in liquid or on solid medium, in the range 75–100 R.H. at 25 °C. (77 °F.). Cardinal temperatures were 12·5 °C., 30 °C. and 44 °C. (55 °F., 86 °F., and 111 °F.). One or sometimes two germ-tubes arose from the sides of a pycnidiospore.

Rotting of pods by *B. theobromae* is attributable to its amylolytic, cellulolytic and pectinolytic activities (King and Eggins 1972).

Vertebrates which damage pods

Over sixty species of vertebrates are listed here as suspected attackers of pods, but only a minority of them (*ca.* 8 per cent), which are asterisked*, have been inculpated, either through direct observation in the act of damaging a pod, or through the presence of cocoa-pod particles in stomach contents, although this is not an entirely satisfactory criterion. The status of the remainder (*ca.* 92 per cent) is uncertain. The absence of cocoa particles from stomach contents may be inconclusive, because food materials may be difficult to determine in this way, through fine mastication and possible rapid digestion (Rosevear 1969). The presence of cocoa particles in stomach contents may not implicate a primary pest. Scavenging animals may feed on rejected pod contents or on pods breached by primary pests. Many of the vertebrates trapped in cocoa plantings are likely to be harmless, whilst caged pests may refuse pods in captivity (Everard 1968; Conway 1971).

The present list of vertebrate species may not be exhaustive. There is always a possibility that 'new' vertebrate pests may attack cocoa through 'learned behaviour' (Strecker and Jackson 1962).

It is not known whether vertebrate pests may transmit pod-rotting fungi from infected pods to healthy ones. In Costa Rica, *Ceratocystis paradoxa* was generally not recovered from mouth parts of jays (*Psilorhinus morio cyanogenys*) feeding on pods (Hansen 1964).

List of vertebrates reported as damaging cocoa pods

Groups of genera listed

Bats (PTEROPODIDAE)
Birds (CORVIDAE, MOMOTIDAE, PICIDAE, PSITTACIDAE)
Carnivores (PROCYONIDAE, VIVERRIDAE)
Marsupials (DIDELPHYIDAE)
Primates (CALLITRICHIDAE, CERCOPITHYCIDAE, LORISIDAE, PONGIDAE)
Rodents (CRICETIDAE, ECHIMYIDAE, GLIRIDAE, HETEROMYIDAE, MURIDAE, SCIURIDAE)
* Indicates cocoa-pest status established (see p. 53).

Aeromys tephromelas (Günther) (SCIURIDAE) Black giant flying squirrel.
    ASIA: Sabah (Conway 1971).
Aeromys thomasi (Hose)   Flat-tailed giant flying squirrel.
    ASIA: Sabah (Conway 1971).
Aethiosciurus poensis (A. Smith) (SCIURIDAE) Green squirrel.
    AFRICA: Ghana (Rosevear 1969, this species probably responsible for most of the damage to cocoa pods, *fide* G. S. Cansdale); Sierra Leone (Jones 1970).
Akodon frustrator
see *Zygodontomys brevicauda brevicauda*
Akodon urichi Allen and Chapman (CRICETIDAE) Field mouse.
    WEST INDIES: Trinidad (Urich 1911*b*).
Alouatta seniculus insulanus (CALLITRICHIDAE) Red howler monkey.
    WEST INDIES: Trinidad (Hart 1911, as *Mycetes seniculus*).
Amazona amazonica tobagensis (PSITTACIDAE) Orange-tipped parrot.
    WEST INDIES: Tobago, Trinidad (Herklots 1961).
Arctogalidia sp.   (VIVERRIDAE) Musang.
    ASIA: Malaysia (Leach, Shepherd, and Turner 1971).
Callosciurus lowii
see *Sundasciurus lowii lowii*
Callosciurus notatus (Boddaert) (SCIURIDAE) Plantain squirrel.
    ASIA: Indonesia (Java) (van Hall 1914, as *Sciurus notatus*).
* *Callosciurus prevostii* (Desmarest)   Prevost's squirrel.
    ASIA: Sabah (Conway 1971).
Cercocebus atys atys (CERCOPITHECIDAE) Sooty mangabey.
    AFRICA: Sierra Leone (Mackenzie 1952).
Cercopithecus campbelli campbelli (CERCOPITHECIDAE) Campbell's monkey.
    AFRICA: Sierra Leone (Mackenzie 1952).
Cercopithecus diana diana   Diana guenon.
    AFRICA: Sierra Leone (Mackenzie 1952).
Cercopithecus mona (Schreber)   Mona monkey.
    AFRICA: West Africa (Burle 1961).
Cercopithecus petaurista buettikoferi   Putty-nosed guenon.
    AFRICA: Sierra Leone (Mackenzie 1952).

Cercopithecus sabaeus (L.) Green monkey.
  AFRICA: Sierra Leone (Mackenzie 1952).
Cercopithecus tantalus Ogilby Guenon.
  AFRICA: West Africa (Burle 1961).
Chloronerpes rubiginosus
see *Piculus rubiginosus* (Swainson)
Colobus badius badius (CERCOPITHECIDAE) Red colobus.
  AFRICA: Sierra Leone (Taylor 1961).
Colobus polykomos polykomos Black and white colobus.
  AFRICA: Sierra Leone (Taylor 1961).
Colobus verus van Beneden Olive colobus.
  AFRICA: Sierra Leone (Mackenzie 1952)
* *Cricetomys gambianus* Waterhouse (MURIDAE) Giant Gambian rat.
  AFRICA: Nigeria (Taylor 1961; Everard 1968).
Dephyomys defua (Miller) (MURIDAE) Defua rat.
  AFRICA: Ghana (Taylor 1961; as *Rattus defua*)
Didelphis karkinophaga
see *Didelphis marsupialis marsupialis*
Didelphis marsupialis marsupialis (DIDELPHIDAE) Manicou.
  WEST INDIES: Trinidad (Urich 1911*b*, as *Didelphis karkinophaga*).
Echimys armatus armatus (ECHIMYIDAE) Spiny rat.
  WEST INDIES: Tobago (Urich 1911*b*, *c* as *Loncheres guianae*).
Echimys trinitatis
see *Proechimys cayennensis trinitatis*
Epomophorus gambianus (Ogilby) (PTEROPODIDAE) Gambian fruit bat.
  AFRICA: Nigeria (Everard 1964).
Euxerus erythropus (Desmarest) (SCIURIDAE) Ground squirrel.
  AFRICA: West Africa (Burle 1961, as *Xerus erythropus*).
Funisciurus anerythrus (Thomas) (SCIURIDAE) Red-less squirrel.
  AFRICA: Nigeria (Taylor 1961; Everard 1968; Delany 1972).
Funisciurus lemniscatus (Le Conte) Rope squirrel.
  AFRICA: Congo (Mayné 1917).
Funisciurus pyrrhopus (F. Cuvier) Side-striped tree squirrel.
  AFRICA: Nigeria (Taylor 1961); Sierra Leone (Jones 1970).
Galago demidovii Fischer (LORISIDAE) Small bush-baby.
  AFRICA: Nigeria (Everard 1964).
Graphiurus hueti Rochebrune (GLIRIDAE) Huet's dormouse.
  AFRICA: Nigeria (Everard 1964).
Heliosciurus gambianus (Ogilby) (SCIURIDAE) Gambian sun squirrel.
  AFRICA: Congo (Mayné 1917, as *Heliosciurus punctatus*, probably in error,
  because *H. gambianus punctatus* occurs from Liberia to Ghana, not in Congo,
  fide Rosevear 1969).
Heliosciurus punctatus
see *Heliosciurus gambianus* (Ogilby)
Heliosciurus rufobrachium (Waterhouse) Red-legged sun squirrel.
  AFRICA: Sierra Leone (Jones 1970).
Heteromys anomalus anomalus (HETEROMYIDAE) Grey pouched rat.
  WEST INDIES: Trinidad (Urich 1911*a*, *b*).

Hylobates moloch (Audebert) (PONGIDAE) Borneo gibbon.
    ASIA: Sabah (Conway 1971).
Hylomyscus stella (Thomas) (MURIDAE) Stella wood mouse.
    AFRICA: Nigeria (Everard 1964).
Lemniscomys striatus (L.) (MURIDAE) Spotted wood mouse.
    AFRICA: Nigeria (Everard 1964).
Loncheres guianae
see *Echimys armatus armatus*
Lophuromys sikapusi sikapusi (MURIDAE) Rusty bellied rat.
    AFRICA: Nigeria (Everard 1964).
Macaca fascicularis (Raffles) (CERCOPITHECIDAE) Long-tailed macaque.
    ASIA: Sabah (Conway 1971).
Macaca nemestrina (L.)   Pig-tailed macaque.
    ASIA: Sabah (Conway 1971).
Marmosa carri (Allen and Chapman) (DIDELPHIDAE) Manicou.
    WEST INDIES: Trinidad (Urich 1911*b*, as *Thylamys carri*).
Marmosa murina L.   Manicou.
    WEST INDIES: Trinidad (Urich 1911*b*).
Mastomys coucha
see *Mastomys natalensis* (A. Smith)
Mastomys natalensis (A. Smith) (MURIDAE) Multimammate rat.
    AFRICA: Nigeria (Everard 1964, as *Mastomys coucha*).
* *Melanerpes striatus* (Müller) (PICIDAE) Carpintero.
    WEST INDIES: Dominican Republic (Ciferri 1929*b*, 1961, *Geotrichum candidum* from beans, following damage by *M. striatus*; Ciferri 1930*a*, *Kloeckera* sp. from pods damaged by *M. striatus*; Ciferri 1942, *Aspergillus phoenicis* from pods damaged by *M. striatus*.
Momotus momota bahamensis (MOMOTIDAE) King of the woods.
    WEST INDIES: Trinidad (Urich 1911*a*, as *Momotus swainsonii*).
Momotus swainsonii
see *Momotus momota bahamensis*
Mus alexandrinus
see *Rattus rattus* (L.)
Mus decumanus
see *Rattus norvegicus* (Berkenhout)
Mus rattus
see *Rattus rattus* (L.)
Mycetes seniculus
see *Alouatta seniculus insulanus*
Nectomys palmipes
see *Nectomys squamipes* Brants
Nectomys squamipes Brants (CRICETIDAE) Water rat.
    WEST INDIES: Trinidad (Urich 1911*b*, as *Nectomys palmipes*).
Oryzomys brevicauda
see *Zygodontomys brevicauda brevicauda*
Oryzomys capito valutinus   Rice rat.
    WEST INDIES: Trinidad (Urich 1911*b*, as *Oryzomys velutinus*).

Oryzomys delicatus Allen and Chapman   Rice rat.
WEST INDIES: Trinidad (Urich 1911*b*).

Oryzomys speciosus Allen and Chapman   Rice rat.
WEST INDIES: Trinidad (Urich 1911*b*).

Oryzomys trinitatis Allen and Chapman   Rice rat.
WEST INDIES: Trinidad (Urich 1911*b*).

Oryzomys velutinus
see *Oryzomys capito velutinus*

* *Paradoxurus hermaphroditus* (Pallas) (VIVERRIDAE) Musang.
ASIA: India (Madras) (Abraham and Padmanaban 1967, as *Paradoxurus niger*); Sabah (Conway 1971).

Paradoxurus niger
see *Paradoxurus hermaphroditus* (Pallas)

Petaurista petaurista (Pallas) (SCIURIDAE) Red giant flying squirrel.
ASIA: Sabah (Conway 1971).

Philander trinitatis (Thomas) (DIDELPHIDAE) Manicou gros-yeux.
WEST INDIES: Trinidad (Urich 1911*a*, *b*).

Piculus rubiginosus (Swainson) (PICIDAE) Blue-headed woodpecker.
WEST INDIES: Trinidad (Urich 1911*a*, as *Chloronerpes rubiginosus*).

Potos flavus (Schreber) (PROCYONIDAE) Kinkajou.
SOUTH AMERICA: Brazil (Bahia) (Silva 1944).

Potos sp.   Kinkajou.
SOUTH AMERICA: Ecuador (Fowler and López 1949).

Praomys morio (Trouessart) (MURIDAE) Soft-furred rat.
AFRICA: Ghana (Taylor 1961, as *Rattus morio*).

Praomys tullbergi (Thomas)   Tullberg's soft-furred rat.
AFRICA: Nigeria (Everard 1964).

Proechimys cayennensis trinitatis (ECHIMYIDAE) Spiny rat.
WEST INDIES: Trinidad (Urich 1911*b*, as *Echimys trinitatis*).

Protoxerus stangeri (Waterhouse) (SCIURIDAE) Giant squirrel.
AFRICA: Nigeria (Everard 1968); Sierra Leone (Jones 1970).

Psilorhinus morio
see *Psilorhinus morio cyanogenys*

Psilorhinus morio cyanogenys (CORVIDAE) Brown jay.
CENTRAL AMERICA: Costa Rica (Hansen 1964, *Ceratocystis paradoxa* from pods damaged by *P. morio*).

Pteropus sp. (PTEROPODIDAE) Flying fox.
AUSTRALASIA: New Britain (Hicks 1967).

Rattus defua
see *Dephomys defua* (Miller)

Rattus exulans (Peale) (MURIDAE) Pacific rat.
AUSTRALASIA: Caroline Islands (Strecker and Jackson 1962); Solomon Islands (Rowe 1966).

Rattus longicaudatus
see *Stochomys longicaudatus* (Tullberg)

Rattus morio

see *Praomys morio* (Trouessart)

* *Rattus mülleri* (Jentink)   Müller's rat.
     ASIA: Sabah (Conway 1971).

Rattus norvegicus (Berkenhout)   Norway rat.
     AFRICA: S. Tomé (Johnson 1912, as *Mus decumanus*).

Rattus rattus (L.)   Black rat.
     AFRICA: S. Tomé (Johnson 1912). WEST INDIES: Trinidad (Urich 1911*a*, as *Mus alexandrinus* and *Mus rattus*). AUSTRALASIA: Caroline Islands (Strecker and Jackson 1962); Solomon Islands (Rowe 1966).

Ratufa affinis (Raffles) (SCIURIDAE) Giant squirrel.
     ASIA: Sabah (Conway (1971).

Rhipidomys couesi Allen and Chapman (CRICETIDAE) Long-tailed cocoa rat.
     WEST INDIES: Trinidad (Urich 1911*b*).

Sciurus aestuans hoffmanni
see *Sciurus granatensis chapmani*

Sciurus granatensis chapmani (SCIURIDAE) Squirrel.
     WEST INDIES: Trinidad (Urich 1911*b*, as *Sciurus aestuans hoffmanni*).

Sciurus notatus
see *Callosciurus notatus* (Boddaert)

Stochomys longicaudatus (Tullberg) (MURIDAE) Target rat.
     AFRICA: Nigeria (Taylor 1961, as *Rattus longicaudatus*).

* *Sundasciurus hippurus* (Geoffroy) (SCIURIDAE) Bushy-tailed squirrel.
     ASIA: Sabah (Conway 1971).

Sundasciurus lowii lowii   Short-tailed squirrel.
     ASIA: Sabah (Berwick 1964, as *Callosciurus lowii*).

Thamnomys rutilans (Peters) (MURIDAE) Thicket rat.
     AFRICA: Nigeria (Taylor 1961).

Thylamys carri
see *Marmosa carri* (Allen and Chapman)

Xerus erythropus
see *Euxerus erythropus* (Desmarest)

Zygodontomys brevicauda brevicauda (CRICETIDAE) Cane rat.
     WEST INDIES: Trinidad (Urich 1911*b*, as *Akodon frustrator* and as *Oryzomys brevicauda*).

Control

Chemical methods

The presence of a fungicide did not repel rodents in Ghana, consequently sprayed pods were lost through fungal infection following rodent attack (Wharton 1962). In these circumstances, control measures have been attempted directly against the vertebrates causing primary damage.

Rodenticides or poisons with a wider 'spectrum' of vertebrate toxicity (e.g. barium carbonate or strychnine) are unlikely to be generally effective in cocoa plantings because affected areas cannot be isolated nor biologically restricted (Davis 1970). However, Friend (1971) reported economical control of damage to cocoa pods in the Solomon Islands by rats (*Rattus exulans* and *R. rattus*) through use of warfarin (Martin 1971) bait distributed in bamboo bait-containers. He suggested, and Murray (1968) also recommended, warfarin-baited paraffin-blocks, as used for rat control in coconut plantings (Smith 1967).

Certain chemicals have been applied to foliage to deter browsing animals, but the problem of protecting cocoa pods against animals which gnaw, but do not consume the husk, is different (Taylor 1961). Thiram has been used successfully as a protective fungicide, and at high doses to repel mice (Martin 1971), but did not protect cocoa pods against vertebrate damage (Taylor 1961; Conway 1971).

Physical methods

Since none of the vertebrates are absolute cocoa pests, control based on extensive slaughter campaigns is likely to be inefficient and ineffective, as was apparently the case in Sierra Leone where nearly a quarter of a million monkeys were destroyed in subsidized 'drives' (Jones 1970). However, over an extended period, small-scale destruction by shooting and trapping has restricted monkey populations elsewhere in West Africa (Urquhart 1955; Sabater Pí and Groves 1972), where there were economic incentives and absence of religious scruples. On the other hand, short-term destruction of mammals by shooting or trapping was costly and doubtfully efficacious in Sabah (Conway 1971).

Cultural methods

Regular and frequent harvesting of ripe pods will restrict their availability. Weekly removal of pods reduced losses through rodent damage in Ghana (Wharton 1955) but not in British Solomon Islands (Friend 1971).

The climbing vertebrates which damage pods visit, but do not generally inhabit, cocoa trees. In Nigeria, damage was greater on trees close to the periphery of plantings adjacent to forest or other uncultivated land (Delany 1972). However, *Cricetomys gambianus*, which is not an adept climber, burrows in cocoa plantings (Taylor 1961). Nevertheless, as a general principle and when practicable, the following statement by Conway (1971) should be heeded. 'Control measures should firstly be directed against damage in plantings adjoining primary or secondary forest. Land should be cleared to leave as bare a strip as possible and at least twenty yards [18 m.] wide between the cocoa and the forest.'

6
CHERELLE WILT

Introduction

The word 'cherelle' which is commonly used for the immature fruits of cocoa may have been derived in Trinidad from a Mexican word apparently used there originally, as implied by Olivieri (1897). He stated that 'the young pods when newly thrown out by the flowers are called "chileros" on account of their shape and resemblance to the well-known "bird pepper" [*Capsicum* sp., cultivar]'. The term 'cherelle' is not well defined but refers to a limited size-range of immature fruits. All cherelles are immature fruits, but not all immature fruits are cherelles because they may be either smaller or larger than the arbitrary size-range. A cocoa tree generally matures a small proportion of the immature fruits which mostly shrivel but usually remain attached. This phenomenon is loosely referred to as 'cherelle wilt', following the reference by Pound (1932c) to 'wilting cherelles'. Nichols (1964b) distinguished 'biotic wilt' (due to damage by insects and/or fungi) from 'physiological wilt' (due to other causes). In this account of cherelle wilt the possible cause of the fruit loss is generally disregarded, except when the above categories are mentioned.

There have been general reviews of cherelle wilt (Voelcker 1938b; Nosti 1953; Hardy 1960a; Burle 1961; Nichols 1965a; Eernstman 1968) and of biotic wilt by Entwistle (1972).

History

The cause of the so-called 'blast' which affected Trinidad cocoa in about 1727 is controversial because contemporary details were inadequate for certain diagnosis (Shephard 1932a). Gumilla (1791) mentioned the abundant flowering of cocoa trees in Trinidad and commented on the production of some fruits throughout the year. His reference to the losses of 'almond-sized' fruits would be applicable to cherelle wilt today. Losses of immature fruits in Venezuela were attributed to unsatisfactory seasonal distribution of rainfall (de Pons 1806).

Economic importance

Without losses of cherelles through wilt, cocoa yields would theoretically be increased about ten-fold (Nosti 1953; Nichols 1965a).

Cheesman (1927) introduced his fundamental study of cocoa embryology by commenting that there was a dearth of information on the biology of *Theobroma cacao*, and he noted the need for further study of the failure of many young pods to mature. The possible reduction of losses through wilt was an immediate objective of the botanical programme (Cheesman 1932*b*) of the Cacao Research Scheme in Trinidad (Evans 1932).

Cherelle wilt differs from fruit shedding in other perennial crops, since it continued despite drastic fruit-thinning (Nichols 1965*a,c*). Some cocoa trees give good yields with much cherelle wilt, and other cocoa trees give poor yields with little cherelle wilt (Nichols 1965*a*). Such a range of cropping behaviour in Ghana was shown by ten trees (designated alphabetically as A–J), which Hewison and Ababio (1930) recorded individually for flowering, setting, wilting, and maturation of pods as summarized in Table 6.1, Cheesman (1932*a*) discussed the data.

TABLE 6.1

Analysis of behaviour of ten trees (A–J) in Ghana from 1 January 1929 to 31 October 1929

Tree	A	B	C	D	E	F	G	H	I	J
Number of flowers	5,350	3,348	4,669	5,842	8,319	1,605	1,099	1,617	1,952	1,991
Number of fruits set	48	43	47	33	97	17	11	21	30	18
Number of fruits wilted	35	18	31	16	46	9	4	6	12	4
Number of pods	13	25	16	17	51	8	7	15	18	14

Table 6.1 shows that tree *E* which gave the best yield (fifty-one pods) also lost the greatest number of immature fruits through wilt (forty-six fruits), in contrast to tree *G* which yielded least (seven pods) and lost fewest immature fruits (four). Tree *E* flowered almost continuously from 5 January to 1 October, whilst tree *G* bore no flowers until 2 April and then bore very few from 18 June until 23 July, when flowering ceased (Hewison and Ababio 1930).

An hypothesis is given below (p. 66) which serves to explain the situations suggested by Nichols (1965*a*) when cherelle wilt might either affect yield (flowering and setting disfavoured, or favoured but with much biotic wilt), or not affect yield (flowering and setting favoured, in combination with little or no biotic wilt). Without data for quantifying these conditions, the possible economic effects of cherelle wilt cannot be assessed.

Symptoms

General

Common names given to immature-fruit losses refer to one or other of two evident symptoms (1 and 2); a less evident one is critical (3).

1. Loss of turgor, hence the term 'cherelle wilt' and 'marchitez' in Venezuela (Nosti 1953).
2. Premature ripening, hence the term 'yellowing', 'mela' in S. Tomé (Patouillard 1922*b*), 'melado' in Fernando Po (Nosti 1953).
3. Cessation of fruit growth occurs shortly before visible symptoms (1 and 2) with loss of natural 'bloom' (Nichols 1961*d*).

Physiological wilt

Wilted fruits, characteristically less than 10 cm. long, differed internally from normal fruits of similar size when examined in median cross-section which showed a 'pentagonal area' of tissue (indicated diagrammatically by Nichols (1961*d*)). In normal fruits, this pentagonal area of tissue was at first creamy white and became oxidized to a brown colour within $1-1\frac{1}{2}$ min. of being cut. In early and later stages of wilt, the pentagonal area of tissue was already discoloured. In explanation of this phenomenon, Nichols (1961*d*) stated that 'in the wilting pod, spatial separation of the enzyme (polyphenol oxidase) and its substrates has broken down and oxidation of the substrate has proceeded'. He used an injection procedure to study the vascular systems in normal and wilted fruits and their stalks. Wilted fruits had vessel occlusions which differed in quantity between early and late wilting stages. In the early stage some vessels were clear, but in the late-wilt stage all vessels had occlusions, which were not tyloses but appeared to be mucilaginous in origin. The progressive development of these 'mucilage plugs' suggested that they were not primarily responsible for wilt. As indicated above, the first indication of this disorder is the cessation of growth and a slight loss of turgor. An immediate shrinkage of the fruit would be expected if blockage of the vessels occurred at the inception of wilting. Daily observations of about fifty small fruits showed that after increase in length ceased, a period of about 4–6 days elapsed before a decrease in length was apparent. It seemed that growth in length ceased through breakdown of fruit-cambium. The pentagonal area considered above, was at first nearly circular, as observed in cross-section of fruits 1–3 days after fertilization. A ring of vascular bundles within this tissue comprised a 'meristematic ring' or cambial band which normally provided new vascular tissue for the pericarp. It seemed that the precocious oxidation of the pentagonal area indicated breakdown of the cambial band with cessation of growth in length and loss of turgor in the early wilt stage. Later, occlusions in the vessels of the fruit-stalk restricted the water supply and caused the shrivelling which characterized the late wilt stage (Nichols 1961*d*).

Through abnormal failure to absciss, wilted fruits are frequently retained, and hence they have been said to 'mummify' on the tree. In the course of development after pollination, there is a period of about 2 weeks when a pollinated ovary may either absciss or wilt. The physiological relationships by which abscission is operative or bypassed are not fully understood. The morphology and anatomy of the constriction where abscission occurs were described and illustrated by Pound (1932b).

Biotic wilt

In Costa Rica, Bartolomé (1952) found that most wilted cherelles had lesions, caused either by insects or by fungi. During 5 years in Venezuela, Reyes, de Reyes, and Armas (1969) recorded sound cherelles and wilted ones which they classified as due to insects, or to fungi, or to 'other causes'. Other workers have found such discrimination difficult to practise because biotic attack may be either primary or secondary, as in S. Tomé (Kaden 1933). Entwistle (1972) discussed fungal infection following insect attack and described wilt symptoms due to direct insect attack, which are beyond present scope. It is difficult to distinguish between physiological wilt and primary or secondary infection of cherelles by *Phytophthora palmivora* (McKelvie 1960). This difficulty may affect cherelle-wilt classification, because cherelles and other immature fruits may together constitute a considerable proportion (*ca.* 70–80 per cent) of the fruits of different ages infected by *P. palmivora* (Wharton 1959). When a large fruit is infected by *P. palmivora*, the symptomatic brown spot is evident for one or more days. When a small fruit is infected by *P. palmivora*, the 'brown spot' immediately involves the whole surface. This brown discoloration of an infected cherelle resembles the brown colour which follows the initial yellowing of a fruit suffering from physiological wilt.

The onset of biotic wilt was studied through its simulation by ring-barking the fruit-stalk (McKelvie 1956). Fruits stabbed with either needles or cork borers also wilted (Nichols 1965b).

Aetiology of physiological wilt

Fruit setting and shedding

Pound (1932c) observed that cherelles which wilted when about 2·3 in. (5·9 cm.) long had evidently been pollinated because there was an insignificant difference between the numbers of ovules in wilted and sound fruits. Using hand-pollination for selfing and crossing among eight different clones, he showed that some were self-compatible (S.C.) whilst others were self-incompatible (S.I.), and he supposed that the fertilization process had failed when the flowers on S.I. trees received their own pollen. By cytological studies, Cope (1939b) confirmed that there was no important difference in the behaviour of pollen tubes in compatible and incompatible matings. Further, he showed that incompatible pollen-tubes penetrated and delivered gametes into the ovules (Cope 1940). Subsequently (Cope 1962a), from the resumption of these investigations in 1948, he concluded that 'the site of the incompatibility reaction in cacao lies not in the style but in the embryo sac. The reaction, indeed is not determined until the

male gametes, delivered into the embryo sac, come to lie in contact with
their female counterparts. Where the pollination is incompatible, the proportion of "non-fusion" ovules in the ovary is either 25 per cent, 50 per
cent, or nearly, if not quite 100 per cent of all ovules receiving male gametes
("fertilized ovules")'.

Losses of flowers and fruits by S.C. and S.I. trees were studied in
Trinidad (Cope 1939a, 1962a). The S.C. trees averaged 3,358 flowers per
tree per year, but the average number of fruits harvested was 7·5 pods per
tree per year. The S.I. trees averaged 5,207 flowers per tree per year, with
an average yield of 4·4 pods per tree per year. The average percentage of
fruits lost through wilt was smaller (47 per cent) for S.I. trees compared
with the average percentage loss for S.C. trees (67 per cent), because the
average number of cherelles set per tree per year was greater for the S.C.
trees (36·6) than for the S.I. trees (13·0).

The incompatibility mechanism is genetically controlled (Cope 1962a,b).
Upper Amazon cocoa was considered to be uniformly S.I., whilst West
African amelonado was uniformly S.C. Trinitario and other heterogeneous
populations contain both S.C. and S.I. trees. It seems that under field
conditions, compatibility may be an important but not necessarily an over-
riding factor determining cherelle-wilt losses. The ranges of losses in Ghana
(22–85 per cent) and in Trinidad (19–93 per cent) were similar (Hewison
and Ababio 1930; Pyke 1933b).

In Trinidad, Humphries (1943b) found that the growth cycle of the fruit
had two phases, the first of these occupied about 75 days, the first period
of the second phase (75–87 days) was one of active metabolism, starting
when the fruit was about 10–11 cm. long and beginning to swell, as indicated by the increase in the ratio of diameter to length (D/L). Nichols
(1964a) considered that the D/L ratio was the only external parameter of
the fruit which could be associated with the change from the wilting to the
non-wilting phase. Initially, this D/L ratio was fairly constant (ca. 0·35) in
Trinidad (Humphries 1940, 1943b) and Ghana (Waters and Hunter 1929;
McKelvie 1956), until at an age of about 80–100 days the diameter increased
relatively more quickly $(D/L$ ca. 0·45). This sudden increase in diameter
occurred when the fruit length was about 10 cm., in Ghana (Waters and
Hunter 1929), in Trinidad (Humphries 1943a), and in Costa Rica (Schroeder 1958), or rarely when the fruit length was about 13 cm. (Dale 1953;
Nichols 1964a). These external modifications are associated with important
internal changes. Cheesman (1927) found that the first division in the
embryo sac (endosperm nucleus) occurred 3–4 days after compatible
pollination. The first division of the fertilized egg did not occur until 40–50
days later. The embryo was recognizable in a fruit 5 cm. long, at an age of
about 50 days. In a fruit about 10 cm. long, aged about 87 days, the embryo
was still small (0·2 mm. long). This is the stage when there is further
division and development of the zygote, and resumed growth of the

endosperm. It also corresponds with the transition from the wilting to the non-wilting phase.

Pollination and fertilization failures

Cheesman (1927) found that pollen germinated quickly when placed on a stigmatic lobe, and 1 hour later the pollen tubes were nearly half-way down the style. They began to reach the ovules in about 4 hours and could be traced to the micropyles. There were discrepancies between numbers of ovules per ovary and numbers of beans per pod in Trinidad (Pound 1932a, 1933a,b). However, variability in bean number (range of means 15·5–47·5 beans per pod) did not arise from variability in ovule number (range of means 40·3–48·3 ovules per ovary). There were seldom, if ever, pods with fewer than about 15 beans per pod. The number of pollinated ovules will presumably be similar to the number of pollen grains reaching the pistil. It was not essential for pollen to be placed on the stigma, since hand-pollination was effective when pollen was placed at the base of the style (Posnette 1938). Cope (1959) reported that 'counted numbers of pollen grains were applied to incompatible stigmas, and the ovules sectioned. In all cases the number of ovules fertilised was only very little less than the number of grains applied'. It seems that cherelles which have received insufficient pollen (less than *ca.* 15 grains) will abort (wilt). There may be many wilted cherelles in this category (having received insufficient pollen). In Indonesia, van der Knaap (1955) reported about 90 per cent pistils with less than 11 pollen grains per pistil.

Table 6.2 summarizes results obtained by Ruinard (1963) in West Irian (formerly West New Guinea), which demonstrated setting failures and successes, and subsequent losses by abscission, with and without hand-pollination (natural pollination was prevented).

TABLE 6,2

Numbers of ovaries remaining on trees in West Irian, expressed as percentages of total numbers of flowers pollinated (compatibly or incompatibly) or not pollinated

Number of days from flower opening or pollination		2 (%)	7 (%)	14 (%)
Compatible pollinations	(790 flowers = 100 %)	85·6	73·5	68·9
Incompatible pollinations	(578 flowers = 100 %)	72·5	2·5	0·0
Not pollinated	(192 flowers = 100 %)	15·6	0·0	—

Table 6.2 shows the prompt (after 2 days) abscission of unpollinated flowers and the transitory 'setting', with complete abscission after 1 week of flowers subjected to incompatible pollination.

Nutrition

An apparent association between incidence of cherelle wilt and occurrence of leaf flushing was noted early in the Trinidad investigations (Pound 1933*d*; Pyke 1933*b*), and was noticed recently in Uganda (Couprie 1972). However, the factors influencing flushing are controversial (Alvim, Machado, and Vello 1972). There is evidence that flushing behaviour is rhythmic and that the major controlling factors are probably endogenous (Greathouse, Laetsch, and Phinney 1971).

Nichols and Walmsley (1965) measured radiation from fruits on small cocoa trees grown in containers to which ^{32}P had been added as orthophosphate. Translocation of phosphorus into a wilting fruit ceased, and there was no movement out again when wilting was well advanced. This restricted movement was in accord with expectation because xylem vessels in the stalk of a wilted fruit became occluded (p. 62). It seemed that this blockage functioned similarly to abscission in separating the wilting fruit from the parent plant. An unforeseen phenomenon was the higher content of phosphate expressed on a dry-weight basis. This may have reflected either a reduced transport of organic substances into wilting fruits, or a loss of carbon through respiration, when wilting began. Seeschaaf (1971) found that wilted cherelles had smaller amounts of carbon and nitrogen than normal cherelles, improbably through back transport to the tree. He considered that lessened amounts of reducing sugars did not cause wilt but resulted through respiration which continued after the onset of yellowing.

The scheme described and illustrated diagrammatically by Nichols (1964*b*) serves conveniently as a possible wilting *modus operandi*. It is supposed that the total number of fruits set (represented as s) is normally in excess of the potential yield (number of potential pods p). The difference may be considered as a reserve of fruits (number $r = s - p$). Accordingly, it follows that actual yield should be equivalent to the potential yield when $s > r$, but actual yield will be less than potential yield if too few fruits are set ($s < r$) because, by definition, $p = s - r$. Nichols (1965*a*) concluded that 'yields are more likely to be reduced by under-setting than oversetting'. Enhanced setting as a possible means of alleviating cherelle wilt is considered below (p. 67).

Amelioration of losses through cherelle wilt

Chemical methods

Pesticides have received attention in connection with possible control of biotic wilt, and with respect to their possible effect on insect pollinators, or on the pollination mechanism, as discussed by Entwistle (1972).

Widespread use of fungicides for control of certain cocoa diseases seems to controvert the drastic effects of copper fungicides on pollen germination and pod production reported in Colombia (Naundorf 1952). Insecticides were also considered to impair pollination in Colombia (Naundorf and Miller 1952; Cardona 1953). Elsewhere, insecticides did not apparently affect pollination: Bahia, Brazil (Ventocilla 1969), Congo (Dessart 1961), Ghana (Entwistle and Hurd 1959; Gerard 1964; Lamb 1957), and Indonesia (Java) (Soerjobroto Widjanarko 1967).

Growth-substances were claimed to have reduced cherelle wilt in Colombia (Murray 1953), but studies in Ghana (McKelvie 1955; 1957a) and in Trinidad (Nichols 1957, 1959b, 1960, 1961a, 1965b) were inconclusive.

Physical methods

The structure of the floral parts of cocoa and the physical character of the pollen are such that wind pollination can occur only rarely if ever (Urquhart 1961). Harland (1925) imitated wind action by shaking the flower but was unable to demonstrate deposition of pollen on stigma or style. Billes (1941) tried shaking, blowing, and exposing flowers to natural air-movement but no pollination occurred when insects were excluded. He studied the possibility that pollen might be water-borne, but this could not be demonstrated. Air movement may affect pollination indirectly. Factors determining both distance and direction were detected and may have operated through the influence of air movement on the flight of pollinators (Glendinning 1962). Enhanced activity of pollinators through turbulence created mechanically was suggested by Knoke and Saunders (1966) as a possible explanation for the increased pollination apparently associated with application of water by mist-blowers at Turrialba, Costa Rica. It is also possible that mechanical pollination occurred because the flowers were agitated more violently than would normally occur through wind action. Soria and Cerdas (1966) claimed increased fruit-setting through using a 'sorghum brush' which was passed over flowering branches, thereby apparently accomplishing some pollination through flower movement.

Small-scale hand-pollination of cocoa flowers was used successfully (Pound 1932c; McKelvie 1956; Hurtado 1960; Soria, J. 1971; Edwards 1972a). There is reason to believe that large-scale hand pollination of cocoa could be practised economically (Edwards 1972b).

Natural pollination

Saunders (1959) commented that cocoa pollination was done largely, if not exclusively, by midges of the genus Forcipomyia (Ceratopogonidae). For present purposes, it is convenient to disregard subgeneric divisions of this genus (Forcipomyia (sensu stricto), Proforcipomyia, Thyridomyia) which were considered by Entwistle (1972). Ten fully identified species are given here (numbered 1–10), which on circumstantial evidence were probable or possible cocoa pollinators. The geographical distributions of these and other species are not fully ascertained. One species (3) was considered to be cosmopolitan, and another (4) had a pantropical distribution (Dessart 1963).

1. *Forcipomyia ashantii* Ingram and Macfie was trapped in a cocoa flower in Ghana (Posnette 1950*a*),

2. *Forcipomyia falcifera* Saunders was reported as breeding in a bromeliad (Chapter 12, p. 170) on a cocoa shade-tree in Trinidad (Saunders 1959).

3. *Forcipomyia fuliginosa* (Meigen) was reported as probably a cocoa pollinator in the Philippine Islands (Fontanilla-Barroga 1965).

4. *Forcipomyia indecora* Kieffer was reported, as *Forcipomyia ingrami* Carter trapped in a cocoa flower in Ghana (Posnette 1950*a*).

5. *Forcipomyia litoraurea* (Ingram and Macfie) was reported as trapped in a cocoa flower in Ghana (Posnette 1950*a*).

6. *Forcipomyia mortuifolii* Saunders was reported as breeding in the leaf-litter of cocoa estates in Trinidad. A single captive female enclosed with cocoa flowers had pollen grains on the thorax (Saunders 1959).

7. *Forcipomyia nana* (Macfie) males and females were taken from cocoa flowers in Trinidad (Macfie 1944).

8. *Forcipomyia setigera* Saunders was breeding in leaf-litter in a Trinidad cocoa estate (Saunders 1959).

9. *Forcipomyia squamipennis* Ingram and Macfie was found resting on cocoa flowers in Ghana (Gerard 1966).

10. *Forcipomyia stylifer* Lutz was taken from a cocoa flower in Trinidad (Macfie 1944).

Forcipomyia quasi-ingrami Macfie (1944) is excluded because this name was given to a congeries of species (Saunders 1956).

It is worth noting that *Atrichopogon brevipalpis* Macfie (Ceratopogonidae) was taken from moss on cocoa trunks in Trinidad (Macfie 1944).

Posnette (1944*b*) explained the dexterity necessary for capture and described the behaviour of individual ceratopogonids from alighting until departure from the flowers. The *Forcipomyia* species studied by Billes (1941) was probably *F. indecora* (as *F. ingrami*), it could not be easily observed in flight except when carrying a ball of pollen which might be nearly half as large as the insect. The procedure by which pollen was acquired and deposited was discussed and illustrated diagrammatically by Posnette and Entwistle (1957). These midges may obtain nutriment from the glandular hairs on various parts of the cocoa flower, which were described by Stejskal (1969). He found that excretion of these hairs contained sugar and he regarded them as nectaries.

In Ghana, Entwistle (1957) found two 'peaks' of cocoa pollination during the day. The major one was from sunrise (about 6 a.m.) until about 9 a.m. The minor one was in the afternoon (2–3 p.m.). Pollination had ceased by

6 p.m. Periodicity in the Philippines was similar to that observed in Ghana (Fontanilla-Barroga 1965). It is likely that periods of activity might be repressed by either wind or rain, as found for similar midges which pollinated *Hevea brasiliensis* flowers in Brazil (Warmke 1952).

The biology of the ceratopogonid pollinators of cocoa flowers has received some attention (Saunders 1959; Dessart 1961), but information is inadequate for rational attempts to promote populations of these insects. There is particular need for such enhancement at times when few (about 5 per cent) flowers are pollinated naturally (Dessart 1961; Soria, S. de J. 1971). Abundant flowering with little setting is exemplified by the incidence of so-called 'crazy flowering' in Trinidad, which was due to a low level of natural pollination, as shown by hand-pollination tests (Voelcker 1938a).

The factors influencing populations of ceratopogonid pollinators are not understood. In Trinidad, these insects were present in soil and litter samples from estates having clay soils, but were absent from samples taken where the soils were described as sand or silt (Strickland 1945).

There is some evidence that certain members of the wingless order Collembola may pollinate cocoa flowers. Other members of this order were caught at heights in the air (Johnson 1969), indicating the likelihood that they may be airborne for considerable distances. Springtails (Collembola) carried *Piper nigrum* pollen in Puerto Rico (Free 1970). Lawrence, P. N. (1971 *in litt.*) reported specimens of *Salina* sp. (Collembola, Paronellidae) from cocoa flowers in New Britain, Territory of Papua and New Guinea. Specimens were subsequently identified by Dr. S. K. Mitra as *Salina celebensis* (Schäffer) (Lawrence, P. N. 1972 *in litt.*). The guts of some specimens contained pollen grains which were examined by Dr. N. K. B. Robson and moss gemmae which were examined by Mr. A. Eddy. Identifications of the pollen grains were uncertain, some might have been those of cocoa but others were not. The gemmae belonged to species of the family Calymperaceae, which is represented by *Calymperes* spp., recorded as epiphytes on cocoa trees (Chapter 12, p. 217). The possibility that *S. celebensis* included cocoa pollen in its diet suggests that such activity might contribute to the pollination of cocoa.

The possible role of springtails as cocoa pollinators is speculative. However, it is worth noting that unidentified Collembola were present in the litter-layers of cocoa estates in Trinidad where Ceratopogonidae were not invariably present (Strickland 1945).

Confirmation is needed for the claim by Vello and Magalhães (1971) that cocoa pollination and yield in Bahia were enhanced through the presence of ants (*Azteca chartifex* Forel, Formicidae) which might excrete a substance that attracted pollinating midges. In Trinidad, *A. chartifex* was inimical to pod production (Entwistle 1972).

7
VIRUS DISEASES

Introduction

Martyn (1968) included five *viruses* and four *suspected viruses* (other reported virus diseases) as affecting cocoa. This separation is used now. 'Virus disease' status has been established through transmission by vector or by grafting, but has not been similarly established for 'suspected virus disease'. All these disorders have in common the departure of cocoa from normality, with potential economic importance. They are grouped together on the negative characters of apparent absence of either pathogenic organism or primary nutritional cause (Chapter 14).

Geographical distribution

Cocoa virus diseases occur in West Africa (Ghana, Ivory Coast, Nigeria, Sierra Leone), in Sri Lanka, and in Trinidad. It is possible that Brunt (1970a) erroneously included Togo Republic among the West African cocoa-belt countries in which swollen-shoot virus disease occurs. This error might have occurred through misinterpretation of the statement by Thresh and Tinsley (1959) that scattered outbreaks occurred in Trans-Volta and Togoland. It is now incorrect to record virus occurrences east of the Volta River as from 'Togoland', 'Togo', or 'Trans-Volta'. Such incidences were within the present Volta Region of Ghana, which extends eastwards from the Volta River to the boundary between the former British and French Mandated Territories of Togoland, as demarcated in 1930 (Massigli and Cadogan 1930). It is not known for certain whether cocoa virus disease occurs in Togo Republic. Krug and Quartey-Papafio (1964) stated for Togo Republic that 'swollen-shoot disease has been discovered, but measures have been taken to control it'. No further details were given.

Suspected virus diseases of cocoa occur elsewhere in Africa (Cameroon and Zanzibar (Tanzania)), in the West Indies (Dominican Republic), and in Asia (Indonesia (Java and Sumatra) and Malaysia (Sabah)).

Tinsley (1959) reviewed worldwide occurrences of cocoa virus diseases. Entwistle (1972) discussed West African cocoa virus diseases and considered occurrences in eastern and western hemispheres.

Economic importance

Steven (1936a,b) applied the term 'swollen-shoot' to a particular disorder of cocoa in the Eastern Region of Ghana. Thresh (1958a) stated that swollen-shoot disease 'is one of the most important factors limiting the production of cocoa and is one of the most economically important plant diseases in the world'. Over a hundred million diseased cocoa trees were destroyed in the Eastern Region of Ghana, and adequate control was not achieved (Legg and Kenten 1968). The eradication procedure is generally referred to as 'cutting-out', and this term is used now, but Entwistle (1972) used the word 'grubbing'. The cutting-out programme has been costly both in monetary terms and through its serious political repercussions (Watson, Dalgleish, and Murray 1948).

Padwick (1956) estimated that the proportion of the world's cocoa crop lost through swollen-shoot was about 10 per cent (> 10 per cent in Ghana; < 10 per cent in Nigeria). He emphasized the seriousness of the economic effects which involved both annual losses of production and 'capital depreciation' through destruction of trees.

Outside West Africa, only in Trinidad have the effects of virus on cocoa yields been analysed statistically, through use of data from clonal trials at River Estate. Affected trees carried non-lethal virus. There was evidence that yields from trees infected with virus might tend to fall to a low level and remain stationary. Although the rate of decline in manured trees was almost four times that in unmanured trees, nevertheless infected trees grown under favourable conditions might still give better yields than less favoured infected trees (Cope 1953b).

Nomenclature and terminology of cocoa viruses

In a publication dated 19 May, Box (1945) used numbers (I, II, III, IV) to designate four viruses affecting cocoa in Ghana. Posnette (1947b) explained that in 1944 he had distributed a mimeograph list of letters in use for viruses, and he discussed strains A, B, and C in a paper dated 23 February 1945, presented at the Cocoa Research Conference held in May–June (Posnette 1945). Therefore his use of letters for cocoa viruses preceded the numbers used by Box (1945), and the use of this alphabet nomenclature continued. The original procedure was to use letters for 'strains' and numbers for 'distinct viruses', as did Posnette (1947b) when he described 1A, 1B, 1C and 1D, and as also did Crowdy and Posnette (1947).

Extensive surveys revealed a tendency for isolated outbreaks to contain new 'virus strains' (Voelcker 1947). The 'labelling' by letters of numerous viruses had exhausted most of the alphabet when Posnette (1950c) considered seventeen viruses (A–Y) from West African localities. He used subjacent numerals to distinguish three Nigerian viruses (O_1 and O_2 from Olanla, O_3 from Ilesha), but this was inconvenient and so the alphabet nomenclature was not further developed. When more than seventy West African isolates were being studied (Tinsley 1953a), Tinsley (1953b) reverted to the locality nomenclature given as synonyms by Posnette (1947b), and this was used for Nigerian isolates (Thresh 1961). Because their proper botanical meanings are too precise for present purposes (Chapter 1, p. 4), it is desirable to avoid the terms 'type' (Mangenot, Alibert, and Basset 1946a) and 'form' (Renaud 1957) used in referring to Ivory Coast viruses. The term 'strain' as used for Trinidad viruses (Baker and Dale 1947a) may also be inappropriate. In accord with the opinion expressed by Thresh and Tinsley (1959), the non-committal term 'isolate' is used for viruses named after the locality in Ghana, Ivory Coast, Nigeria, Sierra Leone, and Trinidad, where virus-infected material originated.

Abbreviations

Tinsley (1953b) and Martyn (1968) used the abbreviation 'C.S.S.V.' and conformable ones were adopted (Brunt and Kenten 1971). The following abbreviations are used here for six viruses infecting cocoa: C.S.S.V. (cocoa swollen-shoot virus), C.M.L.V. (cocoa mottle-leaf virus), C.Y.M.V. (cocoa yellow mosaic virus), C.N.V. (cocoa necrosis virus), C.C.V. (Ceylon cocoa virus), and C.T.V. (cocoa (Trinidad) virus).

Symptom expression in general

Stem and root swellings

Steven (1936a,b) first reported the effects of C.S.S.V. in Ghana, through observing the abnormal thickening of the stems (Fig. 4F(c), p. 12). Sections of hypertrophied stems showed that these swellings were caused by localized increases in amounts of secondary phloem and xylem (Posnette 1947b). The cambial zone averaged eight cells, as opposed to six cells in the normal stem. The phloem cells were distorted and had a greater diameter than normally. The tracheids in swellings were larger than elsewhere and xylem vessels occurred in clusters (Knight and Tinsley 1958). Similar anatomical features characterized the swellings on roots, and necrosis was reported (Goodall 1949). Some isolates produced root swellings but no stem swellings (Thresh and Tinsley 1959). In a limited number of swellings seen in Sri Lanka, there was discoloration involving phloem and adjacent tissues (Orellana and Peiris 1957).

Either the node, or internode or apex of a stem may swell (Brunt and Kenten 1971). When a thin leafless shoot with shortened internodes is affected, this appearance may resemble certain manifestations of witches' broom disease (Chapter 2). However, stems affected by C.S.S.V. are characteristically desiccated (Goodall 1949) and may show a 'brittle twig' symptom. Twigs and chupons of infected trees snap cleanly, in contrast to the ragged 'greenstick' fracture of healthy twigs (Attafuah 1960).

Leaf abnormalities

Leaf symptoms were first reported by Posnette (1941). In the absence of swellings with some virus isolates, leaf symptoms may be transient so that infected plants are at times symptomless.

A healthy young leaf of an amelonado tree contains a red pigment which gives the leaf a pinkish colour at first. Some mesophyll cells adjacent to the veins are filled with red pigment, and are apparently devoid of chloroplasts. At an early stage in its expansion, a healthy leaf becomes green through disappearance of the red colour, which persists in an infected leaf to give a characteristic *red vein-banding* pattern. *Chlorotic areas* develop later, when an infected leaf matures and 'hardens'. They result from a failure of tissues to differentiate, rather than from changes in already differentiated tissues. Consequently, symptoms appear first in leaves produced after infection and seldom in mature leaves. Various manifestations of transient pigmentation, followed by clearing and chlorosis (Fig. 4F(d), p. 12), largely serve to distinguish the syndromes of different cocoa viruses (Posnette 1943c, 1947b; Thresh and Tinsley 1959; Dale 1962).

Transient symptoms may be limited to individual veinlets, or the leaf may be extensively *mottled*. Permanent vein-banding may be restricted to the veinlets, giving the symptom described as *speckling*, or it may extend along larger veins, giving *angular flecks*. A general chlorosis of young leaves, consisting of small irregular chlorotic spots and flecks was described as a *mosaic* (Posnette 1941). Irregular chlorotic bands of varying intensity and width, confined to the main veins, may give a *fern-leaf pattern* or an *oak-leaf pattern*, with zigzag outline (Carter 1956; Orellana and Peiris 1957). Occasionally, severe chlorosis is restricted to only one side of the mid-rib, and then there is usually *distortion* and *crinkling* of the lamina. Some isolates cause *necrosis* of the minor veins, as an initial symptom, in severe cases the leaf or affected shoot may die. In later flushes, the lamina may have *translucent patches*, or leaves may be abnormally narrow. Definite symptom phases characterize the response to inoculation by certain virus isolates. A distinct *acute phase* of infection is then followed by a *chronic phase*, with limited symptoms. With avirulent isolates, the acute phase may be reduced or lacking, and subsequent flushes are usually symptomless ('inapparent infection').

Abnormal pods

Pod symptoms are associated with infection by some virulent West African isolates. Affected pods (Fig. 4F(a), p. 12) are abnormally small, smooth, and rounded (Anon. 1945a). Carter (1956) reported having once seen a rounded pod in Sri Lanka. In West Africa, affected pods may show a characteristic light and dark green *mottling* which persists on ripening but may be overlaid by dark red *marbling* or *blotching*. One Trinidad virus caused red blotches on young fruits of yellow-podded selections (Posnette 1944a; Baker and Dale 1947a). Virus can be recovered from abnormal pods and from normal ones in infected trees, but not from the cotyledons of beans. However, virus can be transmitted from the testa of a bean from an infected pod (Anon. 1950). Therefore, beans from which the testae have been removed, can in certain circumstances be safely imported as seed from countries where C.S.S.V. occurs (Johnston 1963*a*).

To curtail accounts of the symptoms produced by different viruses, it is convenient to reference original descriptions, when available, and/or to cite the tabulation provided by Thresh and Tinsley (1959, Table III). They summarized the syndromes associated with a representative selection of cocoa virus isolates from Ghana and Nigeria, on the basis of presence or absence of particular symptoms discussed above.

Symptoms caused by cocoa virus strains and isolates

C.S.S.V.

Strain A. The symptoms were described from Effiduase (near Koforidua), New Juaben district, Ghana (Posnette 1947*b*). Thresh and Tinsley (1959) summarized the symptoms caused by 'New Juaben isolate' as comprising the following features: swellings, red vein-banding, chlorotic vein-banding, distortion or crinkle, with distinct acute and chronic phases, and pod mottle.

Strain B. The symptoms were described from Bisa, Krobo district, Ghana (Posnette 1947*b*). Thresh and Tinsley (1959) summarized the symptoms caused by 'Bisa isolate' as comprising the following features: swellings, red vein-banding, and mild chlorotic vein-banding.

Strain D. The symptoms were described from Abuorso, near Nkawkaw, Kwahu district, Ghana (Posnette 1947*b*). Young leaves might show either broad red bands along secondary veins or more often a mottle not related to the veins. The first symptoms were usually pin-point yellow spots evenly distributed over the leaf, but becoming invisible as leaves matured. There were acute and chronic phases. Swellings occurred occasionally, as slight internodal inflations. No pod symptoms were recorded.

Strain E. The symptoms were described from Pamen, Eastern Region, Ghana (Voelcker 1946, 1948*c*). There was a cloudy, yellow, non-particulate mottle (flecking) in the acute phase, and a yellow 'oak-leaf' mottle with faint red vein-banding in the chronic phase. Swellings were of medium size.

Strain F. Symptoms were first described from Wiawso, Western Region, Ghana (Voelcker 1946, 1948*b*), but a complexity of viruses was recognized from other localities in the Western Region (Voelcker 1948*c*): Aiyiboso, Amafie, Bosumuoso, Datano, Nsaura, Punekrom, Suhuma, Surawno, and Wiasi. Thresh and Tinsley (1959) summarized the symptoms caused by 'Bosumuoso isolate' as comprising the following features: swellings, red vein-banding, chlorotic vein-banding, distinct acute and chronic phases, and pod mottle.

Strain G. The symptoms were described from Dochi, Eastern Region, Ghana (Voelcker 1946). There was faint red banding of leaves in the acute phase and yellow vein-banding in the chronic phase. No swellings were observed.

Strain H. The symptoms were described from Dawa, Eastern Region, Ghana (Voelcker 1946, 1948*b,c*). They resembled those caused by New Juaben isolate but were less severe. Swellings were produced.

Strain J. This virus was reported from Bosumtwe, Ashanti, Ghana (Voelcker 1948*c*). Thresh and Tinsley (1959) summarized the symptoms produced by 'Bosumtwe isolate' as comprising the following features: swellings, red vein-banding, chlorotic vein-banding, translucent patches, distinct acute and chronic phases.

Strain K. The symptoms were described from Konongo, Ashanti, Ghana (Voelcker 1948*a*). They resembled those caused by New Juaben isolate, but were less severe.

Virus M. Symptom expression with this virus from Mampong, Eastern Region, Ghana, was not fully described originally (Voelcker 1947, 1948*b,c*). Thresh and Tinsley (1959) summarized the symptoms caused by 'Mampong isolate' as comprising the following features: swellings, red vein-banding, chlorotic vein-banding, distinct acute and chronic phases. With New Juaben isolate, the Mampong isolate produced a complex with symptoms typical for neither (Voelcker 1948*b,c*; Tinsley 1953*a*).

Virus N. The symptoms associated with this virus from Akanran, Nigeria, were not described, but an isolate was referred to as 'the Akanran or Egbeda virus' (Voelcker 1948*c*), and an isolate was used in Ghana for transmission tests (Posnette 1950*c*). Thresh and Tinsley (1959) summarized the symptoms produced by 'Egbeda isolate'. Thresh (1961) described symptoms produced by virulent and avirulent viruses from Egbeda.

Viruses O_1 and O_2. The symptoms associated with these isolates from Olanla, Nigeria were not described (Voelcker 1948*c*). Olanla viruses were used for transmission tests in Ghana (Posnette 1950*c*). Symptoms associated with 'Olanla isolate' were summarized by Thresh and Tinsley (1959). Olanla viruses were studied in Nigeria (Thresh 1961).

Virus O_3. The symptoms associated with this virus from Ilesha, Nigeria were not described (Voelcker 1948*c*). Thresh and Tinsley (1959) summarized the symptoms caused by 'Ilesha isolate'. They were similar to those produced by an Olanla isolate (Thresh 1961).

Virus P. This virus from Offa Igbo, Nigeria was used for transmission tests in Ghana and Nigeria (Posnette 1950*c*; Posnette, Robertson and Todd 1950), without description of the symptoms produced. They were summarized by Thresh and Tinsley (1959) for 'Offa Igbo' isolate, and included distinct acute and chronic phases. Thresh (1961) found no clear distinction into acute and chronic phases associated with an isolate from Offa Igbo.

Strain W. Swellings associated with an isolate from Worawora, Volta Region, Ghana were described (Attafuah and Dale 1958). Leaf symptoms were described later (Glendinning, Legg, Lovi, and Martinson 1966).

Virus X. A virulent virus occurring in Kongodia and Apprompronou, Ivory Coast, produced symptoms similar to those associated with infection by the New Juaben isolate (Alibert 1946), and further details were given later (Mangenot *et al.* 1946a; Meiffren 1949). Posnette (1950c) referred to Virus X, from Kongodia.

Virus Y. A virus which was milder in its effects than the Kongodia virus occurred in Yakassé and at Sankadiokro, Ivory Coast (Alibert 1946) .Subsequently it was referred to as 'Sankadiokro virus' (Renaud 1957). Further details were given later (Mangenot *et al.* 1946a; Meiffren 1949). Posnette (1950c) referred to Virus Y, from Yakassé.

Cocoa virus diseases were widespread in the Ivory Coast (Balleyguier 1949), with diversity of symptoms and varying degrees of virulence (Renaud 1957) in the following localities: Abengourou, Agboville, Dalos, Duakoné, Grand Bassam, Issia, Man, and Sinfra.

Virus isolate from Gandorhun, Sierra Leone. Seedlings infected with virus from this outbreak showed distinct acute and chronic phases. Trees known to have been infected for at least 4 years showed no deterioration (Attafuah, Blencowe, and Brunt 1963).

C.M.L.V.

Strain C. Posnette (1947b) described the symptoms produced by strain *C*, from Kpeve, Volta Region, Ghana. He gave two synonyms, one of which was 'Kpeve strain', and the other 'mottle-leaf of cacao' with reference to the syndrome of infection by cherry mottle-leaf virus (Martyn 1968). Thresh and Tinsley (1959) summarized the symptoms caused by 'Kpeve isolate' as comprising the following features: red mottle, red vein-banding, chlorotic mottle, chlorotic vein-banding, and translucent patches. No swellings are produced.

Virus R. The symptoms produced by this virus from Alaparun, Nigeria were described briefly (Anon. 1950). The summarized symptoms associated with Kpeve and Alaparun isolates were similar (Thresh and Tinsley 1959).

C.N.V.

Virus S. Posnette (1950c) described the symptoms produced by infection with this virus from Asalu, Abeokuta Province, Nigeria. Characteristic features were absence of red pigment from the young leaf, and the regular arrangement of small clearings along the midrib to cause distortion which resembled the appearance of the nutritional disorder referred to as 'sickle leaf' (Chapter 14 p. 239). Thresh (1958c) gave the name 'cacao necrosis virus' to isolates from Asalu and neighbourhood, which caused severe necrotic symptoms, with subsequent recovery in young graft-infected plants. Thresh and Tinsley (1959) summarized the similar symptoms produced by isolates from Asalu and from Omi Aboderin, Nigeria as comprising the following features: translucent patches, distortion or crinkle, veinal necrosis, distinct acute and chronic phases. No swellings are produced.

Owusu (1971b) reported a small outbreak of cocoa virus disease due to C.N.V. near Nkoranza, Brong-Ahafo Region, Ghana, which he transmitted by grafting. Symptoms were similar in amelonado, Upper Amazon, and Upper Amazon × Trinitario seedling progenies.

C.Y.M.V.

The symptoms produced by C.Y.M.V. at Benduma, Giehun and Woroma in Sierra Leone were described by Blencowe et al. 1963. The name 'cocoa yellow mosaic' was given to this Sierra Leone virus which resembled turnip yellow mosaic virus (Nixon and Gibbs 1963). Infected trees were not moribund although their leaves had chlorotic blotches, chlorotic mosaic, or were almost completely chlorotic. Some chlorotic patches showed vein necrosis. When the virus was graft-transmitted to cocoa seedlings, circular chlorotic areas appeared at first, but subsequent leaves were symptomless until 12–18 months later when leaves produced the range of symptoms seen in the field.

C.T.V.

Isolate from Diego Martin valley, Trinidad. Posnette (1944a) described the symptoms caused by infection of cocoa trees at River Estate, Diego Martin valley, Trinidad with 'red mottle virus'. Baker and Dale (1947a,b) rejected this designation and substituted the designation 'strain A'. This letter designation was unsuitable because of possible confusion with the earlier letter designations used in Ghana (p. 71). The term red mottle virus should be avoided for fear of possible confusion with the West African cocoa mottle-leaf virus (p. 76). This Trinidad virus caused a red pigmentation of the tissues bordering some or all of the main veins. Consequently this symptom was not visible on trees with dark red young leaves, but was clearly visible on those with green or pink flush-leaves. When leaves hardened the red pigment faded and disappeared. Some forms of mosaic, as cleared areas, varying in size and shape, bordering the main veins, may or may not accompany the red mottle. There was no mosaic with I.C.S. 6, 53, and 60; very slight mosaic with I.C.S. 1; mosaic was pronounced with

I.C.S. 3 and 7 (these I.C.S. clones were described by Pound (1934, 1935a, 1936)). The vein-clearing symptom was generally indefinite, or slightly indicated with I.C.S. 1. The pods of infected I.C.S. 6 trees showed red blotches.

Isolate from Maracas valley, Trinidad. Posnette (1944a) described the symptoms caused by infection of cocoa trees in Maracas valley, Trinidad, with 'vein-clearing virus'. Baker and Dale (1947a,b) rejected this designation and substituted the designation 'strain B', because on certain cocoa selections the symptoms of the vein-clearing virus included red mottling of the leaves. The C.T.V. strain B designation is to be avoided for the same reason as with C.T.V. strain A. There was pronounced vein-clearing, which persisted when the leaves hardened. When I.C.S. 6 trees were infected with this virus, the leaves showed mosaic and red mottling. When I.C.S. 6 trees were infected with the Diego Martin virus, the leaves developed red mottling but no mosaic. Therefore, I.C.S. 6 could be used as a differential host for identifying the two Trinidad viruses. They occurred together in the Santa Cruz valley, Trinidad.

C.C.V.

Viruses from Sri Lanka localities. A survey at the Kundasale Cacao Research Station, Kandy, revealed many trees with a few leaves showing vein-clearing symptoms (Peiris 1953). There were further descriptions of symptoms at the Kundasale Station and at Pallekelly Estate (Carter 1956; Orellana and Peiris 1957). The occurrence of leaf symptoms varying from vein flecking to oak-leaf pattern, with or without stem or root swellings, and presence or absence of rounded fruit, suggested the possibility that more than one cocoa virus occurred in Sri Lanka.

Symptoms associated with occurrence of suspected virus diseases

Africa
Chlorosis. Thorold (1957b) described a chlorosis disease of cocoa in an area between Kumba and Marumba, Cameroon (S.W.). Affected trees had leaves in which light coloration of tissue bordered the veins but there was not actual vein-clearing. In common with certain West African cocoa virus diseases, there was leaf crinkling with tip and marginal necrosis.

The cause of this chlorosis disease was unknown. Two hypotheses were put forward to explain it (nutritional disorder versus virus infection) but neither was entirely acceptable. Patches taken from affected trees were grafted on to healthy seedlings, but they flushed twice during two months without any symptoms being produced (Martini 1959b).

Distortions of cocoa leaf and stem tissues in Zanzibar (Tanzania). These malformations which occurred in association with mealybugs (*Maconellicoccus hirsutus* (Green)) were discussed by Posnette (1950c) and De Lotto

(1964, 1967), but it is not known whether they are 'toxic effects' or due to virus infection.

Central America

Mosaic. This name was given tentatively to a disorder affecting cocoa trees at La Lola, Turrialba, and elsewhere in Costa Rica (Hutchins 1958*b*, 1959*a*). There were chlorotic spots and streaks, and cleared veinlets in restricted areas of affected leaves, accompanied by some distortion. It was not known whether these manifestations were symptoms of a nutritional disorder or of infection by virus.

South America

Narrow dented leaf virus. This designation was provided by Greenwood and Djokoto (1952) as a translation of the expression *virosis de hoja estrecha abollada del cacaotero* proposed by Ciferri (1948) for a suspected virus disease of cocoa observed near Palmira, Valle and elsewhere in Colombia. This disorder was believed to be similar to a disorder of cocoa in the Dominican Republic considered below.

Suspected virus disease in Venezuela. Posnette and Palma (1944) reported that in the Paria Peninsula, Venezuela on nearly every estate a few cocoa trees showed yellow mosaic, sometimes affecting only part of the leaf. These symptoms were unlike those caused by C.T.V. in Trinidad. In Venezuela there were neither stem swellings nor pod mottle. In absence of transmission tests, it was considered unwise to attribute the leaf symptoms to virus infection.

West Indies

Narrow dented leaf virus. Symptoms of a possible cocoa virus disease, first refered to as 'roncet', were observed near Puerto Plata, Santiago Province, Dominican Republic (Ciferri 1930*b*). This disorder (as 'virosis de hoja estrecha abollada del cacaotero') was apparently present also in Colombia (see above). Greenwood and Djokoto (1952) considered that the symptoms of the suspected virus disease resembled the appearance of a nutritional disorder referred to as 'sickle leaf' in Ghana (see p. 239). Therefore, confirmation is required of the claim by Ciferri (1948) that the disorder in the Dominican Republic was graft transmissible.

Asia

Suspected virus disease in Indonesia. Cocoa leaves in different parts of Java (east, central, and west) showed various symptoms, which included mosaic, vein clearing and oak-leaf pattern. Sometimes the leaf shape was asymmetrical. Transmission was not achieved (Semangun 1961).

Blencowe, J. W. (1973 *in litt.*) observed cocoa leaves at Mariendal, near Madan, North Sumatra, with symptoms characteristic of cocoa virus disease, but transmission had not been attempted. Budwood had been introduced to Sumatra from Java.

Suspected virus disease in Malaysia. Leaves of cocoa trees at the Quoin Hill Cocoa Research Station, and at other plantings in Tawau District in Sabah, showed various symptoms, including yellow vein-banding, fern-leaf pattern, and translucent areas (Reddy 1968; Smith 1969; Anon. 1970, 1971). Transmission had not been achieved.

It is uncertain whether there is a cocoa virus disease in Sabah, if so, cocoa may have become infected from an indigenous source-plant. Another possibility would be inadvertent introduction to Sabah, through infected budwood, or other infected cocoa material, from Indonesia or elsewhere in Malaysia.

Virus properties

Chemistry

Early diagnosis of infection is important for practical purposes, particularly in the prosecution of eradication. Accordingly, attention was given to the possibility of testing for infection more rapidly than was possible by transmission experiments. Attempts to develop a satisfactory chemical test were unsuccessful.

Posnette (1947b) reported that sections of stems infected with either of two different C.S.S.V. isolates (strains A and B) stained more rapidly with acidified methyl alcohol than those of healthy stems. Staining was either not affected, or delayed by C.M.L.V. (Kpeve) isolate (strain C). Hancock (1949) experimented further with this laboratory test. The colour reaction was only produced after visible symptoms had appeared. Tinsley and Usher (1954) tested expressed sap from healthy and from virus-infected leaves. Mature-leaf extracts were heated with sodium hydroxide and gave colours ranging from green to brown and red. They claimed that healthy leaves produced green to brownish-green colours whilst infected leaves produced red-brown to crimson colours. Holden (1957) critically examined this test and found that results were erratic.

Although no chemical test for detecting virus infection resulted from these studies, there were important developments which led to mechanical transmissions and preparations used for microscopy and serology.

Physics

Brunt, Kenten, and Nixon (1964) described how electron microscopy was done at Rothamsted Experimental Station, with C.S.S.V. preparations made and tested for infectivity in Ghana and sent to England by air, in chilled vacuum flasks. All virus preparations made from plants infected with the C.S.S.V. isolate tested, contained rod-shaped particles (Fig.

4F(b), p. 12) which were never found in preparations made similarly from healthy plants. More such particles were found in highly infective preparations than in less infective ones. A few particles had one or both ends 'cut off square', but there were no such particles in fresh swollen-shoot virus examined with the electron microscope at Kumasi, Ghana (Kenten and Legg 1968a,b). It was concluded that the few square-ended particles observed in preparations at Rothamsted were either the result of degradation or were artifacts. Milne and Kenten (1970) observed much necrosis but few particles (26 nm. × 130 nm.) occurring as small aggregates of rods in thin sections of parenchyma and veins of young cocoa leaves infected with strain A.

Kenten and Legg (1967) studied C.M.L.V. (Kpeve isolate) extracted from infected cocoa leaves by methods similar to those used by Brunt et al. (1964). Electron microscopy was done at Kumasi and at Rothamsted. Infective preparations contained straight rod-shaped particles with rounded ends, none of the particles was square-ended. Studies of partially purified preparations of C.S.S.V. and C.M.L.V. isolates indicated that they were similar in size, shape and properties in vitro. Kenten and Legg (1971b) summarized the particle sizes of some C.S.S.V. and C.M.L.V. isolates.

C.Y.M.V. from Giehun, Sierra Leone was maintained on cocoa and on Chenopodium amaranticolor Coste and Reyne. Brunt, Kenten, Gibbs, and Nixon (1965) described how C.Y.M.V. preparations were obtained for tests of virus properties and electron microscopy. Extracts of infected cocoa or of C. amaranticolor leaves contained many approximately spherical particles, not found in comparable preparations from uninfected plants. The apparent size of negatively stained C.Y.M.V. particles was almost the same as that recorded by Nixon and Gibbs (1960) for similarly treated turnip yellow mosaic particles.

Nkoranza (C.N.V.) isolate was brought from Ghana to Rothamsted and maintained by subculture in Phaseolus vulgaris L., cv. The Prince, and the properties of the virus were described by Kenten (1972a,b).

Serology

For Nigeria viruses, Okusanya (1965, 1968, 1969) described the testing of antiserum prepared against three C.S.S.V. isolates by injecting into rabbits. For Ghana viruses, Kenten and Legg (1968b, 1971b) studied serological relationships of C.S.S.V. and C.M.L.V. isolates. Brunt et al. (1965) gave details of C.Y.M.V. serological relationships to wild cucumber and turnip mild yellows viruses. No serological relationship was detected between C.Y.M.V. and a number of beetle-borne viruses (Brunt 1970b). Kenten (1972b) stated that C.N.V. is a serotype of tomato black ring virus (T.B.R.V.) and is very distantly related to Hungarian chrome mosaic virus (H.C.M.V.) of grapevine. He suggested that C.N.V. and H.C.M.V.

are Nepoviruses (Valdez 1972). Brunt and Kenten (1971) reviewed the serology of C.S.S.V., C.M.L.V. C.Y.M.V., and C.N.V.

Host range

Preliminary attempts to find a possible alternative host of cocoa virus in Ghana were unsuccessful when transmission from infected cocoa seedlings to seedlings of indigenous plants was attempted by approach-grafting or through use of *Cuscuta* sp. (Voelcker 1946, 1948*b*; Posnette, Robertson, and Todd 1950). Natural infection of *Cola chlamydantha* K. Schum., was detected by use of mealybugs as vectors (Voelcker 1948*b*). Leaf symptoms on a coppiced plant of this species in a Western Region of Ghana outbreak of swollen-shoot led to this discovery (Voelcker 1948*c*). The likelihood that certain other indigenous plants might also be alternative hosts was considered (Voelcker 1948*c*). Posnette *et al.* (1950) gave details of mealybug transmissions of virus from cocoa to indigenous plants, with back transmissions to cocoa for the following species:

Adansonia digitata L., (the baobab tree).
Bombax buonopozense P. Beauv.
Ceiba pentandra (L.) Gaertn.
Cola chlamydantha K. Schum.
Cola gigantea A. Chev., var. *glabrescens* Brenan and Keay, as *C. cordifolia*
    (Tinsley and Wharton 1958; Tinsley 1971).
Hildegardia barteri (Mast.) Kosterm., as *Erythropsis barteri* (Mast.) Ridley.
Sterculia rhinopetala K. Schum.
Sterculia tragacantha Lindl.

Within the above species, natural infection of two *C. pentandra* trees out of fifty-seven tested was demonstrated. Natural infection of one '*C. cordifolia*' seedling was suspected (Posnette *et al.* 1950). Although *C. chlamydantha* does not occur in the Western Region of Nigeria nor in the Eastern Region of Ghana, it appeared to be important as an alternative host in the Western Region of Ghana (Todd 1951). Seedlings of this species were susceptible to all the Western Region isolates (strain F) with which they had been tested and likewise to two viruses in the Ivory Coast (Anon. 1950), where *C. chlamydantha* occurs (Keay 1958). Tinsley (1971) surveyed 1670 farms in Western Region, Ghana, and stated that 'thirty-five per cent of the cacao farms had *C. chlamydantha* growing in close association with the crop and the percentage number of farms with and without swollen-shoot was about the same. However, when *C. chlamydantha* was not found within the farms the incidence of swollen-shoot was less. Thus the local importance of *C. chlamydantha* as a wild host in the Western Province is without question'.

Posnette (1960) explained how dispersal of virus from *C. chlamydantha* may be assisted. Attached fruit of this species split open and some seeds became infected by the feeding of viruliferous mealybugs. Fruit bats (unspecified) are attracted to the seeds of *C. chlamydantha* which they disperse; consequently, infected seeds may be widely distributed in this way.

The significance of natural infection of *C. chlamydantha* in relation to the history of swollen-shoot in West Africa is controversial. Todd (1951) considered that the occurrence of virus-infected specimens, where swollen-shoot of cocoa was unknown, suggested that virus infection of *C. chlamydantha* antedated that of cocoa. Bald and Tinsley (1970) considered evidence which implied that *C. chlamydantha* was originally infected from cocoa.

In addition to that in *C. chlamydantha*, natural infections in *Adansonia digitata*, *Ceiba pentandra*, and *Cola gigantea* var. *glabrescens* were discussed by Attafuah (1965). Legg and Agbodjan (1969) reported infection of a single *Sterculia tragacantha* in Ghana with a virus indistinguishable from strain A. Viruses in *A. digitata* are related to C.M.L.V. (Attafuah and Tinsley 1958; Legg and Bonney 1968c).

Posnette *et al.* (1950) noted that *A. digitata* was seldom found in association with cocoa, but *C. pentandra* and *C. gigantea* did occur in cocoa farms and their possible importance in this connection was discussed by Dale (1962). However, the two latter species and *S. tragacantha* are insensitive to infection, so that virus may be only exceptionally available for transmission to cocoa by mealybug vectors, as explained by Brunt and Kenten (1971). Dale and Attafuah (1957) stated that '*Adansonia digitata* and *Cola chlamydantha* differ from most other tree hosts in the relative ease with which virus can be recovered from them, even after lengthy infection'.

Bald and Tinsley (1970) discussed host-range differences between cocoa virus isolates in relation to previous studies of host-range taxonomic boundaries (Bald and Tinsley 1967a), differentiation between host ranges (Bald and Tinsley 1967b), and congruence of host ranges (Bald and Tinsley 1967c). It will suffice here to consider some of the botanical relationships of experimental host ranges of C.S.S.V. and C.M.L.V. About twenty species which are indigenous or well established in West Africa have been infected by C.S.S.V. and C.M.L.V. isolates in laboratory tests (Posnette *et al.* 1950; Tinsley and Wharton 1958; Dale and Attafuah 1957, 1958; Attafuah and Brunt 1959; Brunt and Kenten 1962a,b,c; Legg and Bonney 1966, 1967, 1968a) These species are either members of the family Sterculiaceae, or of families with affinity to it (Keay 1958) through belonging to the order Tiliales (comprising Bombacaceae, Sterculiaceae, and Tiliaceae), or to the order Malvales (Malvaceae). Certain species of the genera *Byttneria*, *Leptonychia*, and *Scaphopetalum* were not infected by strain A (Tinsley and Wharton 1958). Representatives of these genera were presumably included among those selected for testing because Chevalier (1946) had specified them as possible sources of cocoa virus through their being closely related to *Theobroma*, since they share with this genus, and the genus *Herrania*, the 'hooded' (cucullate) petal character (Cuatrecasas 1964).

It is possible that certain plants which occur commonly in cocoa farms in West Africa but are not infected by cocoa viruses may nevertheless be important indirectly through harbouring mealybug vectors. Strickland (1951*a*) found that *Planococcoides njalensis* was invariably associated with ants inhabiting domatia in the hollow stems of *Canthium subcordatum* DC. (as *C. glabriflorum* Hiern.). This myrmecophyte is a member of the Rubiaceae. *Cola acuminata* (P. Beauv.) Schott and Endl., and *Cola nitida* (Vent.) Schott and Endl., are economic plants in West Africa and commonly grown in cocoa farms. Seedling progenies of these cultivars were tested by Esenam and Ladipo (1967) in Nigeria and found to be immune to C.S.S.V. 'severe Ikire' isolate (Wessel-Riemens and Okusanya 1965). *C. acuminata* is a host of mealybugs (*P. njalensis* and *Planococcus citri*) in Ghana (Forsyth 1966).

Legg and Lovi (1968, 1969) explained that the testing of virus (C.S.S.V and C.M.L.V.) preparations for infectivity would be greatly facilitated if a plant species could be found which would develop local lesions when infected with cocoa viruses. They tested over one hundred species (thirty-three families) with preparations of New Juaben isolate (strain A) at Tafo, Ghana, and some at East Malling Research Station, England. No positive infections with C.S.S.V. were obtained.

C. nitida and *Culcasia scandens* P. Beauv. were apparently infected naturally with C.Y.M.V. (Blencowe *et al.* 1963), but there is a wide range of potential hosts (nine families: Apocynaceae, Araceae, Begoniaceae, Bombacaceae, Chenopodiaceae, Cucurbitaceae, Papilionaceae, Solanaceae, and Sterculiaceae) (Brunt *et al.* 1965).

In limited tests, Martini (1959*a*, 1960) found that some cocoa seedlings showed necrotic symptoms similar to those caused by C.N.V., when grafted with bark patches from *C. nitida* in a C.N.V. outbreak area at Omi Aboderin, Nigeria. He stated that 'the evidence for the susceptibility of *C. nitida* to cocoa necrosis virus is therefore still insufficient'. A range of plants (seven families: Aizoaceae, Amarantaceae, Chenopodiaceae, Cucurbitaceae, Papilionaceae, Solanaceae, and Sterculiaceae) was infected manually with C.N.V. isolates from Nkoranza, Ghana (Kenten and Owusu 1970; Kenten 1972*b*).

No alternative hosts are known for cocoa viruses occurring in Sri Lanka and Trinidad.

Virus transmission

General consideration

Coccoidea (Homoptera) were unimportant cocoa pests in Ghana when Cotterell (1928) recorded only four species. Twenty years later, the mealybugs were still not pests in their own right, and would have remained minor pests if they had not been vectors of the economically serious swollen-shoot disease (Strickland 1948). With the exception of *Aphis gossypii*, all the insects so far proved capable of transmitting one or more of the cocoa viruses are mealybugs of the family-group Pseudococcidae within the Coccoidea. Among eighteen vector species (I–XVIII), thirteen are taxonomically distinct, the remainder are not well defined: some may be distinct but so far unnamed species, others may be found to come within the range of variability of named species.

The vectors, some non-vectors, and some untested species are discussed, and those considered important which are taxonomically well defined are included in an identification key (pp. 94–5). Morphological terms in the text and those used in the key are shown in Fig. 7 (p. 86).

Vector species

Aphis gossypii *Glover (No. XIX not included in key)*. Martini (1961, 1962) showed that *A. gossypii* transmitted Nigerian C.S.S.V. isolates from Ajia and Offa-Igbo (Thresh 1961), when 50 to 150 or more aphids were fed on young flush leaves before transfer to half-beans (Posnette 1947*a*). C.S.S.V. transmission by *A. gossypii* is unconfirmed. Entwistle (1972) stated that 'as *A. gossypii* is rare on cocoa in West Africa and occurs only in small colonies it undoubtedly has a very low status as a vector'. This insect infested shoots and flowers of cocoa in Madras, India (Abraham and Padmanaban 1967). It has a wide geographical distribution, as shown in *Commonwealth Institute of Entomology Series A (Agricultural) Map No. 18* (1968). Aphids transmit other virus diseases (Martyn 1968). Therefore, *A. gossypii* may possibly have some importance as a potential vector of cocoa viruses.

Dysmicoccus brevipes *(Cockerell) (No. I in key)*. This species is widely known as a pest of pineapple, its geographical distribution is shown in *Commonwealth Institute of Entomology Series A Map No. 50* (1955), including occurrences as *Pseudococcus bromeliae* (Bouché), on cocoa (Strickland 1947*a*).

D. brevipes transmitted C.S.S.V. strain A and C.M.L.V. Kpeve isolate (Posnette 1950*c*). All stages (1st, 2nd and 3rd instars and adults) transmitted C.T.V. Diego Martin valley isolate, but not C.T.V. Maracas valley isolate in a limited number of tests (Kirkpatrick 1950).

Ferrisia virgata *(Cockerell) (No. II in key)*. The geographical distribution of this species is shown in *Commonwealth Institute of Entomology Series A (Agricultural) Map No. 219* (1966).

Cotterell (1928) reported this mealybug as attacking cocoa in Ghana, and later he described swollen-shoot virus transmissions by it (Cotterell 1943). Box (1945) confirmed *F. virgata* as a vector of a virulent cocoa virus. All instars fed readily on cocoa beans and gave up to 80 per cent

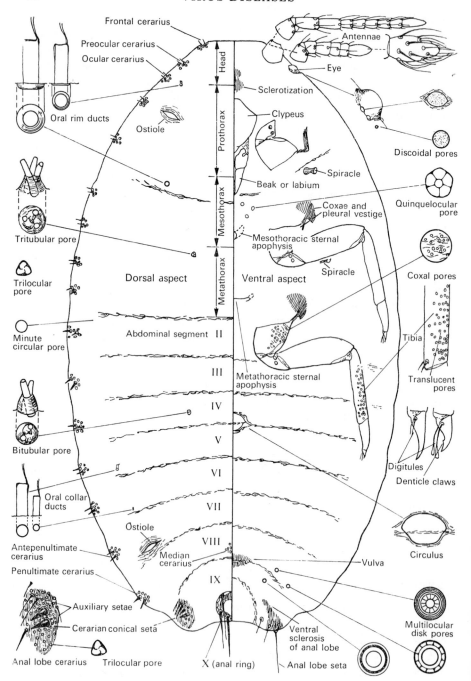

FIG. 7. Diagram illustrating the terms used in connection with mealybug morphology
        (McKenzie 1967).

transmissions of C.S.S.V. strain A, but 'crawlers' (1st and 2nd instar nymphs) were more efficient vectors than adults (Posnette and Strickland 1948).

In West Africa, *F. virgata* transmitted the following viruses: C.S.S.V. A, B, D, F, H, J, K, N, O_1, O_2, P, X, Y (Posnette 1950c; Attafuah and Brunt 1960), and Aboboya, Adiembra, and Anibil isolates from *Cola chlamydantha* (Legg and Bonney 1966).

In Trinidad, *F. virgata* transmitted C.T.V. Diego Martin valley isolate, but transmissions of C.T.V. Maracas valley isolate were not tried (Kirkpatrick 1950).

F. virgata may (Posnette 1950c) or may not transmit C.S.S.V. M (Attafuah and Brunt 1960). The following viruses were not transmitted by *F. virgata*: C.S.S.V. Gandorhun isolate, C.M.L.V. Alaparun and Kpeve isolates, *Adansonia digitata* isolates (A.D. 7, 36, 75), C.N.V. Asalu isolate (Posnette 1950c; Attafuah and Brunt 1960; Legg and Bonney 1966).

Maconellicoccus ugandae *(Laing) (No. III in key)*. Posnette (1950c) reported that a species he designated by number (*Phenacoccus* sp. H 6418) transmitted C.S.S.V. strain M (Mampong isolate). Williams, D. J. (1969 *in litt.*) examined Posnette's 'H 6418' and found it to be *M. ugandae*.

Paraputo anomalus *(Newstead) (No. IV in key)*. Strickland (1947a) gave a description of this species in Ghana as *Paraputo ritchiei* Laing, which is synonymous, and likewise *P. multispinosa* James (Williams 1958a).

This species transmitted C.S.S.V. strain F. complex (Posnette 1950c), and it also transmitted virus from *C. chlamydantha*, Wiawso district, Western Region, Ghana to cocoa beans (Posnette *et al.* 1950).

Planococcoides njalensis *(Laing) (No. V in key)*. Probably the first demonstration of this mealybug as a cocoa virus vector was by Cotterell (1943). He tested a mealybug in Ghana (as *Pseudococcus* sp. No. 1453) which gave 100 per cent transmission of C.S.S.V. According to information provided by Dr. D. J. Williams (Fennah, R. G. 1969 *in litt.*) this mealybug was probably *P. njalensis*. Slides in the Commonwealth Institute of Entomology's Collection (No. I.R.1453 = H 253) were part of a collection studied by Hall (1945), in addition to the type series of *Pseudococcus exitiabilis* Laing, which Hall considered indistinguishable from *P. njalensis*. Box (1945) reported transmission of cocoa virus by *P. njalensis*, as *P. exitiabilis*. All stages transmitted C.S.S.V. strain A, but crawlers (1st and 2nd instars nymphs) and 3rd instar nymphs were more efficient vectors than adults (Posnette and Strickland 1948; Strickland 1951a,b). *P. njalensis* has transmitted all C.S.S.V. and C.M.L.V. strains and isolates with which it has been tested, as follows: C.S.S.V. A, B, D, F, H, J, K, M, N, O_1, O_2, O_3, P, X, Y, Gandorhun isolate, *C. chlamydantha* Aboboya, Adiembra, Anibil isolates, C.M.L.V. Alaparun and Kpeve isolates, *A. digitata* isolates

(A.D. 7, 36, 75) (Posnette 1950c; Attafuah and Brunt 1960; Legg and Bonney 1966).

Planococcus citri *(Risso) Ferris (No. VI in key)*. The 'citrus mealybug' has world-wide tropical and sub-tropical distribution, as shown in *Commonwealth Institute of Entomology Series A Map No. 43* (1954), with indications of occurrences in temperate countries, including Britain (Williams 1962).

When Box (1945) demonstrated transmissions of four virus 'strains' in Ghana, there mistakenly appeared to be selectivity with respect to the particular strains transmitted by *P. citri* and *P. njalensis* (as *P. exitiabilis*). In West Africa, *P. citri* has transmitted all C.S.S.V. and C.M.L.V. strains and isolates with which it has been tested, as follows: C.S.V. A, B, D, F, H, J, K, M, N, O_1, O_2, O_3, P, X, Y, Gandorhun isolate, *C. chlamydantha* Aboboya, Adiembra, Anibil isolates, C.M.L.V. Alaparun and Kpeve isolates, *A. digitata* isolates (A.D. 7, 36, 75) (Posnette 1950c: Attafuah and Brunt 1960; Legg and Bonney 1966).

In Trinidad, *P. citri* transmitted the Diego Martin valley and the Maracas valley isolates, and was considered responsible for most of the natural spread of the disease (Kirkpatrick 1950, 1953a,b).

P. citri transmitted C.C.V. virus in Sri Lanka (Carter 1956).

Planococcus kenyae *(Le Pelley) (No. VII in key)*. This species was identified in 1952 by Williams, D. J. (1969 *in litt.*) from material on cocoa in Ghana. Donald (1953) reported this occurrence, and later in Nigeria (Donald 1955, 1959). In the meantime, some occurrences of *P. kenyae* in Nigeria had been wrongly identified as *P. citri* and/or as *Pseudococcus* sp. near *celtis* (Sutherland 1953; Gregory 1954).

The following virus strains and isolates were transmitted by *P. kenyae* in West Africa: C.S.S.V. A, B, D, F, J, M, P, *C. chlamydantha* Aboboya, Adiembra, Anibil isolates, C.M.L.V. Alaparun and Kpeve isolates, *A. digitata* isolates (A.D. 7, 36, 75) (Attafuah and Brunt 1960; Legg and Bonney 1966).

Planococcus lilacinus *(Cockerell) (No. VIII in key)*. The geographical distribution of this species is shown in *Commonwealth Institute of Entomology Series A Map. No. 101* (1959). Le Pelley (1943) discussed the recognition, occurrences, and biology of this oriental mealybug, and noted that cocoa was one of its chief hosts. *P. lilacinus* transmitted C.C.V. virus in Sri Lanka (Carter 1956).

Pseudococcus comstocki *Kuwana (No. IX in key)*. This species transmitted C.T.V. virus in Trinidad (Kirkpatrick 1953a,b).

Pseudococcus concavocerarii *James (No. X in key)*. This species was studied in Ghana (Strickland 1947a, 1951a) and in Nigeria (Sutherland 1953; Donald 1955, 1959), it also occurs in the Ivory Coast and in Sierra Leone (Entwistle 1972). *P. concavocerarii* fed readily on half-beans (Posnette 1947*a*, Posnette and Strickland 1948) and transmitted the following virus strains and isolates: C.S.S.V. A, D, F, J, M, P, Gandorhun isolate, C.M.L.V. Alaparun and Kpeve isolates (Attafuah and Brunt 1960).

Pseudococcus hargreavesi *Laing (No. XI in key)*. Strickland (1947*a*) gave a description of this species, as *P. bukobensis*, with notes on biology and occurrences in Ghana and Nigeria. From an examination of type material of *P. bukobensis* (Laing), Williams (1958*b*) synonymized it with *P. hargreavesi*. This species transmitted the following virus strains and isolates: C.S.S.V. A, D, F, H, J, K, N, O_1, O_2, O_3, P, Y, *C. chlamydantha* Aboboya, Adiembra, Anibil isolates, C.M.L.V. Alaparun and Kpeve isolates, *A. digitata* isolates (A.D. 7, 36, 75) (Posnette 1950*c*; Attafuah and Brunt 1960; Legg and Bonney 1966).

Pseudococcus longispinus *(Targioni) (No. XII in key)*. The world-wide distribution of this species is shown in *Commonwealth Institute of Entomology Distribution Map No. 93* (1958), with occurrences in temperate countries under greenhouse conditions, including Britain (Williams 1962).

The nomenclature of the 'long-tailed mealybug' was discussed by De Lotto (1964, 1965). *P. longispinus* has been incorrectly cited as *P. adonidum* (*adonidum* auct., not *adonidum* L.).

In West Africa, this species transmitted the following virus strains and isolates: C.S.S.V. M, Gandorhun isolate, C.M.L.V. Kpeve isolate (Posnette 1950*c*; Attafuah and Brunt 1960).

P. longispinus did not transmit the following virus strains and isolates: C.S.S.V. A, B, D, F, K, O_1, O_2, O_3, P, X, Y, *C. chlamydantha* Aboboya, Adiembra, Anibil isolates, C.M.L.V. Alaparun isolate, *A. digitata* isolates (A.D. 7, 36, 75) (Posnette 1950*c*; Attafuah and Brunt 1960; Legg and Bonney 1966).

P. longispinus did not transmit C.T.V. isolates (Kirkpatrick 1950, 1953*b*).

Tylococcus westwoodi *Strickland (No. XIII in key)*. Strickland (1947*a*) described this species from a colony on a cocoa pod at Atikplale, Eastern Region, Ghana.

Lister and Thresh (1954) reported that in Western Region, Nigeria *T. westwoodi* transmitted three virus isolates in preliminary tests, which were not apparently confirmed. This species was categorized as a vector (Heinze 1959; Bigger 1972; Entwistle 1972). Forsyth (1966) listed it as associated with cocoa, but not as a virus vector, therefore, its status in this connection remains uncertain.

Incompletely identified vector species
Dysmicoccus *sp. near* brevipes *(No. XIV not included in key)*. This species from cocoa in Trinidad was considered distinct from *D. brevipes* (Cockerell). It transmitted C.T.V. Diego Martin valley and Maracas valley isolates (Kirkpatrick 1950, 1953*b*).

Pseudococcus *sp. near* celtis *(No. XV not included in key)*. This species was originally referred to by number (H6424), it was collected from cocoa near Asalu, Nigeria. It came close to *P. celtis*, but because there were distinct differences and in the absence of intermediate forms, it was considered as possibly a distinct species (Posnette 1950c). Williams (1958b) transferred *Pseudococcus celtis* Strickland to the genus *Planococcus*. To avoid confusion in referring to previous records, it is convenient to retain the designation '*Pseudococcus* sp. near *celtis*' for the mealybug now being considered, which transmitted the following virus strains and isolates in West Africa: C.S.S.V. A, B, D, F, H, J, M, O_1, O_3, P, X, Gandorhun isolate, *C. chlamydantha* Aboboya, Adiembra, Anibil isolates, C.M.L.V. Alaparun and Kpeve isolates, *A. digitata* isolates (A.D. 7, 36, 75) (Posnette 1950c; Attafuah and Brunt 1960; Legg and Bonney 1966).

Pseudococcus *sp. near* gahani *(No. XVI not included in key)*. This species was originally referred to by number (H6421); it differed from *P. gahani* (Posnette 1950c). Lister (1953) reported a similar species as a vector under another number (H6756). Williams (1958b) noted the possibility that *Pseudococcus gahani* Green should be synonymized with *Pseudoccus fragilis* Brain, and this change was effected by De Lotto (1958, 1964). In spite of the epithet *gahani* being sunk in synonymy, it is convenient to retain it as '*Pseudococcus* sp. near *gahani*', because the substitution of '*Pseudococcus* sp. near *fragilis*' would be confusing with respect to records of the following virus strains and isolates transmitted by this mealybug in West Africa: C.S.S.V. A, D, F, J, M, P, C.M.L.V. Alaparun and Kpeve isolates (Posnette 1950c; Attafuah and Brunt 1960).

Pseudococcus *sp. near* masakensis *(No. XVII not included in key)*. A mealybug species originally referred to by number (H6090) was collected from *C. chlamydantha* in Western Region, Ghana. It was considered not unlike *P. masakensis* James, but the cerarii were different. It transmitted C.S.S.V. strain F complex from *C. chlamydantha* to cocoa (Posnette 1950c). This transmission was confirmed (Posnette *et al.* 1950) with reference to '*Pseudococcus masakensis* Green', probably incorrectly for '*Pseudococcus* sp. near *masakensis*' *(fide* Fennah, R. G. 1969 *in litt.*).

Pseudococcus *sp. near* proteae *(No. XVIII not included in key)*. Lister (1953) reported the mealybug '*Pseudococcus* sp. close to *proteae* Hall' under a number (H6817), as a virus vector. Donald (1953) recorded its occurrence in Ghana, and in Nigeria (Donald 1955, 1959).

Forsyth (1966) listed *P. proteae* Hall as a C.S.S.V. vector, but this mealybug was still considered as 'near *proteae*' (Entwistle 1972). Williams (1958b) placed *Pseudococcus proteae* (Hall) in the genus *Paracoccus*, but for present purposes it is convenient to retain the designation '*Pseudococcus* sp. near *proteae*'.

Non-vectors and some untested species

Cataenococcus loranthi *(Strickland) (No. XX in key)*. Strickland (1947*a*) described this species, as *Farinococcus loranthi*, from *Tapinanthus bangwensis* (Loranthaceae) occurring on *Discoglypremna caloneura* (Pax) Prain (Euphorbiaceae), but it was also collected from *Loranthus* spp., on cocoa and other hosts, and once as a colony on a cocoa pod.

Heinze (1959) erroneously tabulated this mealybug as a C.S.S.V. vector. It was not so categorized by other writers (Forsyth 1966; Entwistle 1972).

Delococcus tafoensis *(Strickland) (No. XXXII in key)*. Strickland (1947*a*) described this species from cocoa at Tafo, Ghana, as *Formicoccus tafoensis*, also from *Ceiba pentandra* and *Cola cordifolia*.

This species was incorrectly listed as a C.S.S.V. vector (Heinze 1959; Bigger 1972). It was not so categorized by other writers (Forsyth 1966; Entwistle 1972).

Geococcus coffeae *Green (No. XXI in key)*. This species was common on roots of cocoa and other plants at Tafo, but not elsewhere in Eastern Region, Ghana (Strickland 1947*a*).

Results from testing *Geococcus* sp., for transmission of C.S.S.V. at Tafo were negative (Lodos and Boafo 1968).

Maconellicoccus hirsutus *(Green) (No. XXXIII in key)*. The geographical distribution of the 'Hibiscus mealybug' is shown in *Commonwealth Institute of Entomology Distribution Map No. 100* (1959). This species was associated with certain maladies of cocoa in Zanzibar, considered above (p. 78).

Nipaecoccus nipae *(Maskell) (No. XXXIV in key)*. The geographical distribution of the 'coconut mealybug' in the New World is shown in *Commonwealth Institute of Entomology Distribution Map No. 220* (1966). Bennett (1955) reported *N. nipae* from cocoa in Trinidad, as a host of a parasite (*Pseudaphycus utilis* Timberlake) (Hymenoptera, Encyrtidae).

There is no report of *N. nipae* having been tested as a possible vector of cocoa virus.

Orthezia insignis *Browne (No. XXII in key)*. The geographical distribution of this species is shown in *Commonwealth Institute of Entomology Distribution Map No. 73* (1957). It is considered to be polyphagous but did not normally feed on cocoa in Trinidad. It did not transmit C.T.V. (Kirkpatrick 1950).

Orthezia praelonga *Douglas (No. XXIII in key)*. This species was sometimes common in Trinidad on cocoa when shaded by *Gliricidia sepium* (Jacq.) Walp. *O. praelonga*, like *O. insignis*, did not transmit C.T.V. (Kirkpatrick 1953*b*).

Phenacoccus madeirensis *Green (No. XXIV in key)*. This mealybug was common as a garden pest in Ghana and Nigeria, but was not found on cocoa. It did not transmit C.S.S.V. strains A and M (Posnette 1950*c*.).

Phenacoccus *sp. near* hirsutus *(No. XXXIX not included in key)*. This mealybug, taken on cocoa in Ghana, was due to be tested as a possible vector of C.S.S.V. (Voelcker 1947; Strickland 1951*a*). It is convenient to retain the original designation because the possible relationship to *Maconellicoccus hirsutus* (Green) is unknown.

Phenacoccus *sp. (No. XXVII not included in key)*. A species of *Phenacoccus* was abundant on *Hibiscus mutabilis* L. in Trinidad. It did not occur naturally on cocoa but fed readily when transferred experimentally. It did not transmit C.T.V. (Kirkpatrick 1950).

Planococcus boafoensis *(Strickland) (No. XXXV in key)*. Strickland (1947*b*) described this species as *Tylococcus boafoensis*, from Tafo, Eastern Region, Ghana, on *Musanga cecropioides* R. Br. (*M. smithii* R. Br.) (Moraceae). There does not appear to be any record of its occurrence on cocoa, nor of its having been tested for possible virus transmission.

Pseudococcus *sp. near* comstocki *(No. XXVIII not included in key)*. This mealybug in Trinidad could not be assigned confidently to *Pseudococcus comstocki* Kuwana. It did not transmit C.T.V. (Kirkpatrick 1953*b*).

Puto barberi *(Cockerell) (No. XXV in key)*. This mealybug was common on garden plants in Trinidad, but apparently occurred only accidentally on cocoa growing under *Gliricidia sepium*. It did not transmit C.T.V. (Kirkpatrick 1950, 1953*b*).

Rastrococcus iceryoides *(Green) (No. XXXVI in key)*. This species infested stems and pods of cocoa in Madras, India (Abraham and Padmanaban 1967). Although it does not appear to have been tested as a possible vector, it is worth noting that its geographical distribution includes Indonesia and Tanzania (Williams 1958*a*; Le Pelley 1968), where suspected virus diseases occur.

Stictococcus sjostedti *Cockerell (No. XXVI in key)*. This scale insect is widespread in West Africa and infestations of cocoa pods may be harmful (Entwistle 1972). It did not transmit C.S.S.V. (Cotterell 1943; Strickland 1951*a*).

Trionymus longipilosus *De Lotto (No. XXXVII in key)*. This mealybug was observed in Zanzibar (Tanzania), where *M. hirsutus* was associated with a suspected virus disease, but was not tested for possible virus transmission (De Lotto 1967).

Tylococcus malacanthae *Strickland (No. XXXVIII in key)*. Strickland (1947*b*) described this species from Tafo, Eastern Region, Ghana, on *Malacantha* sp. (Sapotaceae). There does not appear to be any record of its occurrence on cocoa, nor of its having been tested for possible transmission of cocoa virus.

The following three species (Homoptera and Thysanoptera) have been tested but did not transmit cocoa viruses (Cotterell 1943; Box 1945; Posnette and Strickland 1948; Kirkpatrick 1950).

Mesohomotoma tessmanni *(Aulman) (Psyllidae) (No. XXIX not included in key)*. Other generic names have been used in referring to this species which was originally described in *Udamostigma* and is sometimes placed in *Tyora* (Entwistle 1972).

Selenothrips rubrocinctus *(Giard) (Thripidae) (No. XXX not included in key)*.

Toxoptera aurantii *(Boyer de Fonscolombe) (Aphididae) (No. XXXI not included in key)*.

Identification of potential vectors

The investigation by Posnette (1950*c*) of virus transmission by different vector species had two main objectives. The first was the possible classification of viruses by their vectors, but only limited scope was found for this objective. Some 'key species' were difficult to breed and transmission experiments were difficult to standardize (Thresh and Tinsley 1959). The second objective was to investigate the possible transmission of virus by species different from the one mainly responsible for spread within the crop. Hanna and Heatherington (1957) considered the possible occurrence of unknown vectors to explain the continuing appearance of swollen-shoot in a dimefox-treated plot (p. 106). To the continuing search for hitherto-unrecognized vectors for C.S.S.V. and C.M.L.V. must be added the need to find natural vectors for C.N.V. and C.Y.M.V.

Dr. D. J. Williams has prepared the identification key now provided, for twenty-seven 'good' species associated with cocoa in Africa, Trinidad, and Asia. It is reasonable to suppose that there are so far unrecognized vectors of cocoa viruses in countries where cocoa virus diseases are suspected or inadequately studied.

Factors influencing transmission of virus by vectors

Number of vectors. The earlier transmission experiments seemed to indicate that infection rate tended to increase when larger numbers of mealybugs were used (Posnette and Robertson 1950; Dale 1955*b*, 1957*b*). Results from subsequent tests using different numbers of insects were equivocal, probably because successful transmission depends on a number of factors which may or may not be operative when few insects are used. There does not appear to be a real 'mass action' effect (Entwistle 1972). Tinsley (1955*a*)

Key to mealybug vectors and other species of Coccoidea associated with cocoa

1   Dorsum in life with distinct white wax plates. Abdominal spiracles present; body covered in numerous spines; last antennal segment terminating in a stout spine   2
—   Dorsum without wax plates in life. Abdominal spiracles absent   3
2   Spines occupying most of dorsum   *Orthezia praelonga* Douglas (XXIII)
—   Spines in definite small areas   *Orthezia insignis* Browne (XXII)
3   Anal opening situated towards apex of dorsum
                                Stictococcus sjostedti Cockerell (XXVI)
—   Anal opening situated towards apex of abdomen, mealybugs   4
4   Dorsal setae lanceolate   5
—   Dorsal setae not lanceolate   8
5   Each cerarius with numerous setae on a differentiated plate with some degree of sclerotization   6
—   Each cerarius with never more than 7 setae, not on a sclerotized plate   7
6   Cerarian setae pointed   *Puto barberi* (Cockerell) (XXV)
—   Cerarian setae truncate   *Rastrococcus iceryoides* (Green) (XXXVI)
7   Antennae 9-segmented   *Phenaccocus madeirensis* Green (XXIV)
—   Antennae 8-segmented   *Pseudococcus hargreavesi* Laing (XI)
8   Cerarii absent, anal lobes prominent, terminating in a pair of stout spines
                                Geococcus coffeae Green (XXI)
—   Cerarii present   9
9   Enlarged tubular ducts present, each with orifice surrounded by a sclerotized area bearing 1 or more setae   *Ferrisia virgata* (Cockerell) (II)
—   Without such ducts   10
10 Cerarii forming an almost continuous band around margins
                                Cataenococcus loranthi (Strickland (XX)
—   Cerarii distinct   11
11 Cerarii at apices of very prominent tubercles at least on abdomen   12
—   Cerarii not at apices of prominent tubercles   13
12 Cerarii numbering 18 pairs   *Tylococcus westwoodi* Strickland (XIII)
—   Gerarii numbering at most 12 pairs
                                Tylococcus malacanthae Strickland (XXXVIII)
13 With 18 pairs of cerarii   14
—   With less than 18 pairs of cerarii   18
14 Cerarii each with numerous setae   *Planococcoides njalensis* (Laing) (V)
—   Cerarii each with usually 2 setae   15
15 Cerarii on small tubercles   *Planococcus boafoensis* (Strickland) (XXXV)
—   Cerarii not on small tubercles   16
16 Multilocular pores at anterior and posterior edges of segments   17
—   Multilocular pores at posterior edges of segments only
                                Planococcus kenyae (Le Pelley) (VII)
17 Cisanal setae longer than anal ring setae
                                Planococcus lilacinus (Cockerell) (VIII)
—   Cisanal setae shorter than anal ring setae   *Planococcus citri* (Risso) (VI)

18 Some dorsal setae spine-like and resembling cerarian setae
Nipaecoccus nipae (Maskell (XXXIV)
— Dorsal setae slender not resembling cerarian setae **19**
19 Oral rim ducts present **20**
— Oral rim ducts absent **24**
20 Antennae 8-segmented, with 17 pairs of cerarii **21**
— Antennae 9-segmented, with less than 17 pairs of cerarii **23**
21 With 2 or 3 oral rim ducts of different sizes near most cerarii
Pseudococcus longispinus (Targioni) (XII)
— With a single oral rim duct near most cerarii **22**
22 Anal and pre-anal cerarii each in a deep depression
Pseudococcus concavocerarii James (X)
— Anal and pre-anal cerarii not in a deep depression
Pseudococcus comstocki Kuwana (IX)
23 Dorsal oral rim ducts of 2 sizes, sparse in middle dorsal abdominal
segments *Maconellicoccus ugandae* (Laing) (III)
— Dorsal oral rim ducts of 1 size, numerous in middle dorsal abdominal
segments *Maconellicoccus hirsutus* (Green) (XXXIII)
24 Antennae 6-segmented, anal ring situated a short distance from posterior end
of body **25**
— Antennae 8-segmented, anal ring situated at apex of body **26**
25 Multilocular disc pores present, anal ring with 6 setae
Paraputo anomalus (Newstead) (IV)
— Multilocular disc pores absent, anal ring with numerous setae
Delococcus tafoensis (Strickland) (XXXII)
26 With 17 pairs of cerarii, dorsal setae short
Dysmicoccus brevipes (Cockerell) (I)
— With 1 pair of cerarii, dorsal setae long
Trionymus longipilosus De Lotto (XXXVII)

explained this circumstance in his statement that 'in other words, individual mealybugs do not inject sub-minimal doses of virus which can accumulate to produce infection when groups of these insects are used'.

Maturity of vectors. A belief that crawlers were more efficient vectors than older stages in transmission experiments (Posnette and Strickland 1948) was not substantiated (Dale 1955a). In a duplicated experiment, using relatively unskilled operators, there was a bias in favour of the larger and more robust adult mealybugs because they were less likely to be damaged during manipulation (Dale 1957a). Roivainen (1971) noted that degree of handling was a factor associated with erratic results in transmission experiments.

Acquisition of virus. The procedure in transmission experiments, using mealybugs collected from a cocoa tree, was to starve them for 48 hours to free them from any naturally acquired virus. They were then put on the source plant for a 24-hour acquisition feeding period (A.F.P.), before transferring to cocoa beans which were allowed to germinate for 2 days, for the folds of the cotyledons to open. After a 24-hour test feed period (T.F.P.), the beans were washed in nicotine sulphate and planted. With C.S.S.V. strain A, this procedure gave 50–80 per cent infection rates (Legg and Bonney 1968b).

Attention was given to the effects of preliminary starvation of the insects on transmission rates, with two objectives (Posnette and Robertson 1950; Dale 1955a; Thresh and Tinsley 1959). First, for practical purposes, enhanced infection rates were required. With starvation, infection rate increased with duration of feeding, up to 10 hours, and then declined. Without starvation, infection rate rose slowly and did not decline at 10 hours. This difference was not explained by relative settling rates, with or without starvation (Posnette 1950b). Second, there is scientific interest in connection with the transmission mechanism (Entwistle 1972). Attempts by Longworth and Entwistle (1965) to show whether cocoa virus is stylet or gut-borne in the vector were inconclusive. Roivainen (1971) studied the effects of moulting on virus transmission and reported that virus persisted through moulting, when virus carried on the stylet would be lost. He suggested that C.S.S.V. may be categorized as a 'semi-persistent virus', with transmission referred to as 'circulative' (internal) as discussed by Swenson (1967), and not 'stylet-borne' (external).

Gut-borne viruses affect mainly conducting tissue. Studies on the histology of plants affected by C.S.S.V. showed that it is the conducting tissue which is mainly affected (Mangenot et al. 1946a,b; Knight and Tinsley 1958).

Posnette and Robertson (1950) noted that the length and fineness of mealybug stylets caused the time required for the start of feeding to be longer than for aphids or leaf-hoppers, whose stylets penetrate rapidly. They observed microscopically the feeding mechanism of P. njalensis imprisoned within agar rings. Average stylet length was 988 μm for adults and 492 μm for nymphs. Penetration time was calculated as about 16 mins, from observations on stylet movement (average 0·5 μm. per second). Stylet tracks entered the vascular tissues, but it was uncertain whether they ended in the xylem or phloem. When a cocoa leaf was exposed to $^{14}CO_2$, the P. njalensis adults and crawlers which fed below the leaf became radio active. Autoradiograms showed that only the phloem nearest the cambium was radioactive. It seemed that mealybugs acquired virus from the phloem and must deposit virus into the phloem to infect a plant. Phenacoccus madeirensis was not observed to feed in the phloem, and it seemed that this would be unlikely because of the short length of stylet extruded by this non-vector species (Entwistle and Longworth 1963, 1964).

Feeding site. Different site preferences were observed for F. virgata, P. citri, and P. njalensis (Longworth 1964b; Igwegbe 1966a). F. virgata and P. citri preferred the leaf. *P. njalensis* fed to some extent on leaves but preferred the 'protective' positions offered by leaf axils, crevices between veins and pulvinus, and scars on the stems. Transmission rates were greater with *P. njalensis* from stems (50 per cent) than from leaves (6 per cent), whereas with *F. virgata* they were greater from leaves (48 per cent) than from stems (4 per cent). This difference was in accord with histological studies. *F. virgata* stylets seldom reached the phloem when fed on stems.

Maturity in tolerant and sensitive cocoa selections. Posnette and Todd (1951) considered that 'tolerant varieties which would harbour virulent virus without showing conspicuous symptoms would be a grave menace'. Attempts to determine whether virus was more or less readily available in tolerant than in sensitive cocoa were equivocal (Igwegbe 1966*b*; Owusu 1971*a*). Previously, Dale (1958) used seedling progenies in an attempt to get virus-free cuttings from tolerant infected plants. 'Twinned' seedlings (Posnette 1942; Dale 1956) which had shown only mild transient symptoms were coppiced to give cuttings, some of which were successfully rooted. It appeared that some of the cuttings and perhaps two of the regenerating stumps may have been uninfected, implying that virus distribution at the time of coppicing was discontinuous (non-systemic).

It is difficult to avoid bias when sampling mature trees for virus availability. Nevertheless, there is evidence that virus may be less readily available from mature tolerant trees than from mature sensitive trees, but results from observations of young tolerant and sensitive seedlings may be misleading (Owusu 1971*a*).

Effect of light on symptom expression and virus availability. Under greenhouse conditions, close planting and shading acted similarly in accentuating virus effects (symptom expression and growth depression) with virulent C.S.S.V. in Ghana (Asomaning and Lockard 1964; Asomaning and Kwakwa 1968*b*). In Nigeria, transmission rates were greater for plants kept in darkness than for those grown with full sunlight (Longworth 1965).

Effect of host-plant nutrition. Wharton and Adams (1955) used water-culture methods to study the effects of major nutrients (nitrogen, phosphorus, and potassium) separately and in combination, on virus-infected seedlings. None of these treatments had pronounced effect on leaf symptoms. Extra nitrogen appeared to increase the expression of fern-leaf symptom, but as a reflection of number of leaves present. Without nitrogen there were insufficient leaves for this symptom to develop.

Mealybugs excrete most of the sugar that enters the digestive tract as honeydew but retain most of the amino acids (Entwistle and Longworth 1963). Adomako (1972) studied the composition of cocoa bark and mealybug honeydew, with a view to eventual preparation of diets for the laboratory rearing of mealybugs. Roivainen (1969a) had discussed the possibility of feeding mealybugs on virus incorporated in liquid diets.

Effect of temperature on infected material. C.S.S.V. strains A and B were not inactivated in budwood immersed in water at 45 °C. (113 °F.) for 30 mins., at 50 °C. (122 °F.) for 12 mins., or at 52 °C. (126 °F.) for 10 mins. (Posnette 1947b). Results obtained in Trinidad with C.T.V.-infected material were in general accord with those in West Africa (Murray and Swarbrick 1959). For material infected with cocoa viruses, it seems that heat-treatments which are not fatal to the host tissues have no noticeable effect on the viruses.

Kenten and Legg (1968a) showed that infectivity *in vitro* was retained by preparations of C.M.L.V. at 55 °C. (131 °F.) but was lost at 60 °C. (140 °F.). Therefore the C.M.L.V. thermal inactivation point appeared to be higher than that of C.S.S.V. strain A, preparations of which were unaffected by heating at 45 °C. (113 °F.) for 10 mins., but infectivity was only exceptionally retained at 55 °C. (131 °F.) (Brunt *et al.* 1964).

Effect of temperature on the vectors. There was evidence of a tendency for more mealybugs to be in the cocoa canopy where temperatures rose more rapidly and reached higher maxima than at ground level (Strickland 1951a; Cornwell 1960). Bigger (1972) found that predominance of mealybugs in the canopy region pertained with unshaded cocoa having a thick interlocking canopy, but not with shaded cocoa having a poor canopy. He concluded that further study was needed to determine the factors influencing the distribution of mealybugs within the cocoa tree.

Roivainen (1968a, 1969a) used a radioisotope (^{32}P) as a tracer to estimate the amount of feeding by *P. njalensis*. There was apparently no feeding at 20 °C. (68 °F.), some at 25 °C. (77 °F.) and the uptake was highest at 30 °C. (86 °F.) and not much less at 35 °C. (95 °F.). Therefore, temperature conditions in West Africa are likely to be suitable for acquisition and transmission of virus to proceed uninterrupted for long periods.

Influence of wind on dispersal of vectors. In Ghana, Cornwell (1960) obtained evidence of airborne dispersal of mealybugs up to a distance of 340 ft. (104 m.), and these insects became established on seedlings at a distance of 45 ft. (13·7 m.), from infested cocoa trees. Conditions for 'take-off' were uncertain since tented colonies and mobile instars of *P. njalensis* withstood exposure to air currents of 10 m.p.h. (16 km. h^{-1}). Tests to dislodge mealybugs showed that 1st-instar nymphs of *P. citri* were more readily removed than those of *P. njalensis* and *F. virgata*.

It is possible that gale-force winds experienced at certain seasons in West Africa (Hamilton and Archbold 1945) may carry mealybugs to high altitudes and disperse them over many miles. Vectors from forest-tree hosts may be important in the process of long-distance dispersal through being subjected to wind speeds in excess of those experienced by vectors in cocoa trees. Posnette (1950c) considered the possibility that there may be potential vectors among the mealybug species which occur on wild hosts, where the common vectors are less prevalent than on cocoa. Tall host-trees may therefore be important in connection with 'jump spread' of cocoa virus diseases (Thresh 1958b).

Effect of ants associated with vectors. In a general review of the association of ants with coccids, Nixon (1951) concluded that the extent of mutual benefit was difficult to estimate. There was no proof that ants play an important part in dispersal of coccids nor that they afford much protection by driving away parasites and predators. The role of ants in cocoa virus diseases may be sometimes important but is generally indeterminate.

Le Pelley (1968) discussed ways in which ants may have significant influence with coffee. It seems likely that his comments are applicable also with cocoa. He noted that, over quite short periods, a single ant species may act in more than one way. There is reason to expect longer-term changes in relationships between ants and mealybugs.

Under natural conditions, *P. njalensis* is usually attended by ants, in contrast to *P. citri* which is not invariably attended (Strickland 1951b). For *P. njalensis* the proportion unattended was less than 1 per cent, whilst for *P. citri* the proportion unattended was greater than 10 per cent. Strickland (1951a) showed that *P. njalensis* was the commonest mealybug on cocoa at Tafo (nearly 99 per cent) and *P. citri* came next in order of abundance (nearly 1 per cent). Twenty years later, Bigger (1972) has shown that *P. citri* has taken the place of *P. njalensis* as the commonest mealybug at Tafo, apparently in association with the destruction of forest trees. However, in Trinidad, where *P. citri* was mainly responsible for virus spread (Kirkpatrick 1953a), this species was the dominant mealybug and infestation was negatively correlated with light intensity (Fennah 1959). For Ghana, Bigger (1972) stated that 'if the more mobile *P. citri*, which is not dependent to the same extent on ants, replaces *P. njalensis*, different patterns and rates of spread of virus may occur which may be a change for the worse'. It is worth noting that, despite such a difference in vector species during the same period (1945–51), there were similar increases in percentages of infected trees in Ghana (31–92 per cent) and in Trinidad (16–84 per cent), as discussed by Thresh (1958b).

Ant associations were studied by Cornwell (1956, 1957). Bolton (1972) provided a 'key to ant genera nesting on or in cocoa trees'. Entwistle (1972) discussed the ant species complex in relation to the cocoa ecosystem, including ant associations with mealybugs.

Effect of natural enemies of vectors. Dale (1962) cited Strickland (1951b) and Cornwell (1957) for the opinion 'that parasites and predators are mainly responsible for keeping mealybug populations in Ghana at what is, for such pests, a low level'. Likewise for Trinidad, Kirkpatrick (1953b) commented that *P. citri* was sometimes sufficiently abundant to be a minor pest and it was likely that natural enemies prevented its ranking as a major pest.

Natural enemies were surveyed in Ghana (Donald 1956), Nigeria (Sutherland 1953), and Trinidad (Kirkpatrick 1953a,b). No parasites nor predators were reported for a number of the Coccoidea studied in West Africa and Trinidad. It seems likely that natural enemies of uncommon species may occur but were not observed because surveys were not sufficiently thorough to include all such relatively rare hosts for rearing of possible parasites. In a total of over a quarter of a million mealybugs counted in random collections, several species were represented by fewer than ten individuals (Strickland 1951a).

Insect parasites recorded in Trinidad and in West Africa are grouped as follows and represented by numbers of species/numbers of genera as indicated:

Hymenoptera: Aphelinidae 2/2, Encyrtidae 39/15, Platergasteridae 1/1 (Risbec 1949; Strickland 1951a; Kerrich 1953; 1967, Kirkpatrick 1953b; Sutherland 1953; Bennett 1955, 1957; Donald 1955, 1956, 1957).

Table 7.1 shows that for many parasite species (79 percent), only one host species was reported.

TABLE 7.1
Number of parasite species and number of mealybug host species attacked in Trinidad (W.I.) and in West Africa (W.A.)

	1 host species	2 or 3 host species	More than 3 species	Total species
Number of parasite species (W.I.)	15	0	0	15
Number of parasite species (W.A.)	18	7	2	27
Total	33	7	2	42

Arthropod predators recorded in Trinidad and in West Africa are grouped as follows and represented by numbers of species/numbers of genera as indicated:

Arachnida: Acari 1/1, Araneae 2/2, Pseudoscorpiones 1/1 (Strickland 1951a; Donald 1956).
Coleoptera: Coccinellidae 15/7 (Strickland 1951a; Kirkpatrick 1953b; Donald 1956; Bennett and Simmonds 1964).
Diptera: Cecidomyiidae 9/5, Drosophilidae 1/1, Syrphidae 2/1 (Kirkpatrick 1953b; Donald 1956; Harris 1968).
Lepidoptera: Lycaenidae 2/2, Noctuidae 1/1 (Strickland 1951a; Donald 1956).
Neuroptera: Chrysopidae 5/2 (Kirkpatrick 1953b; Donald 1956).

Table 7.2 shows that for many predator species (72 per cent), only one host species was reported.

TABLE 7.2

Number of predator species and number of mealybug host species attacked in Trinidad (W.I.) and in West Africa (W.A.)

	1 host species	2 or 3 host species	More than 3 species	Total species
Number of predator species (W.I.)	17	2	0	19
Number of predator species (W.A.)	11	7	2	20
Total	28	9	2	39

TABLE 7.3

Mealybugs and associated primary and secondary parasites

Secondary Parasites	Mealybug species	II	V	VI	XIV
43		31	31	31	—
44		—	—	32	—
45		—	—	32	—
46		31, 35	31, 35	31, 35	—
47		—	—	32	—
48		—	—	32	—
49		—	—	—	27
50		36	—	—	—

Mealybug species:
   II *Ferrisia virgata*, V *Planococcoides njalensis*,
   VI *Planococcus citri*, XIV *Dysmicoccus* sp. near *brevipes*.

Primary parasite species:
   27 *Euryhopalus kirkpatricki* (Kerrich)
   31 *Leptomastix bifasciatus* Compere
   32 *Leptomastix dactylopii* (Howard)
   35 *Neodiscodes abengouroui* Risbec
   36 *Pseudaphycus ferrisianae* Bennett

Secondary parasite species:
   43 *Achrysopophagus aegyptiacus* Mercet
   44 *Achrysopophagus dactylopii* (Howard)
   45 *Achrysopophagus seini* Dozier
   46 *Cheiloneurus carinatus* Compere
   47 *Coccidoctonus trinidadensis* Crawford
   48 *Gahaniella tertia* Kerrich
   49 *Kerrichiella coleoptrata* (Kerrich)
   50 *Thysanus hyalipennis* (Girault)

Eight species of secondary parasites (Hymenoptera: Encyrtidae 6/4, Thysanidae 2/2) were reported in association with four species of mealybugs and five species of primary parasites, as shown in Table 7.3 (Risbec 1949; Kerrich 1953; Kirkpatrick 1953*b*; Donald 1956; Bennett, F. D. 1969 *in litt.*). These few records may reflect insufficient study of hyperparasites rather than limited influence of secondary parasites on primary-parasite populations.

There is little information concerning parasites of predators. *Homalotylus africanus* Timberlake (Encyrtidae), and *Homalotylus* sp. were reported from unspecified hosts in West Africa (Donald 1956). Bennett, F. D. (1969 *in litt.*) reported *Homalotylus* sp. near *africanus* from *Hyperaspis* sp. (Coccinellidae) on *P. citri* in Trinidad.

Some other possible means of cocoa virus spread

Human agency. Except for possible occurrences of cocoa viruses in Colombia and in Costa Rica (p. 79), there is no other evidence that cocoa virus diseases occur in the region of Central America and the north-western part of South America within which cocoa cultivation is assumed to have originated (see Chapter 1, pp. 6–10).

Early post-Columbian 'long distance' movements of cocoa (more than 1,000 miles (1,600 km.)) are likely to have been by small plants raised from seed, which would be unlikely to have carried virus infection. Later long-distance movements of cocoa material likely to have carried virus infection were in relatively recent times when suitable techniques were developed for transport and propagation by budding or through rooting of cuttings.

The evidence for spread of virus from planting material and from pods was reviewed by Thresh (1958b). There is circumstantial evidence for 'short-distance' spread (less than 1,000 miles (1,600 km.)) of virus through transport of infected pods. He drew attention to the recognition by Tinsley (1955b) that symptoms produced by C.S.S.V. isolates from Konongo in Ashanti, Ghana and from Kongodia, Ivory Coast were virtually indistinguishable from symptoms produced by isolates otherwise apparently restricted to the New Juaben area of Ghana.

In Trinidad, cocoa virus disease was common in three Northern Range valleys (pp. 77–8), other occurrences elsewhere in Trinidad were attributed to the use of infected budwood (Baker and Dale 1947b). When stem swellings and characteristic leaf symptoms were reported in Sri Lanka, budded and seedling trees showed these symptoms. It seemed likely that the disease had been inadvertently spread through use of infected budwood (Orellana and Peiris 1957). It seemed probable that suspected occurrences of virus disease in Sabah (p. 80) were to be accounted for by introduction of infected propagation-material, despite a previous quarantine period (Anon. 1970). Attafuah and Blencowe (1960) considered the possibility that a virus disease occurrence near a River Moa ferry-crossing in Sierra Leone (Gandorhun isolate, p. 76) originated from infected plant material carried along the trade route from Liberia, but no cocoa virus diseases were reported there (Tinsley 1959).

Mechanical transmission. Brunt and Kenten (1960) described their procedure which was the first to achieve mechanical transmission of C.S.S.V. via *Adansonia digitata* and *Bombax brevicuspe* Sprague seedlings, infected at 2 weeks from germination. Leaf macerates prepared after vacuum-infiltration were applied as slurries to cocoa half-beans. Symptoms sometimes appeared in the first flush-leaves but generally in the second flush of leaves. In subsequent investigations, Brunt and Kenten (1962*a,b,c*) used five isolates, which included Kofi Pare isolate (C.S.S.V. strain A). This isolate, which was not discussed above, was considered similar to New Juaben isolate (Kenten, R. H. 1969 *in litt.*). Brunt and Kenten (1963) and Kenten and Legg (1965, 1968*a,b*) discussed modifications in technique for getting enhanced infectivity. Low infections were at least partly due to the formation of non-infective virus-tannin complexes. Certain proteins preserved infectivity during extraction and in addition indicated the presence of an undescribed virus. Owusu (1969) tested the possibility of using partially purified C.S.S.V. inocula to infect cocoa seedlings manually. One seedling became infected, but further work was necessary for confirmation.

Parasitic plants. Tinsley (1961) reported unsuccessful attempts to use certain parasitic plants (*Cassytha filiformis* L. and *Cuscuta* sp.) to transmit C.S.S.V. and C.M.L.V. isolates from infected cocoa to healthy seedlings.

Control of cocoa virus diseases: direct control

Eradication of infection

Cocoa suffering from swollen-shoot disease conforms to the general rule that plants infected with a virus do not recover: there is no known cure for affected cocoa.

The original control measures proposed were 'to cut out and burn all diseased trees, together with a few of the apparently healthy trees ...' (Steven 1936*a*). The two principles then promulgated were adhered to, throughout subsequent attempts to achieve direct control of cocoa virus diseases. The purpose of destroying 'healthy' trees was two-fold. To eliminate trees which may have already become infected and to form a 'sanitary belt round infected areas'. The desirability of a *cordon sanitaire* as it was referred to later (Johns and Gibberd 1950; Ross and Broatch 1951), became as much an axiom of cocoa virus disease control as the need to destroy some healthy trees because of possible inapparent infection. After comparing different treatments, Posnette (1943*a*) reported that, since repeated treatment was usually necessary, control could be effected most economically by removing only one ring of symptomless trees and those definitely infected. The extent to which apparently healthy trees should be destroyed was one of the most controversial and politically disastrous issues of the campaign for controlling swollen-shoot disease (Anon. 1945*a*; Watson *et al.* 1948). The 'Swollen-Shoot Commission' endorsed the principles of destroying diseased trees and apparently healthy neighbouring ('contact') trees, but emphasized the need for an educational programme to ensure better dissemination of information to farmers (Berkeley, Carter, and Van Slogteren 1948).

At first, when the nature of swollen-shoot and its symptoms were not understood (Voelcker and West 1940), there was uncertainty as to how rigorously the proposed control measures should be enforced (Cadbury, P. S. 1949). Some areas were 'fully' treated (diseased and neighbouring apparently healthy trees destroyed) and subsequently inspected and retreated when new infections were found. Elsewhere, treatments were less effective, because there was no inspection after initial cutting-out. There were also untreated areas, one of these occupied about half an acre in 1937, four and a quarter acres in 1942, and thirty-three acres in 1944 (Anon. 1945a).

After 1940, when transmission of swollen-shoot had been demonstrated (Posnette 1940) and the symptoms were properly understood, there was a rational basis for full resumption of control measures, but the 1941–3 campaign was stopped when a higher priority had to be given to rubber and food production. Posnette (1953) commented that the West African cocoa industry was a 'war casualty'. It is possible that swollen-shoot might have been controlled if eradication had been rigorously enforced in the period immediately after its recognition in 1936. The less severe and slower-spreading virus disease in Trinidad was apparently reduced to negligible importance by destroying all cocoa within an area extending up to 1 mile from the La Pastora Cocoa Propagating Station in the Santa Cruz valley (Thorold 1948; Montserin 1950). According to recent information, there is now little evidence of cocoa virus disease in Trinidad (Murray, D. B. 1970 *in litt.*).

In January 1947 in Ghana, compulsory powers were used to enable the Department of Agriculture to destroy diseased trees without the consent of the owner, but within the following year there was serious opposition so that compulsory cutting-out was suspended in April 1948 (Cadbury ,J. 1949; Linton 1950). Johns and Gibberd (1950) described similar difficulties in Nigeria, resulting in stoppages of the cutting-out campaigns there. Posnette (1953) mentioned that, in the Ivory Coast also, original plans for eradication have had to be abandoned. Neither there nor in Ghana and Nigeria has a way been found to get the co-operation or even consent of enough farmers for treatment to have any permanent value in the worst affected areas. There are areas of 'mass infection' in Nigeria (Longworth 1961) and in Ghana (Quartey-Papafio 1961), which are so heavily infected with C.S.S.V. that direct control has had to be abandoned.

Whilst eradication is impracticable in large areas of 'mass infection', Posnette (1943a, 1953) explained that prompt removal of infected trees in small outbreaks (less than fifty trees) is likely to be effective. The *cordon sanitaire* surrounding a large outbreak area is intended to prevent, or at least limit 'radial spread' but subsidiary ('satellite') outbreaks may be expected (Thresh 1958b) and their treatment by cutting-out, with subsequent inspection, is important.

Cornwell (1956) described the practical procedure of cutting-out and studied the subsequent behaviour of the mealybugs in the 'slash piles' where all the branches were stacked. The trunk bases were stacked separately ('stump piles') to provide evidence of the number of trees cut out. It was generally impracticable to burn the fresh material and undesirable to do so because it provided a valuable source of fuel when dry. The virus became inactivated about 14 days after the construction of the slash pile. There was not much movement of vectors from it and those which did leave it were not capable of migrating to healthy trees at distances greater than 4 ft. (1·2 m.) from the pile in the period during which the virus might persist. There was no reason to believe that the efficiency of cutting-out was seriously reduced by the movement of vectors from the infected trees which were eradicated.

A valuable contribution to the technique of eradicating outbreaks was made by Thresh and Lister (1960). They tested the procedure in Nigeria where all symptomless trees were removed to a distance of 50 yds. (46 m.) from infected trees, thereby an average of ten trees were destroyed for every one obviously infected. To study the justification for this procedure, trees with symptoms were felled and their sites marked. Apparently healthy trees within 30 yds. (28 m.) of the outbreak were 'coppiced' (cut back to a height of 6–9 ins. (15–23 cm.) above ground level). Most of the coppiced trees produced vigorous shoots which were examined for virus symptoms, but about one-third of the treated trees failed to regenerate. Subsidiary experiments indicated that when infected trees were coppiced only half the number survived. Coppicing revealed some infected stumps rapidly (within a period of 3 months), most of them within a year, but some were detected only after 2 years. The procedure recommended and adopted related the extent of apparently healthy trees destroyed (yards) to the size of the outbreak (number of trees) as follows: 1–5 infected (5 yds. (5 m.)), 6–50 infected (10 yds. (9 m.)), 51–200 infected (15 yds. (14 m.)).

Legg (1972) reviewed the cutting-out campaign in Ghana and discussed current rehabilitation and replanting under a scheme supported by the World Bank.

Control of cocoa virus diseases: indirect control

Chemical methods (interpretations of proprietary-pesticide names were provided by Martin 1971, and by Kirby 1973)

Contact insecticides. In preliminary laboratory tests on exposed mealybugs, parathion was rapidly effective against *P. njalensis*, whilst nicotine and D.D.T. were slower acting (Anon. 1950). Under field conditions, insecticides used as smokes or dusts were ineffective compared with emulsions (0·1–0·2 per cent nicotine, or 0·02 per cent parathion) (Anon. 1953*a*).

Because of the protection afforded by carton tents, not all mealybugs were killed even when pesticides were applied to conveniently small trees which were not representative of farmer's cocoa in Ghana. It was to be expected that the chemicals tried would be less effective if applied to large trees. No further tests were made with these materials and methods of application against mealybugs.

Attention was given to the possibility of reducing mealybugs indirectly by disrupting their association with attendant ants. Early attempts to do this by manual removal of ants' nests, grease-banding and insecticides (B.H.C. or D.D.T.) were not generally successful. Dieldrin (0·5–1·0 per cent) disrupted ant activity and *P. njalensis* decreased at first, but subsequently ant and mealybug populations returned to pre-treatment levels and there did not appear to be any control of swollen-shoot disease (Taylor 1958; Entwistle 1959, 1960*b*). Because minor-pest increases followed general applications of dieldrin, different formulations and methods of application were tried (Entwistle 1961*a,b*; Entwistle and Armstrong 1961). Heptachlor and chlordane were tested as possible alternative formicides to dieldrin (Armstrong 1962, 1963). Although some control of ants and mealybugs was achieved, there was still much damage by 'pod miners' ('Marmara' species, Lepidoptera, Lithocolletidae). Although spraying with persistent insecticides (chlordane, dieldrin, heptachlor) stopped ants from tending *P. njalensis* colonies, other mealybug vectors which were not attended by ants (*Ferrisia virgata* and *Planococcus citri*) became more abundant (Gerard 1967).

Systemic insecticides. It was to be expected that the difficulty presented by carton tent protection of *P. njalensis* might be surmounted by the use of a systemic insecticide which should render the whole plant toxic to sucking insects. Dimefox gave 99 per cent mealybug mortality when applied as a liquid in a shallow trench around the base of the cocoa tree (West 1951). Later, this insecticide was used in a commercial formulation called 'Hanane'; it was referred to previously as 'CR409', but the name dimefox is used here. Trees sprayed with either dimefox, paraoxon, or parathion (1 per cent) were badly scorched, but when these insecticides were applied as solutions to the soil in which a cocoa plant was growing, there was appreciable reduction in the number of mealybug colonies. Root uptake of dimefox was demonstrated by Hanna, Judenko, and Heatherington (1955) when this insecticide was effectively applied directly to an exposed cocoa root at the lowest dosage tested (0·005 g. per plant). They determined an exact relationship between tree girth and dosage weight. The cost per treatment was estimated by Hanna and Heatherington (1957). Attempts were made to reduce costs by introducing systemic insecticides directly into the trunks of cocoa trees, since it was expected that smaller quantities would suffice, compared with soil applications. Mealybug populations remained substantially reduced 5 weeks after introducing doses only one-tenth of those prescribed by the girth–weight relationship for soil treatment. However, it seemed that the disadvantage of slowness of the trunk implantation method might outweigh the cost reduction through smaller dosages per tree, compared with soil application. Nicol (1953*a*) discussed the use of dimefox and gave results of tests for toxic residues in beans from pods on treated trees. Residues did not exceed the limit (0·1 p.p.m.) set by the United States Food and Drug Administration (Barnes 1951).

Roivainen (1968*b*, 1969*b*) tested Azodrin and Bidrin, and found that they reduced mealybug populations when painted on the trunk or implanted into holes near the base of the cocoa tree. The period during which cocoa plants treated with Azodrin or Bidrin remain toxic to mealybugs may be shorter than for dimefox. Provided that the number of treatments necessary to rid plants of mealybugs is not excessive, a short persistency period may be advantageous, to circumvent the disadvantage of possible toxicity or taint affecting the beans from treated trees.

Arboricides. Berkeley *et al.* (1948) recommended that research on the chemical destruction of trees should be given high priority because a successful outcome would be of great practical importance. Trials started at Tafo in 1950, but Mapother (1955) concluded that chemical destruction of infected trees was of little practical importance because cutting-out was at least as economical as poisoning and was more rapid. Another objection to the use of arboricides (Asomaning, Quansah, and Lovi 1964), was their apparent harmlessness to mealybugs, whilst C.S.S.V. was not inactivated (Asomaning, Lovi, and Boafo 1964).

There is scope for the use of arboricides to destroy large trees which are virus hosts or otherwise unsuitable as a mixed population with cocoa (Benstead 1953). Large trees in farms cannot be felled without causing some damage to neighbouring cocoa, but by poisoning them they will disintegrate slowly and cause less damage (Benstead 1958).

There is practical experience with large-scale use of arboricides, and the procedure and costs have been described (Liefstingh 1966; Blow 1968).

Cultural methods

Pruning of cocoa to isolate mealybug populations. Since West African cocoa farms are generally poorly maintained, it was unlikely that pruning would be done willingly and effectively enough to reduce canopy spread without affecting productivity (Cornwell 1958). A continuous canopy of foliage is desirable to maintain yields (Longworth 1963).

Planting of cocoa at a wider spacing. Wider spacing would no doubt reduce mealybug migration through the canopy but increased wind speeds in the cocoa would encourage aerial dispersal (Cornwell 1958).

Retention of close spacing with provision of a barrier. Spread of cocoa viruses is aggravated by the close planting and monoculture of the crop over considerable areas. Van der Plank (1948) mentioned cocoa virus disease as an example of the 'crowd diseases' which may be controlled by mixed cropping. Cornwell (1960) considered it unlikely that an economic crop would be found to produce sufficient interrupting foliage to be effective as a 'barrier crop'. Nevertheless, the removal of cocoa on the perimeter of outbreaks and replacement by coffee, was mentioned by Thresh and Lister (1960) as one of the methods used for control of cocoa virus disease in the Ivory Coast. There does not appear to be any report on the possible benefits from this procedure.

Biological methods

Insect antagonism. For mealybugs in Ghana, Bigger (1972) commented that 'control by naturally occurring parasites and predators is not very great'. The first exotic parasite introduced to Ghana was *Anagyrus kivuensis* Compere (Encyrtidae) brought from Kenya in 1948 (Posnette and Strickland 1949). Arrangements were made for further introductions (Anon. 1950). Greathead *et al.* (1971) detailed the introductions of parasites and predators from California and Trinidad into Ghana, through the Commonwealth Institute of Biological Control, in the period 1949–55.

When Nicol (1953b) reviewed the procedure of attempted biological control, more than half a million parasites had been released. Subsequent releases brought the ultimate total to about 1,000,000 parasites liberated in Ghana. A few specimens of *Pseudaphycus angelicus* (Howard) (Encyrtidae) were recaptured (Cornwell 1957). None of the exotic parasites released in Ghana became established. Mortalities after release were not explained.

There was no proved establishment from over 35,000 adult predators (Coccinellidae) released. Nicol (1953b) commented that 'this was not entirely unexpected as these beetles consume a large number of mealybugs during their development and it is unlikely that sufficient mealybugs were present in any of the areas where liberations took place to sustain the introduced species'.

Fungal antagonism. Nicol, Owen, and Strickland (1950) tested *Aspergillus parasiticus* Speare against mealybugs in Ghana. The cultures used were described by Raper and Fennell (1965). Under laboratory conditions, percentage deaths of *Planococcoides njalensis* averaged over 90 per cent following applications of *A. parasiticus* spores as dusts, after 'dilution' with talc. There was no success when similar dusts were applied to mealybug colonies under field conditions (Nicol 1953b).

Another possible parasite was *Cephalosporium* sp., isolated from *Planococcus citri*. A mycelial suspension was sprayed on to half an acre of mature amelonado cocoa. Three weeks later, *Cephalosporium* sp. was recovered from morbid mealybugs and there appeared to be unusually few nymphs in mealybug colonies within the sprayed area (Rojter, Bonney, and Boafo 1966; Rojter, Bonney, and Legg 1966). After 6 months, attempts to isolate

Cephalosporium sp. were not successful (Rojter, Bonney, Boafo, and Dakwa 1968). No further studies with *Cephalosporium* sp. were reported.

Resistance and tolerance

Cocoa material for selection and breeding. To understand the parentage of selections used for breeding and seed production in Ghana and Nigeria, it is necessary to consider their origins and to indicate the code systems employed to designate individual trees and progenies. Material of two different categories was available for selection. They are now referred to conveniently, albeit arbitrarily, as 'early' and 'recent' introductions.

Early introductions comprise the 'original' cocoa populations of farms and experiment stations. All the introductions considered here as 'early' were made before cocoa viruses were recognized in West Africa, in contrast to recent introductions in 1944 (Posnette 1951) and later (McKelvie 1957*b*). These recent introductions originated mainly from the Upper Amazon region.

Posnette (1943*b*) surveyed Ghana cocoa farms and found an unexpectedly large number with more than 30 per cent Trinitario trees, and he assumed 'that the earlier introductions had left their mark'. It seems certain that most of the predominating amelonado cocoa in Ghana and Nigeria originated from Fernando Po and S. Tomé, but the derivation of the intermixture is uncertain.

Dickson (1964) stated that in 1788, the Danish Government in the Gold Coast (later Ghana) entrusted the introduction of various crops, including cocoa, to P. E. Isert who died in 1789. The earliest report of its occurrence there is attributed to van Yzerdoorn (1815), but details are lacking. Monod (1951) provided the earliest authoritative record of cocoa introduction to West Africa (Senegal), which was discussed by Mauny (1953). Although cocoa was listed (as '*Abroma cacao*') among the Richard-Toll, Senegal, plants in 1824, this introduction may have been unsuccessful. Howes (1947) mentioned that records at Kew showed that a shipment of cocoa plants probably raised from West Indian seed was destined for West Africa in 1864, but there were no further details. It is possible that this consignment went to Sierra Leone where the original cocoa is different from West African amelonado (Deighton 1945). Wanner (1962) described attempts by members of the Basel Mission in Ghana to establish cocoa at their Akropong Station, Akwapim, Eastern Region, but the first importation of seeds from Surinam was unsuccessful. More seed was brought from Cape Palmas, Liberia, and one tree survived to produce pods from which seedlings were raised by J. J. Long in about 1868. This planting antedated the illicit introduction of cocoa to Mampong, Akwapim from Fernando Po by Tetteh Quashie (as Tetteh Quarshie, but I have adopted the spelling used by Dickson (1969)). It was the general belief in farming areas that he first introduced cocoa to Ghana (Torto 1959). Posnette (1943*b*) found 'rumour

holds that only a single pod was introduced to the Gold Coast about 1880',
but it is also stated that Tetteh Quashie brought cocoa seedlings from
Fernando Po to Ghana in 1879 (Wanner 1962). Ayorinde (1966) and Lass
and Egbe (1972) discussed the history of cocoa planting in Nigeria where
the origins are also uncertain. It seems that cultivation started there in 1874
with seeds from Fernando Po.

According to Dickson (1969) there was a Government introduction of
cocoa pods from S. Tomé in 1886 for planting at Aburi Botanic Gardens,
Ghana. Posnette, A. F. (1970 *in litt.*) informed me that seedlings from the
cocoa pods introduced in 1886 by Governor Griffiths from S. Tomé, formed
the 'amelonado plot' at Aburi, studied by Auchinleck and Eady (1928) and
later by himself. The plot included some non-amelonado trees, which were
probably 'supplies' resulting from cross-pollination with trees in the
neighbouring Trinitario plot. The original record ledgers show origins as
'red pod criollo' and 'yellow pod criollo' from River Estate, Trinidad.

Selection for possible resistance to swollen-shoot disease was started by
Posnette (1943d). He reported observations on apparently healthy trees
surviving in a C.S.S.V. outbreak area. Although this programme did not
yield any highly resistant progenies, there were indications of tolerance to
infection.

Code system (1). A source reference code was used for early introductions.
Initial letters of the alphabet indicated the locality (farms and experiment
stations), and numerals indicated the position of the tree (Posnette 1943b).

Code system (2). The letter 'C' (for clone) followed by numerals was used
when distributing parent clones (Rogers and Knight 1955; McKelvie
1957b; Glendinning 1967). The 'C' series comprised numbers C1 to C85
(Longworth and Thresh 1963a).

The letter 'C' as prefix, had been previously used for some Trinitario
selections, and did not conform with the 'C' code now being considered
(Posnette 1943b; Posnette and Todd 1951). Accordingly, an earlier 'C85'
was later designated 'ACu85' (Attafuah and Glendinning 1965a,b).

Code system (3). The letter 'T' (for Trinidad) was used when cocoa and
other *Theobroma* species and *Herrania* species were introduced to Tafo,
Ghana (Voelcker 1946, 1947; Anon. 1948). Each pod was designated by a
serial number preceded by the letter T. Pods numbered below T60 were
open-pollinated, whilst T60 and higher numbers were hand-pollinated
(Knight and Rogers 1955). Toxopeus (1964) listed the introductions, from
T1 to T121, and gave their equivalent 'Trinidad code' designations
(considered below).

As the letter T had been used earlier for selections in Ghana, this early
prefix was designated 'TF' to avoid confusion with the later 'T' code.
Likewise, when a Nigerian selection referred to originally at 'T38' (Russell

1952), was used in Ghana, it was designated 'N38' to avoid confusion with the later 'T' code.

Code system (4). Various combinations of letters were used in Trinidad ('Trinidad code') to indicate where parent trees were growing, notably 'I.C.S.' for Imperial College selections, Trinidad. The two designations now in common use for Upper Amazon selections, which refer to particular rivers, are 'Na' (for Nanay), and 'Pa' (for Parinari). The abbreviation 'IMC' used by F. J. Pound (Baker and Holliday 1957), meant 'Iquitos Mixed Calabacillo', according to Posnette, A. F. (1970 *in litt.*), not 'Iquitos Maranon Clones' as suggested by Fisher, Soderholm, and Kahn (1967).

Code system (5). A 'W' code system referred to progenies at W.A.C.R.I. (Tafo, Ghana), for plant breeding purposes there. It was adopted to designate selected material as follows (Anon. 1953*b*): prefix 'WA' for amelonado selections, 'WB' for hybrid selections, 'WC' for criollo selections, 'WD' for Trinitario selections, 'WE' for Upper Amazon selections, and 'WAE' for crosses (A × E, etc.).

Code system (6). Letters A–M were used to designate selections in trials away from Tafo (Glendinning and Edwards 1961; Glendinning 1963*b*, 1967; Longworth and Thresh 1963*b*, 1964; Longworth 1964*a*; Longworth, Are, and Freeman 1965; Glendinning and Martinson 1966; Amponsah and Abrokwa 1969; Edwards 1969; Toxopeus 1969).

The above account of code systems is relevant to published references to Tafo (C.R.I.G., formerly W.A.C.R.I.) selections. The usage of codes there was shown comprehensively in 'Check List, W.A.C.R.I. Breeding Material and Varieties' (mimeograph, undated (*ca.* 1960), compiled by Glendinning, D. R. (1972 *in litt.*).

The use of tolerant and/or resistant selections. The planting of cocoa trees having inapparent infection was opposed because it would frustrate the procedure of control by cutting-out trees with symptoms (Posnette and Todd 1951; Blencowe 1961). However, one of the factors limiting successful control by cutting-out was the occurrence of infected but temporarily symptomless trees which were inadvertently overlooked in the course of surveys when trees were marked for cutting-out. It is now realized that elimination of all potential reservoirs of infection is impracticable in certain areas of Ghana (Legg and Kenten 1968) and Nigeria (Longworth 1961). For profitable cocoa cultivation to continue or be resumed in such areas, consideration was given to the use of selections tolerant to infection, particularly if these also showed resistance to infection.

Posnette (1969) commented that 'tolerance appears to be more widespread than other forms of virus resistance in crop plants'. He mentioned swollen-shoot of cocoa as one of three virus diseases for which tolerance might be the only feasible way to overcome them. Cocoa swollen-shoot in

West Africa fulfils the four conditions which favour the use of tolerance: no immunity or hypersensitivity has been found; virus-free material is available for planting; virus spreads rapidly into and within the crop; virus reservoirs occur outside the crop. There have been discussions of possible developments in the planting of resistant and/or tolerant trees for the control of swollen-shoot disease (Kenten and Legg 1971*a*; Legg and Kenten 1971*a,b*).

It is not within present scope to give detailed consideration to tolerant selections now available because they are likely to be replaced through the scheme for assessing candidate progenies which aims at producing cocoa trees with a high level of resistance to virus infection, as discussed by Legg (1972).

Lockwood (1973) discussed a trial at Tafo, Ghana, of 4-year-old seedlings of twenty-eight hybrid progenies infected with C.S.S.V. A. There was rapid decline of infected trees. Some important conclusions were stated as follows: 'the results from the experiment suggest that the tolerance of a clone does not necessarily indicate its value as a parent in breeding for tolerance . . . future breeding for tolerance must therefore depend on screening the progenies of new parents, using a tester parent . . . amelonado would probably be the best tester parent because it is homozygous for many characters and is widely available.'

8

WILT DISEASE

Introduction

Rorer (1918a) attributed a rot of pods and bark in Ecuador to a fungus of the genus *Sphaeronaema*. Nowell (1923) considered this disease as 'Sphaeronema black spot and bark rot' and explained that inoculations with pure cultures of this fungus had proved that it was the cause of these maladies, due to infection following careless use of cutlasses, whence the names 'enfermedad del machete' and 'mal de machete' were given to it by Rorer (1918a). The causal fungus was subsequently considered to belong to the genus *Ceratostomella*, but later to *Ceratocystis*. It occurred as a wound parasite associated with damage by implements and by beetle borers, especially *Xyleborus* spp. The importance in most of the affected countries of the association with these borers, was recognized by referring to the disease as '*Xyleborus-Ceratocystis* Complex'. This was the designation under which the disease was discussed by Entwistle (1972). A severe manifestation of the disease was described by Spence and Moll (1958) as a 'wilt condition' in Trinidad, where Iton (1959) investigated it as 'wilt disease'. This noncommittal name is used here because the nature of the disease is not fully understood. Cocoa is affected by different permanent-wilt disorders, the syndromes of which are not clearly defined and their aetiologies are uncertain (Thorold 1967).

Geographical distribution

Wilt disease occurs in South America (Brazil, Colombia, Ecuador, Guayana, Peru, Venezuela) in Central America, (Costa Rica, Guatemala, Mexico), in the West Indies (Dominican Republic, Trinidad, and probably in Haiti), in Asia (Philippines, Sri Lanka), and in Australasia (Fiji, New Guinea).

References to occurrences of *Ceratocystis fimbriata* in association with cocoa are given in Chapter 12. This fungus occurs in West Africa (*C.M.I. Distribution Map No. 91*, ed. 4, 1971) on hosts other than cocoa, but 'wilt disease' as discussed now, was not reported there.

Economic importance

In 1918, the cocoa industry of Ecuador was seriously affected by the more important witches' broom and Monilia diseases, so that the simultaneous occurrence of wilt disease was generally overlooked. Lass (1970) reported that 40,000 cocoa trees were lost through wilt disease at Clementina Estate, Ecuador.

After about 1940, wilt became widespread in Colombia (Idrobo 1958*a*) and many cocoa-growing areas were affected (Caldas, Cauca, Choco, Huila, Nariño, Santander, and Valle Provinces). Moll (Spence and Moll 1958) visited Colombia in 1958 and in Puerto Tajada saw more than 50 per cent tree losses. The need to find a remedy prompted the Campaña Nacional de Cacao to promote the study of this disease (Benavides 1955).

Malaguti (1958*a*) described wilt incidence in the central irrigated area of Venezuela (Ocumare de la Costa, Chuao, and Choroní).

Imle and Cuatracasas (1967) believed that the disorder, referred to as a 'blast' which affected cocoa in 1727 (Gumilla 1791), may have been an epiphytotic of *Ceratocystis* wilt, but this seems improbable because immature fruits were lost, rather than whole trees (p. 60). Damage to Trinidad cocoa, associated with *Xyleborus* species towards the end of the nineteenth century, was discussed (Potter 1894, 1895). Although no associated fungus was reported, it seems likely that *C. fimbriata* was implicated. Among factors affecting tree productivity in Trinidad considered by Shephard (1937*a*), was severe wounding by careless use of cutlasses. The associated black streaks in the wood were probably symptomatic of *C. fimbriata* infection. There was no serious or widespread recurrence of wilt in Trinidad until 1958 (Spence and Moll 1958). Murray (1966) reported that 4,800 trees were lost through this disease at River Estate.

Altson (1926*b*) observed bark rot in Costa Rica, causing death of 7- to 9-year-old cocoa trees. Wilt was reported as endemic in Costa Rica plantations (Siller 1958).

A general estimate of loss from wilt is not available because it is difficult to dissociate the direct economic effects of *C. fimbriata* from other factors. Saunders (1965) considered that millions of trees had been killed by it.

Host range

C. fimbriata affects species in fifteen Angiosperm families (Morgan-Jones 1967*a*; MacFarlane 1968).

Symptoms

This account of wilt disease symptoms follows the one by Iton (1959). In the most serious form of the disease, there is wilting of the foliage of the whole tree or branch above the affected part which may be dark in colour with slightly sunken surface. Wilted leaves change colour irregularly through yellow to brown and become rolled longitudinally. They characteristically remain attached to the dead branch for several weeks. A lesion or canker may be formed, with discoloured tissue, from which a dark-coloured liquid may drip during damp weather. A yellowish or reddish internal discoloration extends some distance beyond the wound. A dark line delimits the affected tissue.

An uncertain length of time elapses between natural infection and the appearance of visible signs of attack. Spence and Moll (1958) examined some apparently healthy trees and found extensive damage to bark and wood, before wilting of leaves occurred.

The holes made by *Xyleborus* spp. were about 1 mm. diameter, and penetrated the bark and wood more or less at right angles to the axis. Iton (1959, 1961) used the term 'frass' for the small coiled plugs which protruded from the holes and consisted of wood dust, not insect excrement. The internal discoloration of the wood decreased towards the healthy areas and changed from a uniform expanse to discrete lenticular patches in transverse section. Other fungi, including *Calonectria rigidiuscula* (conidial state) may be present (Iton and Conway 1961). Variation in the colour of the stained wood is probably due to the participation of different fungi.

Wilt disease symptoms may be confused with those of the disorder termed 'sudden death' ('morte súbita'), but with the latter, the crown was lost in the early stages, although there was occasional recovery. Sometimes there was 'ashy-blue' necrosis of vessels and small brown lesions in the bark. The necrosis caused by *C. fimbriata* was generally darker and nearer the base of the trunk (Manco and Medeiros 1969).

Aetiology

The main pathogen

Taxonomy. The fungus described on sweet potato in 1890, as *Ceratocystis fimbriata* Ellis and Halstead, was later transferred to the genus *Sphaeronaema*, as *S. fimbriatum* (Ell. and Halst.) Saccardo. When the perithecia with evanescent asci were no longer misinterpreted as pycnidia, the fungus was designated *Ceratostomella fimbriata* (Ell. and Halst.) Elliott, and then transferred to *Ophiostoma*, as *O. fimbriatum* (Ell. and Halst.) Nannfeldt. Through subsequent generic amendments, the original name is maintained. *Ceratostomella* now contains only species with persistent asci. It is important that the use of the name *Ceratostomella* for the cocoa-wilt fungus should be discontinued, since evanescence of the asci characterizes the three species of *Ceratocystis* associated with cocoa (*C. fimbriata, C. moniliformis* (Hedgcock) C. Moreau, and *C. paradoxa* (Dade) C. Moreau). There is no species of *Ceratostomella*, as now understood, recorded on cocoa.

Description. There are full descriptions of *C. fimbriata* by Iton (1961) and by Morgan-Jones (1967a). There are three kinds of spore. The elliptical ascospores have a gelatinous sheath, which forms a brim and gives a hat-shaped appearance; they are hyaline, non-septate, 4·5–8 × 2·5–5·5 μm.

The conidia are of two forms, either thin-walled endoconidia or thick-walled endoconidia. There are also thick-walled chlamydospores. These asexual spores are cylindrical, obovate or oval, and measure *ca.* 9 μm. Pure cultures were obtained from the base of a tree recently killed by this pathogen. A thin, grey mycelial mat was produced, with numerous phialides (Ainsworth 1971), extruding endoconidia (Iton 1959).

The optimum temperature for growth of *C. fimbriata* in culture was between 24 °C. (75 °F.) and 27 °C. (81 °F.), for all isolates tested (Webster and Butler 1967). Numbers of perithecia were greatest at 23 °C. and least at 30 °C. (Small 1966).

Biochemistry. Vegetative growth was sparse in the absence of thiamine. All self-fertile isolates tested produced fertile perithecia when thiamine was added (Webster and Butler 1967).

Variation and pathogenic specialization. Isolates of *C. fimbriata* were separated into three groups on the basis of colour, and distribution of perithecia in cultures on malt extract agar. Isolates from cocoa and sweet potato comprised one group, with smoky grey to olive-green colonies and perithecia produced either singly or in small scattered clumps. Isolates from a particular host from different geographical areas appeared to be identical (Webster and Butler 1967).

Cross inoculation experiments showed much variation in pathogenicity of isolates from different hosts. Cross inoculations on cocoa, coffee, and sweet potato plants indicated that cocoa was the most susceptible of the three and the coconut isolate was the most pathogenic (Barba and Hansen 1962*b*). Cocoa seedlings were not infected when inoculated with *C. fimbriata* isolates which caused wilt of *Mangifera indica* L. (Ribeiro and Coral 1968).

It is likely that for cocoa hosts of *C. fimbriata*, there are 'aggressive' and 'non-aggressive' variants of this pathogen, either of which may predominate periodically, as for the elm host of *Ceratocystis ulmi* (Buism.) C. Moreau in temperate countries (Gibbs and Brasier 1973). This phenomenon would explain periods when wilt disease of cocoa is not serious but with severe outbreaks occurring occasionally, through possible predominance of an aggressive variant of *C. fimbriata*.

Spore production. Chlamydospores were produced in abundance internally, particularly in the vascular rays and in the cells immediately surrounding the tunnels made by *Xyleborus* borers, commonly referred to as 'galleries'. Iton (1961) suggested that rapid colonization of the wood might occur through upward translocation of spores in the transpiration stream, in accord with the observation that discoloration tends to spread faster in an upward direction. The thin-walled endoconidia were abundant on mycelium lining the galleries and also on mycelium growing in frass heaps at gallery entrances. Microscopic examination of frass showed chlamydospores present intracellularly in the finely divided wood particles and also lying freely between them. Thin-walled endoconidia were also present sometimes in fresh frass. When wood chips were incubated in the laboratory for 7–10 days, both perithecia and conidia were produced on the wood surfaces. Therefore, spores will probably be produced naturally on exposed wood under suitable conditions. Perithecia were produced on the surfaces of inoculated plants when these had been covered by a polythene sleeve, which functioned as a moist chamber.

Spore germination. Ascospores germinated within 24 hours on malt agar medium. Germ tubes emerged either from the top or through the area of the spore surrounded by the brim. The production of one germ tube was generally followed by that of another. Thick-walled endoconidia germinated *in situ* in cultures 8–10 days old (Webster and Butler 1967). Iton (1961) used frass for tests of spore viability. Thin-walled endoconidia germinated both in liquid medium and in a moist atmosphere without liquid. Their germination percentages were commonly greater than 60 per cent in 24 hours. Relatively poor germination of chlamydospores (0–7 per cent) probably indicated that the optimal conditions for this process were not understood.

Other pathogens

Evidence was adduced in Colombia (Naundorf 1956) and in Costa Rica (Saunders 1964), for a belief that *Xyleborus* species tended to attack areas of branches cankered by *Phytophthora palmivora*. Disease complexes, considered to be due to attack by *Phytophthora, Ceratocystis* and *Xyleborus*, were discussed by Tollenaar (1958) and by Thorold (1967).

Iton (1959) explained that isolations from the discoloured wood and from adjacent apparently 'healthy' wood consistently produced *Fusarium* species and *C. fimbriata*. Inoculations with pure cultures of the *Fusarium* species did not produce symptoms in the test plants, but similar inoculations with *C. fimbriata* produced symptoms, and death occurred in four of the thirty-four cuttings inoculated. Iton and Conway (1961) confirmed occurrences of *Calonectria rigidiuscula* (conidial state) and *C. fimbriata* in discoloured wood associated with *Xyleborus* galleries. Iton (1961) used these fungi in further inoculation experiments. None of the plants inoculated with *C. rigidiuscula* or with sterile culture medium developed symtoms. All the plants inoculated with *C. fimbriata* or with a mixture of *C. fimbriata* and *C. rigidiuscula* developed symptoms and died within a period of 7–20 days.

Spread of wilt disease

Dispersal pattern. The distribution of wilt occurrences in Trinidad did not suggest spread from a focal point. Occurrences in widely separated localities seemed to be sporadic. The spatial distribution of apparently successive occurrences at River Estate, suggested that inoculum might have been carried from field to field through the prevailing north-east wind (Spence and Moll 1958; Iton 1959).

Main dispersal agents. Iton (1959, 1960, 1961, 1966) and Iton and Conway (1961) considered the possibility that insects contaminated with *C. fimbriata*, when aided by wind, might transmit the disease, but the distance traversed would in the case of *Xyleborus* borers, be restricted through their susceptibility to desiccation. Such agents might be responsible for the establishment of infection foci in different fields within an estate. To test the possibility of airborne dispersal of *C. fimbriata*, the air spora was sampled at heights ranging from 1–6 ft. (0·3–1·8 m.) above soil level and at 3–6 ft. (0·9–1·8 m.) from the trunks of diseased trees, by exposing vaselined slides. Trapped spores included those of *Fusarium* sp. and chlamydospores, the latter not occurring freely but embedded in microscopic bits of wood, similarly to the particles composing the frass coils extruded by *Xyleborus* species infesting the cocoa trees. There was visual evidence for short-distance dispersal of frass which generally contained *C. fimbriata* chlamydospores. Heaps of frass collect at the base of infested trees, having fallen there or having been washed down by rain from the gallery entrances above. Leaves and trunks surrounding an infested tree were often coated with this wood dust. The infectivity of frass was established by successful inoculations of test plants when control plants remained healthy. It was evident that *Xyleborus* borers may be responsible indirectly for dispersal of *C. fimbriata* through production of spore-laden frass which was suitably placed for successful take-off since it was extruded from the galleries as friable plugs projecting several millimetres into the air. Other observations indicated that *Xyleborus* beetles may transmit the pathogen directly. Naturally emerging beetles often carried *C. fimbriata* spores externally. When the alimentary canals of several *Xyleborus* species were removed and examined, chlamydospores of *C. fimbriata* were found in the rectum of most of the species. The viability of these thick-walled spores, after passage through the alimentary tracts of the beetles was demonstrated. When *Xyleborus* beetles were caged on test plants in the greenhouse, some beetles transmitted *C. fimbriata*, which produced chlamydospores in the host cells. Some *Xyleborus* beetles caged on healthy plants in the field tunnelled into the trees and frass was extruded but no disease symptoms developed.

Trees with and without *Ceratocystis* inoculations, in an area with large *Xyleborus* populations were examined in the laboratory. Trees which had been inoculated with agar cultures of *C. fimbriata*, or with a mixture of *Fusarium* sp. and *C. fimbriata* were consistently bored by *Xyleborus* beetles, but trees inoculated with *Phytophthora palmivora* or with sterile agar were not bored. *C. fimbriata* and *Fusarium* sp. are wound parasites which may infect recent injuries readily but may be unable to develop on older wounds when there has been time for some natural healing to occur. This supposition was tested in an experiment in which wounding was followed by inoculation after various intervals of time. There was little or no borer attack on wounded uninoculated trees, but the inoculated trees were attacked by borers and especially when the interval between wounding and inoculation was minimal.

In Trinidad, the greatest incidence of borer galleries in the majority of wilted trees, occurred at the base of the trunk. Infestation of roots was also observed (Iton and Conway 1961). Norris, Bishop, Knoke, and Saunders (1968) suggested that the tendency to attack trunk bases might be attributable to a positive geotropic response. However, infestation at ground level might indicate some association with the soil litter-layer, which favoured either beetle attack or fungal invasion.

Iton and Conway (1961) discussed evidence supporting their suggestion 'that attractiveness is a function of infection and that infection precedes infestation'. Iton (1968) stated that 'further experiments revealed that *Xyleborus* spp., migrate from wilting cacao trees and almost invariably attack newly *Ceratocystis*-infected hosts in preference to healthy ones. These insects are contaminated with the pathogen from their old galleries and, whilst tunnelling into new hosts, they deposit inoculum, thus augmenting host infection and hastening disease development. Such diseased hosts then attract beetles *en masse*'.

It seems that consideration should be given to the possible occurrence of 'population aggregating pheromones' such as have been claimed for other bark beetles (*Dendroctonus* spp.), as discussed by Wood and Silverstein (1970).

Iton (1960) listed the following *Xyleborus* species from wilted cocoa trees in Trinidad: *X. corniculatus* Schedl, *X. ferrugineus* (Fabr.), *X. posticus* Eichhoff, and *X. theobromae* (Hopkins), the last as *X. hirtellus* Schedl.

X. ferrugineus was considered to be a primary pest of cocoa in Costa Rica, where it attacked trees not showing obvious symptoms of deterioration (Saunders, Norris, and Knoke 1967). Entwistle (1972) discussed the biology of this beetle.

Other possible dispersal agents. Iton (1966) found that mites (Acarina) commonly ingest mycelium and spores of *C. fimbriata*. Possible dispersal by mites may be aided by beetles, since the former were attached to the bristles on the legs, body, and elytra of *Xyleborus* species.

Nematodes were observed in *Xyleborus* galleries, apparently feeding on *Fusarium* sp., whilst spores of *Ceratocystis* and *Fusarium* were observed adhering to the surfaces of nematodes which in turn were attached to mites. The possible role of this complex association of nematodes, mites, beetles, and fungi, in the spread of wilt disease, was not demonstrated (Iton 1966).

Springtails (Collembola) were observed in *Xyleborus* galleries. These wingless insects are nevertheless very active. Spores may become attached to their hairy bodies, and thereby be transported in air currents for considerable distances (Iton 1966) as mentioned in Chapter 6 (p. 69).

Human agency. Malaguti (1952) reported necrosis of trunks and main branches of cocoa in Venezuela, caused by *C. fimbriata* acting as a wound parasite. Subsequent field tests indicated that 66 per cent of the trees became infected, apparently through being wounded by cutlasses previously used on infected trees. Only 18 per cent of the trees damaged by sterilized cutlasses became infected (Malaguti 1958*a*).

Factors influencing incidence of wilt disease

There have been suggestions that some form of environmental stress may predispose cocoa to attack by *C. fimbriata*. Drought was associated with serious incidences of wilt in Colombia (Spence and Moll 1958), Ecuador (Wood 1959), and Trinidad (Spence and Moll 1958). On the other hand, Malaguti (1952) in Venezuela found more disease after rainy periods, and so did Siller (1958) in Costa Rica.

Saunders (1964) suggested that ecological factors, especially drought or flooding, might weaken large numbers of cocoa trees and initiate a cycle of deterioration and infection leading to the occurrence of wilt. He considered that the nature of the bark was probably the most important factor predisposing trees to beetle attack. Number of *Xyleborus* attacks and their tunnelling were dependent on wood moisture.

There were not marked seasonal fluctuations of *Xyleborus* populations in Costa Rica and in Trinidad where wilt was serious. Contrariwise, in West Africa where wilt disease caused by *C. fimbriata* did not occur, Entwistle (1960*a*) found marked seasonal fluctuations in populations of *Xylosandrus compactus* Eichhoff (as *X. morstatti* (Hagedorn)). *Botryodiplodia theobromae* and *Calonectria rigidiuscula*, but not *Ceratocystis fimbriata*, were isolated from lesions associated with beetle attack in West Africa.

Control

Chemical methods

Regular applications of an insecticide in Costa Rica (Saunders 1964) and in Trinidad (Iton 1966; Bartley and Small 1966; Small 1967*b*) did not control wilt disease, probably because fungal infection may precede insect infestation (Iton and Conway 1961).

Oechsli (1957) claimed that a mixture of a copper fungicide (Banocobra) and an insecticide (D.D.T.) applied three times a year to trunks and main branches at Clementina Estate, Ecuador, lessened loss of trees from wilt. However, Tollenaar (1958) commented that the apparent success of this treatment might have been due to control of *Phytophthora palmivora*,

which might otherwise have favoured attack by *Xyleborus* in association
with *C. fimbriata*.

Sanitation

To reduce the amount of infective material available for dispersal,
Iton (1966) advised that the root and lower part of the trunk of an affected
tree should be burnt. The upper part of the tree, which was uninfected,
might be left in the field.

The efficacy of sanitation as a control measure was doubtful (Saunders
and Knoke 1967). Wilt disease was not controlled at River Estate, Trinidad,
despite a rigorous sanitation programme there (Murray 1966).

Cultural methods

Because canker and bark-rot manifestations of *C. fimbriata* infection
may result from certain field practices, special precautions should be taken.
Cutlasses might be sterilized by incorporating a fungicide in the scabbard,
to prevent spreading the fungus. It is important to lessen risk of infection
by minimizing damage. When in the course of normal pruning it may be
necessary to expose large surfaces, these should be suitably protected
against possible infection. It may be possible to arrange for pruning to be
timed so as to promote healing of wounds, thereby preventing their
becoming infected.

Malaguti (1958a) observed that harvesting of pods by plucking generally
produced a lesion in the bark which might permit entry of the fungus.
Therefore, pods should be removed from the tree by cutting the stalk.

Resistance

Trees with a predominance of criollo characters were more severely
affected than forastero cocoa in Colombia (Idrobo 1958a), in Ecuador
(Desrosiers 1957) and in Venezuela (Malaguti 1958a). Therefore attention
has been given to the possibility of breeding and/or selecting cocoa for
resistance to wilt disease. To reduce the inevitable delay through observing
responses in field trials, there have been attempts to develop laboratory
screening procedures.

The production of toxins by *C. fimbriata* was demonstrated in Colombia
(Idrobo and Naundorf 1956), and Idrobo (1958b) tested for resistance to
this fungus by using water-extracts of bark and wood from affected trees
to immerse young cocoa plants. Sensitivity to the disease was assessed by
the extent of withering after 36 hours.

In Costa Rica, Delgado and Echandi (1965) developed a quantitative
screening procedure, which was employed subsequently, with or without
modification and referred to as the 'Delgado and Echandi method'. Blocks
of wood and bark from normal cocoa branches about 10 mm. diameter
were inoculated with a suspension of *C. fimbriata* spores and mycelium.

Reaction was assessed and marks awarded on a numerical scale of mycelial growth. Mycelium soon totally covered the blocks from susceptible trees. *Theobroma angustifolium* and *T. mammosum* showed resistance, whilst *Herrania* species were susceptible. Within *T. cacao*, two Upper Amazon selections, I.M.C. 67 and P. 12 (Pound 12) were resistant. These cocoa clones were described by Enriquez and Soria (1967). Further tests of the Delgado and Echandi method in Costa Rica (Soria and Esquivel 1969) confirmed the resistance of I.M.C. 67 and P. 12, and likewise for I.M.C. 67 in Ecuador (Vitori and Delgado 1969) and in Trinidad (Small 1966, 1967a).

Ruiz, Jiménez and Soria (1969a,b) inoculated three *Theobroma* species and six cocoa clones, and assessed their resistance or susceptibility quantitatively by colorimetric estimation of the degree of chlorosis induced in leaves in response to *C. fimbriata* infection. They claimed that this technique gave reproducible results and was as efficient as the Delgado and Echandi method.

De Reyes and Reyes (1971) used another method which was described fully by Domínguez (1971). Paper disks impregnated with a suspension of *C. fimbriata* spores, were placed on pieces of bark previously separated from the wood, under conditions of high relative humidity. I.M.C. 67 and P. 12 were resistant compared with a local (Venezuela) selection (O.C. (Ocumari) 61). Resistance was maintained when I.M.C. 67 was crossed with O.C. 61, but progeny from O.C. 61 × P. 12 were less resistant. Nevertheless, Domínguez (1971) advised use of this cross where wilt disease was economically important. I.M.C. 67 was presumably disfavoured as a parent because of its small bean-size (Chapter 2, pp. 24-5).

The immutability of cocoa-host resistance is uncertain. Webster and Butler (1967) found that *C. fimbriata* isolates were fundamentally homothallic but some ascospore progenies were self-fertile and cross-fertile. The 'strains' studied evidently comprised a single species because they crossed readily and produced a high percentage of viable ascospores, hence there was likelihood of new strains arising through hybridization. Therefore, it is interesting to note that a new and virulent phase of *C. fimbriata* was detected at Pichilingue, Ecuador. Chalmers (1969) commented that wilt disease was not abating there, compared with Trinidad. De Reyes and Reyes (1971) concluded that resistance appeared to be controlled by recessive inheritance, in agreement with the conclusion reached by Soria and Esquivel (1969).

9

DIEBACK ASSOCIATED WITH MIRID ATTACK AND FUNGAL INFECTION

Introduction

Plant-feeding 'bugs' (Miridae) of the subfamily Bryocorinae attack cocoa and other tropical beverage-plants containing purines, of which cocoa has both theobromine and caffeine. Leston (1970a) suggested that these substances may be mirid attractants. He reviewed mainly West African cocoa pests and retained the name 'capsids', because it was the long-standing 'vernacular term'. This account considers these insects on a cocoa-world basis and 'mirids' is the name used here for them. The group name Capsidae is a junior synonym of Miridae. It may be noted that 'capsid' is a term used in connection with the structural components of viruses (Fraenkel-Conrat 1969).

Severe debility and degeneration of the vegetative parts of cocoa is comprehensively described as 'dieback'. This disorder may develop through invasion of stems by weakly parasitic fungi (Turner 1967). Opportunity for fungal infection and internal spread may arise through damage to superficial tissues by mirids, which puncture the plant and weaken it by feeding on the cell contents.

Geographical distribution

There is not a close biological relationship between mirids and fungi associated with dieback, consequently it is difficult to state precisely the geographical areas where damage by mirids is in excess of direct injury, through subsequent fungal infection. This lack of precision is partly due to less intensive study of dieback associated with mirids in areas where this disorder is of lesser economic importance compared with West Africa. Another factor contributing to uncertainty is the apparent mutability of feeding-site selection. There have been fluctuations in preferences for either pods, with unimportant damage, or for vegetative parts, with sometimes serious debilitation.

The fungus mainly concerned in causing the dieback now to be considered is *Calonectria rigidiuscula*, which is physiologically variable and widespread throughout the tropics (Booth and Waterston 1964a; Booth 1971). Two fungi commonly associated with *C. rigidiuscula* are *Botryodiplodia theobromae* and *Phytophthora palmivora*, which are virtually co-extensive with cocoa (for details and references, see Chapter 12, pp. 174, 197). Although the pathogens are widespread, the species of Miridae infesting cocoa have restricted distributions. It follows that the aetiology of dieback associated with mirids varies because the insect–pathogen relationship is mutable in both place and time. Particular groups of cocoa mirids occur in Africa, America, Asia and Australasia (Entwistle and Youdeowei 1964; Leston 1970a; Entwistle 1972).

Squire (1947) listed more than twenty species of Miridae in Central and West Africa from various hosts, five species were recorded from cocoa but only two of these are of major importance by causing serious tree losses through association with *C. rigidiuscula*. *Sahlbergella singularis* Haglund is widespread in West Africa and the Central African extension of the cocoa-belt, from Sierra Leone eastwards to Kasai, Congo, as shown in *Commonwealth Institute of Entomology Distribution Map No. 22* (1952). *Distantiella theobroma* (Distant) ranges less widely than *S. singularis*, as indicated by *Commonwealth Institute of Entomology Distribution Map No. 21* (1952). *D. theobroma* occurs from Sierra Leone eastwards to Cameroon (S.E.), and occasionally in Central Africa (Boulard 1967). There is consensus of opinion that *D. theobroma* and *S. singularis* are the important cocoa mirids which in association with *C. rigidiuscula* cause dieback and death of cocoa trees in Africa (Entwistle 1972).

Morales and Matarrita (1961) reported species of *Colletotrichum* and *Fusarium* in association with *Monalonion* sp. causing cocoa dieback in Costa Rica.

In Asia and Australasia, where cocoa has been established recently, in contrast with its long existence in the New World, it seems that this crop is being 'exploited' by insects from other hosts. Szent-Ivany (1961) noted that new mirid infestations by forest insects occurred in plantations abandoned during the last war. There were probably mirid hosts among the forest plants. In Sri Lanka, Green (1901) found only pod damage but referred to damage to young leaves and stems of cocoa there *ca.* 1880, presumably caused by *Helopeltis antonii* Signoret. The original description of this mirid (1858) did not mention the host plant. It seems that *H. antonii* was replaced by another species within a period of about 20 years after the 1880 infestation. The mirid causing pod damage in Sri Lanka was not critically studied until De Silva (1957) described a 'new' species (*H. ceylonensis*) which fed preferentially on pods. He was unable to find *H. antonii* in the major cocoa-growing areas of Sri Lanka.

For Sabah, Malaysia, Conway (1964) reported that the feeding habits of *Platyngomiriodes apiformis* Ghauri had changed over a period of a few years. At first this mirid caused pod damage, then chupons were attacked, and later branches and trunks were affected. During this period, *Helopeltis clavifer* Walker had attacked pods but also stems, causing dieback. It was being replaced by *P. apiformis* which caused larger lesions, so that the ensuing fungal infections were said to be more serious than with *H. clavifer*. A number of fungi, including *B. theobromae*, but not *C. rigidiuscula*, were reported from pods attacked by *H. clavifer* and by *P. apiformis*. Isolations from stems were not reported (Anon. 1963; 1964*b*, 1965).

In the Gazelle Peninsula, New Britain, Dun (1954) found *Pseudodoniella typicus* (China and Carvalho) causing dieback, but apparently without fungal infection. Whilst this mirid occasionally attacked flush growth, it caused the loss of pods, at least partly through infection by *Gloeosporium* sp., which grew in and around the mirid lesions on the pod surface. It was expected that the effects of dieback might become more serious if fungal infection occurred later in mirid lesions on the vegetative parts.

The West Indies are exceptional in their freedom from important mirid pests affecting cocoa (Entwistle 1972).

Economic importance

Early in the course of mirid investigations in Ghana, it was realized that a small 'resident' population or larger fluctuating ones could cause damage out of proportion to the numbers present (Voelcker 1947).

The depredations of mirids in Ghana earned for them the vernacular (Akan) phrase 'sankonuabe' which Schweizer (1933) rendered as 'go back pick oil palms'. The first edition of the dictionary by Christaller (1881) did not include sankonuabe. According to Wanner (1962) there were only a few cocoa plants in Mission Stations in the period 1860–80, but one may speculate whether mirids may possibly have been the pests which he referred to as hampering early attempts to establish cocoa in Ghana. Quansah (1964) stated that Ghana cocoa farmers were referring to mirids as sankonuabe in 1908, 'realizing that they might find cocoa a more difficult crop to grow successfully than the oil palms previously grown'. The injunction was apparently unheeded, since Dudgeon (1910*a,b*) observed young plantings attacked by mirids. Production of cocoa in Ghana increased five-fold from 40,000 metric tons in 1910–11 to more than 200,000 metric tons in 1923–4 (Viton 1955), despite occurrences of severe dieback associated with mirid attack, as described by Dade and Patterson (1922). A 'peak' was reached with in excess of 300,000 metric tons in 1936–7, but production was subsequently depressed by mirid attack and incidence of virus disease.

Thresh (1960) studied virus-infected and uninfected trees in Nigeria. He stated that 'the condition of the trees was more closely related to the incidence of capsid damage and associated dieback caused by *Calonectria rigidiuscula* (Berk. and Br.) Sacc., than it was to swollen-shoot virus infection'.

Padwick (1956) considered losses due to 'canker' caused by *Calonectria rigidiuscula* as under 10 per cent but crop losses resulting from mirid damage, as discussed by Kay (1961), were assessed at 20 per cent or more. The term 'canker' was used also by Deighton (1956) in connection with mirid attack in Sierra Leone, probably because Dade and Patterson (1922) mentioned that affected trees had been described as suffering from 'dry canker'. The term 'canker' is used here for the 'wet canker' associated with *Phytophthora palmivora* infection (Chapter 12, pp. 165–7). It has not been practicable, so far, to assess losses due to mirid infestation with and without *C. rigidiuscula* infection. Taylor and Wharton (1954, 1955) attempted to do this through differential spraying, using either a fungicide, or an insecticide, or these chemicals in combination, but their experiment was vitiated by difficulties in assessing damage, based on counts of infected and uninfected lesions.

Before 1957, crop losses due to mirid attack may have been under-estimated, at about 10–20 per cent. Vernon (1961, 1964) showed that there may have been crop increases ranging between 50 per cent and 100 per cent through wide-scale use of insecticides (lindane and aldrin) for mirid control in Ghana and Nigeria.

Host range

Alternative hosts of cocoa mirids were listed and discussed (Taylor 1954; Johnson 1962a; Entwistle and Youdeowei 1964; Entwistle 1972). Booth and Waterston (1964a) listed families containing hosts of *C. rigidiuscula*. In West Africa, these insects and this fungus are likely to have some hosts in common, within the families Bombacaceae, Malvaceae, and Sterculiaceae. Because of taxonomic difficulties indicated by Leston (1970a), the host ranges are not clear for some mirid genera, notably *Helopeltis* and *Monalonion*.

Aetiology

Dieback associated with mirid attack is mainly, but not always primarily an entomological problem. Kay (1959) isolated *C. rigidiuscula* from dieback tissues in the absence of mirid attack (see p. 129). At first, the necrosis of tissue following feeding by mirids was believed to be due to a combination of mechanical damage and injection of phytotoxic saliva. Later, with recognition that damage was persistent and progressive, the invasion of mirid-damaged tissue by *C. rigidiuscula* was noted (Voelcker 1946).

The anatomy and physiology of the digestive system of *D. theobroma* and *S. singularis* were described by Goodchild (1952). Following entry of the stylets, which are about 2 mm. long in adult mirids, saliva is injected under high pressure, filling the intercellular spaces and producing the appearance described as a 'water-soaked area' which may be up to 3–4 mm. diameter. A toxic action was indicated by the strong acidity of freshly ingested food. Through death of the cells, their walls became permeable and soluble contents were leached out, insoluble carbohydrates being dissolved by salivary amylase. The punctured area became depressed through collapse of the underlying tissue and darkened within a few hours, to give a black elliptical lesion. Crowdy (1947) confirmed that the lesions made by the two species of mirids behaved similarly. Tissue-collapse through damage to the medullary ray parenchyma usually extended into the medullary rays in the xylem, but the phloem and adjoining cambium were largely unaffected. Soon after attack, secondary wound cambium formed, cutting off the dead cortical tissues and reconstituting the parts of the primary cambium damaged in the medullary ray region. A characteristic feature was the fine network of phloem fibres, adhering to the surface of the lesion, the dead cortical tissues having fallen away.

In contrast to the limited extent of uninfected lesions, involving only medullary rays of the peripheral tissues, the presence of *C. rigidiuscula* involved damage to both phloem and xylem, with abnormal thickening and darkening of cell walls in the conducting tissue, in contrast to only slight discoloration in the disorganized region of uninfected xylem. Infected tissues died, producing a deep-seated lesion, but at some stage healing generally occurred through development of callus, thereby forming an 'occluded lesion'. Meanwhile, phellogen activity produced the characteristic 'roughened bark' which was always associated with 'a series of black, distinct, oval lesions on the surface of a central cylinder in the xylem' (Crowdy 1947). The roughened bark, typifying infected lesions, probably persisted throughout the whole life of the branch. This was confirmed by Owen (1956), who found that the presence in stems of infected lesions, which had been occluded for some years, could be detected by the characteristic roughened bark.

Using cultures of *C. rigidiuscula*, Crowdy (1947) successfully inoculated wounded stems of different ages ranging from 'soft green shoots to trunks 15–20 years old'. The fungus became established in tissues of all ages, but normally developed very slowly; it remained alive when its growth was halted (occluded) by callus. The xylem of young wound-inoculated stems was discoloured but it was unaffected in wounded but uninoculated control stems. In uninfected mirid lesions, damage was localized and confined to the area originally injected by the feeding insect.

Crowdy (1947) studied outbreaks in Ghana and distinguished a state he described as 'acute dieback' in which 'a close examination of dying branches showed that the dieback was spreading down the tree mainly in the cortex and cambium; the infected tissues were claret-coloured, and there was a clear line separating them from the healthy tissues'. Another state described as 'chronic dieback' was associated with severely affected trees, damaged by acute dieback, mirid attack or by injury caused through a fallen shade-tree. Infection spread from the ends of branches towards the main trunk, as in the acute form, but in 'chronic dieback' the fungus spread more rapidly in the wood than in the peripheral tissues. In the infected xylem, he distinguished three distinct zones. The blackish-grey dead wood contained both *C. rigidiuscula* and *B. theobromae* and could be distinguished from a more recently infected claret-coloured zone which contained *C. rigidiuscula* alone. A straw-coloured, water-soaked zone which rarely contained fungus, separated the infected area from the healthy xylem. When Owen (1956) studied dieback in Ghana, he found many examples lacking the zonation described by Crowdy (1947) and whilst *C. rigidiuscula* was often isolated, sometimes only *B. theobromae* was obtained. To study incidences of infection, he sampled and cultured from mirid lesions and from other kinds of damage (non-mirid lesions). Two kinds of occluded mirid lesions were sampled. One kind was from chupons up to 1 in. (2·5 cm.) diameter and comprised 'recent' lesions, the other kind was from mature stems and comprised 'old' lesions. Cultures made from these different kinds of material showed interesting similarities and differences, expressed as percentages (frequency of isolation as percentage of total lesions in each category). The isolations with their percentage frequencies were classified as *C. rigidiuscula*: recent (42 per cent) and old (40 per cent); *B. theobromae*: recent (32 per cent) and old (26 per cent); other fungi:* recent (20 per cent) and old (24 per cent); sterile: recent (6 per cent) and old (15 per cent). Therefore *C. rigidiuscula* was most frequently isolated from each kind of material with similar percentages. *B. theobromae* was less common but likewise with similar percentages, as also for the other fungi, comprising species of several genera but individually with frequencies below 10 per cent (*other fungi included *Gliocladium roseum* Bainier, and species of *Fusarium, Pestalotiopsis, Phoma,* and *Phomopsis*).

With wounding and using either spore suspensions in water, or mycelium grown on agar as inocula, Crowdy (1947) showed that *C. rigidiuscula* can infect young or older stems, via quarter in. (6 mm.) diameter holes in mature stems and through needle punctures in soft green stems. Owen (1956) tested the pathogenicities of *C. rigidiuscula* and *B. theobromae* by puncturing and inoculating cocoa plants which were sampled and examined over a period of 40 weeks to observe rates of fungal spread, as mean length of lesion produced. *Calonectria*-inoculated punctures increased faster (average *ca.* 0·4 mm. per week) than *Botryodiplodia*-inoculated punctures (average *ca.* 0·1 mm. per week) which did not increase in size after about 28 weeks from inoculation, whilst the *Calonectria*-inoculated punctures were still enlarging at 40 weeks from inoculation when observations ceased. He concluded that *C. rigidiuscula* was the important fungus in Ghana, causing dieback following mirid attack. *B. theobromae* generally occurred shortly behind *C. rigidiuscula*, but under conditions of artificial culture, *B. theobromae* was more vigorous and tended to overrun *C. rigidiuscula*, which probably explained why only *B. theobromae* was sometimes obtained from lesions which may have originally contained both fungi. The *C. rigidiuscula* isolate which he used did not persist indefinitely in all lesions, since there was a decrease in the frequency of isolation with time. He found that *C. rigidiuscula* infection resulted from artificial inoculations with or without fungal inoculation. This fungus was recovered from 85 per cent of punctures inoculated with a particular isolate, whilst another ('wild') isolate of *C. rigidiuscula* was obtained from 12 per cent of the 'control punctures' which had been inoculated with sterile water. This observation is in accord with the evidence that trees may become infected by *C. rigidiuscula*, leading to dieback, in the absence of mirid attack. Cocoa trees in Nigeria which had been sprayed with insecticide to prevent mirid attack, nevertheless had *C. rigidiuscula* in dead wood with spread to living tissue (Kay 1959, 1961). Some non-mirid lesions were infected by *C. rigidiuscula* (16 per cent), a few by *B. theobromae* (4 per cent), some (52 per cent) by 'other fungi' (named above) and others were sterile (28 per cent). Non-mirid lesions occurred mainly near the base of the tree and probably resulted from implement wounds, made accidentally during weeding or pruning operations (Owen 1956).

Mirid lesions on a pod are discrete spots which do not spread (Johnson 1962*a*). They were seldom, if ever infected by *C. rigidiuscula* in Ghana (Voelcker 1948*b*).

Symptoms

In general, the younger the shoot the more rapid is the development of damage initiated by mirids. When they feed on the tips of fan branches, the dead twigs remain for some time, giving the scorched appearance which Voelcker and West (1940) described as 'blast'. The retention of dead leaves was characteristic of this disorder and served to distinguish it from the effects of drought, when dieback proceeds slowly, with the leaves first becoming flaccid and turning yellow before falling. Williams (1953) observed that blast was sometimes a seasonal phenomenon, occurring in January and February. Later, such affected trees might recover, so that their general health and yielding ability were not apparently affected. Much more serious was the disorder he referred to as 'perennial blast' when growth flushes were persistently attacked by mirids and the incidence of *C. rigidiuscula* infection produced a 'stagheaded' appearance, with concomitant yield-reduction. Voelcker and West (1940) reported areas affected by blast in Nigeria and less extensive occurrence in Ghana. Squire (1947) commented that in Nigeria and elsewhere in West Africa, the growing of cocoa with little or no shade was associated with a 'diffuse form' of mirid attack. In Ghana, where the cocoa was generally shaded, mirid attack tended to be restricted, and was described as a 'pocket'.

Spread of infection

It is possible that *C. rigidiuscula* may be widely dispersed through transport on the legs and bodies of mirids. These insects may have a single-flight range of over 1 mile (2 km.) according to unpublished data for *Distantiella* discussed by Leston (1970a). Usher (1957) considered it was unlikely that spores of *C. rigidiuscula* were airborne, but he mentioned the possible operation of rain in this connection. It is likely that rain-splash may add spores of this fungus to the air spora, as discussed by Ingold (1967). It seems that tropical air-temperatures will not be immediately lethal, since Usher (1957) found that 9 per cent of the *C. rigidiuscula* spores germinated in water after heating for 5 minutes at 113 °F. (45 °C.).

Goodchild (1952) inoculated a nutrient-agar 'slope' with contents of the mirid alimentary canal, and abundant growth resulted, which comprised yeasts and bacteria, including *Micrococcus* sp., but no extraneous 'filaments'; only the filamentous outgrowths of the third mid-gut were observed. Although the flora of the digestive system of mirids has not been studied exhaustively, in the absence of evidence to the contrary it may be concluded that *C. rigidiuscula* is not carried internally by mirids.

There was conflicting evidence regarding the extent to which *C. rigidiuscula* might be carried externally by mirids. In early experiments, when live mirids representing various instars collected in the field, were placed on nutrient agar for about 1 minute, there was no development of *C. rigidiuscula*, nor of *B. theobromae* (Voelcker 1948b). Later, Kay (1961) reported an observation by Usher (1957) that *C. rigidiuscula* was occasionally recovered from the body surface of mirids. When 216 adults of *D. theobroma* and *S. singularis* collected in the field, were placed on cassava-dextrose-agar for half an hour, Usher (1957) isolated *C. rigidiuscula* from 11 per cent of these insects. In a further experiment, seventy-three mirids were dissected into legs, body and mouth-parts, these were cultured separately, but *C. rigidiuscula* was isolated only from bodies and legs.

Factors influencing incidence of dieback

Shade

Williams (1953) stated that breaks in the cocoa canopy 'normally precede, rather than result from mirid attack'. He showed that pockets could be induced experimentally by breaking the canopy. In the absence of overhead shade-trees, a pocket might be started initially by mirids, and maintained by their continued attack in association with invasion by *C. rigidiuscula*.

The interaction of degree of overhead shade and amount of mirid damage has received attention (Johnson 1962a,b).

Water stress

Owen (1956) believed that *C. rigidiuscula* might remain alive in the xylem for 10 years or more, without spreading until some adversity weakened the tree and severe dieback resulted. Gibbs and Pickett (1966) reported an instance of this resurgence phenomenon in a plant which had been maintained without wilting, when it was subjected to water stress. Severe infections leading to dieback also occurred with increased water status of plants previously subjected to periodic wilting. Such circumstances occurred in West Africa in association with the recovery of cocoa at the onset of the rains, following a period with unusually dry air, referred to as 'harmattan' (Anon. 1949). Thomas (1932) noted that damage by mirids was enhanced when a severe dry season had checked the growth of cocoa, and was followed by a flush of new leaves and stems.

Virus infection

Since the mealybug vectors of cocoa viruses and mirids were both widespread in Ghana and Nigeria, it was to be expected that some cocoa trees would be infected by both *C. rigidiuscula* and virus.

Thresh (1960) concluded that deterioration of swollen-shoot affected trees in Nigeria was due mainly to *C. rigidiuscula* infection. This opinion was upheld by Brunt (1970a) who considered that most C.S.S.V. strains were non-lethal unless there was simultaneous infection by *C. rigidiuscula*.

Control

Sanitary methods

In swollen-shoot affected areas of Ghana and Nigeria, when the behaviour of trees was observed after stumping (cutting at a distance of 1 ft. (30 cm.) or less from the ground), some symptomless trees did not recover by production of chupons from the stumps (Voelcker 1947; Thresh and Lister 1960). Such failures to regenerate were not investigated, but it seems likely that some, if not all, were too extensively infected by *C. rigidiuscula* for recovery to occur. Crowdy (1947) discussed possible procedures for treating dieback-affected areas, and stressed the importance of eliminating material affected by *C. rigidiuscula*. In chronic dieback patches, trees should be stumped or removed entirely, so that the gaps could be replanted. New shoots are liable to mirid infestation, therefore such attack must be prevented. Growth of young cocoa may be seriously checked by mirids, as noted by Voelcker and West (1940). They stated that in Ghana, 'in the early years of the development of the cacao industry a farm was expected to commence bearing after four years, it is now estimated that there is a lapse of as much as ten years between planting and first reaping'.

Chemical methods

Fungicides. Kay (1959) tried pruning dead wood from the trees, alone and in combination with applications of copper fungicide by spraying. There was some benefit from pruning alone, but better results were claimed for pruning combined with fungicide.

Whilst fungicide applications may prevent new infections, they will be ineffective against internal infections and occluded lesions which should be removed by appropriately severe pruning.

Since the prevention of infection through conventional fungicides is uncertain, the feasible alternative procedure is the chemical control of mirids.

Insecticides. Gamma-B.H.C. was successfully applied by mist-blower for mirid control in West Africa (Ali 1972), until the discovery of resistance to chlorinated hydrocarbons in Ghana (Peterson and Bond 1964) and in Nigeria (Entwistle, Youdeowei, and Eguagie 1964), showed the need for biochemically different insecticides. The carbamate insecticide arprocarb (Baygon) gave good results in the Ivory Coast (Lavabre, Piart, and Nguyen Ban 1965) and in Ghana (Marchart 1969a), although side effects included a decline in numbers of *Oecophylla* (Marchart 1969b). Marchart (1971a screened forty insecticides as possible substitutes for gamma-B.H.C. A number of carbamates was suitable in this respect. Field trials with arprocarb gave no evidence of taint or off-flavour in beans from trees which had received as much as 24 oz. a.i. per acre 11 days before harvest, nor following 12 oz. a.i. per acre 1 day before harvest. The only drawback was the relatively high cost of arprocarb. Some organophosphorus compounds were effective systemic insecticides but their possible use was limited by high mammalian toxicity (Collingwood 1971a).

The possible use of carbamates as an alternative to cyclodiene insecticides may be vitiated by the likely development of resistance to two or more chemically unrelated groups of toxicants (Entwistle 1972; Georghiou 1972).

Biological methods

Bruneau de Miré (1969) tested *Wasmannia auropunctata* (Roger) (Formicidae) which was used by cocoa growers in Cameroon (S.E.) to control mirids and some other insects. It appeared that *W. auropunctata* drove away mirids, and ants of the genus *Crematogaster*, but numbers of some insects apparently increased. It is probable that *W. auropunctata* had localized effects on insect populations through its being an alien. Although recorded from Gabon nearly 50 years ago, *W. auropunctata* was originally described from Cuba (Wheeler 1922).

Radio-isotope tagging of mirids (Marchart and Leston 1968, 1969) revealed large numbers of individuals and much diversity of predator species. None were apparently dependent on mirids because similar numbers occurred in non-infested cocoa. The encouragement of ants has been proposed as a possible control measure (Williams 1954). Leston (1970a) discussed this possibility. He advocated an integrated control programme (Collingwood 1972), and he opposed routine applications of an insecticide. In no circumstances should cocoa trees be sprayed when they had nests of *Oecophylla longinoda* (Latreille) (Hymenoptera, Formicidae) (Leston 1971). However, Marchart (1971b) noted that for over half a century, no insecticidal control was practised in Ghana. Therefore in that period ants and other natural enemies were operative without interference from spraying. Chemical control of mirids was introduced because natural control had failed.

Entwistle (1972) considered the possible future use of sex attractants for mirid control. *D. theobroma* females release a sex attractant to lure males but such behaviour was not demonstrated for *S. singularis* (Collingwood 1971*b*).

Resistance to infection

A range of amelonado, Trinitario, and Upper Amazon selections was tested by Owen (1956) for possible resistance to *C. rigidiuscula*, using artificial inoculations with this fungus followed by measurement of lesion dimension. Seedling progenies from some Upper Amazon hybrids showed significantly lower mean lesion lengths in these comparisons. Although some Upper Amazon selections grew more vigorously than West African amelonado cultivar, there was no correlation between apparent resistance to *C. rigidiuscula* infection and general vigour of the host.

Bell and Rogers (1957) noted that genetic resistance to *C. rigidiuscula* had not been demonstrated. Therefore, cocoa breeding aimed at resistance to infection could not be recommended.

Resistance to infestation

Sometimes in mirid-infested areas, some cocoa plants of different age from the generality appeared to escape attack, but at other times there was no obvious basis for apparent discrimination in selection of feeding sites. Using unattacked stems of similar age, selected from young and older trees, Posnette (1943*e*) found no support for a belief that *D. theobroma* showed a preference for young trees and that *S. singularis* showed a preference for mature trees. When stems from unattacked trees were compared with stems from attacked trees, there was no consistent discrimination for the 'attacked' as opposed to the 'unattacked' selection.

It seemed unlikely that consistently unpalatable trees would be found. Bell and Rogers (1957) considered that cocoa breeding for possible resistance to mirids could not be recommended.

IO

CUSHION GALL DISEASES

Introduction

When abnormal growths of flowering cushions were first noticed in Guyana (Bartlett 1905), Trinidad (Rorer 1911), and Ghana (Bunting 1927*a*), they seemed unimportant. Serious occurrences were reported later in Colombia by Garcés (1940) who named the disease 'verruga del cojín floral' which has been translated and generally adopted as the name 'cushion gall'. Studies initiated by Hutchins (1958*a,b*, 1959*a,b* 1960) showed that five kinds of gall could be distinguished, two of them (green-point and flowery galls) being commoner than knob, fan, and disk galls. Green-point gall is the most important kind and has received particular attention because flower production ceases and since successively more cushions and additional trees may be affected, productivity of an area can be reduced. Ford, Bourret, and Snyder (1967) restricted the term 'cushion gall' to the green-point kind, the aetiology of which is better understood than that of flowery and other kinds of gall. Since occurrences are not always specially designated, it is convenient now to use the comprehensive name to cover all kinds with special indication when a particular kind of cushion gall is being considered.

The comprehensive term 'cushion gall' is in general use and is preferable to the term 'chupon gall' suggested by Bartley (1960).

Geographical distribution

Cushion galls have been reported in most of the cocoa-growing countries.

AFRICA: Ghana (Bunting 1927*a*), Ivory Coast (Renaud 1959), Nigeria (Longworth 1960), Sierra Leone (Anon. 1961). CENTRAL AMERICA: Belize (Hopkins 1960), Costa Rica (Hutchins, Desrosiers, and Martin 1959), Guatemala (Hutchins 1959*b*), Mexico (Escamilla 1960), Nicaragua (Kevorkian 1951), Panama (Hutchins 1958*a*). SOUTH AMERICA: Brazil (Hutchins 1959*b*), Colombia (Garcés 1940), Ecuador (Escamilla 1960), Guyana (Bartlett 1905), Peru (Hunter 1958), Surinam (van Suchtelen 1955*a*), Venezuela (Malaguti 1958*b*). WEST INDIES: Dominica (von Faber 1909), Dominican Republic (Ciferri 1930*b*), Grenada (Krug and Quartey-Papafio 1964), Jamaica (James 1957), Trinidad (Rorer 1911). ASIA: Philippines (Ocfemia and Celino 1933), Sri Lanka (Orellana 1959*b*). AUSTRALASIA: New Britain, New Guinea, New Ireland, Papua (Shaw and Burnett 1969).

Economic importance

It is difficult to assess the economic importance of cushion gall disease because incidences vary greatly from one country to another, and even between different plantings of similar clones within the same country. Long-term effects are imponderable since disease outbreaks occur intermittently.

Bates (1963) drew attention to evidence that green-point gall existed for 50 years in an area of Guyana where it was 'rediscovered' in 1959. Bunting (1927a) noted galls in Ghana but no disease assessment was made until 1958. Brunt (1960) commented on this initial survey which indicated that the incidence of the disorder was no greater than it was a quarter of a century earlier. In a later survey about half a million acres of cocoa were inspected between August 1958 and August 1960, but only fifty-seven gall-bearing trees were found (Brunt and Wharton 1961c, 1962c,d).

Green-point gall disease seems to have been present for many years in Ghana and Guyana, but has remained unimportant. This is perhaps not unexpected in Guyana where cocoa plantings are sparse and localized, but in Ghana they are dense and continuous over large areas. No rational explanation can be offered for apparently similar disease incidences in two such dissimilar cocoa-producing areas.

Cushion abnormalities in Trinidad mentioned by Rorer (1910b), may have been cushion gall, but the disease seems to have been unimportant until about 1958 when all cocoa areas were surveyed (Goberdhan and Ganpat 1960). At Marper Estate (Anon. 1945b) the numbers of affected trees doubled from December 1958 to December 1959.

In Colombia, Garcés (1940) reported cushion gall disease in Valle and Antioquia, and Holliday (1953) observed cushion proliferation, giving large wart-like growths. Hutchins (1958b) observed the disease in a planting approximately 40 years old near Sopetrán, where 90 per cent of the trees were affected, and nearly every cushion appeared to have a gall. One tree was estimated to have 2,000 galls, and pod production had practically ceased.

Kevorkian (1951) observed cushion gall in western Nicaragua, where percentages of affected trees ranged from 25 per cent to 75 per cent. In an estate planted about 1880, where the disease was believed to have been present for about 10 years, Hutchins (1958a) found 44 per cent of the trees affected. Bourret and Ford (1965) reported a planting where almost all the cushions of many trees were affected.

In Costa Rica, Siller (1963) estimated the effects of cushion gall on yields of trees about 45 years old, using fifty pairs of trees randomly selected. One individual of each pair was apparently healthy and the other was affected by cushion gall. Yields were recorded weekly for a period of 21 months. The total yield of the affected trees (310 lb. (141 kg.)), was less than half the total yield of the healthy trees (773 lb. (351 kg.)). These observations appeared to show a reduction of yield due to cushion gall, but it was possible that this disorder affected only low-yielding trees. Also in Costa Rica, yield reductions were fairly closely related to flowery gall incidence (Molina and Desrosiers 1965). Yield was lowered appreciably when a large proportion of cushions on trunks and main limbs was affected (Hutchins, L. M. 1970 *in litt.*).

Gall development may affect pod production indirectly (Jiménez, Llano, and Hutchins 1966), through diversion of nutrients to growth of galls instead of to maturation of pods. Green-point galls may measure 4–6 in. (10–15 cm.) in diameter, and the diameter may increase as much as 3 in. (7·6 cm.) in a year (Hutchins and Siller 1960).

Symptoms

Green-point gall

The swollen flower cushions produce numerous flower initials but these do not develop into normal flowers with pedicels, instead the buds remain green and sessile, typically as a profusion of green 'points' on the corrugated, brown surface of the gall. These galls are usually globose and semi-hard, bright green at first. They generally die after about a year, when all tissues become black, carbonaceous and easily crumbled, but before that stage is reached, the green points may disappear on parts of the gall which die first. The galls are generally borne on a short central stalk ($\frac{1}{4}$–$\frac{1}{2}$ in. (6–13 mm.) diameter), and were generally described as easily broken off. In Ghana, the galls were firmly attached by a tough central stalk (Brunt and Wharton 1961*a*). The inner tissues of the enlarging gall are light coloured, somewhat soft in texture, branching laterally and vertically from the central stalk. The lower surface of the gall may be flattened against the trunk or branch, without adhering to it except by the central supporting stalk.

These galls typically occur on flower cushions, but they occasionally develop at other sites. Malaguti (1959) reported galls on seedlings in Venezuela, less than 1 year old, which presumably had not produced flower cushions. Gorenz (1960) noted large non-flowery galls at the base and near suckers originating from old plants, especially when they were cut back.

Flowery gall

This kind of gall may bear hundreds of closely packed flowers. When they die, the darkened mass of dead flowers clings to the gall for a time but eventually falls to the ground as a mat, giving way to a new 'flush' of flowers. The flowers on flowery galls develop fully. Soria (1960*b*) showed by hand pollinations that pollen is viable and ovules are capable of producing normal seeds. Lack of fruit setting on flowery galls is thus apparently due to failure of natural pollination.

The galls are generally borne on a semi-hard stalk which branches laterally. Over the stalk and its branches a layer of parenchymatous tissue is formed, through which the flower initials emerge. Occasionally flowery galls are more or less flat on the trunk without the central stalk being evident, they are not then easily broken off.

In the absence of self-pollination attempts, symptoms of flowery gall are likely to be confused with the profuse flowering of self-incompatible cocoa trees. They are referred to as 'male' cocoa trees and cannot produce normal fruits when self-pollinated (Pound 1935b).

Brunt and Wharton (1961a) did not observe flowery galls in Ghana, but only the so-called 'male' trees, which they considered to be unlike true galls in having swollen cushions composed of spongy parenchymatous tissue, and without a central stalk and internal branching.

Knob gall

In Costa Rica, this kind of gall was hard, woody and with smooth surface, up to 1 in. (2·5 cm.) or more in diameter. Knob galls occurred in flower cushions but did not bear flowers. An affected tree generally had not more than 10–15 galls, usually less (Hutchins and Siller 1960).

Shaw and Burnett (1969) reported trees with knob galls in New Britain and New Ireland. Some trees had galls on the main trunk below the jorquette, often in rows on both sides of the fan branches, apparently reflecting distichous phyllotaxy (Brooks and Guard 1952). These knob galls were mostly about 1·5 in. (4 cm.) diameter, but occasionally were as much as 6 in. (15 cm.) long. There was no pith nor lysigenous cavity within the gall, but sometimes there were near-by 'vertical lysigenous traumatic canals' (Shaw 1968).

Disk gall

This kind of gall was first called 'hard flat gall' thereby distinguishing it from both green-point and flowery galls, which are generally globose. Disk galls measured 2–3 in. (5–7·6 cm.) and were woody, very hard, and firmly united to the tree. The surface was dark, corrugated, and undulating. They may bear flowers and set some fruit (Hutchins and Siller 1960).

Fan gall

This name was given to cushion galls in Costa Rica bearing branched, stem-like outgrowths, up to a few inches in length, having very short internodes. These outgrowths may be produced singly or as a group in the form of a fan (Hutchins and Siller 1960).

Shaw and Burnett (1969) reported trees with fan galls in New Guinea, Papua, and New Britain. When first observed, one affected tree had apparently normal flowering on all branches except one. This exceptional branch had fan galls on small twigs which would not normally have carried flowers. Trees with fan galls were bearing apparently normal pods.

Aetiology

Green-point gall

Hutchins (1959b) in Costa Rica and Gorenz (1960) in Nicaragua successfully transmitted green-point by grafting gall tissue on to healthy plants. The use of peeled beans and half-beans as test plants (Posnette 1947a; Brunt 1963) showed that gall extracts were infectious, in Costa Rica (Hutchins 1960), Ghana (Brunt and Wharton 1960), and Guyana (Archibald 1961). Subsequently, similar causal organisms were recognized contemporaneously in Africa and in America.

In West Africa, Brunt, and Wharton (1961a) isolated bacteria resembling *Agrobacterium tumefaciens* (Smith and Townsend) Conn from gall material but they were non-infectious. Spherical tumours were formed on the cotyledons of cocoa beans after inoculation with an authentic culture of *A. tumefaciens*, but these tumours were morphologically distinct from the galls produced by inoculation with gall extracts (Brunt and Wharton 1961b). Typical galls resulted from inoculating seed and a pod stalk with one isolate of *Calonectria rigidiuscula*. Later, Brunt and Wharton (1962b) reported further unsuccessful attempts to transmit the disease using isolates from gall material, including bacteria (*A. tumefaciens, Corynebacterium* spp., and *Xanthomonas* spp.), and a fungus (*Botryodiplodia theobromae*). When *C. rigidiuscula* isolations and re-isolations were confirmed as capable of producing typical gall symptoms, experiments were made to establish whether the infectious culture of this fungus was free from extra-cellular bacteria and virus. Brunt and Wharton (1962b) stated that 'the filtration and dilution experiments together with the non-systemic nature of the disease suggest that a virus is not associated with the cultured isolates of *C. rigidiuscula*'. However, it has been suggested that this fungus might produce a substance which interfered with the host's metabolism (Hansen 1963a). Attempts to demonstrate the presence of such substances have been inconclusive (Mitchell, Hutchins, and Marth 1965)

Fungi and bacteria were isolated from galls in Costa Rica, Nicaragua, and Venezuela by Hansen (1963a), and Hansen and de Reyes (1963). Gall-inducing isolates from Costa Rica and Venezuela were identified as *C. rigidiuscula* (imperfect state), but the Nicaraguan isolate was identified as *Fusarium roseum*. The symptoms induced by this species were similar to those appearing after inoculation with the *C. rigidiuscula* isolates, including also the gall-inducing cultures originating in Ghana (identified as *C. rigidiuscula*), which were tested in parallel by Hansen (1963a). Accordingly, he suggested that the name green-point cushion gall should be applied to the disease regardless of which of the two pathogens was the agent. Ford *et al.* (1967) described further studies of *C. rigidiuscula* in relation to green-point gall and noted that there had not been confirmatory reports of *F. roseum* as a cushion-gall pathogen. This name is taxonomically 'incertae sedis', through being used in accord with the 'nine species system'. Booth (1971) stated that 'this system means that all the species previously in the sections Roseum, Arthrosporiella, Gibbosum, and Discolor were all referred to *F. roseum*'.

The gall-inducing isolates studied by Brunt and Wharton (1962*a*,*b*) in Ghana were considered as constituents of one group within the complex species (*C. rigidiuscula*), the other group comprising the weakly parasitic isolates associated with cocoa dieback and the production of lesions in weakened trees. The gall-forming isolates will produce lesions identical in appearance to those formed by dieback isolates but the latter will not induce galls. No cultural or morphological differences between isolates of the two groups were recognized. Hutchins (1965) found that *C. rigidiuscula* cultures started from ascospores produced in perithecia on rotted pods did not induce green-point galls. This observation followed the demonstration of heterothallic forms of *C. rigidiuscula* (Reichle and Snyder 1964). Ford *et al.* (1967) showed that gall-inducing isolates of this fungus were hetero-thallic. Ascospores were produced in culture when two complementary isolates were mated. Naturally occurring perithecia were homothallic and ascospore isolates from them were not capable of inducing green-point galls. All isolates from gall tissue were pathogenic and either heterothallic or non-fertile.

Because it was considered important to distinguish pathogenic and non-pathogenic isolates, Ford *et al.* (1967) designated and described a pathogenic 'forma specialis' (f. sp.). Booth (1971) explained that the names *Fusarium rigidiusculum* published by Snyder and Hansen (1945) and *F. rigidiusculum* f. sp. *theobromae* proposed by Ford *et al.* (1967) are invalid. The object was to distinguish a pathogenic forma specialis with a perfect state in *Calonectria rigidiuscula* f. sp. *theobromae*, from the non-pathogenic forma specialis with a perfect state in *C. rigidiuscula*.

Flowery gall

Attempts to transmit flowery gall were at first unsuccessful (Hutchins 1960). Later, Hutchins (1963) succeeded in transmitting it. He confirmed that flowery gall is 'communicable by contact inoculation when galls are applied to normal flower cushions in gall-free trees' (Hutchins 1964).

Flowery gall and green-point gall may occur together on the same tree or even on the same cushion (Hutchins 1959*b*). Hutchins (1966) tested whether a non gall-inducing, or possibly gall-inhibiting *Fusarium* species isolated from a flowery gall might lessen green-point gall incidence. In laboratory experiments, unexpectedly few galls were produced when seeds were doubly inoculated, using a gall-inducing (*C. rigidiuscula* (imperfect state)) isolate together with the gall-inhibiting isolate. The observation that green-point gall incidence in Costa Rica had recently declined concurrently with the spread of flowery gall, suggested the possibility that interaction between gall-inducing and gall-inhibiting isolates might be affecting numbers and kinds of gall in the field.

Currently, *C. rigidiuscula* (imperfect state) has been uniquely reported as associated with flowery galls in Sabah (Anon. 1973).

Knob gall

At Turrialba, Costa Rica, Hutchins (1964) observed that typical knob galls developed within a period of several weeks on wounded cushions where flowery galls had been removed without damaging the cambium. These galls continued to enlarge over a period of many months. Knob galls did not develop when normal cushions were removed.

Tollenaar (1966) observed trunk swellings and production of knob galls on cocoa growing in boron-deficient volcanic soils in Ecuador. Contrariwise, in the Territory of New Guinea and Papua, there was no evidence from leaf analyses that occurrences of knob galls were associated with boron deficiency or other mineral deficiencies. Sometimes there, new galls appeared when knob galls were removed by cutting flush with the stem surface. When internal gall-tissue was cultured, *C. rigidiuscula* was not obtained. *B. theobromae* often developed, but gall symptoms were not produced when this fungus was used as inoculum. Attempts to transmit the disorder, using gall tissue or gall tissue macerates as inoculum were unsuccessful. Electron microscopy of sap extracts from knob-gall tissue did not reveal any virus-like particles in these preparations. Biochemical studies of gall-affected and gall-free material, did not show any important differences in gibberellin or auxin contents between 'galled' and 'normal' tissues (Shaw and Burnett 1969).

Host range

The medical term 'buba' has been applied to cushion galls of cocoa and probably indicated conjectures that there was possibly a relationship with gall-like structures occurring in other plants (Wellman and Orellana 1955; Malaguti and de Reyes 1964).

In Guyana, Archibald (1961) employed the half-bean technique (Posnette 1947*a*; Brunt 1963), and transmitted a gall disease to cocoa, using distilled-water gall-washings and aqueous extracts (unfiltered), from galls on cocoa, mango (*Mangifera* sp.), and pigeon pea (*Cajanus* sp.).

When melon (*Cucumis melo* L.) and sunflower (*Helianthus annuus* L.) seeds were soaked in a spore suspension of a Costa Rica (Zent) gall-inducing isolate of *C. rigidiuscula* (imperfect state) from cocoa, germination percentages were lowered and cotyledonary buds developed slight swellings (Hansen 1963*a*).

Small galls were formed on *Vigna unguiculata* (L.) Walp., (*V. sinensis* (L.) Savi ex Hassk.) seedlings when Brunt and Wharton (1962*a*) wound-inoculated buds with a gall-forming isolate of *C. rigidiuscula* (imperfect state) from cocoa.

Gall-inducing isolates of *C. rigidiuscula* (imperfect state) can invade coffee (Ford *et al.* 1967) and other plants mentioned above, but there is no evidence for the role of these or other possible hosts in nature. The host range for green-point gall has probably not been fully determined. No alternative hosts are known for flowery gall and other kinds of cushion gall.

Spread of cushion gall

Symptoms appeared sooner when spores (imperfect state of *C. rigidiuscula*) were used to inoculate beans (12–14 days) (Brunt 1963), than when washings from gall surfaces or suspensions of gall tissue were used (59–90 days) (Hutchins 1960). It seems that inoculum potential may have to build up for infection to occur, as was demonstrated by experiments to test the infectivity of diluted spore suspensions (Brunt and Wharton 1962*b*). Dry, powdered green-point gall tissue remained infective for many months (Hutchins 1963).

Brunt and Wharton (1962*b*) found that *C. rigidiuscula* was not evident on the external surfaces of galls but sporulated within the cavities of the condensed branching system.

Ford *et al.* (1967) suggested that the incidence and spread of green-point gall may generally depend on limited insect and water dispersal of conidia. Wider spread may result from airborne dispersal of ascospores.

Wharton and Brunt (1959) noted that no insects or other pests likely to induce gall-formation had been observed within galls in West Africa, but since the earliest stages of gall formation had not been observed, it was not possible to eliminate causes which might operate only at time of gall initiation. Nymphs and adult mealybugs (*Ferrisia virgata* and *Planococcoides njalensis*) transmitted the disorder from galls on mature trees and from galls produced on inoculated seedlings (Brunt and Wharton 1960). There have been casual observations of various pests associated with cushion galls but no causal relationships have been demonstrated (Losada 1958; Shenefelt, Stelzer, and Lara 1960).

There have been unsuccessful attempts to establish whether cushion gall disease is systemic in the plant (Hansen 1966), or even whether there is internal spread of infection within the plant (Gorenz 1960; Brunt and Wharton 1961*a*; Hansen 1963*a*). Nevertheless, Hutchins (1959*a*) found evidence that cushion gall might be carried over long distances and accidentally introduced into new areas by taking propagating material from affected trees.

Factors influencing incidence of cushion gall

In Nicaragua, increased number and size of galls coincided with the active growth of the cocoa in the rainy season. Galls frequently died back at the end of the growing season but started to develop again the next year (Gorenz 1960). Similarly in Trinidad, more galls were produced during wet weather. Conversely, galls disintegrated in dry weather, so that trees tended to have fewer galls than in the wet season. Trees in flat areas had more galls than trees on hills where the soils were presumably drier through being better drained (Goberdahn and Ganpat 1960).

There was conflicting evidence with regard to the possible effects of shade on cushion gall incidence. In Trinidad, Goberdahn and Ganpat (1960) found that clones under shade had more numerous, larger, and greener green-point galls than unshaded clones. In Costa Rica, Molina and Desrosiers (1965) tested urea and found that the incidence and spread of flowery gall were greater in unshaded than in shaded cocoa, and were related positively to nitrogen-application levels.

Control

Cultural methods

Surveys of two estates in Nicaragua, one affected by cushion gall (Valle Menier), the other not affected (Tierra Dorada) indicated the importance of taking propagating material from healthy trees growing in an area where careful inspection had failed to reveal the presence of gall disease (Hutchins 1958a). Observations in a planting at Quepos, Costa Rica, showed the importance of prompt removal of trees showing galls and of those suspected of having the disease. One objective was to ensure the maintenance of gall-free areas to supply propagating material. To achieve this objective, there should be frequent inspection (intervals of 4–6 months) by trained observers (Hutchins 1959a).

Chemical methods

Since natural spread of cushion gall diseases is not fully understood, attempts to prevent it by pesticide application have been empirical.

In Costa Rica, Siller (1960) tried malathion, which apparently reduced the number of green-point galls but the number of flowery galls may have been enhanced. Helfenberger and Hutchins (1966) tested fungicides against green-point gall in the laboratory, and to a limited extent under field conditions. It may be concluded that the chemical prevention or control of cushion-gall disease under field conditions has not yet been adequately demonstrated.

Resistance

In Costa Rica, some 'U.F.' (United Fruit Company selection) clones appeared to be resistant to both flowery gall and green-point gall, when other clones showed various degrees of susceptibility (Hutchins *et al.* 1959; Hutchins, Soria, and Siller 1964). In Ecuador, S.C.A. 6 and some local (E.E.T.) selections were among clones without cushion-gall symptoms. No explanation was offered for the behaviour of certain hybrid progenies which were apparently more severely affected by cushion gall than their parents (Alvaredo, Ampuero, and Doak 1960). In Trinidad, there was some indication that green-point gall incidence was greater in Trinitario clones than in Upper Amazon selections (Goberdahn and Ganpat 1960). In Nigeria, cushion gall disease spread within non-amelonado selections as compared with apparent lack of spread to adjacent amelonado trees (Longworth 1960; Gorenz 1969). Tinsley (1960) commented that the incidence of galls in West Africa appeared to be more prevalent in Trinitario clones than in amelonado cultivars.

II
ROOT DISEASES

Introduction

Garrett (1970) commented that the investigation of root diseases was neglected in the earlier years, mainly through technical difficulties and partly because appropriate research was not forthcoming through failure to recognize the economic importance of the root diseases of perennial crops.

Economic importance

The economic loss occasioned by root diseases of cocoa has been difficult to estimate because of the 'patchiness' of their incidences. One reason for such discrete occurrences was believed to be the attack of cocoa roots through proximity of other hosts which were susceptible to infection. Such associations arose either through the planting of cocoa on previously forested land (wholly or partially cleared), or through subsequent establishment of certain shade-tree species in particular.

During the half-century from about 1870 in Trinidad and elsewhere in the West Indies, much cocoa was planted in forested land (Shephard 1932b). Root diseases were rife in that period (Nowell 1923). In the meantime, cocoa was planted throughout the forest country of Ghana (Dickson 1969), with consequent prevalence of root diseases there also (Bunting and Dade 1924). Since ca. 1930, the importance attached to root diseases declined, partly because economic outlook focused on diseases which seemed likely to be more crippling for cocoa industries, notably 'witches' broom' in Trinidad (Chapter 2) and 'swollen-shoot' in West Africa (Chapter 7).

It has been a common experience that certain perennial economic crops are more prone to root diseases than others. Padwick (1956) categorized root diseases of cocoa, coffee, and tea, as causing small or very small economic losses, in comparison with the more economically important root diseases of Para rubber. In lieu of precise estimates of financial losses, it is convenient to adopt an arithmetical assessment of 'interest' (Table 11.1), derived from the 'Plant host–pathogen index to Vols 1–40 (1922–61)' of the *Review of Applied Mycology* (RAM) (MacFarlane 1968), as used by Ainsworth (1961) to analyse the scope of RAM.

On the assumption that 'interest' may be positively equated with 'economic importance', the totals across in Table 11.1 show that root-

TABLE 11·1

Interest in six root-diseases pathogens of four crop-plant hosts, as number of annual volumes of RAM (total 40) each with one or more references to a particular host–pathogen relationship

Host	Rubber	Tea	Cocoa	Coffee	Total
Pathogen*					
Armillariella mellea	14	25	16	20	75
Ganoderma pseudoferreum	33	17	11	3	64
Phellinus noxius	24	13	8	13	58
Rigidoporus lignosus	37	9	13	16	75
Sphaerostilbe repens	15	12	5	1	33
Ustulina deusta	24	19	8	3	54
Total	147	95	61	56	359

* Pathogens: considered on pp. 148–54.

disease importance for the four economic crops diminishes as follows: rubber (147 > tea (95) > cocoa (61) > coffee (56).

Aetiology

Root-systems of cocoa

Cocoa roots originate in different ways, as described by McCreary, McDonald, Mulloon, and Hardy (1943), Hurd (1961), Swarbrick (1964), and Purseglove (1968b). The relationship between soil profiles and different kinds of root systems was shown diagrammatically by Hardy (1960a).

A tap-root is produced at germination and grows vertically downwards to a depth of about 1 ft. (0·3 m.) to 4 ft. (1·2 m.), or exceptionally to 6 ft. (1·8 m.) depending upon soil porosity and water level in the soil. The tap-root generally forks at a depth which depends upon the physical properties of the soil.

Lateral roots develop below the junction of tap-root and trunk, which is the region referred to as the 'collar'. They grow horizontally, some quite near the soil surface, coming from the top of the tap-root. They branch repeatedly and terminate as fibrous rootlets, which may have mycorrhizal associations in the leaf-litter layer on the surface of the soil. Normally, lateral roots are produced in whorls at intervals along the tap-root.

Sinker roots, also referred to as 'anchor roots', are sometimes produced from the lateral roots and grow vertically downwards to a depth of several feet.

Adventitious roots may be produced by multi-stemmed trees, particularly with abnormally moist conditions near the base of the tree. Such 'aerial' (stilt) roots grow vertically or diagonally into the soil (Fig. 8(b). They may be specially encouraged (Pyke 1932), but sometimes they occur naturally in old, multi-stemmed, feral trees (Myers 1930, 1934).

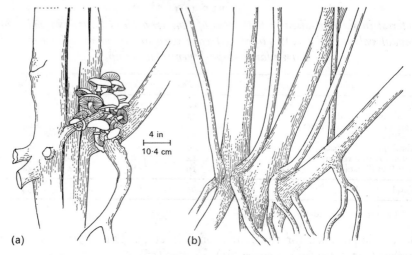

4 in
10·4 cm

(a)   (b)

FIG. 8. (a) Shows symptoms of collar-crack disease, with *Armillariella mellea* fructifia-
cations (Dade 1927*a*). (b) Shows the multiple-stemmed habit, with adventitious
rooting.

Pyke (1932) found that ring-barking to isolate chupons from the main
stem-system was important for encouragement of extra rooting.

The root system from vegetative propagation of both 'fan' and 'chupon'
cuttings (Pyke 1932, 1933*a*, 1934*a*), developed two or three vertical sinker
roots which took the place of the 'true' tap-root of a seedling root system.
Cheesman (1936) concluded that there was no difference at age approximately $2\frac{1}{2}$ years, between the root systems of different types of cutting
material. It seemed that the initial difference noticed by Pyke (1933*a*) was
not maintained.

Hurd (1961) showed that tap, lateral, and sinker roots can all absorb
water and nutrients from the soil, but Swarbrick (1964) commented that
'there can be no doubt that under normal conditions the lateral root
system with its numerous fibrous roots is the most important in this
respect'. Nevertheless, the partial defoliation response, with subsequent
recovery, was similar when different parts of the root system were severed
(Hurd 1961).

Symptoms

Bunting and Dade (1924) observed that root disease symptoms in general
are such as would be expected from the interruption of nutrient and/or
water intake. The result of root infection may be sudden and severe for a
young tree, with wilted leaves remaining attached to the branches. Leaves
may be shed progressively from the branches of an older infected tree, with
accompanying dieback symptoms and ultimately a moribund 'stag-headed'

appearance. Sometimes the tap-root is affected and weakened, so that the cocoa tree is liable to be blown over. On the other hand, when horizontal roots are affected, there is likely to be a slower decline in general health, or only part of the tree may be affected when the root system is not totally infected. A partially affected tree may persist with a degree of debility determined by ability to regenerate a new root system.

Fungi associated with cocoa roots

The relationship between the host and important root-disease fungi is such that much of their life-cycles is spent in a sterile mycelial state, with a tendency for fructifications to be produced only when the host is dying or dead. Common names for some cocoa root-diseases characterize the colour of aggregations of microscopic hyphae ('red root disease' due to *Ganoderma pseudoferreum*, 'brown root disease' due to *Phellinus noxius*, 'white root disease' due to *Rigidoporus lignosus*).

The tendency for delayed fructification of most 'specialized' root fungi (*Ustulina deusta* is exceptional in this respect), in contrast to the less tardy sporulation of many 'unspecialized' (Garrett 1970) root fungi, caused some early misconceptions as to the economic importance of certain fungi associated with the roots of debilitated cocoa. Prillieux and Delacroix (1894) described a tropically ubiquitous and weakly parasitic fungus (*Botryodiplodia theobromae*) as *Macrophoma vestita*, from cocoa roots in South America. The possibility of equivocal deductions from the presence of weak pathogens commonly associated with stem infections, was noticed by Small (1925) in Uganda. It appeared that a severe dieback there frequently killed cocoa trees. This disorder was associated with the presence of *B. theobromae* and *Colletotrichum* sp. The simultaneous presence of root disease was suspected and cases of root rot due to *Armillariella mellea* were found.

Twenty-three species of fungi reported as associated with cocoa roots are listed below. Details of their geographical distributions, with literature references, are given in Chapter 12. The taxonomy and biology of the more aggressive and/or conspicuous of the root fungi are considered. These fungi are widespread and have extensive host-ranges commensurate with the probable antiquity of the main groups within the classes to which they belong (Ascomycetes, Basidiomycetes, and Phycomycetes) (Demoulin 1973).

The fungi infecting cocoa roots which are considered below, comprise both 'soil inhabitants' and 'soil invaders' (Garrett 1938). They are mostly (83 per cent) members of the three taxonomic classes mentioned above, the remainder (17 per cent) are classified as either Fungi Imperfecti, or as Mycelia Sterilia. Despite some diversity of taxa, the above-ground symptoms associated with root infection are generalized and not diagnostic for a particular root-infecting species.

It is convenient to include here (p. 155) an account of root mycorrhiza.

This cocoa phenomenon has been studied insufficiently for a proper assessment of its possible pathological or benign (commensal) status.

Armillariella mellea. Pegler and Gibson (1972*a*) gave a description and general account of this fungus. It has numerous hosts (MacFarlane 1968) throughout its range in temperate and tropical countries (*C.M.I. Distribution Map No. 143,* 1969). Associated with this widespread occurrence, there are differences in morphology and temperature relationships (Gibson 1961). Reported occurrences on cocoa are given on p. 173.

In temperate climates, *A. mellea* commonly spreads by rhizomorphs which transmit inoculum from one substrate to another (Garrett 1956), but these fungal organs are not invariably present. In tropical climates, when mycelium invades the host tissues, particularly along the medullary rays, it thickens, thereby splitting the wood through mycelial structures referred to as 'xylostromata'. This phenomenon gave rise to the common name 'collar crack' which Dade (1927*a*) applied to Armillaria root disease of cocoa in Ghana (Fig. 8(a)). The xylostromata disintegrated in the dead (see page 146) plant, leaving fissures about 2 in. (5 cm.) deep (Weststeijn 1967).

In Ghana, infection spread from tree to tree through contact of adjacent root systems, in absence of transmission by rhizomorphs. Such aggregations of mycelium were not found in the field, but were readily produced in the laboratory when large pieces of infected material taken from a tap root or collar region were kept damp. Rhizomorphs were also produced in 'tube cultures' (Dade 1927*a*).

Elsewhere, when rhizomorph growth-rates were studied in relation to the interaction between temperature and nutrition (Garrett 1956, 1970; Rishbeth 1968), the optimum temperature for rhizomorph growth-rate was lower (22 °C. (72 °F.)) when nutrition was sub-optimal, as happens if *A. mellea* is subjected to a food-base restriction in the field. With unrestricted nutrition, as when *A. mellea* was grown in culture on nutrient media, the optimum temperature for rhizomorph growth was higher (*ca.* 25 °C. (77 °F.)). Accordingly, an explanation was provided for the observation in Ghana (Dade 1927*a*) that *A. mellea* under field conditions was without rhizomorphs but these developed when abundant substrate-material was specially provided and when *A. mellea* was grown in culture.

Dade (1927*a*) correlated severity of collar-crack disease in Ghana with wetness induced by high atmospheric humidity and associated luxuriance of ground vegetation and epiphytes. Weststeijn (1967) reported collar-crack disease of cocoa in Nigeria, and stated that 'sometimes infected trees were found growing in waterlogged soil'.

A range of introduced and indigenous West African plants was listed by Dade (1927*a*) as hosts of *A. mellea* in Ghana, including oil palm (*Elaeis guineensis* Jacq.). Infection of the latter plant was not detected by Fox (1964) in Nigeria, nor was it listed as a host plant there by Bailey (1966), but it was so reported in the Congo (Turner 1971*a*). Dade (1927*a*) reported *A. mellea* as growing saprophytically in Ghana on a root of 'Eriodendron' (presumably *Ceiba pentandra* (L.) Gaertn., syn. *Eriodendron anfractuosum* DC.) from which six cocoa trees had become infected. In S. Tomé, Rishbeth (1972) found that among cocoa shade-trees there, *C. pentandra* and likewise *Musanga cecropioides* R.Br. were more resistant to *A. mellea* than *Albizzia falcata* (L.) Backer (as *A. moluccana* Miq.) and *Erythrina velutina* Willd. He stated that 'yet others, such as *Carapa procera* DC. and *Pentaclethra macrophylla* Benth., are apparently even more resistant'.

Armillariella tabescens. In Malagasy (Madagascar), Orian (1954) reported this fungus, as *Clitocybe tabescens*, causing root rots of cocoa, coffee, and other plants. Subsequently, Roger (1960) referred to this coffee root rot as caused by *Clitocybe* sp., and commented that this fungus was not definitely identified as *C. tabescens*.

Attack of cocoa by *A. tabescens* may have been unrecognized elsewhere, or it may be unrecognizable taxonomically (Gibson 1961; Gibson and Corbett 1964; Rishbeth 1968). However, Riker (1961), whilst disregarding *A. mellea*, proposed that the root rot caused by *A. tabescens* should be regarded as an internationally dangerous forest disease. It seems that *A. tabescens* is recognizable in America but not necessarily elsewhere.

Botryodiplodia theobromae. Mention is made above (p. 147) of one synonym of this fungus (*Macrophoma vestita*), and another is *Thyridaria tarda*. Van Hall (1914) referred to a 'thyridaria root rot' of cocoa.

Infection by *B. theobromae* follows damage by mirids (Chapter 9) and root infection may also follow mechanical damage. This fungus is likely to occur on moribund roots but probably unimportantly.

Ceratocystis fimbriata. This fungus is considered in Chapter 8 as the wilt-disease pathogen. It was reported on cocoa roots in Fiji (Firman 1972).

Ceratocystis moniliformis forma *theobromae*. Morgan-Jones (1967*b*) gave a description of *C. moniliformis*. Luc (1952) designated a form of this species which was isolated from cocoa roots in Malagasy (Madagascar). Barba and Hansen (1962*a*) isolated a fungus which they considered similar to *C. moniliformis* from above-ground parts of cocoa in Costa Rica.

Corticium rolfsii. Seymour (1929) listed this fungus, as *Sclerotium rolfsii*, under *Theobroma cacao*, but without details. No report of *C. rolfsii* in association with cocoa was listed by MacFarlane (1968), although this fungus has other woody-plant hosts in many tropical countries (*C.M.I. Distribution Map No. 311*, 1969).

Ganoderma pseudoferreum. This fungus was characterized as having mycelial aggregations on roots, with definite tissue differentiation and a toughened outer skin (Garrett 1944). In Papua and New Guinea, there was

a tendency for some soil to be attached to the infected cocoa roots. Although
the reddish colour of the rhizomorph gave rise to the usual common name
('red root disease'), this root disease was referred to there as 'wet root rot'
because the cocoa wood became soft and spongy (Thrower 1956). Occurrences on cocoa are given on p. 184, and the geographical distribution on
other hosts is shown in *C.M.I. Distribution Map No. 98* (1965).

This root disease of cocoa was very common in Malaya where it was
considered more serious than either 'brown' or 'white' root diseases
(Thompson and Johnston 1953; Johnston 1959). It may be inadvisable to
interplant cocoa in rubber because the latter is a severely affected host
(Blencowe 1968).

Helicobasidium longisporum. Wakefield (1917) distinguished this fungus
from other species of the genus by its purple- to violet-coloured hymenium
and long, coloured spores. It does not appear to have been reported from
cocoa since it was observed in association with *Macrophomina phaseolina*
on some cocoa roots in Uganda (Small 1925).

Macrophomina phaseolina. Physiologic strains on different hosts vary con-
siderably (Ashby 1927; Tarr 1962; Holliday and Punithalingam 1970).
Williams (1968) reported this fungus from dying roots of cocoa in Sabah.

Garrett (1960) commented that *M. phaseolina* (as *M. phaseoli*) 'has
certainly been credited with causing many more "diseases" than it has
deserved'.

Phellinus noxius and *Phellinus lamaensis.* The pathogen of brown root
disease was at first recognized in the sterile state and later with atypical
fructification, whence this fungus was initially placed in the genus *Hymenochaete (H. noxia)*, with later transfer to *Fomes*, and now to *Phellinus*. When
the validity of the epithet 'noxia' was questioned, the fungus was referred
to as *Fomes lamaoensis*. Because of this confused nomenclature (Thrower
1965), and since *P. lamaensis* and *P. noxius* are separated microscopically
(Pegler and Waterston 1968a), and as they are possibly not separable patho-
genically, it is convenient to consider them together here (*P. noxius* 'sensu
lato'). Only limited importance need be attached to the single record of
P. lamaensis in association with cocoa by Piening (1962) for Ghana, where
P. noxius is the generally accepted pathogen of brown root disease.

Occurrences of this fungus on cocoa are given on p. 196, and its geographical distribution on various hosts was shown in *C.M.I. Distribution
Map No. 104* (1969).

The mycelium on roots has a characteristic encrustation of soil and small
stones (Sharples 1922). Dissection of this sheath reveals the typical brown
colour of the mycelium which later becomes black on the outside. The
bark disintegrates under the encrustation and mycelium in the wood
appears as brown lines in advanced stages of the disease. There may be

some aggregation of fungal hyphae (Garrett 1944), but definite rhizo-morphs were not noticed in Nigeria on standing trees, however, they formed after an infected tree was uprooted. Lethal instances of brown root disease in Nigeria were found in cocoa plantings aged 2–7 years (West-steijn 1966b).

A different manifestation of *P. noxius* infection was observed in the Gazelle Peninsula, New Britain District of New Guinea (Thrower 1965). A crust of mycelium spread from ground level to *ca.* 1·5–3 ft. (0·5–1 m.) on the trunk. Affected trees usually died about 6 months after the appearance of the crust. Because the crust on the trunk was sometimes associated with mycelium on the roots, it is reasonable to consider this disease as an unusual manifestation of attack by the brown root disease pathogen.

Phytophthora palmivora. Turner and Asomaning (1962) studied the infec-tion of the roots of young cocoa seedlings by *P. palmivora*, and they sug-gested that young feeding roots of older trees, in the uppermost soil layers, might also be attacked. There does not appear to have been confirmation of this expectation.

Rhizoctonia lamellifera. Hansford (1937; 1943a) reported this fungus from the roots of cocoa suffering from dieback in Uganda, but he considered that it was probably not the primary cause of the disorder.

The taxonomic status of *R. lamellifera* is dubious. It is uncertain whether *R. lamellifera* is separable from *Rhizoctonia bataticola* (Small 1925; Hopkins 1933) or not (Small 1926a; Holliday and Punithalingam 1970).

Rigidoporus lignosus. Pegler and Waterston (1968b) gave a description and resolved a confused nomenclature to the effect that diseases associated with similar fungi (*R. lignosus*) occur within the tropics of the eastern and western hemispheres (*C.M.I. Distribution Map No. 176* (1966)).

White root disease is characterized by the pale-coloured strands of mycelium on the exterior of affected roots, usually on the underside of horizontal ones. Older strands (rhizomorphs) are cord-like and yellow, brown or sometimes slightly reddish. The advancing portion consists of fine hyphae from the external mycelium entering the bark and wood at intervals, to cause their decay. Leaves are lost prematurely after dis-coloration and wilting. Only part of the root system may be attacked at first, so that the whole tree above ground is not uniformly affected. In Nigeria, infected trees had a thin canopy and did not show the excessive defoliation associated with *A. mellea* attack (Weststeijn 1966b).

Attack by *R. lignosus* depends on proximity of roots of living hosts or other suitable food base for the rhizomorphs, because of its ectotrophic growth habit. The 'inoculum potential' concept is important in this connec-tion (Garrett 1960). Through the wide host range of this fungus (MacFar-lane 1968), coupled with the diversity of tropical vegetation, there have been opportunities for 'polyphagous parasitism', exemplified by dramatic advances involving cocoa (Petch 1928b; Staner 1930). At other times, the fungal food-source may be a stump left when a forest tree was felled (Akinrefon 1967). Peries and Irugalbandara (1973) discussed fungal entry into host tissue.

Rosellinia arcuata. Sivanesan and Holliday (1972c) gave a description of this species and stated that it was 'plurivorous but only of serious importance on tea *(Camellia sinensis)*'.

Possible occurrences of this fungus on cocoa roots are based on an uncertain determination in Ghana (Dade 1940), and an association with 'black root rot' in Indonesia (Hubert 1957).

Rosellinia australis. This species was reported by Weir (1926) on cocoa in Brazil, but there do not appear to have been any subsequent reports.

Rosellinia bunodes. Sivanesan and Holliday (1972a) gave a description of this species, discussed its plurivorous pathogenicity and noted that cocoa was one of the perennial economic crops affected. They added occurrences in Central America to those already shown in *C.M.I. Distribution Map No. 358* (1970).

R. bunodes and *R. pepo* are two 'forest root fungi' which were destructive in the West Indies when forest land was used for agricultural development (Nowell 1923).

Rosellinia necatrix. Sivanesan and Holliday (1972b) gave a description of this species, discussed its pathogenicity, and noted that its optimum soil temperature was *ca.* 20 °C. (63 °F.) The authenticity of an unlocalized report of *R. necatrix* in association with cocoa (Burle 1961), seems doubtful.

Rosellinia paraguayensis. This species was reported by Nowell (1923) from lowland cocoa in Grenada, where it was associated with dieback in several groups of cocoa trees. Waterston (1941) found *R. paraguayensis* at 1,200 ft. (370 m.) altitude, where the rainfall (> 200 in. (5,000 mm.) per year) was probably greater than in the lowland area. Perithecia occurred on a wounded cocoa branch. Apparently there was no penetration of healthy tissue. It seems that the pathogenicity of this species is doubtful.

Rosellinia pepo. Booth and Holliday (1972) gave a description of this fungus and considered its pathogenicity. Authentic occurrences of *R. pepo* are solely within the northern tropical region of the New World (*C.M.I. Distribution Map No. 298* (1968)).

R. pepo differs from other species of *Rosellinia* associated with cocoa in being markedly parasitic as Waterston (1941) demonstrated by inoculation experiments. The perithecial state rarely occurs. The conidial state is referable to *Dematophora* rather than to *Graphium* (Booth and Holliday 1972); it appears at an early stage on exposed roots and at the base of the stem. A characteristic feature is the production of 'fans' or 'stars' of white mycelium between the bark and wood of the roots. From this layer of mycelium in the cambium, the wood is penetrated via the medullary rays.

Waterston (1941) found that root disease due to *R. pepo* was not invariably associated with abundance of organic matter, but tended to occur on soils of light texture. Garrett (1944) explained that with high rainfall, overhead shade, and associated accumulation of humus, *R. pepo* advances unrestrictedly as a mycelial sheet which parasitizes the roots and stems of plants engulfed in the course of this advance. Under drier conditions, with less humus or surface litter, the advance is slower and restricted to roots or fragments of plants which may serve as food-bases.

Sphaerostilbe repens. This fungus has a tropicopolitan distribution (*C.M.I. Distribution Map No. 288* (1968)), on various hosts, which are mainly but not exclusively woody plants (MacFarlane 1968). Details of occurrences on cocoa are given on p. 202.

Ashby (1929*b*) explained that the conspicuous colour of the rhizomorphs had suggested the common name 'red root disease' for the wet rot which affected limes (*Citrus aurantiifolia* (Christm.) Swingle) in Dominica, and the roots of cocoa also (Briton-Jones 1934). To avoid confusion through duplication of the same common name used for the disease caused by *Ganoderma pseudoferreum* (p. 149), it is preferable to use the unequivocal name 'Sphaerostilbe root disease' (Thompson and Johnston 1953).

The imperfect (conidial) state occurs on exposed bark of roots or on soil in contact with them. The reddish-brown conidiophores bear white 'heads' of hyaline conidiospores. The perfect (perithecial) state occurs rarely, as clusters of flask-shaped, dark red perithecia intermingled with the conidial state.

Garrett (1944) summarized opinions that Sphaerostilbe root disease was associated with such soil conditions as impeded drainage and lack of aeration, which were presumed to lower the resistance of the roots to attack by *S. repens*.

Ustulina deusta. Hawksworth (1972) gave a description of this fungus, considered its pathogenicity to various hosts and mentioned its cosmopolitan distribution (*C.M.I. Distribution Map No. 417* (1966)). Petch (1923) referred to this species as 'one of the most protean of tropical fungi'.

Unlike the behaviour of most of the other fungi affecting cocoa rhizospheres, the presence of *U. deusta* is not manifested by external mycelium on roots but it is conspicuous on the exterior of the above-ground parts. These occurrences gave rise to the common names 'collar rot' (Bunting and Dade 1924) and 'stem rot' (Thompson and Johnston 1953). It seems advisable not to use the name 'collar rot', to avoid possible confusion with the common name 'collar-crack disease' used for the root disease caused by *Armillariella mellea* (p. 148).

Affected wood becomes dry when dead and it may be divided internally by mycelial sheets, which appear as black lines ('zone-lines') in cross-section and these may be misinterpreted as 'cracks' (cf. 'collar-crack disease'). The bodies of mycelium in the wood have been referred to as 'pseudosclerotia' (Garrett 1970). Beneath the bark, there are white or brownish-white fan-shaped mycelial patches. Mycelium emerges through the bark and spreads over the surface to form a white plate on which conidia are produced. Through periodical growth-interruptions, the plate of mycelium becomes concentrically marked by furrows occasioned by arrested growth and its subsequent resumption after a period of dry weather. In sheltered situations, the surface may remain white, elsewhere the plate changes colour to purplish-grey, and finally black. The production of conidia on the plate confers a greenish-grey colour. Later, the surface becomes dotted with numerous black points which are the openings of perithecia embedded in white tissue.

Root disease caused by *U. deusta* spreads slowly because this fungus does not grow through the soil (Briton-Jones 1934). Generally, a healthy root becomes infected through contact with an infected one. Henderson (1954) reported that Ustulina root disease was common in New Guinea, where infections were believed to occur through mechanical wounds. There were instances when *U. deusta* apparently behaved as a wound parasite, because infection sometimes started in the stem and spread to roots.

There may be air-borne spore-infection of tree-stumps and other exposed surfaces above ground (Garrett 1944).

Verticillium dahliae. Hawksworth and Talboys (1970) gave a description of this fungus and discussed its pathogenicity to a wide range of dicotyledonous plants in temperate and sub-tropical regions (*C.M.I. Distribution Map No. 366* (1969)).

Leakey (1965) described a 'sudden death' disorder of cocoa in Uganda. An apparently healthy tree might, as a result of infection by *V. dahliae*, become entirely moribund in about a week, with brown, brittle leaves hanging vertically on the affected tree. At other times, parts of a tree wilted successively. There was noteworthy resemblance to the scorched appearance and deaths of trees previously reported by Snowden (1921).

Initial attempts to establish the pathogenicity of *V. dahliae* to cocoa were unsuccessful (Leakey 1965). Subsequently, Emechebe and Leakey (1968) reported that *V. dahliae* was recovered from surface-sterilized wilted cocoa shoots following inoculation of the roots with a suspension of *V. dahliae* conidia. Emechebe, Leakey, and Banage (1971) studied the Verticillium wilt syndrome and also the behaviour of this fungus in cocoa roots (Emechebe, Leakey, and Banage 1972).

Ectotrophic mycorrhiza. This manifestation of the phenomenon was described and illustrated by Pyke (1935) and by Laycock (1945), as branched unseptate hyphae anastomosing among the root hairs. Microscopical observations indicated hyphal penetration of the epidermis, with development of mycelium in the root cortex. Rombouts (1954) found that it was difficult to distinguish 'a genuine mycorrhizal mantle' from what appeared to be fortuitous fungi, which might be 'normal' constituents of the cocoa rhizosphere. Pyke (1935) had studied the 'superficial mycelium' of small roots (up to 1 mm. diameter) and noticed casual epiphytic fungi of three genera (*Fusarium, Mucor,* and *Penicillium*). Turner and Asomaning (1962) reported fungi of twelve genera on surfaces of feeding roots in Ghana (*Aspergillus, Cephalosporium, Chalaropsis, Cladosporium, Cunninghamella, Fusarium, Hormiscium, Penicillium, Pestalotiopsis, Rhizoctonia, Spicaria,* and *Trichoderma*).

Endotrophic mycorrhiza. There was apparently continuity with ectotrophic mycorrhiza, via an appressorium, with penetration of fine ultimate rootlets, within a length range of about 2–6 mm. Longer rootlets, described as 'runner roots' were without internal mycelium, as were root-tips and root-initials. Entry was by fine hyphae from below the larger ones (appressoria) adpressed to the root surface. Hyphae sometimes increased in diameter on becoming internal, then branched to form an inter- and intra-cellular network in the cortex to a depth of 1–5 cells according to the size of the root, but without penetrating every cell. The endodermis of the stele was not entered. Septa were seen occasionally in the internal mycelium, particularly of larger roots.

Some hyphae transformed to coiled masses filling the lumina of the cells and were referred to as 'arbuscules' which seemed to disintegrate later, but Laycock (1945) emphasized that this phase should not be interpreted as 'digestion' which Pyke (1935) had suggested. There was no evidence that the cocoa host derived benefit from apparent fragmentation of the so-called arbuscules, which may have been artefacts.

Attempts to obtain cocoa mycorrhiza in pure culture were unsuccessful. Species of *Endogone* and *Rhizoctonia* were associated with rootlets of both cocoa and rubber in the Congo (Anon. 1953c). Except for reported occurrence of cocoa mycorrhiza in Venezuela (Laycock 1945), there is no further knowledge of the possible geographical range of cocoa mycorrhiza.

When cocoa roots were sampled from two Trinidad estates representing 'good' cocoa (Tortuga) and 'poor' cocoa (Las Hermanas) for estimation of mycorrhiza incidence, there was no clear indication of the possible nutritional significance of mycorrhiza (Laycock 1945). Sampling at three depths in different Trinidad cocoa-estate soils suggested that the number of rootlets with mycorrhiza was positively associated with good soil-aeration rather than with amount of organic matter (Rombouts 1954).

Control of root diseases

Chemical methods

Garrett (1970) discussed the use of a volatile fumigant (carbon disulphide), and the use of a fungicide with high stability in soil (P.C.N.B., also known as Quinozene) against root-disease fungi. Application cost would be excessive for ordinary commercial purposes in the case of cocoa.

The possible use of arboricides to destroy diseased, or otherwise unwanted trees, is considered in Chapter 7 (p. 107).

Cultural methods

Preparation of land for planting. Leach (1937, 1939) suggested that forest trees should be ringed in advance of felling, so that the roots would die earlier through depletion of starch reserves. Gibson and Goodchild (1961) demonstrated in Kenya that ring-barking, if properly applied, did have the desirable effect of restricting colonization of roots by *Armillariella mellea*. It was important that the trees should not die before exhaustion of root starch.

Selective clearing is commonly practised in West Africa, it involves the felling of soft-wooded trees and leaving the hard-wooded ones if suitable to provide shade. Some stumps and moribund trees are likely to remain and thereby constitute a possible root-disease hazard. Complete clearing to prevent root disease in a cocoa planting may be too costly and otherwise undesirable through exposure of subsoil (Allison and Cunningham 1959).

Petch (1923) recommended that 'in dealing with *Rosellinia* the surface of the soil must be made as bare as a tennis court'. As pointed out by Hardy (1953), an approach to this condition had been disadvantageous for the Trinidad cocoa industry, albeit having possibly achieved inadvertent control of Rosellinia root disease.

Sanitation. The removal and destruction of affected cocoa trees was difficult to enforce in West Africa (Bunting and Dade 1924). Dickson (1969) discussed the lack of success in attempting legislative control of cocoa diseases in Ghana. Nevertheless, it was recommended that cocoa trees in Ghana affected by root disease should be burnt and sources of infection traced and destroyed (Wharton 1962).

Regular inspection of rubber roots for removal of the epiphytic rhizomorphs of *Rigidoporus lignosus* was considered to be an effective control method (Garrett 1970). Peries and Irugalbandara (1973) considered that regular inspection was undesirable because some damage to roots was inevitable. Instead, reliance should be placed on disease detection from leaf symptoms. However, for cocoa in Nigeria, above-ground symptoms were not evident until infection had reached an advanced stage (Weststeijn 1966b).

For plantations in Papua and New Guinea, Shaw (1962) emphasized the need to record the position of affected trees so that appropriate control measures might be applied, in accordance with the scale of ascertained losses.

Cover crops. Fox (1967) discussed the beneficial effects of cover crops in relation to the replanting of rubber, apparently through the action of cover-crop roots in disintegrating and exhausting massive woody inocula of *R. lignosus*, as explained by Garrett (1970). Some form of ground cover is generally considered desirable to avoid soil deterioration after clear-felling (Acquaye and Smith 1965). Cover crops under cocoa are likely to suffer through too much shade from the cocoa canopy, compared with their persistence through less shade from the rubber canopy.

Encouragement of adventitious rooting. Development of a multi-stemmed habit and the encouragement of adventitious rooting is suggested as a possible procedure for mitigating losses in an area liable to root disease (Fig. 8(b)). This procedure was tried with apparent success, in Cameroon, when the roots of cocoa trees were attacked by basidiomycetes, as described by Ludwigs (1920). Provided that the root system was not yet completely destroyed, regeneration by chupons followed cutting the main stem near ground level (stumping). These chupons grew well and their production of adventitious roots was promoted by heaping soil around the regenerating stump. Mycelial growth in the stump apparently ceased but it was not known for how long the attack might be halted in this way.

There is support for the above recommendation, through evidence that within the four woody crop-plants considered in Table 11.1 (p. 145), diminishing proneness to root disease (in the order: rubber, tea, cocoa, coffee) is negatively associated with ability to form adventitious roots (ease of propagation), which is a reflection of certain anatomical features. Examples of 'ready-rooting' plants are cocoa (Pyke 1932, 1933a, 1934a; Toxopeus and Okoloko 1967), and coffee (Trench, Gillett, and McClelland 1937; Wellman 1961). Rubber is 'shy-rooting' (Beakbane 1961, 1969). Tea appears to be in an intermediate category (Purseglove 1968b).

Beakbane (1961, 1969) showed that ease of propagation was mainly, but not entirely related to the anatomical structure of the primary phloem. 'Shy-rooting' was associated with presence of a continuous cylinder of thick-walled fibres without living protoplasts. In contrast, with 'ready-rooting' plants, the sclerenchymatous cylinder was discontinuous. Sclerification is an aspect of tissue senescence, and in this respect rooting capacity is associated with delayed differentiation of primary phloem parenchyma into fibres and sclereids. This retardation is achieved in practice by such procedures as partial etiolation, earthing up and marcotting. The anatomy of cocoa (Metcalfe and Chalk 1950) seems to conform with expectation for 'ready-rooting', although ease of rooting stem cuttings varies with the clone (Purseglove 1968b).

12

PARASITES, SAPROPHYTES, AND EPIPHYTES ASSOCIATED WITH COCOA TREES

Introduction

The entire floras of cocoa trees merit attention here, in accord with the statement by Butt (1972) that '. . . A. J. P. Oort described epidemiology as a branch of ecology dealing with ecosystems in which a predatory, parasitic, or pathogenic relationship exists between an organism and its host'. However, the status of the cocoa tree as host or substrate, with respect to components of its resident flora, may vary in space and time. Leben (1965) discussed the location of micro-organisms on higher plants and stated 'that it will be difficult to determine precisely "in" or "on" for many organisms'. It is important to note the phenomenon that most plants are resistant to invasion by most micro-organisms, as discussed by Wood (1972). Hence the comprehensive heading of this chapter, which is concerned with cocoa-tree ecosystems (Leftwich 1973).

Economic importance

A possible deleterious effect of sub-aerial intrusive plants on perennial tropical crops is controversial. Carruthers (1904) commented that '. . . it is also supposed that in some cases the buds are prevented from bursting at the places where these lichens are found. I have examined a very large number of tea bushes and cacao trees to obtain evidence of this suppression of leaf and flower buds, but without finding any proof that this often, if ever, takes place . . .'. Nevertheless, a contrary opinion persisted. Johnson (1912) stated that 'epiphytes, such as mosses, lichens, and small orchids, often interfere with the development of young cocoa buds, and should be carefully removed from the tree'. Bunting and Dade (1924) considered numerous plants (algae, aroids, ferns, fungi, lichens, mosses, orchids) which might interfere with the supply of light available to plants supporting them, and might induce the attack of parasitic organisms by increasing humidity. Burle (1961) also expressed the opinion that epiphytes might have a harmful 'smothering effect' or be conducive to pathogenic attack. Ruinen (1953) studied a syndrome which she referred to as 'epiphytosis', due to undetermined mycorrhizal fungi associated with host and epiphyte relationships.

A survey of cocoa plantings in Nigeria showed that the presence or absence of particular epiphytes (expressed as 'epiphyte ratings') was a useful indicator of rainfall and humidity regimes of different localities, in connection with studies of black pod disease caused by *Phytophthora palmivora* (Thorold 1952). In the drier areas (rainfall < 60 in. (1,520 mm.) per year), the trunks and branches of cocoa trees carried crustose and foliose epiphytes (lichens and hepatics). In the wetter areas (rainfall > 60 in (1,520 mm.) per year), trunks and branches of cocoa trees carried foliaceous epiphytes (mosses and vascular plants). Prevalence of foliaceous epiphytes might be expected to have a 'smothering effect', if such exists, because they are bulkier than the crustose and foliose epiphytes. Table 12.1 summarizes some results from the survey, for localities representing a range of annual precipitations (46–109 in. (1,168–2,770 mm.) per year).

TABLE 12.1

Rainfall, productivity, and prevalence of trees with foliaceous epiphytes in Nigeria

Locality	Rainfall (average) (in. per year)	Number of trees with foliaceous epiphytes, expressed as percentage of total number of trees observed (%)	Number of fruits per tree
Ibadan	46	2	23
Ondo	56	26	7
Benin	78	64	21
Warri	109	98	8

The presence of foliaceous epiphytes might either enhance the number of fruits through harbouring pollinators (Chapter 6), or it might tend to suppress flowering and/or fruiting through a conjectural smothering effect. Table 12.1 shows that the presence or absence of foliaceous epiphytes was without apparent effect on the number of fruits.

Conspectus of parasites, saprophytes and epiphytes associated with cocoa

Plant groups associated with the above-ground parts of cocoa trees comprise such diverse taxa as bacteria and bromeliads. Species are listed, with their geographical occurrences and literature references on pp. 175–229. First, it is convenient to consider within most of the main groups, a few representatives which are of some economic importance or of particular scientific interest.

Yeasts and saprophytic bacteria

Ruinen (1961, 1963*a*) studied the organisms populating cocoa leaves in Surinam, and found yeasts and nitrogen-fixing bacteria (*Azotobacter* and *Beijerinckia* spp.), so that total nitrogen increased in dew collected from cocoa leaves (Ruinen 1965). This observation is in accord with the comment by Tukey (1971) that leaves of some tropical plants, including cocoa, are easily wetted and easily leached. There is reason to believe that such leachates may benefit the cocoa plant (Bhat, Limaye, and Vasantharajan 1971).

Norris and Chapman (1968) reviewed the genus *Azotobacter* and noted that the ability to fix atmospheric nitrogen was not restricted to the azotobacters. Many species assigned to this genus were inadequately described, or evidently minor variants of six fully described species which they discussed, three of them having been reported from cocoa (*Azotobacter agilis, A. chroococcum*, and *A. vinelandii*). Some other '*Azotobacter*' species have been separated and placed in the genus *Beijerinckia* which Breed, Murray, and Smith (1957) rejected, pending further comparative studies. Nevertheless, it is necessary to use this generic name now, but without indicating occurrence of particular *Beijerinckia* species on cocoa.

Ruinen (1956) discussed the widespread occurrence in tropical soils of bacteria assigned to *Beijerinckia*, in contrast to their absence from soils in temperate regions. It seems likely that nitrogen-fixing bacteria on leaves will augment populations in the soil. Meiklejohn (1962) stated that 'forest soils kept for a long time under bare fallow contained very few aerobic nitrogen fixers, however'. She found cells of *Azotobacter* on leaves of four species of forest trees and cells of *Beijerinckia* on leaves of nine species of forest trees, at Tafo, Ghana (Meiklejohn 1962). Apparently cocoa leaves were not examined there, but it is reasonable to suppose that these bacteria would have occurred, either by dispersal from leaves of nearby forest-trees, or from the soil.

It is to be expected that a variety of micro-organisms may be deposited on pods from leaves above them, by the leaching action of dew or rainfall, since bacteria and yeasts occurred in layers on leaves, varying from $1-22\,\mu m$ in thickness (Ruinen 1961). Some of these yeasts produced lipids extracellularly, and through lipolytic activity there was breakdown of the plant cuticle and/or prevention of its formation. Consequently, there was diffusion of substances at the surface, through enhanced permeability of the epidermis (Ruinen 1963a,b, 1966). Nutrient availability promoted microbial activity (Ruinen 1965, 1970, 1971). Last and Deighton (1965) discussed ways in which different members of the leaf flora may interact. They commented that 'leaf saprophytes may act as scavengers "mopping-up" energy sources, such as amino acids and sugars, which otherwise might stimulate the growth of plant parasites'. It is reasonable to suppose that there may be saprophyte populations on fruits which are similar to those on leaves. Leben (1965) drew attention to a possible parallel between a nutritional explanation for soil fungistasis (considered for *P. palmivora* by Thorold (1955b) and Turner (1965a)), and the inhibition of fungus pathogens on the leaf. He noted 'the skewed nature of infectivity–titration

curves for leaf-infecting fungi . . .', which he exemplified by the phenomenon 'that 100 germinable conidia of a pathogen may be required to
produce one leaf lesion'. A similar phenomenon was observed when a
suspension of *P. palmivora* sporangia was sprayed on to apparently healthy
attached cocoa fruits in Nigeria. The mean number of infections (black pod
spots) per fruit was 1·4 in one typical series of observations (Thorold
1955*b*). This paucity of multiple infections has remained unexplained.
Hislop and Park (1962*a*) confirmed that the number of spots (lesions)
averaged less than 2 per pod at normal tropical temperatures. When otherwise untreated pods were chilled (10 °F. (5 °C.) below ambient temperature
for 18 hours) and subsequently inoculated with *P. palmivora* zoospore
suspensions, they found that the mean number of lesions per pod was
greater (34·3 ± 18 to 68·3 ± 11). It is suggested that the greater number
of lesions after chilling, may have been due to suppression of microbial
activity on the pod surface. When chilled pods were inoculated and taken
into a warmer room, it seems likely that with prolonged motility, zoospores
may have caused infection before the chilled saprophytes resumed normal
activity on the pod surface. Contrariwise, at normal tropical temperatures
(> 20 °C. (68 °F.)), the activity of microbial epiphytes on the pod surface
may account for the paucity of *P. palmivora* lesions, through 'competition'
with this parasite. It is important to note that the optimum temperature for
Azotobacter agilis and *A. chroococcum* was given as 25 °C., (77 °F.) to 28 °C.
(82 °F.) by Bergey, Breed, Murray, and Hitchens (1939). Yeasts which
occur on cocoa leaves (*Candida, Cryptococcus, Rhodotorula*, and *Sporobolomyces* spp.) have elevated maximum temperatures (*ca.* 34 °C.) (93 °F.)
(Phaff 1970; Phaff and Ahearn 1970; Phaff and Fell 1970; van Uden and
Buckley 1970).

Incidental suppression of microbial activity by copper fungicides may
partially account for the unsatisfactory reduction of black pod losses due
to *P. palmivora* (Hislop and Park 1962*a,b*). The writer noted absence of
epiphytes from cocoa trees when copper fungicide was used to control
black pod, and this toxic effect on epiphytes persisted for at least a year
after spraying had ceased (Thorold 1955*a*). Therefore, a fruit on a sprayed
tree might be without microbial epiphytes and thereby deprived of the
partial protection from infection by *P. palmivora* from which it might
benefit in the absence of fungicide application. It is conceivable that
inefficient spraying may be worse than no spraying.

Parasitic bacteria

Bunting (1927*b*) illustrated and described a disorder of cocoa pods in
Ghana which he referred to as 'stripe disease'. There were reddish-brown
to black discolorations arranged longitudinally along ridges on the surface
of a pod exposed to maximum light. Internal lesions were confined to the
pericarp. They were at first water-soaked in appearance, later becoming

reddish-brown, then slaty and mucilaginous, when they were demarcated by a black border. The whole pericarp ultimately became black and rotten. Bacteria in the lesions were considered to be *Erwinia aroideae* (originally as *Bacillus aroideae*). Little attention was given to this stripe disease of cocoa pods in Ghana, and it may be presumed to be unimportant there.

Possible infection by *Agrobacterium tumefaciens* is considered in Chapter 10.

Fungi

Botryodiplodia theobromae. The term 'warty pod' was applied by Posnette (1943d) but was published previously (Waters 1941) with reference to a disorder of cocoa fruits in Ghana. There were pyramid-shaped protuberances ('warts') scattered over the surfaces of fruits of all ages. These warts were described as soft and water-soaked. *B. theobromae* was isolated from protuberances of different sizes but Wharton (1962) considered that this fungus was probably not primarily responsible for the disorder which might be initiated by insect punctures. He stated that 'losses from this disease are negligible and do not warrant control measures' (Wharton 1962).

Colletotrichum brachytrichum. Corbett (1964) stated that in Malawi this fungus 'forms large ashy-white leaf spots in which the ascervuli appear as distinct black points'. This anthracnose is likely to be amenable to control by fungicide if necessary.

Corticium salmonicolor. The 'pink disease' caused by this fungus is characterized by the bright pinkish colour and coarse hyphae on bark and small branches. There is rapid superficial spread on the tree, but some deeper penetration of tissues may have a ring-barking effect so that distal parts are affected. The extent to which leaves may wilt, turn brown, and fall, depends on the part of the tree which is attacked. Although damage is localized, it may be quite severe. Pink disease occurs when the climate is warm and moist for sufficiently long periods (Burt 1926). The fungus is not host specific (MacFarlane 1968), and the disease it causes has a wide geographical distribution within the tropics and sub-tropics (*C.M.I. Distribution Map No. 122* (1971)).

Manual removal and destruction of affected branches was recommended as a remedial measure (Rorer 1916). Fortnightly applications of Bordeaux mixture controlled pink disease in Trinidad, and there appeared to be at least a twelvemonth residual effect from spraying (Thorold 1953a). Fungicidal control of this disease was exceptionally difficult at an estate in Sabah (Wood 1971).

Corticium stevensii. External rhizomorphic fungal strands occur on above-ground plant-parts in warm and moist climates. The term 'thread blight' was reported by Berkeley (1873) for a malady of tea plantations in India.

Talbot (1965) considered *Corticium stevensii* to be a *Ceratobasidium* species. Dennis (1970) used the character of sclerotia on the rhizomorphic threads to distinguish this thread-blight fungus from *Koleroga noxia* which lacks sclerotia.

Crinipellis sarmentosa. Petch (1915) mentioned that the origin of the term 'horsehair blight' was unknown, and he discussed the uncertain status of this horsehair fungus. Dennis (1952) considered that it seemed to be a rhizomorphic state of *Crinipellis stupparia* (Berk. and Curtis) Pat.

Glomerella cingulata. Several maculicolous species of *Colletotrichum* which are considered to be conidial states of *G. cingulata*, infect leaves, stems, and fruits of cocoa (Desrosiers 1960). *G. cingulata*, commonly reported as *C. gloeosporioides*, has a world-wide distribution on many hosts (MacFarlane 1968). Corbett (1961) reported the conidial state of *G. cingulata* from young cocoa leaves in Malawi, and stated that 'it also caused a pod rot, and in the latter phase may well become serious in the rather severe climatic conditions of the lower Shire River valley'.

Koleroga noxia. Nowell (1923) described thread-blight diseases attributed to *C. stevensii* and *K. noxia*, as *Pellicularia koleroga*. Burt (1918) and Talbot (1965) illustrated and discussed these fungi. They may penetrate leaf tissues, thereby causing localized discoloration, debility, and dieback. Attacks may be controlled by applications of Bordeaux mixture.

Marasmiellus scandens. Bunting and Dade (1924) illustrated and discussed the 'white thread' disease caused by this fungus, which was originally described from Ghana (Dennis and Reid 1957). Shaw (1962) in Papua and New Guinea, and Leston (1970b) in Ghana observed that affected leaves died prematurely.

Leston and Gibbs (1969) believed that *M. scandens* might be spread by *Usingeria mirabilis* Schouteden (Heteroptera, Aradidae) which feeds on mycelia and might disperse viable fragments.

Marasmius equicrinis and *M. trichorhizus.* The status of these taxa is uncertain (Petch 1915; Dennis 1951, 1970; Singer 1964). Horsehair blight fungi commonly lack fructifications (Shaw 1963). Bunting and Dade (1924) illustrated and discussed the appearance of cocoa in Ghana with the horsehair fungus which was considered to be *M. equicrinis*. Occurrences of these fungi are sporadic and seemingly unpredictable. In the course of a survey of cocoa farms in Nigeria, no predilection for any particular cocoa ecoclimate was detected (Thorold 1952).

The tangles of horsehair fungi retain dead leaves. A false impression may be gained of abnormal losses of leaves, because some suspended leaves may have matured and dehisced normally. Attempts to control horsehair blight by fungicide are likely to be unjustifiable economically.

Oncobasidium theobromae. Turner (1967, 1971*b*) discussed various causes of cocoa dieback. Severe dieback was differentiated from minor kinds of dieback in the Territory of Papua and New Guinea since about 1966 (Keane 1971), and since about 1956 in West Malaysia (Turner 1971*b*; Keane and Turner 1972). A new genus was proposed and its *species typica* was described as *Oncobasidium theobromae* Talbot and Keane (1971) (Fig. 9). When first observed at Keravat, New Guinea, mycelium of this fungus emerged from xylem vessels of *Theobroma cacao*; then fruit bodies developed on leaf-scars and adjoining stems. This fungus was isolated from

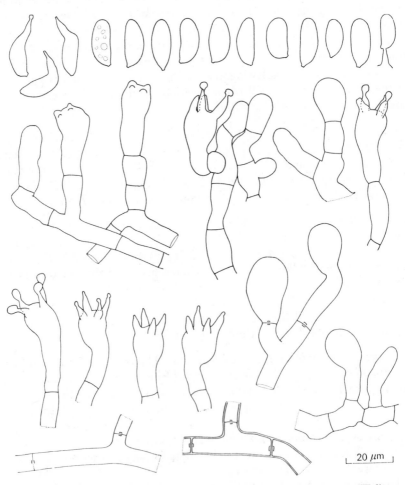

FIG. 9.   Basidiospores, basidia, and hyphae of *Oncobasidium theobromae* (Talbot and Keane 1971).

diseased cocoa stems and was apparently lethal to young (unbranched) seedlings, and was associated with destructive dieback affecting older cocoa plants, as described by Keane, Flentje, and Lamb (1971). They proposed the name 'vascular-streak dieback' because of the characteristic brown-black streaking of the xylem as viewed in longitudinal sections of affected stems. In a detailed account of this disease, Keane, Flentje, and Lamb (1972) explained that the name they proposed distinguished a particular disease from general 'tip-dieback', and in particular replaced the term '*Botryodiplodia* dieback' (Shaw 1962) which was a misnomer.

O. theobromae basidiospore production, deposition, and infection of unhardened cocoa leaves were dependent on rainfall and/or high humidity. The first external indication of infection was a characteristic yellowing of one or two leaves, which might be those of the second or third flush behind the growing tip, but tip leaves of tardily growing stems may discolour first. Such affected leaves shed after a few days (Keane *et al.* 1971, 1972).

Fungicidal control of vascular-streak dieback was not yet developed. Prompt removal of affected stems was recommended, to restrict possible sources of inoculum. There was evidence that some Upper Amazon selections were less affected by this disease than amelonado cocoa (Turner 1971*b*; Keane and Turner 1972).

Phytophthora palmivora. Ainsworth (1971) defined the term 'canker' as 'a plant disease in which there is sharply limited necrosis of the cortical tissue . . .'. The aetiology of cocoa canker is not fully understood because initial infection is cryptic, and manifested tardily, whilst the 'chupon-wilt' symptom (Fig. 4C(c)) is the prompt response to infection of young stems (Rorer 1910*a*; Thorold 1955*b*). The first obvious manifestation of canker may be dieback or debilitation, as a secondary effect from the presence of one or more lesions in the stem. Some early misunderstanding was due to description and study of canker in an advanced stage.

Barrett (1907) visited Trinidad and commented that 'the term "canker" is here used in its broad sense to include the destruction of woody plant tissues by any parasitic fungus. Strictly speaking, cankers are caused by species of the genus *Nectria* . . .'. Much attention was given at first to fungi associated with pod rot and canker which belonged to the order Hypo-creales (*Calonectria, Nectria,* and *Sphaerostilbe* spp.), as discussed by Rorer (1910*a*). He reviewed the studies of pod rot and canker diseases in different countries, from the first definite mention of canker symptoms (Porter 1833) until the successful outcome of his experiments. In Trinidad, in response to stem inoculation with *P. palmivora*, bark became claret coloured. There was generally a surrounding dark line in the bark cambium. This appearance was similar to that of some naturally-occurring cankers. In Ghana, Dade (1928*a*) demonstrated a causal relationship between bark canker and black pod disease. When a canker started, the exposed diseased bark had at first a pale maroon colour, with brighter reddish-brown margin. There were red 'zone lines' which marked the limits of periodical fungal growth. Some blackening of the wood was associated with older bark cankers which attained a maximum length of 5–6 in. (13–15 cm.) (Dade 1929*a*).

Criollo cocoa was mainly affected in the Caroline Islands where several thousand trees were lost in the course of a few years, through canker caused by *P. palmivora*. Inoculations of criollo seedlings or trees up to *ca*. 4 in. (10 cm.) diameter, with either diseased bark or isolates of the causal fungus, were rapidly lethal (11–60 days), since the resulting cankers soon completely encircled the stems. Necrosis of the cambium did not extend into the wood. Trees with large cankers shed most of their leaves and then produced new flushes of smaller leaves. Concurrently, there was abundant flowering but the cherelles failed to develop before trees succumbed. In the course of this dramatic outbreak, there was opportunity to test and successfully demonstrate mechanical transmission. Many healthy trees were infected when pruned with knives which were contaminated through being used to cut affected trees. The frequency of such transmission was lessened by rinsing pruning knives in sodium hypochlorite solution in combination with treatment of cut surfaces with tar. Such treatment was successful for early stage cankers but severely diseased trees were removed and burnt (Zaiger and Zentmyer 1965).

In Fiji, Firman and Vernon (1970) and Firman and Sundaram (1970) used local isolates of *P. palmivora* to inoculate stems of seedling populations and clonal selections, to observe their reactions to infection under controlled conditions in relation to their response to natural infection. At first the inoculation was by insertion of small pieces of agar cultures of *P. palmivora* into bark flaps, which measured 25 mm. × 10 mm. on 4-year-old trees (Firman and Vernon 1970). Later, the preferred procedure was the insertion of infected pieces of agar beneath disks of bark removed with a cork borer, thereby measurement of a canker was facilitated because the wound was smaller and neater than that of the bark flap (Firman and Sundaram 1970). Responses to inoculation were measured at intervals within periods up to 23 weeks from inoculation, and assessed in terms of scar length and width, and cambial spread with or without secondary outbreaks. Natural infections were assessed by awarding marks (1–5) by scoring trees for number of lesions and their condition ('active' or otherwise). Although duration of *P. palmivora* at the inoculation site and cambial spread were probably more important than scar length, the latter criterion of susceptibility was more objective (Firman and Vernon 1970). Firman and Sundaram (1970) stated that 'scar length was sufficiently discriminatory for numerical analysis'.

Mycological investigations of cocoa dieback or debilitation have shown that several fungi may participate at different times in various countries.

In cankers, there may be a succession of fungi (*P. palmivora* and *Calonectria rigidiuscula*), each having periods of more or less vigorous and suppressed activity (Firman and Vernon 1970; Firman and Sundaram 1970). It is possible that early occurrence of *P. palmivora* may have been overlooked in the succession of fungi (*C. rigidiuscula* and *B. theobromae*) associated with mirid attack (Chapter 9), as discussed by Owen (1956).

Necrotic bark from the margin of active lesions often yields *C. rigidiuscula*. A special medium containing antibiotics described by Eckert and Tsao (1960, 1962) may be needed to obtain *P. palmivora* from canker lesions (Zaiger and Zentmyer 1965). Waterhouse and Stamps (1969) noted that *Phytophthora* spp. usually outgrew bacteria on water agar, except under tropical conditions when there might be considerable bacterial contamination so that an antibiotic was necessary. Bacterial activity may be associated with the deliquescence and exudation of reddish liquid from cankers reported by Nowell (1923) in the West Indies, by Bunting and Dade (1924) in West Africa, and in the Caroline Islands (Zaiger and Zentmyer 1965).

Trachysphaera fructigena. This fungus causes 'mealy pod' disease in Ghana, which was illustrated and described by Bunting and Dade (1924). The vegetative parts of cocoa trees are not attacked. *T. fructigena* occurs in tropical Africa (*C.M.I. Distribution Map No. 249* (1971)), on species of four genera (*Coffea, Mimusops, Musa, Theobroma*). Holliday (1970c) gave a description and illustrated the conidia, oogonia, and antheridia of *T. fructigena*. He stated that this fungus 'can only infect wounded cacao pods . . .'. Bunting and Dade (1924) observed in the field that pods were infected when otherwise apparently undamaged, whilst the fungus grew on otherwise unwounded detached pods kept in moist chambers. However, under field and laboratory conditions, damage facilitates infection by *T. fructigena*. At Tafo, Ghana, pods damaged by rodents (Chapter 5) were infected either by *T. fructigena* or by *B. theobromae* (Anon. 1953a). These two fungi are readily distinguishable by coloration and gross morphological characters. Microscopical examination or isolation and culture of the pathogen concerned may be necessary sometimes to distinguish between 'mealy pod' and 'black pod' caused by *P. palmivora*. They can generally be distinguished because *T. fructigena* attacks nearly mature pods, not fruits of all ages as does *P. palmivora*. The brown spot which develops following infection by the latter is clearly defined in contrast to the diffuse brown coloration of the lesion following infection by *T. fructigena* (Fig. 4D(a, b)). The white to pinkish-brown masses of conidia are produced promptly and more abundantly than the sporangia of *P. palmivora*. The latter pathogen is harmful because it commonly destroys the beans through infecting immature fruits. Invasion of nearly mature fruits by *T. fructigena* may not reach or extend beyond the testae of the seeds.

Algae

Cephaleuros virescens. Rorer (1918*b*) suggested the name 'algal disease' for the disorder due to attack by *C. virescens*. A reddish pigmentation is associated with carotenoid, referred to as haematochrome (Prescott 1969). Because of this coloration and since the outbreaks were noticed particularly where cocoa trees were unduly exposed, this disease seemed to be similar to the disorder affecting other trees, referred to as 'sun scald' or 'red rust' (Mann and Hutchinson 1904, 1907). 'Sun scald' was an unsuitable appellation because this disease was not restricted to over-exposed cocoa. 'Red rust' was a misnomer because there was no connection with true 'rust', caused by species of Uredinales, which do not attack cocoa.

In Trinidad, the branches of cocoa trees affected by algal disease lost their leaves and sometimes died from their tips. In the dry season, affected stems had dark purplish or black spots which sometimes coalesced. During the wet season, a yellowish, or rusty-red velvet-like bloom developed on the spots (Rorer 1918*b*). Nowell (1923) discussed abnormal growing conditions which might promote algal-disease damage. In S. Tomé, severe debilitation of cocoa trees by algal disease, was associated with thrips *(Selenothrips rubrocinctus)* attack (Urich 1928).

The severity of algal disease depends upon environmental conditions, but probably also upon pathogenicity. In his redescription of *C. virescens*, Printz (1939) noted its variability and commented that several different species might be included under this name. Joubert and Rijkenberg (1971) stated that 'it is evident that the taxonomy of the genus *Cephaleuros* is in need of revision'.

Sporangia are formed on the vertical threads constituting the 'bloom' on the branches. The sporangia produce biflagellate zoospores which may enter stomata, to form a thallus of several layers of algal threads beneath the epidermis (Fritsch 1965). Entrance may also be via cracks in the bark.

Shaw (1962) reported another species *(C. minimus)*, on young cocoa twigs, but not apparently on the leaves. *C. minimus* occurred particularly on twigs of inadequately shaded cocoa (Shaw, D. E. *in litt.* 1964, 1970, 1971), notably in the Markham valley, near Lae (see map, in Shaw, Gee, and Dunn 1958). The extent of penetration into the cocoa host could not be determined from material recently examined, which was unsuitable for sectioning (Hibberd, D. J. *in litt.* 1970, 1971).

Trentepohlia spp. occur on trunks and branches of cocoa trees, generally as green growths where shaded, and varying through yellow to orange-red in well-lighted situations (Fritsch 1965). These algae tend to follow the flow of rain, as they do on buildings in the tropics (Whiteley 1966). In the absence of evidence to the contrary, it is assumed that these epiphytic algae are harmless to cocoa. They are mentioned here because they may be confused with *Cephaleuros* spp. Bourelly (1966) provided a key for the separation of the genera *Cephaleuros, Phycopeltis,* and *Trentepohlia.*

Lichens.

Corticolous species. *Temnospora fulgens* was common and conspicuous on cocoa trunks in Nigeria. It was difficult to separate from the bark, as noticed by Harper and Letcher (1966). They showed that pinastric acid is a constituent of this lichen. Otherwise, except for about eight species on cocoa in the genera *Anaptychia, Parmelia, Physica,* and *Ramalina* considered by Culberson (1969, 1970), the chemical constituents of lichens reported on cocoa have not been studied. Since some lichen substances are antibiotic (Hale 1967), it is possible that some corticolous lichens occurring on cocoa may have anti-fungal properties. Infection of stems by fungi might thereby be prevented or delayed. Since mature amelonado trunks in Nigeria were generally more or less completely covered by corticolous lichens except when shade suppressed them (Thorold 1952), it is worth noting that canker (caused by *P. palmivora*) and pink disease (caused by *C. salmonicolor*) occurred infrequently in Nigeria where shade was seldom excessive.

Foliicolous species. Last and Deighton (1965) considered the common epiphytes of living leaves and noted the occurrence of lichens on leaves in the wet tropics.

There are no stomata on the upper surface of cocoa leaves (Evans and Murray 1953*b*). Fordham (1972) gave stereoscan photographs which show the distribution of wax particles on the upper surface, and the distribution of stomata on the lower surface.

In common with the generality of foliicolous lichens on various hosts, the species on cocoa are epiphyllous and mostly occur supracuticularly. Species of the genus *Strigula* occur subcuticularly, but do not penetrate the epidermis and invade the leaf tissue, as explained by Santesson (1952). He depicted *S. nemathora* on a cocoa leaf.

Limited observations indicated that foliicolous lichens might only become well developed when cocoa leaves in Nigeria were about 12 months old (Thorold 1952). Unlike corticolous lichens, they mostly become fertile very quickly. *Phyllophiale alba* is exceptional because this monotypic genus lacks fructification. This lichen is dispersed and propagated by dish-like isidia incorporating both algal and fungal tissues, whilst most foliicolous lichens are without isidia (Santesson 1952).

Bryophytes

None of the bryophytes is parasitic (Garjeanne 1932). Their occurrence on cocoa is influenced by amounts of illumination and moisture (Richards 1932), and at least that of the mosses by the supply of mineral nutrients, as discussed for some species in Britain by Grubb, Flint, and Gregory (1969). They suggested that mosses may benefit through compounds originating from nitrogen-fixing bacteria on leaves and bark. By accumulating dust and debris, the more robust bryophytes in particular may conserve nutrients for slow release later. These compounds may reach the cocoa roots either through leaching by rain, or through decomposition when bryophyte colonies are dislodged or shed with part of the stem-system on which they are growing.

Ferns

Richards (1952) discussed the accumulation of humus and debris by 'bracket epiphytes', exemplified by species of the genera *Drynaria* and *Platycerium* having two kinds of fronds. These epiphytes may benefit cocoa trees through contributing to soil fertility, in a manner similar to that indicated for bryophytes.

Flowering plants

Acanthosyris paulo-alvinii. This parasitic tree grew to a height of over 66 ft. (20 m.) in the cocoa-growing areas of southern Bahia, especially in the municipalities of Canavieiras and Una, where it was referred to as 'mata cacau' because old cocoa trees near to it died and younger ones failed to develop (Reis 1938). *A. paulo-alvinii* trees had few branches and sparse foliage, so that their harmful effect on cocoa was not through casting too much shade. Their roots were thick and fleshy, with protuberances from which 'shoots' emerged. The root system radiated widely (> 10 m.) but not deeply (1–30 cm.), and apparently without adversely depleting the soil moisture. Reis (1938) considered that the cocoa possibly suffered through toxins excreted by the roots of the other plant. This supposition was not substantiated experimentally. Alvim and Seeschaaf (1968) studied 'mata cacau' as *A. paulo-alvimii* (it was described and named *A. paulo-alvinii* by Barroso 1968). Cocoa trees near (2–3 m.) *A. paulo-alvinii*, did not invariably show dieback although they were not normally vigorous. Under experimental conditions, cocoa seedlings did not suffer through proximity of *Acanthosyris* when their root systems were separated by an impenetrable barrier. When both kinds of plant were grown together in the same container without separation of root systems, the cocoa died or showed dieback symptoms within a period of 11 months. Examination of associated root systems showed that *Acanthosyris* roots formed haustoria which penetrated cocoa tap-roots and reached the phloem region but not the xylem. Haustoria were not formed when *Acanthosyris* roots were in contact with other kinds of cocoa roots (see Chapter 11, pp. 145–6).

Bromeliaceae. In the western hemisphere, 'tank' epiphytes (Richards 1952) which belong to the family Bromeliaceae, may affect the nutrition and eco-climate of cocoa trees. When they fall or are dislodged, 'tank brome-liads' add water and nutrients to the soil, because the liquid they hold contains decomposing organic matter (Fonaroff 1966). *Gravisia aquilega*, which occurs on cocoa, may hold a quarter of a gallon, whilst a large arboreal species (*Glomeropitcairnia erectiflora* Mez), may hold 1 gal. (Pittendrigh 1948).

Two species of *Erythrina* referred to collectively as 'immortelles' and specifically as 'Anauca' (*E. poeppigiana* (Walp.) O. F. Cook) and 'Bocare' (*E. glauca* Willd.) were commonly used to shade cocoa trees in Trinidad, particularly the latter in the lower and wetter areas. An average immortelle shade-tree spacing in mature cocoa was 24 ft. × 48 ft. (7·3 m. × 14·6 m.), or *ca.* 38 trees per acre (Thorold 1945*b*).

The crown and branches of the Bocare immortelle were generally colonized by epiphytes, mainly Bromeliaceae (Pittendrigh 1948; Fonaroff 1966). *G. aquilega* was a prevalent bromeliad and its average frequency was about fourteen per tree (Pittendrigh 1950*c*).

Smith (1953) discussed attempts to eradicate or control bromeliads because 'bromelicolous anophelines' breed in the water they contain. In Trinidad, two such species of mosquito were considered to be important (Pittendrigh 1950*a,b*). *Anopheles bellator* Dyar and Knab is known to be a malaria vector, but the vectorial capacity of *A. homunculus* Komp was not conclusively established (Fonaroff 1966). Copper sulphate solution was propelled into immortelles to destroy bromeliads at 15–25 ft. (4·5–7·6 m.) above ground, where the greatest larval frequencies occurred (Fonaroff 1966). Charles (1959) discussed the incidence of *A. bellator* malaria in Guyana, in relation to possible spread of cocoa cultivation there. Ferreira, Corrêa, Tomich, and De Sá (1969) discussed the need to destroy brome-liads in southern Brazil. Simazine gave excellent control of *Tillandsia recurvata* L. (Cardenas 1971).

Loranthaceae. Dalziel (1937) referred to *Loranthus* spp. as 'African mistle-toe'. Species of Loranthaceae were sometimes called 'mistletoe' in Trinidad (Williams and Williams 1951). Willis (1948) accepted this generalized use of the trivial name which is especially applicable to *Viscum album* L. in temperate countries. The genus *Loranthus* has been subdivided (Keay 1958), but 'not very satisfactorily' according to Hutchinson (1969).

Various mistletoes damaged permanent crops in Ghana (Bunting and Dade 1924) and elsewhere, including Costa Rica (Kuijt 1969). Room (1971*a,b*) studied the damage caused by *Tapinanthus bangwensis* in West Africa. Attachment of the parasite to the cocoa host was by a haustorium, the growth of which, together with that of surrounding host tissues, formed a cankerous growth referred to as the 'junction'. This hypertrophy might attain a volume of 800 ml.

The succulent part of the fruit was eaten by birds (unspecified), which might deposit the seeds on cocoa trees. Infection was aided by the seed being covered with a viscous substance which set hard after exposure to the air. The bark needed to be thin enough for initial haustorial penetration. Another factor determining successful establishment of *T. bangwensis* was the degree of insolation. Heavily shaded farms were without mistletoe, whilst cocoa trees with some shade had a smaller proportion of infested trees (*ca.* 6 per cent) than unshaded cocoa trees (*ca.* 37 per cent infested). An infested tree tended to occur next to other infested trees. Such groups of affected cocoa trees were referred to as 'pockets'.

The part of the cocoa branch beyond (i.e. distal to) the point of attack was invariably killed through occlusion accompanied by hypertrophy. Deep penetration of the haustorium severed the nutrient supply to the distal part of the cocoa branch. Experimental subjection of leaves of host and parasite to radioactive carbon dioxide (from ^{14}C barium carbonate) showed that the parasite took products of photosynthesis from its cocoa host, but photosynthates produced by the parasite were not translocated to the host.

Mistletoes should be removed regularly. In West Africa, August was a suitable time, for two reasons. There was generally a peak flowering then, so that the parasite was conspicuous, and this time would be coincident with an inter-crop period when labour should be available for mistletoe control. Future chemical control of mistletoe was conceivable but available herbicides were not sufficiently specific, safe, or cheap (Room 1970).

Thonningia sanguinea. This root parasite has a wide distribution in the forest areas of tropical Africa, where it attacks the roots of indigenous and introduced trees, including cocoa and Para rubber (Dalziel 1937; Bullock 1948). The subterranean rhizome may be several feet long, it becomes tuberous at the point of attachment to the host (Keay 1958).

Occurrences of Parasites, Saprophytes, and Epiphytes

Bacteria

Agrobacterium tumefaciens (E. F. Smith and Townsend) Conn

AFRICA: Ghana (Dade 1940, uncertain determination as *Bacterium tumefaciens* associated with trunk hyperplasia; Brunt and Wharton 1962*b*, isolates from galls, buds, and cushions resembled *A. tumefaciens*). SOUTH AMERICA: Colombia (Garcés 1941, as *B. tumefaciens,* supposed cause of cushion hypertrophy).

Azotobacter agilis Beijerinck

SOUTH AMERICA: Surinam (Ruinen 1961, on leaf).

Azotobacter chroococcum Beijerinck

SOUTH AMERICA: Surinam (Ruinen 1961, on leaves).

Azotobacter vinelandii Lipman

SOUTH AMERICA: Surinam (Ruinen 1961, on leaves).

Bacillus aroideae Townsend
see *Erwinia aroideae* (Townsend) Holland
Bacterium tumefaciens E. F. Smith and Townsend
see *Agrobacterium tumefaciens* (E. F. Smith and Townsend) Conn
Erwinia aroideae (Townsend) Holland
   AFRICA: Ghana (Bunting 1927*b*, uncertain determination as *Bacillus aroideae* associated with 'stripe disease' of pods).

Fungi

Acrostalagmus cinnabarinus Corda
see *Nectria inventa* Pethybridge
Aleurodiscus acerinus (Pers.) Höhnel and Litsch.
   ASIA: Indonesia (Java) (Burt 1924).
Alternaria consortiale (Thüm.) Hughes
see *Ulocladium consortiale* (Thüm.) Simmons
Androsaceus equicrinis (Müll.) Pat.
see *Marasmius equicrinis* Müll.
Annellophora borneoensis M. B. Ellis
   ASIA: Sabah (Ellis 1965, 1971, on leaves).
Anthostomella bahiensis (Hempel) Speg.
see *Calonectria bahiensis* Hempel
Anthracophyllum nigritum (Lév.) Kalchbr.
   ASIA: Philippines (Teodoro 1937, on dead wood).
Anthromycopsis filiformis Pat.
   AFRICA: S. Tomé (Patouillard 1922*b*).
Apiospora montagnei Sacc.
   WEST INDIES: Jamaica (Leather 1967, as *Papularia arundinis,* on stem).
   ASIA: Sri Lanka (Petch 1925*a*, as *Epicoccum theobromae,* on leaves).
Armillaria mellea (Vahl ex Fr.) Kummer
see *Armillariella mellea* (Vahl ex Fr.) P. Karst.
Armillariella mellea (Vahl ex Fr.) P. Karst.
   AFRICA: Cameroon (S.E.) (Grimaldi 1954*a*, as *Armillaria mellea*); Congo (Steyaert 1948); Fernando Po (Nosti 1953); Ghana (Dade 1940); Ivory Coast (Mallamaire 1935*a*); Nigeria (Bailey 1966); Sierra Leone (Deighton 1956); S. Tomé (Gravier 1907); Uganda (Hansford 1943*a*). CENTRAL AMERICA: Mexico (Zevada, Yerkes, and Niederhauser 1955). SOUTH AMERICA: Brazil (Averna-Saccá 1920); Colombia (Polania 1957). WEST INDIES: Dominican Republic (Ciferri 1961, uncertain determination). AUSTRA-LASIA: Papua and New Guinea (Dumbleton 1954).
Armillariella tabescens (Scop. ex Fr.) Singer
   AFRICA: Malagasy (Madagascar) (Orian 1954, as *Clitocybe tabescens*).
Asbolisia citrina Bat. and Cif.
   WEST INDIES: Haiti (Batista and Ciferri 1963, on leaves).
Aspergillus delacroixii Sacc. and Syd.
see *Aspergillus olivaceus* Delacr.
Aspergillus elegans Gasperini
   WEST INDIES: Jamaica (Leather 1967, associated with pod rot).

Aspergillus ochraceus Wilhelm
WEST INDIES: Dominican Republic (Ciferri 1927*b*, on pods).
Aspergillus olivaceus Delacr.
ASIA: Philippines (Teodoro 1937, as *A. delacroixii*, on pods).
Aspergillus parasiticus Speare
AFRICA: Ghana (Nicol, Owen, and Strickland 1950, introduced, and parasitized *Planococcoides njalensis*, under laboratory conditions).
Aspergillus phoenicis (Corda) Thom
WEST INDIES: Dominican Republic (Ciferri 1942, on pods, associated with damage by *Melanerpes striatus* (see Chapter 5)).
Aspergillus terreus Thom
ASIA: Sabah (Williams 1965*b*, from mirid lesion on pod).
Aspergillus ustus (Bain.) Thom and Church
AFRICA: Cameroon (S.W.) (Anon. 1968, from mirid lesion); Ghana (Owen 1956, from artificial stem-lesion).
Aspergillus versicolor (Vuill.) Tirab.
ASIA: Sabah (Williams 1965*b*, from mirid lesion on pod).
Asterostomella paraguayensis Speg.
UNLOCALIZED: (Seymour 1929).
Auerswaldia maxima Massee
AFRICA: Cameroon (S.E.) (Grimaldi 1954*a*, on branches).
Auricularia auricula (Hook.) Underw.
AUSTRALASIA: Papua and New Guinea (Shaw 1963, as *A. auricula-judae*, probably incorrectly determined (Lowy 1952)).
Auricularia auricula-judae (L. ex Fr.) Schroet.
see *Auricularia auricula* (Hook.) Underw.
Auricularia cornea (Ehrenb. ex Fr.) Ehrenb. ex Endl.
ASIA: Philippines (Teodoro 1937, as *Hirneola cornea*, on dead wood).
Auricularia delicata (Fr.) P. Henn.
AFRICA: Sierra Leone (Herb. Kew, on stump).
Auricularia fuscosuccinea (Mont.) Farl.
CENTRAL AMERICA: Costa Rica (Lowy, B. 1969 *in litt.*, on rotting wood); Mexico (Lowy, B. 1969 *in litt.*, on rotting wood)
Auricularia mesenterica Pers.
ASIA: Philippines (Teodoro 1937, on dead branches).
Auricularia polytricha (Mont.) Sacc.
CENTRAL AMERICA: Mexico (Lowy, B. 1969 *in litt.*, on rotting wood). WEST INDIES: Guadeloupe (Duss 1903, on live stems). ASIA: Philippines Teodoro 1937, on dead branches).
Beltrania africana Hughes
AFRICA: Ghana (Hughes 1952, on dead branches).
Botryodiplodia elasticae Petch
see *Botryodiplodia theobromae* Pat.
Botryodiplodia theobromae Pat.
AFRICA: Cameroon (S.E.) (Grimaldi 1954*a*); Cameroon (S.W.) (Hennings 1895, as *Diplodia cacaoicola*); Congo (Buyckx 1953, as *Lasiodiplodia theobromae*); Dahomey (Berthault 1913); Fernando Po (Nosti 1953); Gabon (Krug and Quartey-Papafio 1964); Ghana (Hughes 1953); Guinea (Spanish)

(Resplandy, Chevaugeon, Delassus, and Luc 1954); Malagasy (Madagascar) (Bouriquet 1946); Malawi (Corbett 1964, 1965); Mozambique (Anon. 1956); Nigeria (West 1938); Principe (Navel 1921); Sierra Leone (Deighton 1956); S. Tomé (da Camara and Cannas Mendes 1910, as *Macrophoma scaphidiospora*); Tanzania (Tanganyika) (Riley 1960); Tanzania (Zanzibar) (Briant 1959); Uganda (Small 1915, as *Thyridaria tarda*). CENTRAL AMERICA: Costa Rica (McLaughlin 1956); El Salvador (Ancalmo 1959, as *Diplodia natalensis*, and as *D. theobromae*); Guatemala (Palm 1932); Mexico (Limón 1945); Nicaragua (Litzenberger and Stevenson 1957). SOUTH AMERICA: Bolivia (Alandia and Bell 1957); Brazil (Averna-Saccá 1920); Colombia (Polania 1957); Ecuador (Desrosiers and Diaz 1956a); Guyana (Martyn 1933); Peru (Crandall and Javier Dieguez 1948); Surinam (van Hall, A. E. and Drost 1909): Venezuela (Müller 1941). WEST INDIES: Cuba (Cook and Otero 1939); Dominica (Howard 1901b); Dominican Republic (Ciferri 1961, as *Macrophoma vestita*; Voorhees 1942, as *Physalospora rhodina*); Grenada (Howard 1901b); Haiti (Orellana 1956a); Jamaica (Larter and Martyn 1943); Martinique (Baker 1940); Puerto Rico (Fragoso and Ciferri 1928); St. Lucia (Howard 1901b); St. Vincent (Howard 1901b); Trinidad (Baker and Dale 1951). ASIA: Brunei (Peregrine 1972); Indonesia (Java) (Hubert 1957); Malaysia (West) (Thompson and Johnston 1953); Philippines (Saccardo 1916); Sabah (Anon. 1972b); Sarawak (Turner 1967); Sri Lanka (Petch 1906, as *Chaetodiplodia grisea*); Thailand (Chandrasrikul 1962); Vietnam (Bugnicourt 1932). AUSTRALASIA: British Solomon Islands (Johnston 1960b); Fiji (Harwood 1959); New Hebrides (Dadant 1953); Papua and New Guinea (Thrower 1960a); Samoa (American) (Dumbleton 1954); Samoa (West) (Johnston 1963c); Samoa (Appel and Laubert 1906, as *Lasiodiplodia nigra*). UNLOCALIZED: (Seymour 1929, as *Botryodiplodia elasticae*).

Botryosphaeria minuscula Sacc.

ASIA: Philippines (Saccardo 1916, on moribund branches).

Calonectria bahiensis Hempel

SOUTH AMERICA: Brazil (Hempel 1904; Spegazzini 1906b, as *Anthostomella bahiensis*).

Calonectria cremea Zimm.

CENTRAL AMERICA: Mexico (Zevada *et al.* 1955). ASIA: Indonesia (Java) (Zimmermann 1901a, b); Sri Lanka (Petch 1910b). AUSTRALASIA: Samoa (Gehrmann 1913, as *Nectria cremea* auct., not *N. cremea* Grimaldi).

Calonectria diploa (Berk. and Curt.) Wollenw.

ASIA: Indonesia (Java) (Zimmermann 1901a,b, as *Nectria coffeicola*, on pods).

Calonectria flavida Massee

see *Calonectria rigidiuscula* (Berk. and Br.) Sacc.

Calonectria gigaspora Massee

WEST INDIES: Unlocalized (Roger 1953).

Calonectria rigidiuscula (Berk. and Br.) Sacc.

AFRICA: Cameroon (S.E.) (Grimaldi 1954b); Cameroon (S.W.) (Brick 1908, as *Fusarium decemcellulare*); Congo (Buyckx 1953); Ghana (Crowdy 1947); Guinea (Spanish) (Booth 1960); Ivory Coast (Resplandy *et al.* 1954); Malagasy

(Madagascar) (Bouriquet 1946); Nigeria (Bailey 1966); Sierra Leone (Deighton 1956); Uganda (Hansford 1943*a*). CENTRAL AMERICA: Costa Rica (Ford *et al.* 1967, as *Fusarium rigidiusculum*); Mexico (Zevada *et al.* 1967, as *Calonectria flavida*); Panama (Reinking and Wollenweber 1927). SOUTH AMERICA: Brazil (Averna-Saccá 1920); Colombia (Booth 1960); Ecuador (Hansen 1963*a*); Surinam (van Hall 1909, as *Spicaria colorans* (*Fusarium spicaria-colorantis*)); Venezuela (Hansen 1963*a*). WEST INDIES: Dominican Republic (Hansen 1963*a*); Grenada (Booth 1960); Jamaica (Seaver 1928, as *Scoleconectria tetraspora*); Trinidad (Baker and Dale 1951, as *Calonectria tetraspora*). ASIA: Brunei (Johnston 1965); Indonesia (Anon. 1960); Malaysia (West) (Johnston 1960*a*); Philippines (Gandia 1962); Sabah (Anon. 1973); Sarawak (Johnston 1960*d*); Sri Lanka (Petch 1920, as *Nectria rigidiuscula*); Vietnam (Bugnicourt 1939). AUSTRALASIA: British Solomon Islands (Johnston 1960*b*); Caroline Islands (Zaiger and Zentmyer 1965); Fiji (Firman 1972); New Hebrides (Johnston 1963*b*); Papua and New Guinea (Shaw 1963); Samoa (West) (Johnston 1963*c*); West Irian (Johnston 1961).

Calonectria tetraspora (Seaver) Sacc. and Trott.
see *Calonectria rigidiuscula* (Berk. and Br.) Sacc.

Calospora bahiensis Speg.
  SOUTH AMERICA: Brazil (Spegazzini 1906*b*).

Calospora theobromae Camara
  AFRICA: S. Tomé (da Camara 1925, on bark).

Calostilbe striispora (Ellis and Everh.) Seaver
  AFRICA: Malagasy (Madagascar) (Bouriquet 1946). SOUTH AMERICA: Surinam (van Suchtelen 1955*a*, associated with bark disease and dieback); Venezuela (Malaguti and Sirotti 1952). WEST INDIES: Jamaica (Ashby 1915, as *Sphaerostilbe musarum*, on cankered branches); Trinidad (Seaver 1928, as *Macbridella striispora*).

Camarosporium megalosporum Camara
  AFRICA: S. Tomé (da Camara and Cannas Mendes 1910, on bark).

Candida parapsilosis (Ashford) Langeron and Talice
  AFRICA: Ivory Coast (Ruinen 1963*a*, as *C. parapsilosis* var. *intermedia*, from leaves).

Candida parapsilosis (Ashford) Langeron and Talice var. *intermedia* van Rij and Verona
see *Candida parapsilosis* (Ashford) Langeron and Talice

Capnodium brasiliense Puttemans
  AFRICA: Uganda (Snowden 1921, on leaves).

Cephalosporium acremonium Corda
  AFRICA: Ghana (Turner 1960*d*, from pod).

Cephalosporium humicola Oudem.
  AFRICA: Ghana (Turner 1960*d*, from pod).

Ceratocarpia theobromae von Faber
  AFRICA: Cameroon (S.W.) (von Faber 1909, associated with *Meliola theobromae*, on leaves).

Ceratocystis fimbriata Ellis and Halst.
  CENTRAL AMERICA: Costa Rica (Siller 1958, as *Ceratostomella fimbriata*); Guatemala (Schieber and Sosa 1960); Mexico (Desrosiers and Diaz 1956*b*).

SOUTH AMERICA: Brazil (Knoke 1965); Colombia (Arbelaez 1957, as *Ophiostoma fimbriatum*); Ecuador (Desrosiers and Diaz 1956b); Guyana (Bisessar 1965); Peru (Krug and Quartey-Papafio 1964); Venezuela (Malaguti 1952, 1963). WEST INDIES: Dominican Republic (Schieber 1969); Haiti (Orellana 1956a); Trinidad (Baker 1936; Iton 1959, 1961). ASIA: Philippines (Eloja and Gandia 1963); Sri Lanka (Speyer 1923, probably occurred in association with *Xyleborus fornicatus* Eichh. attack (see Chapter 8)). AUSTRALASIA: Fiji (Graham 1965); Papua and New Guinea (Szent-Ivany 1963, probably occurred in association with *X. confusus* Eichh. attack).

Ceratocystis moniliformis (Hedgc.) C. Moreau
CENTRAL AMERICA: Costa Rica (Barba and Hansen 1962a, uncertain determination).

Ceratocystis moniliformis (Hedgc.) C. Moreau forma *theobromae* Luc
AFRICA: Malagasy (Madagascar) (Luc 1952, as *Ophiostoma moniliforme* forma *theobromae*, from root).

Ceratocystis paradoxa (Dade) C. Moreau
AFRICA: Cameroon (S.W.) (Grimaldi 1954b, as *Thielaviopsis ethaceticus*, from pods); Ghana (Dade 1928c, as *Ceratostomella paradoxa*, on husks); Nigeria (Gorenz 1972b, pods infected). CENTRAL AMERICA: Costa Rica (Hansen 1964, from pod rot, associated with damage by *Psilorhinus morio* (see Chapter 5). SOUTH AMERICA: Ecuador (Desrosiers and Diaz 1956a). WEST INDIES: Jamaica (Larter and Martyn 1943); Trinidad (Baker and Dale 1951). UNLOCALIZED: (Seymour 1929, as *Thielaviopsis paradoxa*).

Ceratostomella fimbriata (Ellis and Halst.) Elliott
see *Ceratocystis fimbriata* Ellis and Halst.

Ceratostomella paradoxa Dade
see *Ceratocystis paradoxa* (Dade) C. Moreau

Cesatiella polyphragmospora Camara
AFRICA: S. Tomé (da Camara and Cannas Mendes 1910, on bark).

Chaetodiplodia grisea Petch
see *Botryodiplodia theobromae* Pat.

Chaetomium funicola Cooke
AFRICA: Ghana (Anon. 1973, from root tissue-culture); Sierra Leone (Herb. I.M.I., from root).

Chaetospermum chaetosporum (Pat.) A. L. Smith and Ramsbottom
AUSTRALASIA: New Hebrides (Huguenin 1964).

Chaetospermum elasticae Koord.
AFRICA: Nigeria (Waterston, J. M. 1959 *in litt.*, on husk). ASIA: Indonesia (Java) (Zimmermann 1902, on pods); Sri Lanka (Petch and Bisby 1950, as *Ciliospora gelatinosa*).

Chaetothyrium boedijnii Hansf.
AUSTRALASIA: New Britain (Herb. I.M.I., on leaves); Papua and New Guinea (Shaw 1963).

Chaetothyrium vermisporum Hansf. var. *glabrum* Hansf.
AUSTRALASIA: New Guinea (Hansford 1957, on leaves).

Chaetothyrium womersleyi Hansf.
AUSTRALASIA: Papua and New Guinea (Shaw 1963).

Chlamydomyces palmarum (Cooke) Mason
AFRICA: Sierra Leone (Herb. I.M.I., on pods). ASIA: Malaysia (West) (Herb. I.M.I.).

Choanephora cucurbitarum (Berk. and Rav.) Thaxt.
AFRICA: Cameroon (S.E.) (Grimaldi 1952); Ghana (Dade 1929c, on husks).

Ciliciopodium theobromae Camara
AFRICA: S. Tomé (da Camara 1920, on pods).

Ciliospora gelatinosa Zimm.
see *Chaetospermum elasticae* Koord.

Circinella muscae (Sorokine) Berl. and de Toni
SOUTH AMERICA: Colombia (Chardon and Toro 1930, as *Circinella spinosa*, associated with Monilia disease lesions (see Chapter 3)).

Circinella spinosa van Tiegh. and Le Monnier
see *Circinella muscae* (Sorokine) Berl. and de Toni

Cladoderris infundibuliformis (Klotzsch) Fr.
AFRICA: Sierra Leone (Herb. I.M.I., from trunk).

Cladoderris spongiosa Fr.
AFRICA: Nigeria (Wakefield 1917, on dead branches).

Cladosporium cladosporioides (Fres.) de Vries
AFRICA: Ghana (Turner 1960d, as *Hormodendrum cladosporioides,* from pod).

Cladosporium herbarum (Pers.) Link ex S. F. Gray
WEST INDIES: Dominican Republic (Ciferri 1927b, on pods).

Cladosporium theobromicola Averna-Saccá
SOUTH AMERICA: Brazil (Averna-Saccá 1920, on leaves).

Clitocybe tabescens (Scop. ex Fr.) Bres.
see *Armillariella tabescens* (Scop. ex Fr.) Singer

Clonostachys theobromae Delacr.
SOUTH AMERICA: Colombia (Delacroix 1897, on pods).

Clypeosphaeria theobromicola Speg.
SOUTH AMERICA: Brazil (Spegazzini 1906b, on bark).

Coccoidella stevensonii (Cif. and Bat.) E. Müller
CENTRAL AMERICA: Guatemala (Ciferri and Batista 1957, as *Systremma stevensonii,* on dry leaves).

Cochliobolus geniculatus Nelson
AFRICA: Ghana (Herb. I.M.I., from bark). AUSTRALASIA: New Hebrides (Dumbleton 1954, as *Curvularia geniculata*).

Colletotrichum brachytrichum Delacr.
AFRICA: Cape Province (Verwoerd and du Plessis 1933, on leaves); Ivory Coast (Mallamaire 1935b); Malawi (Corbett 1964, associated with leaf spot). WEST INDIES: Dominican Republic (Ciferri 1961); Trinidad (Delacroix 1905, on leaves). ASIA: Malaysia (West) (Johnston 1960a); Sabah (Berwick 1964, on leaves); Sri Lanka (Petch and Bisby 1950, on leaves).

Colletotrichum coffeanum Noack
see *Glomerella cingulata* (Stonem.) Spauld. and Schrenk

Colletotrichum cradwickii Bancroft
see *Glomerella cingulata* (Stonem.) Spauld. and Schrenk

Colletotrichum fructi-theobromae Averna-Saccá
SOUTH AMERICA: Brazil (Averna-Saccá 1925, on pods).

Colletotrichum gloeosporioides (Penz.) Sacc.

see *Glomerella cingulata* (Stonem.) Spauld. and Schrenk

Colletotrichum gloeosporioides (Penz.) Sacc. var. *minus* Simmons

see *Glomerella cingulata* (Stonem.) Spauld. and Schrenk var. *minor* Wollenw.

Colletotrichum incarnatum Zimm.

see *Glomerella cingulata* (Stonem.) Spauld. and Schrenk

Colletotrichum luxificum van Hall and Drost

see *Glomerella cingulata* (Stonem.) Spauld. and Schrenk

Colletotrichum theobromae App. and Strunk

see *Glomerella cingulata* (Stonem.) Spauld. and Schrenk

Colletotrichum theobromicolum Delacr.

see *Glomerella cingulata* (Stonem.) Spauld. and Schrenk

Coniothecium effusum Corda

> WEST INDIES: Dominican Republic (Fragoso and Ciferri 1928, on dry branches).

Coniothyriella theobromae Roger

> AFRICA: Ivory Coast (Roger 1936, on pods).

Cookeina sulcipes (Berk.) O. Kuntze

> AFRICA: Sierra Leone (Herb. I.M.I., on dead trunk).

Coprinarius disseminatus (Pers. ex Fr.) Quél.

see *Coprinus disseminatus* (Pers. ex Fr.) S. F. Gray

Coprinus disseminatus (Pers. ex Fr.) S. F. Gray

> AFRICA: S. Tomé (Coutinho 1925, as *Coprinarius disseminatus,* on dead trunks).

Coriolus occidentalis (Klotzsch) G. H. Cunn.

> WEST INDIES: Trinidad (Fidalgo, O. and Fidalgo, Maria 1966).

Corticium invisum Petch

> ASIA: Unlocalized (Roger 1951).

Corticium javanicum Zimm.

see *Corticium salmonicolor* Berk. and Br.

Corticium koleroga (Cooke) Höhnel

see *Koleroga noxia* Donk

Corticium laeve Pers. ex Fr.

> UNLOCALIZED: (Seymour 1929).

Corticium lilaco-fuscum auct.

see *Corticium salmonicolor* Berk. and Br.

Corticium roseum Pers.

> AFRICA: Congo (Hendrickx 1948).

Corticium rolfsii Curzi

> UNLOCALIZED: (Seymour 1929, as *Sclerotium rolfsii*).

Corticium salmonicolor Berk. and Br.

> AFRICA: Cameroon (S.E.) (Grimaldi 1954*a*); Congo (Hendrickx 1948); Ghana (Wharton 1962); Ivory Coast (Mallamaire 1935*b*); Nigeria (Bailey 1966); Sierra Leone (Deighton 1956); S. Tomé (Patouillard 1921, as *Necator decretus*). CENTRAL AMERICA: Belize (Baker 1940). SOUTH AMERICA: Brazil (Bondar 1925, as *Corticium lilaco-fuscum*); Colombia (Polania 1957); Guyana (Martyn 1933); Surinam (van Suchtelen 1955*a*). WEST INDIES:

Dominica (Stockdale 1908); Dominican Republic (Ciferri 1930*b*); Martinique (Baker 1940); Puerto Rico (Fawcett 1914); St. Lucia (Stockdale 1908); Trinidad (Baker and Dale 1951). ASIA: Indonesia (van der Knaap 1956, as *Pellicularia salmonicolor*; von Faber 1909, as *Corticium javanicum*); Malaysia (West) (Johnston 1960*a*); Philippines (Krug and Quartey-Papafio 1964); Sabah (Berwick 1960); Sarawak (Anon. 1960); Thailand (Anon. 1960). AUSTRALASIA: British Solomon Islands (Johnston 1960*b*); Brunei (Johnston 1964*a*); Fiji (Harwood 1959); New Hebrides (Johnston 1963*b*); Papua and New Guinea (Henderson 1954); Samoa (Smith 1955).

Corticium solani (Prill. and Delacr.) Bourd. and Galz.
see *Rhizoctonia solani* Kühn

Corticium stevensii Burt
 WEST INDIES: Trinidad (Burt 1918).

Corymbomyces albus App. and Strunk
 AFRICA: Cameroon (S.W.) (Appel and Strunk 1904, on pods).

Creonectria bainii (Massee) Seaver
see *Nectria bainii* Massee

Crinipellis perniciosa (Stahel) Singer
 SOUTH AMERICA: Bolivia (Alandia and Bell 1957, as *Marasmius perniciosus*); Brazil (Silveira 1954); Colombia (Polania 1957); Ecuador (Fowler and Lopez 1949); Guyana (Martyn 1933); Peru (Hunter 1958); Surinam (Stahel 1915); Venezuela (Müller 1941). WEST INDIES: Grenada (Baker and Cope 1949); Tobago (Muir 1948); Trinidad (Baker and Dale 1951).

Crinipellis sarmentosa (Berk.) Singer
 WEST INDIES: Unlocalized (Petch 1915, as *Marasmius sarmentosus*).
 AUSTRALASIA: Papua and New Guinea (Dumbleton 1954).

Cryptococcus laurentii (Kufferath) Skinner
 AFRICA: Ivory Coast (Ruinen 1963*a*, from leaves). SOUTH AMERICA: Surinam (Ruinen 1963*a*, from leaves).

Cryptococcus neoformans (Sanfelice) Vuill.
 AFRICA: Ivory Coast (Ruinen 1963*a*, from leaves).

Cunninghamella elegans Lendner
 SOUTH AMERICA: Colombia (Chardon and Toro 1930, on pods).

Curvularia geniculata (Tracy and Earle) Boedijn
see *Cochliobolus geniculatus* Nelson

Curvularia lunata (Wakker) Boedijn var. *aeria* (Bat., Lima and Vasconcelos) M. B. Ellis
 WEST INDIES: Jamaica (Anon. 1973).

Cylindrocarpon album (Sacc.) Wollenw.
 WEST INDIES: Trinidad (Baker and Dale 1951, as *Fusarium album*, on stem).

Cylindrocarpon curvatum Hochapfel
see *Cylindrocarpon olidum* Wollenw.

Cylindrocarpon gracile Bugn.
 ASIA: Malaysia (West) (Booth 1966).

Cylindrocarpon lucidum Booth

see *Nectria lucida* Höhn.
Cylindrocarpon olidum Wollenw.
   AUSTRALASIA: New Hebrides (Dumbleton 1954, as *Cylindrocarpon curvatum*).
Cylindrocarpon suballantoideum Wollenw.
see *Nectria jungneri* P. Henn.
Cylindrocarpon tenue Bugn.
   AFRICA: Ghana (Booth 1966); Sierra Leone (Booth 1966). ASIA: Sabah (Booth 1966).
Cylindrocarpon theobromicola Bugn.
   AUSTRALASIA: New Britain (Booth 1966).
Cylindrocarpon tonkinense Bugn.
   AFRICA: Nigeria (Booth 1966).
Cylindrocarpon victoriae (P. Henn. ex Fr.) Wollenw.
see *Nectria jungneri* P. Henn.
Cylindrocladium scoparium Morgan
   AFRICA: Ghana (Turner 1960c, on pods).
Cyphella holstii P. Henn.
see *Phaeosolenia densa* (Berk.) W. B. Cooke
Cyphella pulchra Berk. and Br.
see *Marasmius pulcher* (Berk. and Br.) Petch
Cyphella variolosa Kalchbr.
see *Phaesoloenia densa* (Berk.) W. B. Cooke
Deflexula fascicularis (Bres. and Pat.) Corner
   AUSTRALASIA: Papua and New Guinea (Shaw 1963, on old wood).
Deflexula subsimplex (P. Henn.) Corner
   SOUTH AMERICA: Colombia (Corner 1952, on bark).
Didymium iridis (Ditm.) Fr.
   WEST INDIES: Trinidad (Barnes 1963, on witches' brooms in trays).
Didymium squamulosum Fr.
   AFRICA: Sierra Leone (Herb. I.M.I.).
Diplodia cacaoicola P. Henn.
see *Botryodiplodia theobromae* Pat.
Diplodia cococarpa Sacc.
   AFRICA: S. Tomé (Henriques 1917, on pods).
Diplodia natalensis Pole Evans
see *Botryodiplodia theobromae* Pat.
Diplodia theobromae (Pat.) Nowell
see *Botryodiplodia theobromae* Pat.
Diplodina corticola App. and Strunk
   AFRICA: Cameroon (S.W.) (Appel and Strunk 1904, on dry branches); S. Tomé (da Camara 1920, on bark).
Discella cacaoicola App. and Strunk
   AFRICA: Cameroon (S.W.) (Appel and Strunk 1904, on pods); Ghana (Dade 1940, on pods. SOUTH AMERICA: Brazil (Averna-Saccá 1920, on branches).
Duportella tristicula (Berk. and Br.) Reinking
   AUSTRALASIA: New Hebrides (Johnston 1963b, uncertain determination, on trunk of dying tree).

Echinodia theobromae Pat.

see *Polyporus theobromae* (Pat.) Lloyd

Epicoccum theobromae Petch

see *Apiospora montagnei* Sacc.

Epochnium monilioides Link

WEST INDIES: Dominican Republic (Ciferri 1927*b*, uncertain determination, on pods).

Eutypa erumpens Massee

WEST INDIES: Trinidad (Baker and Dale 1951).

Eutypa phaselina (Mont.) Sacc.

WEST INDIES: Trinidad (Hart 1911, as *Eutypa phasetina*).

Eutypella theobromicola Wakef.

AFRICA: Cameroon (S.E.) (Grimaldi 1954*a*); Ghana (Wakefield 1918).

Exosporium ampullaceum (Petch) M. B. Ellis

AFRICA: Nigeria (Ellis 1961, on branches). AUSTRALASIA: Papua and New Guinea (Shaw 1963, as *Helminthosporium ampullaceum*, on old wood).

Favolus brasiliensis Fr.

AFRICA: Sierra Leone (Herb. Kew., on stump); S. Tomé (Patouillard 1921, on branches).

Fenestella gigaspora P. Henn.

AFRICA: Ivory Coast (Resplandy *et al.* 1954).

Fomes auberianus (Mont.) Murrill

see *Rigidoporus lignosus* (Klotzsch) Imazeki

Fomes lamaensis (Murrill) Sacc. and Trott.

see *Phellinus lamaensis* (Murrill) Heim

Fomes lamaoensis auct.

see *Phellinus noxius* (Corner) G. H. Cunn.

Fomes noxius Corner

see *Phellinus noxius* (Corner) G. H. Cunn.

Fomes pectinatus (Klotzsch) Gill.

AFRICA: S. Tomé (Coutinho 1925, on trunks).

Fomes semitostus (Berk.) Cooke

see *Rigidoporus lignosus* (Klotzsch) Imazeki

Fracchiaea broomeiana (Berk.) Petch

AFRICA: Ghana (Hughes 1953, on branches).

Fuligo cinerea Morg.

AFRICA: Nigeria (Farquharson and Lister 1916, on old pods); ASIA: Sri Lanka (Petch 1910*a*, as *Fuligo ellipsospora*, on pods).

Fuligo ellipsospora Lister

see *Fuligo cinerea* Morg.

Fusarium album Sacc.

see *Cylindrocarpon album* (Sacc.) Wollenw.

Fusarium allescherianum P. Henn.

see *Glomerella cingulata* (Stonem.) Spauld. and Schrenk

Fusarium anthophilum Braun

see *Fusarium moniliforme* Sheldon var. *anthophilum* Wollenw.

Fusarium aquaeductum Lagerh.

ASIA: Philippines (Wollenweber 1931, as *F. aquaeductum* var. *elongatum*, on rotting pods).

Fusarium aquaeductum Lagerh. var. *elongatum* Wollenw.

see *Fusarium aquaeductum* Lagerh.

Fusarium avenaceum (Corda ex Fr.) Sacc.

AFRICA: Nigeria (Anon., 1968, from seedling).

Fusarium camptoceras Wollenw. and Reinking

CENTRAL AMERICA: Costa Rica (Anon. 1973); Honduras (Wollenweber and Reinking 1925). ASIA: Vietnam (Bugnicourt 1939, on pods).

Fusarium decemcellulare Brick

see *Calonectria rigidiuscula* (Berk. and Br.) Sacc.

Fusarium equiseti (Corda) Sacc.

AFRICA: Ghana (Owen 1956, from artificial stem-lesion); Nigeria (Bailey 1966, associated with wilt). ASIA: Sabah (Herb. I.M.I.); Vietnam (Bugnicourt 1939, as *F. equiseti* var. *bullatum*, on branches).

Fusarium equiseti (Corda) Sacc. var. *bullatum* (Sherb.) Wollenw.

see *Fusarium equiseti* (Corda) Sacc.

Fusarium javanicum Koord.

see *Fusarium solani* (Mart.) Sacc.

Fusarium lateritium Nees

CENTRAL AMERICA: Nicaragua (Bourret and Ford 1965, from galls).

Fusarium moniliforme Sheldon

AFRICA: Ivory Coast (Resplandy *et al.* 1954, on pods); Uganda (Anon. 1925, on stem). CENTRAL AMERICA: Costa Rica (Alexander, Cook and Bourret 1965, from galls). WEST INDIES: Trinidad (Gordon 1956, on dead branch). ASIA: Indonesia (Reddy 1970a); Sabah (Anon. 1967, associated with *Helopeltis* sp., punctures). AUSTRALASIA: Samoa (Gehrmann 1913, as *F. samoense*, from cankered bark).

Fusarium moniliforme Sheldon var. *anthophilum* Wollenw.

CENTRAL AMERICA: Honduras (Wollenweber and Reinking 1925, as *F. anthophilum*). WEST INDIES: Jamaica (Hansford 1926, on rotting pod).

Fusarium moniliforme Sheldon var. *subglutinans* Wollenw. and Reinking

UNLOCALIZED: (Booth and Waterston 1964b, as *Gibberella fujikuroi* var. *subglutinans*, associated with pod rot).

Fusarium orthoceras Schlecht.

see *Fusarium oxysporum* Schlecht.

Fusarium oxysporum Schlecht.

CENTRAL AMERICA: Costa Rica (Alexander *et al.* 1965, from galls). SOUTH AMERICA: (Orejuela 1939, uncertain determination, in roots). WEST INDIES: Jamaica (Reinking and Wollenweber 1927, as *F. orthoceras*, on pod). ASIA: Sabah (Anon. 1967, from rotting pod).

Fusarium rigidiusculum Snyder and Hansen

see *Calonectria rigidiuscula* (Berk. and Br.) Sacc.

Fusarium roseum Link

CENTRAL AMERICA: Nicaragua (Hansen 1963a, associated with cushion gall).

Fusarium sambucinum Fuckel

AFRICA: Malawi (Corbett 1964, from rotting pod). UNLOCALIZED: (Roger 1953, as *F. sarcochroum*).

Fusarium samoense Gehrmann

see *Fusarium moniliforme* Sheldon

Fusarium sarcochroum (Desm.) Sacc.

see *Fusarium sambucinum* Fuckel

Fusarium semitectum Berk. and Rav.

ASIA: Sabah (Williams 1965a, associated with branch dieback).

Fusarium solani (Mart.) Sacc.

AFRICA: Cameroon (S.E.) (Grimaldi 1952, as *F. theobromae*; 1954a, as *Nectria ipomoeae*); Cameroon (S.W.) (Appel and Strunk 1904, on husks); Ghana (Dade 1940, as *Hypomyces ipomoeae*, hyperparasite on *Armillariella mellea*); Ivory Coast (Roger 1934, as *Nectria cacaoicola*; Roger and Mallamaire 1937, as *F. javanicum*); Malagasy (Madagascar) (Bouriquet 1946); Sierra Leone (Booth 1960). CENTRAL AMERICA: Costa Rica (Alexander *et al.* 1965, from galls); Honduras (Reinking and Wollenweber 1927, as *F. solani* var. *suffuscum*). SOUTH AMERICA: Colombia (Booth 1960). WEST INDIES: Trinidad (Booth 1960). ASIA: Indonesia (Java) (Rutgers 1913, as *Nectria cancri*, on cankered bark); Malaysia (West) (Thompson and Johnston 1953, on stem); Philippines (Teodoro 1937, as *Hypomyces haematococcus*, on bark); Sabah (Johnston 1960c, as *Nectria haematococca*, associated with pod rot); Sri Lanka (Petch 1910b, as *Nectria diversispora*, on pods); Vietnam (Bugnicourt 1939, as *F. solani* var. *minus*, on trunk). AUSTRALASIA: British Solomon Islands (Johnston 1960b, on branches); Papua and New Guinea (Anon. 1968); West Irian (Johnston 1961, associated with stem rot).

Fusarium solani (Mart.) Sacc. var. *minus* Wollenw.

see *Fusarium solani* (Mart.) Sacc.

Fusarium solani (Mart.) Sacc. var. *suffuscum* Sherb.

see *Fusarium solani* (Mart.) Sacc.

Fusarium spicaria-colorantis Sacc. and Trott.

see *Calonectria rigidiuscula* (Berk. and Br.) Sacc.

Fusarium theobromae App. and Strunk

see *Fusarium solani* (Mart.) Sacc.

Fusarium theobromicolum Averna-Saccá

SOUTH AMERICA: Brazil (Averna-Saccá 1925, on pods).

Fusarium tumidum Sherb.

ASIA: Sabah (Herb. I.M.I., from branch cankers).

Ganoderma applanatum (Pers. ex Wallr.) Pat.

AFRICA: Ivory Coast (Mallamaire 1935a).

Ganoderma fulvellum Bres.

AFRICA: S. Tomé (Patouillard 1922a, on old trunks).

Ganoderma laccatum (Kalchbr.) Bourd. and Galz.

AFRICA: Ivory Coast (Mallamaire 1935b).

Ganoderma lucidum (Leyss. ex Fr.) Karst.

WEST INDIES: Trinidad (Baker and Dale 1951, uncertain determination).

Ganoderma pseudoferreum (Wakef.) Overeem and Steinmann

SOUTH AMERICA: Surinam (van Suchtelen 1955a); Venezuela (Desrosiers and Diaz 1956*b*). ASIA: Indonesia (Java) (Hubert 1957); Malaysia (West) (Thompson and Johnston 1953); Philippines (Rombouts 1937); Sarawak (Anon. 1960). AUSTRALASIA: Papua and New Guinea (Thrower 1956).

Gibberella fujikuroi (Sawada) Ito ap. Ito and Kimura var. *subglutinans* Edwards see *Fusarium moniliforme* Sheldon var. *subglutinans* Wollenw.

Glaziella vesiculosa Berk.
   WEST INDIES: Trinidad (Herb. I.M.I., on leaves).

Gliocladium catenulatum Gilman and Abbott
   AFRICA: Malawi (Corbett 1964, from pod rot).

Gliocladium penicilloides Corda
see *Nectriopsis aureonitens* (Tul.) Maire

Gliocladium roseum Bain.
   AFRICA: Ghana (Hughes 1953, on bark); Sierra Leone (Herb. I.M.I., from pod).

Gliomastix luzulae (Fuckel) Mason ex Hughes
   AFRICA: Ghana (Dickinson 1968, on pods).

Gliomastix murorum (Corda) Hughes var. *polychroma* (van Beyma) C. H. Dickinson
   AFRICA: Ghana (Dickinson 1968, on pod).

Gloeosporium affine Tehon
see *Glomerella cingulata* (Stonem.) Spauld. and Schrenk

Gloeosporium allescherianum (P. Henn.) Wollenw.
see *Glomerella cingulata* (Stonem.) Spauld. and Schrenk

Gloeosporium theobromae Zimm.
   ASIA: Indonesia (Java) (Zimmermann 1902, on pods).

Gloeosporium theobromicola M. F. Vincens
see *Glomerella cingulata* (Stonem.) Spauld and Schrenk)

Glomerella cingulata (Stonem.) Spauld. and Schrenk
   AFRICA: Cameroon (S.E.) (Grimaldi 1954*a*, as *Colletotrichum gloeosporioides*); Cameroon (S.W.) (Appel and Strunk 1904, as *C. theobromae*; Busse 1905*a*, *b*, as *C. incarnatum*); Congo (Steyaert 1948, as *C. theobromicolum*, on pods); Ghana (Dade 1940, as *C. coffeanum*); Ivory Coast (Resplandy *et al.* 1954); Malawi (Corbett 1964, from angular leaf-spot and pod rot); Mauritius (Wiehe 1948); Nigeria (Swarbrick 1964, on seedlings in nursery; Bailey 1966, as causing pod anthracnose); S. Tomé (Patouillard 1922*b*); Tanzania (Tanganyika) (Riley 1960); Uganda (Hansford 1943*a*). NORTH AMERICA: U.S.A. (Shear and Wood 1913, on leaves in glasshouse). CENTRAL AMERICA: Costa Rica (Newhall 1948); Guatemala (Müller 1950); Mexico (Orellana 1955); Nicaragua (Orellana 1955). SOUTH AMERICA: Brazil (Averna-Saccá 1920, as *Gloeosporium affine*; Vincens 1918, as *Gloeosporium theobromicola*); Colombia (Polania 1957); Ecuador (Desrosiers and Diaz 1956*a*); Guyana (Bisessar 1965); Surinam (Van Hall and Drost 1907, as *C. luxificum*). WEST INDIES: Cuba (Venning and Gertsch 1958); Guadeloupe (Baker 1940); Haiti (Orellana 1956*a*); Jamaica (Bancroft 1910, as *C. cradwickii*); Martinique (Baker 1940); Puerto Rico (Stevenson 1926); Trinidad (Baker, Crowdy, and McKee 1940). ASIA: Brunei (Peregrine 1971); Malaysia (West) (Johnston 1960*a*); Philippines (Gandia 1963); Sabah (Johnston 1960*c*); Sri Lanka (Petch and Bisby 1950). AUSTRALASIA: New Hebrides (Anon. 1960). EUROPE:

Czechoslovakia (Cejp 1930, as *Fusarium* (*Gloeosporium*) *allescherianum*); Germany (Hennings 1895, as *Gloeosporium affine*, on leaves); U.S.S.R. (Bondarzewa-Monteverde, Gutner and Novosselova 1936, on leaves in glasshouse).

Glomerella cingulata (Stonem.) Spauld. and Schrenk var. *minor* Wollenw.

AUSTRALASIA: Queensland (Simmonds 1965, 1966, as *C. gloeosporioides* var. *minus*, associated with leaf spotting).

Graphium rhodophaeum Sacc. and Trott.

see *Nectria dealbata* Berk. and Br.

Helicobasidium longisporum Wakef.

AFRICA: Uganda (Wakefield 1917, 1920, on roots).

Helminthosporium ampullaceum Petch

see *Exosporium ampullaceum* (Petch) M. B. Ellis

Helminthosporium capense Thüm.

see *Spiropes capensis* (Thüm.) M. B. Ellis

Helminthosporium guianense Stev. and Dowell

SOUTH AMERICA: Guyana (Stevens and Dowell 1923, on *Irenopsis guianensis*); Venezuela (Chardon and Toro 1934, on *I. guianensis*).

Helminthosporium theobromae Turc.

EUROPE: Italy (Turconi 1920, on leaves).

Helminthosporium theobromicola Cif. and Frag.

WEST INDIES: Dominican Republic (Fragoso and Ciferri 1928, on leaves).

Helotium miniatum Pat.

WEST INDIES: Guadeloupe (Duss 1903, on bark).

Hemimycena marbleae (Murrill) Dennis

WEST INDIES: Trinidad (Dennis 1951, as *Mycena marbleae,* on rotting pod).

Hemimycena micropapillata (Dennis) Dennis

WEST INDIES: Trinidad (Dennis 1951, as *Mycena micropapillata,* on rotting leaves).

Hermatomyces sphaericum (Sacc.) Hughes

AFRICA: Ghana (Hughes 1953, as *Stemphylium sphaericum,* on bark).

Heterochaete flavida Pat.

AFRICA: S. Tomé (Patouillard 1921, on bark).

Hexagonia discopoda Pat. and Har.

AFRICA: Nigeria (Herb. Kew.); Sierra Leone (Herb. I.M.I.); S. Tomé (Patouillard 1922*a*).

Hirneola cornea (Ehrenb. ex Fr.) Fr.

see *Auricularia cornea* (Ehrenb. ex Fr.) Ehrenb. ex Endl.

Holstiella bahiensis Speg.

SOUTH AMERICA: Brazil (Spegazzini 1906*a*, on branches and pods).

Hormiscium splendens (Cooke) Sacc.

WEST INDIES: Dominican Republic (Ciferri 1927*b*, uncertain determination, on pods).

Hormodendrum cladosporioides (Fres.) Sacc.

see *Cladosporium cladosporioides* (Fres.) de Vries

Hymenochaete castanea Wakef.

AFRICA: Nigeria (Wakefield 1914, on dead branches).

Hymenochaete noxia Berk.

see *Phellinus noxius* (Corner) G. H. Cunn.

Hymenula socia Sacc.

see *Nectria pityrodes* Mont. var. *saccharina* Berk. and Br.

Hypochnus theobromae von Faber

AFRICA: Cameroon (S.W.) (von Faber 1909, on branches).

Hypomyces haematococcus (Berk. and Br.) Wollenw.

see *Fusarium solani* (Mart.) Sacc.

Hypomyces ipomoeae (Halst.) Wollenw.

see *Fusarium solani* (Mart.) Sacc.

Hypoxylon rubiginosum (Pers. ex Fr.) Fr.

AFRICA: Ghana (Hughes 1953, on bark); Sierra Leone (Herb. I.M.I., on dead stems). SOUTH AMERICA: Brazil (Sydow and Sydow 1909, in bark and on branches). WEST INDIES: Haiti (Ciferri 1961); Trinidad (Hart 1911).

Hysteriopsis brasiliensis (Speg.) Sacc. and Trott.

SOUTH AMERICA: Brazil (Spegazzini 1906*b*, on stems).

Hysteropsis cinerea Speg.

SOUTH AMERICA: Brazil (Spegazzini 1906*a*, on leaves and pods).

Irenopsis guianensis (Stev. and Dowell) Stev.

SOUTH AMERICA: Guyana (Stevens and Dowell 1923, as *Meliola guianensis*, on leaves); Venezuela (Chardon and Toro 1934). WEST INDIES: Trinidad (Baker and Dale 1951).

Isaria cretacea van Beyma

AFRICA: Ghana (Anon. 1973, on beans).

Isaria ochracea Boud.

WEST INDIES: Trinidad (Barrett 1907, uncertain determination, on *Diabrotica* sp., (Coleoptera, Chrysomelidae) on leaf).

Kloeckera africana (Klöcker) Janke

WEST INDIES: Dominican Republic (Ciferri 1930*a*, as *K. domingensis*, on rotten pods).

Kloeckera domingensis Cif.

see *Kloeckera africana* (Klöcker) Janke

Knyaria vulgaris (Tode) Kunze

see *Nectria cinnabarina* (Tode ex Fr.) Fr.

Koleroga noxia Donk

AFRICA: Congo (Hendrickx 1948, as *Pellicularia koleroga*); Ivory Coast (Resplandy *et al.* 1954, as *Corticium koleroga*). CENTRAL AMERICA: Costa Rica (Newhall 1948); Panama (Hardy 1957). SOUTH AMERICA: Bolivia (Murray 1968); Brazil (Deslandes 1944); Ecuador (Desrosiers and Diaz 1956*a*); Guyana (Martyn 1933); Surinam (van Suchtelen 1955*a*). WEST INDIES: Haiti (Pierre-Louis and Dadaille 1956); Trinidad (Collens 1909, on leaves). ASIA: Malaysia (West) (Heath 1958); Philippines (Krug and Quartey-Papafio 1964). AUSTRALASIA: New Hebrides (Cohic 1953).

Kretzschmaria cetrarioides (Welw. and Currey) Sacc.

AFRICA: Tanzania (Tanganyika) (Riley 1960, on dead stump).

Labrella theobromicola Averna-Saccá

SOUTH AMERICA: Brazil (Averna-Saccá 1925, on pods).

Lasiodiplodia nigra App. and Laubert
see *Botryodiplodia theobromae* Pat.
Lasiodiplodia theobromae (Pat.) Griff. and Maubl.
see *Botryodiplodia theobromae* Pat.
Lasionectria cacaoicola Averna-Saccá
  SOUTH AMERICA: Brazil (Averna-Saccá 1925, on pods).
Lenzites repanda (Pers.) Fr.
  AFRICA: S. Tomé (Coutinho 1925, on trunks).
Leptoporus microstomus (Berk. and Curt.) Pat.
see *Polyporus microstomus* Berk. and Curt.
Leptosphaeria theobromicola Frag. and Cif.
  WEST INDIES: Dominican Republic (Fragoso and Ciferri 1928, on leaves).
Letendraea bahiensis Speg.
  SOUTH AMERICA: Brazil (Spegazzini 1906*b*, on trunk).
Lopharia mirabilis (Berk. and Br.) Pat.
  ASIA: Malaysia (West) (Johnston 1960*a*, from branch dieback).
Lophodermium theobromae Pat.
  WEST INDIES: Guadeloupe (Duss 1903, on fallen leaves).
Macbridella striispora (Ellis and Everh.) Seaver
see *Calostilbe striispora* (Ellis and Everh.) Seaver
Macrophoma scaphidiospora Camara
see *Botryodiplodia theobromae* Pat.
Macrophoma vestita Prill. and Delacr.
see *Botryodiplodia theobromae* Pat.
Macrophomina phaseolina (Tassi) Goid.
  AFRICA: Uganda (Small 1926*b*, as *Sclerotium bataticola*). ASIA: Sabah
  (Williams 1967, on dying roots); Sri Lanka (Small 1928, as *Rhizoctonia bata-
  ticola,* on roots). AUSTRALASIA: British Solomon Islands (Johnston 1960*b*,
  associated with seedling dieback).
Macrosporium commune (Rabenh.) Sacc.
see *Macrosporium sarcinula* Berk.
Macrosporium sarcinula Berk.
  AFRICA: S. Tomé (da Camara 1920, as *M. commune,* on leaves, branches, and
  fruits).
Macrosporium verrucosum Lutz
  AFRICA: S. Tomé (Lutz 1906, on pods).
Marasmiellus goniosporus Reid
  AUSTRALASIA: Papua and New Guinea (Reid 1966, on leaves).
Marasmiellus scandens (Massee) Dennis and Reid
  AFRICA: Cameroon (S.E.) (Grimaldi 1954*a*, as *Marasmius scandens*); Congo
  (Krug and Quartey-Papafio 1964); Ghana (Massee 1910, as *Marasmius scan-
  dens*; Petch 1928*a*, as *Marasmius byssicola*); Ivory Coast (Guillaumin 1971);
  Malagasy (Madagascar) (Barat 1954); Nigeria (West 1938); Sierra Leone
  (Deighton 1956); Togo Republic (Berard 1956). SOUTH AMERICA:
  Guyana (Procter and Pires 1958). ASIA: Indonesia (Reddy 1970*a*); Malaysia
  (West) (Turner 1968*b*); Sabah (Berwick 1964). AUSTRALASIA: Fiji
  (Morwood 1956); New Hebrides (Johnston 1963*b*); Papua and New Guinea
  (Anon. 1960); West Irian (Johnston 1961).

Marasmius atropurpureus Murrill
see *Marasmius tageticolor* Berk.
Marasmius byssicola Petch
see *Marasmiellus scandens* (Massee) Dennis and Reid
Marasmius cyphella Dennis and Reid
   AUSTRALASIA: Papua and New Guinea (Shaw 1963).
Marasmius equicrinis Müll.
   AFRICA: Cameroon (S.E.) (Grimaldi 1954*a*, as *Marasmius trichorhizus*);
   Congo (Hendrickx 1948); Ghana (Dade 1940); Ivory Coast (Resplandy *et al.*
   1954); Nigeria (Bailey 1966); Sierra Leone (Deighton 1956); S. Tomé
   (Patouillard 1921, as *Androsaceus equicrinis*); Togo Republic (Berard 1956).
   CENTRAL AMERICA: Costa Rica (Orellana 1955). SOUTH AMERICA:
   Brazil (Bondar 1939). WEST INDIES: Grenada (South 1912); Trinidad
   (Hart 1911). ASIA: Malaysia (West) (Thompson and Johnston 1953); Sabah
   (Anon, 1967). AUSTRALASIA: New Hebrides (Dadant 1953); West Irian
   (Johnston 1961).
Marasmius haedinus Berk.
   WEST INDIES: Dominica (Dennis 1951, on fallen leaves).
Marasmius inoderma (Berk.) Singer
   ASIA: Malaysia (West) (Thompson 1950, as *Marasmius semiustus,* associated
   with death of plants in baskets).
Marasmius longipes Mont.
   WEST INDIES: Trinidad (Dennis 1951, on fallen leaves).
Marasmius ochraceoniger P. Henn.
   AUSTRALASIA: Fiji (Herb. Kew.).
Marasmius pandoanus Singer
   SOUTH AMERICA: Bolivia (Singer 1964, on fallen leaves).
Marasmius perniciosus Stahel
see *Crinipellis perniciosa* (Stahel) Singer
Marasmius perniciosus var. *ecuadoriensis* Stahel
   SOUTH AMERICA: Ecuador (Stahel 1923).
Marasmius pulcher (Berk. and Br.) Petch
   ASIA: Sri Lanka (Roger 1951, as *Cyphella pulchra*).
Marasmius sarmentosus Berk.
see *Crinipellis sarmentosa* (Berk.) Singer
Marasmius scandens Massee
see *Marasmiellus scandens* (Massee) Dennis and Reid
Marasmius semiustus Berk. and Curt.
see *Marasmius inoderma* (Berk.) Singer
Marasmius stenophyllus Mont.
   ASIA: Malaysia (West) (Anon. 1960, as cause of seedling stem canker).
Marasmius tageticolor Berk.
   WEST INDIES: Dominica (Dennis 1951, on leaves); Trinidad (Rayner 1941,
   uncertain determination, as *Marasmius atropurpureus*, on leaves).
Marasmius theobromae von Faber
   AFRICA: Cameroon (S.W.) (von Faber 1909, on dead leaves).
Marasmius trichorhizus Speg.
see *Marasmius equicrinis* Müll.

Megalonectria nigrescens (Kalchbr. and Cooke) Sacc.
    AFRICA: S. Tomé (Patouillard 1921, on bark).
Megalonectria pseudotrichia (Schwein.) Speg.
see *Thyronectria pseudotrichia* (Schwein.) Seeler
Melanographium citri (Frag. and Cif.) M. B. Ellis
    AFRICA: Ghana (Dade 1940, as *Pseudocamptoum fasciculatum*, on leaves;
    Ellis 1963); Sierra Leone (Mason 1933, on twigs).
Melanomma henriquesianum Bres. and Roum.
    AFRICA: S. Tomé (Bresadola 1891, on bark).
Melanospora zamiae Corda
    AFRICA: Uganda (Anon. 1925).
Meliola guianensis Stev. and Dowell
see *Irenopsis guianensis* (Stev. and Dowell) Stev.
Meliola theobromae von Faber
    AFRICA: Cameroon (S.W.) (von Faber 1909, as 'sooty mould' on leaves).
Memnoniella subsimplex (Cooke) Deighton
    AFRICA: Ivory Coast (Moreau and Moreau 1951, as *Stachybotrys subsimplex*).
Menisporopsis theobromae Hughes
    AFRICA: Ghana (Hughes 1952, on fallen leaves).
Metasphaeria theobromae Camara
    AFRICA: S. Tomé (da Camara 1920, on branches).
Microcera coccophila Desm.
see *Nectria flammea* (Tul.) Dingley
Microcera lacerata Pat.
    AFRICA: S. Tomé (Patouillard 1921, on *Pseudaonidia* sp., (Coccidae) on
    leaves, and *M. lacerata* var. *brachyspora* Pat., on *Aulacaspis* sp., (Coccidae) on
    leaves).
Micropeltis heterosperma (Syd.) Bat.
    ASIA: Philippines (Teodoro 1937).
Micropeltis theobromae Bat.
    SOUTH AMERICA: Brazil (Batista and Gayão 1953, on leaves).
Microporus sanguineus (L. ex Fr.) Petrak
see *Polyporus sanguineus* L. ex Fr.
Monilia carbonaria Cooke
see *Neurospora sitophila* Shear and Dodge
Monilia cinerea Bon.
see *Sclerotinia laxa* Aderh. and Ruhl.
Monilia roreri Cif. and Parodi
    SOUTH AMERICA: Colombia (Ciferri and Parodi 1933); Ecuador (Des-
    rosiers and Diaz 1956*a,b*); Peru (Hunter 1958); Venezuela (Müller 1941).
    CENTRAL AMERICA: Panama (Orellana 1956*b*).
Monilia sitophila (Mont.) Sacc.
see *Neurospora sitophila* Shear and Dodge
Mucor mucedo (L.) Fres.
    ASIA: Philippines (Saccardo 1916, on rotting pods).
Mycena citricolor (Berk. and Curt.) Sacc.
    CENTRAL AMERICA: Costa Rica (Sequeira 1958, on leaves).

Mycena marbleae (Murrill) Dennis
see *Hemimycena marbleae* (Murrill) Dennis
Mycena micropapillata Dennis
see *Hemimycena micropapillata* (Dennis) Dennis
Mycena theobromicola (Murrill) Dennis
WEST INDIES: Grenada (Dennis 1951, on rotten pods); Trinidad (Dennis 1951, on rotten pods).
Mycogone aurantiaca Camara
AFRICA: S. Tomé (da Camara 1920, on roots and fruits).
Mycogone cervina Ditm. var. *theobromae* Sacc.
ASIA: Philippines (Saccardo 1916, on young fruits).
Myriangium duriaei Mont. and Berk.
AFRICA: S. Tomé (Patouillard 1921, on leaves and bark, associated with insects (Coccidae)).
Myrothecium roridum Tode ex Fr.
AFRICA: Sierra Leone (Deighton 1956, causing seedling leaf-spot).
Mystrosporium polytrichum Cooke
WEST INDIES: Dominican Republic (Fragoso and Ciferri 1928, on rotting pods).
Myxosporium theobromae van Breda de Haan
ASIA: Indonesia (Java) (van Breda de Haan 1900, on stems and petioles).
Necator decretus Massee
see *Corticium salmonicolor* Berk. and Br.
Nectria albiseda Pat.
AFRICA: S. Tomé (da Camara and Coutinho 1925).
Nectria bactridioides Berk. and Br.
ASIA: Malaysia (West) (Johnston 1960a, from dieback).
Nectria bainii Massee
AFRICA: Congo (Mayné and Vermoesen 1914, uncertain determination, on pods); Nigeria (Bailey 1966, associated with pod damage). SOUTH AME-RICA: Guyana (Bancroft 1919). WEST INDIES: Dominican Republic (Fragoso and Ciferri 1928, as *Creonectria bainii*, on stems and branches); Puerto Rico (Whetzel and Olive 1920, on pods); Trinidad (Baker and Dale 1951). ASIA: Philippines (Teodoro 1937). AUSTRALASIA: Samoa (Gehrmann 1913).
Nectria bainii Massee var. *hypoleuca* Sacc.
ASIA: Philippines (Saccardo 1916, on young pods).
Nectria cacaoicola Roger
see *Nectria haematococca* Berk. and Br.
Nectria camerunensis App. and Strunk
AFRICA: Cameroon (S.W.) (Appel and Strunk 1904, on dead pods). ASIA: Philippines (Teodoro 1937, on dry pod).
Nectria cancri Rutg.
see *Fusarium solani* (Mart.) Sacc.
Nectria cinereo-papillata P. Henn. and Nym.
see *Nectria jungneri* P. Henn.
Nectria cinnabarina (Tode ex Fr.) Fr.
WEST INDIES: Dominican Republic (Fragoso and Ciferri 1928, as *Knyaria*

vulgaris, on discarded pods).

Nectria coffeicola Zimm.

see *Calonectria diploa* (Berk. and Curt.) Wollenw.

Nectria cremea auct.

see *Calonectria cremea* Zimm.

Nectria cremea Grimaldi

AFRICA: Cameroon (S.E.) (Grimaldi 1954*a*).

Nectria dealbata Berk. and Br.

AFRICA: Ghana (Hughes 1952, as *Graphium rhodophaeum*, on branches); Sierra Leone (Herb. I.M.I., on dead branches); Uganda (Hansford 1943*b*, on twig). WEST INDIES: Jamaica (Leather 1961, associated with false 'witches' broom'). ASIA: Sri Lanka (Petch 1910*b*, on pod). AUSTRALASIA: West Irian (Johnston 1961, from stem rot).

Nectria discophora (Mont.) Mont.

WEST INDIES: Trinidad (Baker and Dale 1951). ASIA: Philippines (Teodoro (1937).

Nectria ditissima Tul.

ASIA: Sri Lanka (Carruthers 1900, uncertain determination; Petch 1910*b*, from stem cankers).

Nectria diversispora Petch

see *Fusarium solani* (Mart.) Sacc.

Nectria flammea (Tul.) Dingley

AFRICA: S. Tomé (da Camara 1920, as *Microcera coccophila,* and as *M. coccophila* var. *platyspora*, on insects (Coccidae) on leaves; Patouillard 1921, as *Sphaerostilbe coccophila,* on insects (Coccidae), on leaves).

Nectria flavolanata Berk. and Br.

AFRICA: Ghana (Hughes 1952, on pods); Uganda (Wakefield 1920, on dead stem). ASIA: Indonesia (Reddy 1970*a*); Malaysia (West) (Johnston 1960a, associated with cherelle rot); Philippines (Teodoro 1937, on rotting pods). AUSTRALASIA: West Irian (Johnston 1961, from pod and stem rots).

Nectria haematococca Berk. and Br.

see *Fusarium solani* (Mart.) Sacc.

Nectria inventa Pethybridge

AFRICA: Ghana (Hughes 1952, as *Acrostalagmus cinnabarinus,* on dry pods); S. Tomé (Dias, Lucas, de Vasconcelos and da Camara 1953, on wood).

Nectria ipomoeae Halst.

see *Fusarium solani* (Mart.) Sacc.

Nectria jungneri P. Henn.

AFRICA: Cameroon (S.E.) (Grimaldi 1954*a*); Cameroon (S.W.) (Hennings 1895); Ghana (Booth 1966, as *Cylindrocarpon victoriae*); Ivory Coast (Resplandy *et al.* 1954); Nigeria (Bailey 1966, on bark); Sierra Leone (Anon. 1973); Tanzania (Tanganyika) (Booth 1966). CENTRAL AMERICA: Mexico (Zevada *et al.* 1955). SOUTH AMERICA: Colombia (Booth 1966); Surinam (Booth 1966). WEST INDIES: Dominican Republic (Ciferri 1929*b*, 1961, uncertain determination, as *N. theobromae*); Grenada (Massee 1908, as *N. theobromae,* from cankers); Trinidad (Booth 1966). ASIA: Malaysia (West) (Johnston 1960*a*, from dieback); Philippines (Teodoro 1937, as *N. cinereopapillata,* on rotting pods); Sabah (Johnston 1964*b*, from dying branch).

AUSTRALASIA: New Hebrides (Dadant 1953; 1954, as *C. suballantoideum*, on diseased pods and branches); Samoa (American) (Dumbleton 1954); Samoa (West) Johnston 1963c).

Nectria lucida Höhn.
CENTRAL AMERICA: Belize (Booth 1966, as *Cylindrocarpon lucidum*).

Nectria nkoemvonensis Grimaldi
AFRICA: Cameroon (S.E.) (Grimaldi 1954a, on branches).

Nectria ochroleuca (Schw.) Berk.
AFRICA: Ghana (Herb. I.M.I., on pods); Nigeria (Herb. I.M.I., on pods); Sierra Leone (Anon. 1964a); S. Tomé (Patouillard 1922b, on old pods). WEST INDIES: Jamaica (Leather 1961, associated with false 'witches' broom'); Trinidad (Herb. I.M.I., on dead branch). ASIA: Malaysia (West) (Anon. 1973). AUSTRALASIA: New Hebrides (Johnston 1963b, from dieback); Papua and New Guinea (Shaw 1963, on old wood); Samoa (West) (Reddy 1970b); West Irian (Johnston 1961).

Nectria pityrodes Mont. var. *saccharina* Berk. and Br.
AFRICA: Ghana (Hughes 1953, as *Hymenula socia*, on twigs); Sierra Leone (Herb. I.M.I., on dead branch). WEST INDIES: Trinidad (Herb. I.M.I., on dead branch).

Nectria portoricensis Stev.
SOUTH AMERICA: Guyana (Stevens and Dowell 1923, uncertain determination, as hyperparasite on *Irenopsis guianensis*, on leaves).

Nectria rigidiuscula Berk. and Br.
see *Calonectria rigidiuscula* (Berk. and Br.) Sacc.

Nectria stenospora Berk. and Br.
ASIA: Sri Lanka (Petch 1910b, on pods).

Nectria striatospora Zimm.
AFRICA: Ghana (Anon. 1925, on pods). ASIA: Indonesia (Zimmermann 1901a, b, on bark); Sri Lanka (Petch and Bisby 1950, on stems).

Nectria subquaternata (Berk. and Br.) Sacc.
AUSTRALASIA: Papua and New Guinea (Shaw 1963, on old wood).

Nectria suffulta Berk. and Curt.
AFRICA: Sierra Leone (Herb. I.M.I., on pod). WEST INDIES: Trinidad (Herb. I.M.I., on pod).

Nectria theobromae Massee
see *Nectria jungneri* P. Henn.

Nectriopsis aureonitens (Tul.) Maire
AFRICA: Ghana (Turner 1960d, as *Gliocladium penicilloides*, from pod).

Neurospora sitophila Shear and Dodge
AFRICA: Ghana (Dakwa 1968, from dying tree). WEST INDIES: Dominican Republic (Ciferri 1927a, b, as *Spicaria lateritia*, on pods; 1961, as *Monilia carbonaria*, on dead stems).

Niesslia crucipila (Höhnel) E. Müller
AFRICA: Sierra Leone (Herb. I.M.I., on dead wood).

Nigrospora sphaerica (Sacc.) Mason
AFRICA: Ghana (Owen 1956, from artificial stem-lesion; Turner 1960d, from pod).

Nummularia anthracodes (Fr.) Cooke var. *gliricidiae* Rehm
  AFRICA: Ghana (Hughes 1952, on branches).
Oncobasidium theobromae Talbot and Keane
  ASIA: Malaysia (West) (Keane and Turner 1972). AUSTRALASIA: Papua
  and New Guinea (Talbot and Keane 1971).
Oospora candidula Sacc.
  ASIA: Philippines (Saccardo 1916, on rotting pods).
Oospora roseoflava Sacc.
  WEST INDIES: Dominican Republic (Fragoso and Ciferri 1928, on pod).
Ophiobolus calathus Massee
  WEST INDIES: Trinidad (Hart 1911, on branches).
Ophioceras majusculum Penzig and Sacc.
  AFRICA: S. Tomé (Dias, Lucas, de Vasoncelos, and da Camara 1953, on
  pods).
Ophionectria theobromae Pat.
  WEST INDIES: Guadeloupe (Duss 1903, on twigs). ASIA: Philippines
  (Teodoro 1937, on branches). AUSTRALASIA: Samoa (American) (Dumble-
  ton 1954).
Ophionectria trichospora (Berk. and Br.) Sacc.
  SOUTH AMERICA: Unlocalized (Herb. I.M.I.). WEST INDIES: Trini-
  dad (Herb. I.M.I.).
Ophiostoma fimbriatum (Ellis and Halst.) Nannf.
  see *Ceratocystis fimbriata* Ellis and Halst.
Ophiostoma moniliforme (Hedgc.) H. and P. Syd. forma *theobromae* Luc
  see *Ceratocystis moniliforme* (Hedgc.) C. Moreau forma *theobromae* Luc
Papularia arundinis (Corda) Fr.
  see *Apiospora montagnei* Sacc.
Patellaria theobromatis d'Almeida and Camara
  AFRICA: S. Tomé (d'Almeida and da Camara 1909, on bark). SOUTH
  AMERICA: Brazil (Averna-Saccá 1920, on branches).
Pellicularia koleroga Cooke
  see *Koleroga noxia* Donk
Pellicularia salmonicolor (Berk. and Br.) Dastur
  see *Corticium salmonicolor* Berk. and Br.
Penicillium crustaceum Fr.
  see *Penicillium expansum* series
Penicillium expansum series
  WEST INDIES: Dominican Republic (Ciferri 1961, as *P. crustaceum,* on
  pods).
Penicillium janthinellum Biourge
  ASIA: Sabah (Williams 1965*b*, from insect lesion on pod).
Penzigia dealbata (Berk. and Curt.) Sacc. and Paol.
  see *Xylosphaera fockei* (Miq.) Dennis
Perichaena chrysosperma (Currey) List.
  WEST INDIES: Trinidad (Barnes 1963, on witches' brooms in trays).
Perichaena pulcherrima Petch
  ASIA: Sri Lanka (Petch 1909, on dead branches).

Periconia byssoides Pers. ex Schw.

WEST INDIES: Dominican Republic (Ciferri 1927*b*, as *Periconia picnospora*, on pods).

Periconia pycnospora Fres.

see *Periconia byssoides* Pers. ex Schw.

Pestalotia funerea Desm.

AFRICA: S. Tomé (da Camara and Cannas Mendes 1910, on leaves).

Pestalotia guepini Desm.

SOUTH AMERICA: Brazil (Averna-Saccá 1920, on leaves). AUSTRAL-ASIA: Samoa (Brick 1908, on seedlings).

Pestalotia menezesiana Bres. and Torrend

AFRICA: Ghana (Guba 1961, from lesions).

Pestalotia theobromae Petch

ASIA: Philippines (Guba 1961, on pods); Sri Lanka (Petch 1925*a*, on leaves).

Pestalotiopsis aquatica (Ellis and Everh.) Steyaert

ASIA: Sabah (Williams 1965*a*, from branch dieback); Sarawak (Reddy 1969).

Pestalotiopsis mangiferae (P. Henn.) Steyaert

AFRICA: Ghana (Steyaert 1953, from mirid lesion).

Pestalotiopsis neglecta (Thüm.) Steyaert

ASIA: Malaysia (West) (Steyaert 1953, on seedling leaves).

Pestalotiopsis owenii Steyaert

AFRICA: Ghana (Steyaert 1953, from artificial lesion).

Pestalotiopsis owenii Steyaert var. *major* Steyaert

AFRICA: Ghana (Steyaert 1953, from artificial lesion).

Pestalotiopsis papposa Steyaert

AFRICA: Ghana (Steyaert 1953, from artificial lesion).

Pestalotiopsis theae (Sawanda) Steyaert

ASIA: Sabah (Anon. 1972*b*, associated with necrotic leaf-blotch).

Pestalotiopsis theae (Sawanda) Steyaert var. *minor* Steyaert

AFRICA: Ghana (Steyaert 1953, from artificial lesion).

Pestalotiopsis versicolor (Speg.) Steyaert

AFRICA: Ghana (Steyaert 1953, from artificial lesion).

Phaeobotryosphaeria plicatula (Berk. and Br.) Petch

AFRICA: Ghana (Hughes 1953, on bark); Sierra Leone (Herb. I.M.I., on dead branch). ASIA: Malaysia (West) (Johnston 1960*a*, from twig dieback).

Phaeoisaria clematitidis (Fuckel) Hughes

AFRICA: Ghana (Herb. I.M.I., on dead wood); Sierra Leone (Herb. I.M.I., on dead branch). ASIA: Sabah (Berwick 1964, as *P. cornui,* on dead branch).

Phaeoisaria cornui (Bain.) Mason

see *Phaeoisaria clematidis* (Fuckel) Hughes

Phaeosolenia densa (Berk.) W. B. Cooke

ASIA: Malaysia (West) (Johnston 1960*a*, as *Cyphella variolosa*); Philippines (Teodoro 1937, as *Cyphella holstii,* on dead tree). AUSTRALASIA: British Solomon Islands (Herb. Kew.); New Hebrides (Huguenin 1964); Papua and New Guinea (Shaw 1963, on wood); West Irian (Johnston 1961).

Phellinus lamaensis (Murrill) Heim

AFRICA: Ghana (Piening 1962, as *Fomes lamaensis*).

Phellinus noxius (Corner) G. H. Cunn.

AFRICA: Cameroon (S.W.) (Ludwigs 1920, as *Hymenochaete noxia*, on roots and stem bases); Congo (Fraselle 1962, associated with root disease); Fernando Po (Nosti 1953); Ghana (Dade 1940); Ivory Coast (Mallamaire 1935*a*, as *Fomes lamaoensis*); Nigeria (West 1938). ASIA: Indonesia (van der Knaap 1956); Malaysia (West) (Johnston 1960*a*); Sabah (Berwick 1964); Sri Lanka (Anon. 1936); Taiwan (Sawada 1928). AUSTRALASIA: Fiji (Harwood 1959); Papua and New Guinea (Thrower 1956); Samoa (Henderson 1954).

Phellinus pachyphloeus Pat.

AFRICA: S. Tomé (Patouillard 1921, on trunks).

Phlyctaena anomala Petch

AFRICA: Uganda (Petch 1917, on bark).

Phoma theobromae Pat.

AFRICA: S. Tomé (Patouillard 1921, 1922*b*).

Phomopsis theobromae (d'Almeida and Camara) Bondarzewa-Mont.

AFRICA: Cape Province (Verwoerd and du Plessis 1933, as *Phyllosticta theobromae*, on leaves); Ivory Coast (Mallamaire 1935*b*); S. Tomé (d'Almeida and da Camara 1903, on leaves). SOUTH AMERICA: Brazil (Batista and Vital 1952, on leaves); Surinam (van Suchtelen 1955*a*, on leaves). WEST INDIES: Dominican Republic (Ciferri 1929*a*, *b*, on leaves, associated with thrips (*Selenothrips rubrocinctus*) damage). ASIA: Indonesia (Java) (Stevenson 1926, on leaves); Malaysia (West) (Thompson and Johnston 1953, associated with seedling leaf disease); Sri Lanka (Petch and Bisby 1950). EUROPE: U.S.S.R. (Bondarzewa-Monterverde *et al.* 1936, on leaves).

Phomopsis theobromae forma *dominicana* Frag. and Cif.

WEST INDIES: Dominican Republic (Fragoso and Ciferri 1928, as *Phyllosticta theobromae* forma *dominicana*, on leaves).

Phyllosticta theobromae d'Almeida and Camara

see *Phomopsis theobromae* (d'Almeida and Camara) Bondarzewa-Mont.

Phyllosticta theobromae forma *dominicana* Frag. and Cif.

see *Phomopsis theobromae* forma *dominicana* Frag. and Cig.

Phyllosticta theobromicola M. F. Vincens

SOUTH AMERICA: Brazil (Vincens 1918, on leaves).

Physalospora affinis Sacc.

ASIA: Philippines (Saccardo 1916, on pod).

Physalospora rhodina (Berk. and Curt.) Cooke

see *Botryodiplodia theobromae* Pat.

Physalospora theobromae Turc.

ASIA: Malaysia (West) (Thompson and Johnston 1953, associated with seedling root disease). EUROPE: Italy (Turconi 1920, on leaves).

Physalospora theobromicola Frag. and Cif.

WEST INDIES: Dominican Republic (Fragoso and Ciferri 1928, on leaves).

Physarum bubalinum Farr

WEST INDIES: Dominica (Farr 1969, on rotting husk).

Physarum compressum Alb. and Schw.

AFRICA: Nigeria (Farquharson and Lister 1916, on old pods). WEST INDIES: Dominica (Farr 1969, on rotting fruit).

Physarum nutans Pers. var. *leucophaeum* List.
WEST INDIES: Dominican Republic (Fragoso and Ciferri 1928, on dry pods).

Physarum pezizoideum (Jungh.) Pavillard and Lagardo
ASIA: Malaysia (West) (Herb. I.M.I.).

Phytophthora arecae (Coleman) Pethybridge
NORTH AMERICA: U.S.A. (Wilson 1914, pods artificially infected).

Phytophthora botryosa Chee
ASIA: Malaysia (West) (Chee 1969a, pods artificially infected).

Phytophthora cactorum (Leb. and Cohn) Schroet.
see *Phytophthora palmivora* (Butler) Butler

Phytophthora capsici Leonian
NORTH AMERICA: U.S.A. (Tucker 1931, seedlings artificially infected).

Phytophthora cinnamomi Rands
NORTH AMERICA: U.S.A. (Zentmyer *et al.* 1968, stems artificially infected).

Phytophthora citrophthora (R. E. Smith and E. H. Smith) Leonian
WEST INDIES: Jamaica (Leather 1967, associated with wilt).

Phytophthora colocasiae Racib. emend. Thomas and Ramakrishnan
see *Phytophthora palmivora* (Butler) Butler

Phytophthora faberi Maublanc
see *Phytophthora palmivora* (Butler) Butler

Phytophthora heveae Thompson
ASIA: Malaysia (West) (Turner 1968a, b); Sabah (Berwick 1965, from rotting pod; Anon. 1972b, from cushions).

Phytophthora hydrophila Curzi
NORTH AMERICA: U.S.A. (Tucker 1931, seedlings artificially infected).

Phytophthora meadii McRae
NORTH AMERICA: U.S.A. (Tucker 1931, pods and seedlings artificially infected).

Phytophthora megasperma Dreschler
SOUTH AMERICA: Venezuela (de Reyes, Reyes, and Escobar 1972; Anon. 1972a, as cause of 'water spot' pod rot).

Phytophthora nicotianae van Breda de Haan
NORTH AMERICA: U.S.A. (Tucker 1931, pod and seedlings artificially infected).

Phytophthora nicotianae var. *parasitica* (Dastur) Waterhouse
NORTH AMERICA: U.S.A. (Tucker 1931, pod and seedlings artificially infected).

Phytophthora omnivora de Bary
see *Phytophthora palmivora* (Butler) Butler

Phytophthora palmivora (Butler) Butler
AFRICA: Angola (Turner 1961a); Cameroon (S.E.) (Grimaldi 1954a); Cameroon (S.W.) (West and Voelcker 1942); Congo (Hendrickx 1948, as *P. cactorum*); Fernando Po (Nosti 1953); Gabon (Turner 1961a); Ghana (Dade 1940): Ivory Coast (Resplandy *et al.* 1954); Liberia (Krug and Quartey-Papafio 1964); Malagasy (Madagascar) (Krug and Quartey-Papafio 1964); Nigeria (West 1938); Principe (Navel 1921); Sierra Leone (Deighton 1956); S. Tomé

(da Camara and Cannas Mendes 1910, as *P. faberi*); Tanzania (Tanganyika) (Riley 1960); Tanzania (Zanzibar) (Urquhart 1958); Togo Republic (Berard 1956); Uganda (Hansford 1943*a*). CENTRAL AMERICA: Belize (Evans, Mitchell, Greenidge, Harkness, Beasley, Gregory-Smith, and Marnham 1948); Costa Rica (Wood 1957); Guatemala (Palm 1932); Mexico (Desrosiers and Diaz 1956*b*); Nicaragua (Orellana 1955); Panama (Orellana 1956*b*). SOUTH AMERICA: Brazil (Lellis and Filho 1957); Colombia (Polania 1957); Ecuador (Desrosiers and Diaz 1956*a*, *b*); Guyana (Martyn 1933); Peru (McLaughlin 1950*b*); Surinam (Ashby 1929*a*, as *P. parasitica* (Thomas and Ramakrishnan 1948)); Venezuela (Müller 1941). WEST INDIES: Carriacau (Baker 1940); Cuba (Venning and Gertsch 1958); Dominica (South 1912); Dominican Republic (Fragoso and Ciferri 1928); Grenada (South 1912); Haiti (Pierre-Louis and Dadaille 1956); Jamaica (Topper 1960); Martinique (Baker 1940); Puerto Rico (Chardon and Toro 1934); St. Kitts (South 1912); St. Lucia (Brooks 1916); St. Vincent (South 1912); Tobago (Freeman 1925); Trinidad (Massee 1899, as *P. omnivora*). ASIA: India (Ramakrishnan and Thankappan 1965); Indonesia (Hubert 1957); Malaysia (West) (Barcroft 1961); Philippines (Teodoro 1937); Sabah (Johnston 1960*c*); Sri Lanka (Petch and Bisby 1950; Vasudeva 1960, as *P. colocasiae*, with reference to Coleman 1910*a*, *b*, probably on Ceylon material); Thailand (Reinking 1921); Vietnam (Krug and Quartey-Papafio 1964). AUSTRALASIA: Caroline Islands (Zaiger and Zentmyer 1965); Fiji (Harwood 1959); New Hebrides (Dadant 1953); Papua and New Guinea (Thrower 1960*a*,*b*); Samoa (American) (Dumbleton 1954); Samoa (West) (Anon. 1973); West Irian (Johnston 1961).

Phytophthora palmivora var. *piperis* Muller
    ASIA: Indonesia (Muller 1936, cocoa was infected).
Phytophthora parasitica auct.
see *Phytophthora palmivora* (Butler) Butler
Piricularia caudata App. and Strunk
see *Trichoconis caudata* (App. and Strunk) Clem.
Pirostoma tetrapsecadiosporium Camara
    AFRICA: S. Tomé (da Camara and Cannas Mendes 1910, on bark).
Pleospora infectoria Fuckel
    AFRICA: S. Tomé (da Camara 1929, on bark).
Pleurotus testudo Berk.
    ASIA: Malaysia (West) (Johnston 1960*a*, associated with dieback).
Podospora striata (Ellis and Everh.) Ellis and Everh.
    WEST INDIES: Trinidad (Herb. I.M.I., on dead wood).
Podosporium theobromicolum Averna-Saccá
    SOUTH AMERICA: Brazil (Averna-Saccá 1920, on branches).
Pogonomyces hydnoides (Sw. ex Fr.) Murrill
see *Polyporus hydnoides* (Sw. ex Fr.) Murrill
Polylagenochromatia theobromae Camara
    AFRICA: S. Tomé (da Camara 1929, on bark).
Polyporus cinnabarinus Jacq. ex Fr.
    SOUTH AMERICA: Brazil (Averna-Saccá 1920, as *Polystictus cinnabarinus*).

Polyporus hydnoides Sw. ex Fr.
WEST INDIES: Trinidad (Fidalgo and Fidalgo 1966, as *Pogonomyces hydnoides*).
Polyporus korthalsii Lév.
WEST INDIES: Martinique (Duss 1903, as *Xanthochrous korthalsii*).
Polyporus lignosus Klotzsch
see *Rigidoporus lignosus* (Klotzsch) Imaseki
Polyporus microstomus Berk. and Curt.
WEST INDIES: Guadeloupe (Duss 1903, as *Leptoporus microstomus*).
Polyporus rugulosus Lév.
ASIA: Philippines (Teodoro 1937, on dead wood).
Polyporus sanguineus L. ex Fr.
AFRICA: Ivory Coast (Moreau and Moreau 1951, as *Microporus sanguineus*);
S. Tomé (Coutinho 1925, as *Trametes sanguinea*).
Polyporus sulphureus Fr.
AFRICA: S. Tomé (Patouillard 1921, as *Polyporus sulfureus*, on trunks).
Polyporus theobromae (Pat.) Lloyd
ASIA: Malaysia (Singapore) (Patouillard 1918, as *Echinodia theobromae*, on dead branches).
Polyporus zonalis Berk.
AFRICA: S. Tomé (Coutinho 1925, on trunks). SOUTH AMERICA: Brazil (Spaulding 1961).
Polystictus cinnabarinus (Jacq. ex Fr.) Sacc.
see *Polyporus cinnabarinus* Jacq. ex Fr.
Polystictus cryptomeriae P. Henn.
ASIA: Philippines (Teodoro 1937, on dead wood).
Polystictus persoonii Fr.
see *Trametes corrugata* (Pers.) Bres.
Poria ferruginosa (Schrad. ex Fr.) Karst.
AFRICA: S. Tomé (Coutinho 1925, on trunks).
Poria hypobrunnea Petch
AFRICA: Ghana (Dade 1940; Pegler and Gibson 1972*b*, uncertain determination).
Poria hypolateritia auct.
ASIA: Indonesia (Reddy 1970*a*; Pegler and Gibson 1972*b*, uncertain determination and taxonomy).
Poria incarnata Fr.
WEST INDIES: Trinidad (Baker and Dale 1951, uncertain determination).
Pseudocamptoum fasciculatum (Cooke and Massee) Mason
see *Melanographium citri* (Frag. and Cif.) M. B. Ellis
Pyrenotrichum bicolor Sant.
AFRICA: Nigeria (Thorold 1952, on leaf).
Pyrenotrichum irregulare Sant.
AFRICA: Fernando Po (Thorold 1955*a*, on leaf); Nigeria (Thorold 1952, on leaf).
Pyrenotrichum splitgerberi Mont.
AFRICA: Nigeria (Thorold 1952); Principe (Santesson, R. 1957 *in litt.*, on leaf).

Pyricularia caudata App. and Strunk
see *Trichoconis caudata* (App. and Strunk) Clem.
Pythium complectens Braun
ASIA: Malaysia (West) (Johnston 1960*a*, associated with seedling root disease).
Pythium debaryanum Hesse
CENTRAL AMERICA: Costa Rica (Bowman 1951, uncertain determination).
Ramularia necator Massee
EUROPE: England (Massee 1907, on cotyledons).
Rhabdospora theobromae App. and Strunk
AFRICA: Cameroon (S.W.) (Appel and Strunk 1904, on dead pods).
Rhizoctonia bataticola (Taubenh.) Butler
see *Macrophomina phaseolina* (Tassi) Goid.
Rhizoctonia lamellifera Small
AFRICA: Uganda (Hansford 1937, 1943*a*, on roots, associated with dieback).
Rhizoctonia solani Kühn
AFRICA: Ghana (Dade 1940; Piening 1962, as *Corticium solani*). CENTRAL AMERICA: Costa Rica (Hansen 1963*b*, causing leaf spotting); Guatemala (Hansen 1963*b*, possibly causing leaf spotting). ASIA: Sabah (Anon. 1972*b*, from cushions).
Rhizophydium fungicola Zimm.
ASIA: Indonesia (Java) (Zimmermann 1902, on pod).
Rhizopus arrhizus Fischer
AFRICA: Ghana (Turner 1960*d*, as *R. nodosus,* from pod).
Rhizopus nodosus Namysl.
see *Rhizopus arrhizus* Fischer
Rhizopus oryzae Went and Geerl.
AFRICA: Ghana (Anon. 1968, on husk).
Rhodophyllus hypoporphyrius Berk. and Curt.
WEST INDIES: Guadeloupe (Duss 1903).
Rhodotorula glutinis (Fres.) Harrison
AFRICA: Ivory Coast (Ruinen 1963*a*, from leaves).
Rhodotorula mucilaginosa (Jörgensen) Harrison
see *Rhodotorula rubra* (Demme) Lodder
Rhodotorula rubra (Demme) Lodder
AFRICA: Ivory Coast (Ruinen 1963*a*, as *R. mucilaginosa,* from leaves).
Rhopalopsis coenopus (Fr.) Cooke
WEST INDIES: Trinidad (Rorer 1911, on fallen branches).
Rhytidhysterium rufulum (Spreng.) Speg.
AFRICA: Cameroon (S.E.) (Grimaldi 1954*a*); Ghana (Hughes 1952, as *Tryblidiella rufula*, on branches); Sierra Leone (Herb. I.M.I., on dead twigs). SOUTH AMERICA: Brazil (Sydow and Sydow 1909, on branches). WEST INDIES: Haiti (Ciferri 1961). ASIA: Malaysia (West) (Johnston 1960*a*, associated with twig dieback).
Rigidoporus lignosus (Klotzsch) Imaseki
AFRICA: Cameroon (S.E.) (Grimaldi 1954*a*); Congo (Staner 1928); Fernando Po (Nosti 1943); Ghana (Dade 1940); Ivory Coast (Resplandy *et al.* 1954); Nigeria (West 1938); Sierra Leone (Deighton 1930, uncertain determination);

S. Tomé (Patouillard 1922a, as *Polyporus lignosus*). SOUTH AMERICA: Brazil (Weir 1926). WEST INDIES: Trinidad (Rayner 1941; Baker and Dale 1951, uncertain determination as *Fomes auberianus*). ASIA: Malaysia (West) (McIntosh 1951); Sabah (Anon. 1960); Sarawak (Anon. 1960, 1966); Sri Lanka (Petch 1917, 1918, as *Fomes semitostus*). AUSTRALASIA: New Hebrides (Johnston 1963b); Papua and New Guinea (Thrower 1956).

Rosellinia arcuata Petch

AFRICA: Ghana (Dade 1940, uncertain determination). ASIA: Indonesia (Hubert 1957, associated with 'black root rot').

Rosellinia australis Sacc. and Trott.

SOUTH AMERICA: Brazil (Weir 1926, on dead roots).

Rosellinia bunodes (Berk. and Br.) Sacc.

CENTRAL AMERICA: Mexico (Limón 1945). SOUTH AMERICA: Brazil (Weir 1926). WEST INDIES: Cuba (Anon. 1952); Grenada (Waterston 1941); Jamaica (Larter and Martyn 1943); Puerto Rico (Cook and Otero 1939); St. Lucia (Walters 1928, as *Rosellinia* root disease (probably *R. bunodes* and *R. pepo*, in *Rev. appl. Mycol.* 8, 20 (1929)); Trinidad (Nowell 1923). ASIA: Indonesia (Reddy 1970a). AUSTRALASIA: Papua and New Guinea (Dumbleton 1954).

Rosellinia necatrix (Hartig) Berl. ex Prill.

AFRICA: Unlocalized (Burle 1961, as *Rosellinia necatrix* Berk.).

Rosellinia paraguayensis Starb.

CENTRAL AMERICA: Mexico (Zevada *et al.* 1955). WEST INDIES: Grenada (Waterston 1941). AUSTRALASIA: Papua and New Guinea (Dumbleton 1954).

Rosellinia pepo Pat.

CENTRAL AMERICA: Costa Rica (Wood 1957); Mexico (Limón 1945). SOUTH AMERICA; Brazil (Weir 1926); Surinam (van Suchtelen 1955a). WEST INDIES: Cuba (Anon. 1952); Dominican Republic (Ciferri 1961); Grenada (Waterston 1941); Jamaica (Larter and Martyn 1943); St. Lucia (Brooks 1916); Trinidad (Baker and Dale 1951). AUSTRALASIA: Papua and New Guinea (Dumbleton 1954; doubtful record, see p. 152).

Sarcosoma javanicum Rehm

AFRICA: Ghana (Herb. I.M.I., on dead wood).

Sarcoxylon deightonii Petrak

AFRICA: Sierra Leone (Petrak and Deighton 1952, on trunk).

Schizophyllum alneum (L.) Schroet.

AFRICA: Ghana (Hughes 1953, as *S. commune*, on branches). SOUTH AMERICA: Brazil (Teixeira 1946); Peru (Cooke 1961, locality given by Cooke, W. B. 1962 *in litt.*).

Schizophyllum commune Fr.

see *Schizophyllum alneum* (L.) Schroet.

Sclerotinia laxa Aderh. and Ruhl.

WEST INDIES: Dominican Republic (Ciferri 1927b, 1961, uncertain determination as *Monilia cinerea*, from branches).

Sclerotium bataticola Taubenh.

see *Macrophomina phaseolina* (Tassi) Goid.

Sclerotium rolfsii Sacc.

see *Corticium rolfsii* Curzi

Scoleconectria tetraspora Seaver

see *Calonectria rigidiuscula* (Berk. and Br.) Sacc.

Scopulariopsis fusca Zach
    AFRICA: Ghana (Morton and Smith 1963, on leaves).

Sebacina calcea (Pers.) Bres.
    ASIA: Malaysia (West) (Johnston 1960a, associated with branch dieback).

Septobasidium spongia (Berk. and Curt.) Pat.
    WEST INDIES: Cuba (Burt 1916, on bark).

Septoria theobromicola Cif. and Frag.
    WEST INDIES: Dominican Republic (Fragoso and Ciferri 1928, on leaves).

Spegazzinia tessarthra (Berk. and Curt.) Sacc.
    AFRICA: Ghana (Herb. I.M.I.).

Sphaerella theobromae von Faber
    AFRICA: Cameroon (S.W.) (von Faber 1909, on pods). SOUTH AMERICA:
    Brazil (Lizer 1914).

Sphaeronaema mirabile (Speg.) Jacz.
    AFRICA: Ghana (Herb. I.M.I.). Sierra Leone (Herb. I.M.I.).

Sphaeronaema theobromae Cost. and Gallaud
    UNLOCALIZED: (Costantin and Gallaud 1903, on pods).

Sphaerostilbe coccophila (Desm.) Tul.

see *Nectria flammea* (Tul.) Dingley

Sphaerostilbe musarum Ashby

see *Calostilbe striispora* (Ellis and Everh.) Seaver

Sphaerostilbe ochracea Pat.
    WEST INDIES: Guadeloupe (Duss 1903, on rotten pod).

Sphaerostilbe repens Berk. and Br.
    AFRICA: Cameroon (S.E.) (Grimaldi 1954a); Congo (Fraselle 1962); Uganda
    (Snowden 1921). WEST INDIES: Trinidad (Stell 1929, as *Sphaerostilbe* sp.,
    probably *S. repens* (*Rev. appl. Mycol.* **9**, 20, 1930)). ASIA: Sri Lanka (Gadd
    1928). AUSTRALASIA: Papua and New Guinea (Dumbleton 1954).

Spicaria colorans de Jonge

see *Calonectria rigidiuscula* (Berk. and Br.) Sacc.

Spicaria lateritia Cif.

see *Neurospora sitophila* Shear and Dodge

Spiropes capensis (Thüm.) M. B. Ellis
    WEST INDIES: Trinidad (Baker and Dale 1951, as *Helminthosporium capense*,
    on *Meliola* sp., on leaf).

Sporidesmium aburiense M. B. Ellis
    AFRICA: Ghana (Ellis 1958, as a hyperparasite, on leaves).

Sporidesmium crassisporum M. B. Ellis
    AFRICA: Ivory Coast (Herb. I.M.I., from dead branch).

Sporidesmium tropicale M. B. Ellis
    AFRICA: Ghana (Ellis 1958). ASIA: Malaysia (West) (Johnston 1960a,
    associated with twig dieback).

Sporobolomyces roseus Kluyver and van Niel
    AFRICA: Ivory Coast (Ruinen 1963a, from leaves).

Sporobolomyces salmonicolor (Fischer and Brebeck) Kluyver and van Niel
  AFRICA: Ivory Coast (Ruinen 1963*a*, from leaves).
Sporotrichum flavissimum Link
  WEST INDIES: Dominican Republic (Ciferri 1927*b*, on pod).
Stachybotrys subsimplex Cooke
see *Memnoniella subsimplex* (Cooke) Deighton
Stachybotrys theobromae Hansf.
  AFRICA: Ghana (Hughes 1952, on branches and dry pods); Sierra Leone
  (Herb. I.M.I., on dead branch); Uganda (Hansford 1943*b*, on dead branch).
  WEST INDIES: Trinidad (Herb. I.M.I.). ASIA: Sabah (Anon. 1973).
  AUSTRALASIA: Papua and New Guinea (Shaw 1963, on old wood).
Stachylidium bicolor Link ex S. F. Gray
  AFRICA: Ghana (Hughes 1952, on pods). ASIA: Malaysia (West) (Thompson and Johnston 1953, associated with leaf spotting).
Stachylidium theobromae Turc.
see *Verticillium theobromae* (Turc.) Mason and Hughes
Stemonitis ferruginea Ehrenb.
  WEST INDIES: Dominican Republic (Ciferri 1961, on dead leaves).
Stemphylium sphaericum Sacc.
see *Hermatomyces sphaericum* (Sacc.) Hughes
Stereum petalodes Berk.
  WEST INDIES: Dominican Republic (Ciferri 1961, uncertain determination).
Stilbella erythrocephala (Ditm. ex Fr.) Lindau
  WEST INDIES: Dominican Republic (Fragoso and Ciferri 1928, on rotten pods).
Stilbella proliferans Stev.
  AFRICA: Ghana (Herb. I.M.I., on bark); Sierra Leone (Herb. I.M.I.).
  CENTRAL AMERICA: Costa Rica (Stevens 1927, on bark). WEST INDIES:
  Trinidad (Herb. I.M.I.). ASIA: Malaysia (West) (Anon. 1973). AUSTRA-
  LASIA: Papua and New Guinea (Shaw 1963, on old wood).
Stilbochalara dimorpha Ferd. and Winge
  SOUTH AMERICA: Venezuela (Ferdinandsen and Winge 1910, on rotting pods).
Stilbospora cacao Massee
  WEST INDIES: Trinidad (Massee 1906, on branches).
Stilbum aurantio-cinnabarinum Speg.
  WEST INDIES: Trinidad (Herb. I.M.I.).
Stilbum cinnabarinum Mont.
see *Thyronectria pseudotrichia* (Schw.) Seeler
Stilbum fasciculatum Berk. and Br.
  AFRICA: Uganda (Hansford 1943*b*).
Stilbum nanum Massee
  WEST INDIES: Trinidad (Lewton-Brain 1905, uncertain determination, associated with thread blight). ASIA: Indonesia (Anon. 1960, associated with thread blight).
Stilbum seabra Pat.
  AFRICA: S. Tomé (Patouillard 1922*b*, associated with 'Mela' disease of pods).

Systremma stevensonii Cif. and Bat.
see *Coccoidella stevensonii* (Cif. and Bat.) E. Müller
Teichospora loculosa Camara
    AFRICA: S. Tomé (da Camara 1920, on branches).
Teichospora theobromae Camara
    UNLOCALIZED: (Roger 1953).
Thielaviopsis ethaceticus Went
see *Ceratocystis paradoxa* (Dade) C. Moreau
Thielaviopsis paradoxa (De Seynes) Höhnel
see *Ceratocystis paradoxa* (Dade) C. Moreau
Thyridaria tarda Bancroft
see *Botryodiplodia theobromae* Pat.
Thyronectria pseudotrichia (Schw.) Seeler
    AFRICA: Cameroon (S.E.) (Grimaldi 1954*b*, on branches); Ghana (Dade
    1940, as *Megalonectria pseudotrichia*); Sierra Leone (Herb. I.M.I., on bran-
    ches); S. Tomé (Patouillard 1921, as *Stilbum cinnabarinum*, on bark; Dias *et al.*
    1953, on pod); Uganda (Snowden 1921, on dead stem). WEST INDIES:
    Jamaica (Leather 1967, on pod). ASIA: Malaysia (West) (Johnston 1960*a*,
    from dieback); Sabah (Johnston 1960*c*, from dieback); Sri Lanka (Petch 1910*b*,
    on stems). AUSTRALASIA: Papua and New Guinea (Shaw 1963, on old
    wood).
Trachysphaera fructigena Tabor and Bunting.
    AFRICA: Cameroon (S.E.) (Grimaldi 1954*a*); Congo (Fraselle 1962); Ghana
    (Tabor and Bunting 1923); Ivory Coast (Resplandy *et al.* 1954); Nigeria
    (Bailey 1966); Sierra Leone (Deighton 1956).
Trametes corrugata (Pers.) Bres.
    AFRICA: Ghana (Piening 1962); Sierra Leone (Herb. Kew.); S. Tomé (da
    Camara and Cannas Mendes 1910, as *Polystictus persoonii*). WEST INDIES:
    Trinidad (Rayner 1941, as *Trametes cubensis*). ASIA: Philippines (Teodoro
    1937, as *Trametes persoonii,* on dead wood). AUSTRALASIA: New Hebrides
    (Johnston 1963*b*, associated with dieback).
Trametes cubensis (Mont.) Sacc.
see *Trametes corrugata* (Pers.) Bres.
Trametes gibbosa (Pers. ex Fr.) Fr.
    AFRICA: S. Tomé (Coutinho 1925, on trunks).
Trametes persoonii Mont.
see *Trametes corrugata* (Pers.) Bres.
Trametes sanguinea (L. ex Fr.) Lloyd
see *Polyporus sanguineus* L. ex Fr.
Trametes sepium (Rav.) Berk.
    AFRICA: S. Tomé (Coutinho 1925, uncertain determination, on trunks).
Trametes sprucei Berk.
    AFRICA: S. Tomé (Coutinho 1925, on dead trunks).
Trichoconis caudata (App. and Strunk) Clem.
    AFRICA: Cameroon (S.W.) (Appel and Strunk 1904, as *Piricularia* (*Pyri-
    cularia*) *caudata,* on pods); Sierra Leone (Deighton and Pirozynski 1972, on
    wilting pods, associated with *Botryodiplodia theobromae*).

Trichoderma viride Pers. ex S. F. Gray
    AFRICA: Ghana (Owen 1956, from artificial stem-lesion).
Trichosphaeria dactylosporifera Petch
    AFRICA: Ghana (Herb. I.M.I., on dead wood); Sierra Leone (Herb. I.M.I., on dead wood).
Trichothecium roseum (Pers.) Link ex S. F. Gray
    ASIA: Malaysia (West) (Herb. I.M.I.).
Tryblidiella rufula (Spreng.) Sacc.
see *Rhytidhysterium rufulum* (Spreng.) Speg.
Ulocladium consortiale (Thüm.) Simmons
    UNLOCALIZED: (Joly 1964, as *Alternaria consortiale,* on pods).
Unguiculella caespitosa Dennis
    AFRICA: Sierra Leone (Dennis 1950, on dead tree).
Ustulina deusta (Hoffm. ex Fr.) Lind
    AFRICA: Cameroon (S.E.) (Grimaldi 1954a, as *U. maxima*); Fernando Po (Nosti 1953, as *U. zonata*); Ghana (Dade 1940); Tanzania (Tanganyika) (Riley 1960). WEST INDIES: Trinidad (Baker and Dale 1951). ASIA: Indonesia (Reddy 1970a); Sri Lanka (Anon. 1936). AUSTRALASIA: Fiji (Harwood 1959); New Hebrides (Johnston 1963b); Papua and New Guinea (Thrower 1956).
Ustulina maxima (Weber) Wettst.
see *Ustulina deusta* (Hoffm. ex Fr.) Lind
Ustulina zonata (Lév.) Sacc.
see *Ustulina deusta* (Hoffm. ex Fr.) Lind
Verticillium albo-atrum Reinke and Berth.
    SOUTH AMERICA: Brazil (Rudolph 1931).
Verticillium cinnamomeum Petch
    ASIA: Malaysia (West) (Herb. I.M.I., on 'whitefly' (Aleyrodidae sp.)).
Verticillium dahliae Kleb.
    AFRICA: Uganda (Leakey 1965, causing 'sudden death' disease).
Verticillium ochrorubrum Desm.
    SOUTH AMERICA: Colombia (Chardon and Toro 1930, on pod lesions, associated with *Monilia roreri* infection).
Verticillium theobromae (Turc.) Mason and Hughes
    EUROPE: Italy (Turconi 1920, as *Stachylidium theobromae,* on leaves).
Virgatospora echinofibrosa Finley
    AFRICA: Sierra Leone (Herb. I.M.I.). ASIA: Malaysia (West) (Anon. 1973). AUSTRALASIA: New Guinea (Herb. I.M.I.).
Wallrothiella subiculosa Höhnel
    AFRICA: Ghana (Dickinson 1968).
Xanthochrous korthalsii (Lév.) Pat.
see *Polyporus korthalsii* Lév.
Xerotus nigritus Lév.
    ASIA: Philippines (Reinking 1920, on dead wood).
Xylaria anisopleura (Mont.) Mont.
    AFRICA: Sierra Leone (Herb. I.M.I., on dead trunks).
Xylaria fastigiata Fr.
    AFRICA: Sierra Leone (Herb. I.M.I., on dead trunks).

Xylaria feejeensis (Berk.) Fr.
see *Xylosphaera feejeensis* (Berk.) Dennis
Xylaria ianthino-velutina (Mont.) Fr.
see *Xylosphaera ianthino-velutina* (Mont.) Dennis
Xylocladium clautriavii (Pat.) Syd.
 WEST INDIES: Trinidad (Herb. I.M.I.).
Xylosphaera feejeensis (Berk.) Dennis
 ASIA: Sabah (Berwick 1964, as *Xylaria feejeensis,* on dead branch).
Xylosphaera fockei (Miq.) Dennis
 WEST INDIES: Martinique (Duss 1903, as *Penzigia dealbata,* on rotting
 wood).
Xylosphaera ianthino-velutina (Mont.) Dennis
 SOUTH AMERICA: Colombia (Dennis 1957, as *Xylaria ianthino-velutina,*
 on fallen pods).
Zignoella büttneri Rehm.
 AFRICA: S. Tomé (da Camara 1929, uncertain determination, on bark).
Zygosporium echinosporum Bunting apud Mason
 AFRICA: Sierra Leone (Herb. I.M.I.).
Zygosporium oscheoides Mont.
 AFRICA: Ghana (Hughes 1952, on leaves).

Algae

Cephaleuros minimus Karst.
 ASIA: Indonesia (Reddy 1970*a*); Malaysia (West) (Herb. I.M.I.); Sri Lanka
 (Petch 1922). AUSTRALASIA: Papua and New Guinea (Shaw 1962, 1963);
 West Irian (Johnston 1961).
Cephaleuros mycoidea Karst.
see *Cephaleuros virescens* Kunze
Cephaleuros virescens Kunze
 AFRICA: Cameroon (S.E.) (Grimaldi 1954*a*); Cameroon (S.W.) (Thorold
 1952); Congo (Claessens 1914); Fernando Po (Nosti 1953); Ghana (Dade
 1940, as *C. mycoidea*); Ivory Coast (Mallamaire 1935*b*); Malagasy (Madagas-
 car) (Bouriquet 1946); Nigeria (West 1938); S. Tomé (de Seabra 1922);
 Uganda (Snowden 1921). SOUTH AMERICA: Brazil (Silva and Lellis
 1947); Colombia (Garcés 1941, as 'algal disease'); Ecuador (Desrosiers and
 Diaz 1956*a*). WEST INDIES: Dominican Republic (Ciferri 1929*a, b*);
 Grenada (Baker 1940); Guadeloupe (Baker 1940); Haiti (Orellana 1956*a*);
 Jamaica (Larter and Martyn 1943); Martinique (Baker 1940); St. Lucia
 (Brooks 1918); St. Vincent (Baker 1940); Trinidad (Rorer 1918*b*). ASIA:
 Indonesia (Java) (Rombouts 1937); Malaysia (West) (Heath 1958); Sabah
 (Johnston 1960*c*); Thailand (Thet Su 1935). AUSTRALASIA: Fiji (Graham
 1964); Papua and New Guinea (Shaw 1962; 1963); Samoa (Smith 1955).
Chroococcus minutus (Kützing) Naegeli
 AFRICA: Nigeria (Thorold 1952).
Phormidium retzii Gomont
 AFRICA: Nigeria (Thorold 1952).
Phycopeltis flabelligera (de Toni) Hansgirg
 AFRICA: S. Tomé (Johnson 1912).

Trentepohlia abietina (Flot.) Hansgirg
    AFRICA: Principe (Cribb, A. 1959 *in litt.*); S. Tomé (Cribb, A. 1959 *in litt.*).
Trentepohlia arborum (C. Agardh) Har.
    AFRICA: Cameroon (S.W.) (Thorold 1952, as *T. wainioi*).
Trentepohlia aurea (L.) Mart.
    AFRICA: Nigeria (Thorold 1952).
Trentepohlia aurea var. *polycarpa* (Nees and Mont.) Har.
    AFRICA: Cameroon (S.W.) (Thorold 1952); Nigeria (Thorold 1952).
Trentepohlia bossei de Wild.
    AFRICA: Cameroon (S.W.) (Cribb, A. 1959 *in litt.*); Fernando Po (Cribb, A. 1959 *in litt.*); Nigeria (Cribb, A. 1959 *in litt.*); Principe (Cribb, A. 1959 *in litt.*).
Trentepohlia lagenifera (Hildebrand) Wille var. *africana* Printz
    AFRICA: Nigeria (Thorold 1952).
Trentepohlia rigidula (Müll. Arg.) Har.
    AFRICA: Principe (Cribb, A. 1959 *in litt.*).
Trentepohlia wainioi Har.
see *Trentepohlia arborum* (C. Agardh) Har.

Lichens (Corticolous)

Anaptychia speciosa (Wulf.) Massal.
    ASIA: Sri Lanka (Wright 1907, uncertain determination, as *Physcia speciosa*).
Anthracothecium cinerosum (Ach.) Müll. Arg.
    AFRICA: Cameroon (S.W.) (Dodge 1964); Principe (Dodge 1964); S. Tomé Dodge 1964).
Anthracothecium guineensis (Nyl.) Zahlbr.
    AFRICA: Nigeria (Dodge 1964); Principe (Dodge 1964); S. Tomé (Dodge 1964).
Arthonia subcaesia Dodge
    AFRICA: Nigeria (Dodge 1964).
Bacidia golungensis (Vain.) Zahlbr.
    AFRICA: Nigeria (Dodge 1953).
Bacidia molybditis (Tuck.) Zahlbr.
    WEST INDIES: Trinidad (Herb. I.M.I.).
Bacidia nigeriensis Dodge
    AFRICA: Nigeria (Dodge 1953).
Bathelium subalbens (Nyl.) Dodge
    AFRICA: Cameroon (S.W.) (Dodge, C. W. 1958 *in litt.*).
Bombyliospora domingensis (Pers.) Zahlbr.
    AFRICA: Nigeria (Thorold 1952, probably wrong determination).
Bombyliospora nigeriensis Dodge
    AFRICA: Nigeria (Dodge 1953).
Bombyliospora thoroldii Dodge
    AFRICA: Nigeria (Dodge 1953).
Candelariella isidiosa Dodge
    AFRICA: Principe (Dodge 1971).

Collema byrsaeum Ach.
see *Physma byrsaeum* (Ach.) Tuck.
Collema cameroonense Dodge
    AFRICA: Cameroon (S.W.) (Dodge 1964).
Collema minutum (Hue) Dodge
see *Collema nigrescens* (Huds.) DC. var. *minutum* Hue
Collema nigrescens (Huds.) DC.
    AFRICA: Nigeria (Thorold 1952).
Collema nigrescens (Huds.) DC. var. *minutum* Hue
    AFRICA: Cameroon (S.W.) (Dodge 1953); Nigeria (Dodge 1953; 1964, as
    C. minutum (Hue) Dodge, not *C. minutum* Magn.); S. Tomé (Dodge 1964).
Cryptothecia nigeriensis Dodge
    AFRICA: Nigeria (Dodge 1953).
Cryptothecia thoroldii Dodge
    AFRICA: Nigeria (Dodge 1953).
Diplotomma thoroldii Dodge
    AFRICA: Nigeria (Dodge 1971).
Glyphis cicatricosa Ach.
    AFRICA: Cameroon (S.W.) (Dodge 1964).
Graphina albonotata (Nyl.) Dodge
    AFRICA: Principe (Dodge 1964).
Graphina ambrizensis (Vain.) Zahlbr.
    AFRICA: Cameroon (S.W.) (Dodge 1964).
Graphina arthothelioides Dodge
    AFRICA: Cameroon (S.W.) (Dodge 1964); S. Tomé (Dodge, C. W. 1961 *in
    litt.*).
Graphina collatinensis Red.
    AFRICA: Ivory Coast (des Abbayes 1955).
Graphina fecunda Zahlbr.
    AUSTRALASIA: Fiji (Dodge, C. W. 1968 *in litt.*).
Graphina ulcerata (Vain.) Zahlbr.
    AFRICA: Cameroon (S.W.) (Dodge 1964); Nigeria (Dodge 1964).
Graphis angolensis Dodge
    AFRICA: S. Tomé (Dodge 1964).
Graphis guineensis Dodge
    AFRICA: Cameroon (S.W.) (Dodge 1964).
Graphis nigeriensis Dodge
    AFRICA: Cameroon (S.W.) (Dodge 1964); Nigeria (Dodge 1953, 1964).
Graphis ondensis Dodge
    AFRICA: Nigeria (Dodge 1953).
Graphis striatula (Ach.) Spreng.
    AFRICA: Cameroon (S.W.) (Dodge 1964).
Graphis thoroldii Dodge
    AFRICA: Nigeria (Dodge 1953).
Graphis timidula Nyl.
    AFRICA: Cameroon (S.W.) (Dodge 1964).
Gyrostomum scyphuliferum (Ach.) Fr.
    AFRICA: Principe (Dodge 1964).

Laurera nigeriensis Dodge
  AFRICA: Nigeria (Dodge 1953).
Lecanora aequinoctialis Stizenb.
  AFRICA: Nigeria (Dodge 1953).
Lecidea granifera (Ach.) Vain.
  AFRICA: Nigeria (Dodge 1953).
Lecidea nigeriensis Dodge
  AFRICA: Nigeria (Dodge 1953).
Lecidea rubina Ach.
  AFRICA: Cameroon (S.W.) (Dodge, C.W. 1958 *in litt.*); Nigeria (Dodge 1953).
Lecidea tenuis Müll. Arg.
  AFRICA: Nigeria (Dodge 1953).
Leptogium cameroonense Dodge
  AFRICA: Cameroon (S.W.) (Dodge 1964); Nigeria (Dodge 1964).
Leptogium marginelloides Dodge
  AFRICA: Cameroon (S.W.) (Dodge 1964); S. Tomé (Dodge 1964).
Leptogium nigeriense Dodge
  AFRICA: Nigeria (Dodge 1964).
Leptogium phyllocarpum (Pers.) Nyl.
  WEST INDIES: Guadeloupe (Duss 1904; Vainio 1915, as *L. phyllocarpum* var. *macrocarpa*).
Leptogium stipitatum Vain.
  WEST INDIES: Guadeloupe (Duss 1904).
Leptogium thoroldii Dodge
  AFRICA: Cameroon (S.W.) (Dodge 1964).
Leptogium tremelloides (L.f.) S. F. Gray var. *foliolosa* Dodge
  AFRICA: Nigeria (Dodge 1964); Principe (Dodge 1964).
Leptogium verpiforme Dodge
  AFRICA: Cameroon (S.W.) (Dodge 1964).
Leptogium vesiculosum (Sw.) Malme
  AFRICA: Nigeria (Thorold 1952).
Melanotheca cameroonensis Dodge
  AFRICA: Cameroon (S.W.) (Dodge 1953).
Melanotheca nigeriensis Dodge
  AFRICA: Nigeria (Dodge 1953, 1964).
Melanotheca porosa Dodge
  AFRICA: Nigeria (Dodge 1964).
Ocellularia cavata (Ach.) Müll. Arg.
  AFRICA: Nigeria (Dodge 1953).
Ocellularia fumosa (Ach.) Müll. Arg.
  AFRICA: S. Tomé (Dodge 1964).
Ocellularia scolecospora Dodge
  AFRICA: Nigeria (Dodge 1953).
Ocellularia trypanea (Ach.) Dodge
  AFRICA: Nigeria (Dodge 1953).
Opegrapha nigeriensis Dodge
  AFRICA: Nigeria (Dodge 1953).

Opegrapha prosodea Ach.
AFRICA: Nigeria (Dodge 1953).
Pannaria thoroldii Dodge
AFRICA: Cameroon (S.W.) (Dodge 1964).
Parmelia austrosinensis Zahlbr.
AFRICA: Ivory Coast (des Abbayes 1958, as *P. meridionalis*).
Parmelia claudelii Vain. var. *clemensiae* Vain.
see *Parmelia cristifera* Tayl.
Parmelia cristifera Tayl.
AFRICA: Principe (Dodge, C. W. 1961 *in litt.*, as *P. gossweileri*). AUSTRA-
LASIA: Fiji (Dodge, C. W. 1968 *in litt.*, as *P. claudelii* var. *clemensae*).
Parmelia gossweileri Dodge
see *Parmelia cristifera* Tayl.
Parmelia meridionalis Tav.
see *Parmelia austrosinensis* Zahlbr.
Parmelia pseudotinctorum Abb.
AFRICA: S. Tomé (Dodge, C. W. 1961 *in litt.*).
Parmelia sanctae-helenae Dodge
AFRICA: Annobon (Dodge, C. W. 1960 *in litt.*).
Parmelia sancti-angelii Lynge
AFRICA: Ivory Coast (des Abbayes 1958).
Parmelia sulphurata Nees and Flot.
WEST INDIES: Guadeloupe (Duss 1904).
Phaeographina deducta Zahlbr.
AFRICA: Fernando Po (Dodge 1953).
Phaeographina leptotremoides Dodge
AFRICA: Cameroon (S.W.) (Dodge 1953, 1964).
Phaeographina scriptitata Dodge
AFRICA: Cameroon (S.W.) (Dodge 1964).
Phaeographis dendriticella Müll. Arg.
AFRICA: Cameroon (S.W.) (Dodge 1964).
Phaeographis impexella (Stirt.) Zahlbr.
AFRICA: Cameroon (S.W.) (Dodge 1964).
Phaeographis lynceodes Zahlbr.
AFRICA: Cameroon (S.W.) (Dodge 1953); Nigeria (Dodge 1964); Principe
(Dodge 1964).
Phaeographis navicularis (Vain.) Zahlbr.
AFRICA: Cameroon (S.W.) (Dodge 1964); Principe (Dodge 1964).
Phaeographis ochracea Dodge
AFRICA: Cameroon (S.W.) (Dodge 1953, 1964).
Phaeographis sexlocularis (Vain.) Zahlbr.
AFRICA: Cameroon (S.W.) (Dodge 1964).
Phaeographis subnivescens (Nyl.) Zahlbr.
AFRICA: Cameroon (S.W.) (Dodge 1964); Principe (Dodge 1964).
Phyllopsora buettneri (Müll. Arg.) Zahlbr.
AFRICA: Ghana (Dodge 1953); Nigeria (Dodge 1953); Principe (Dodge
1964).

Physcia integrata Nyl. var. *sorediosa* Vain.
SOUTH AMERICA: Brazil (Averna-Saccá 1920).
Physcia nigeriensis Dodge
AFRICA: Nigeria (Dodge 1971).
Physcia poncinsii Hue
AFRICA: Cameroon (S.W.) (Dodge 1953); Nigeria (Dodge 1953).
Physcia speciosa (Wulf.) Nyl.
see *Anaptychia speciosa* (Wulf.) Massal.
Physma byrsaeum (Ach.) Tuck.
AFRICA: S. Tomé (Dodge 1964). WEST INDIES: Guadeloupe (Duss 1904, as *Collema byrsaeum*).
Pseudopyrenula deightoni Dodge
AFRICA: S. Tomé (Dodge 1964).
Pyrenastrum parathelioides Dodge
AFRICA: Nigeria (Dodge 1953); S. Tomé (Dodge 1964).
Pyrenula aspistea (Afz. in Ach.) Ach.
AFRICA: S. Tomé (Dodge 1964).
Pyrenula convexa (Nyl.) Müll. Arg.
SOUTH AMERICA: Peru (Dodge, C. W. 1965 *in litt.*).
Pyrenula eucalypta Vain.
AFRICA: Cameroon (S.W.) (Dodge 1953).
Pyrenula fuscolurida Vain.
AFRICA: Nigeria (Dodge 1953).
Pyrenula heteroclita Ach.
AFRICA: Cameroon (S.W.) (Dodge 1953); Nigeria (Dodge, C. W. 1952 *in litt.*).
Pyrenula mamillana (Ach.) Trev.
AFRICA: Cameroon (S.W.) (Dodge 1953); Nigeria (Dodge 1953).
Pyrenula trombetana Vain.
AFRICA: Nigeria (Dodge 1953).
Pyxine coccoes (Sw.) Nyl.
AFRICA: Nigeria (Thorold 1952, probably wrong determination).
Pyxine copelandii Vain.
AUSTRALASIA: Fiji (Dodge, C. W. 1968 *in litt.*).
Ramalina dendriscoides Nyl. var. *subnuda* Müll. Arg.
AFRICA: S. Tomé (Dodge 1971).
Ramalina denticulata Nyl. var. *pseudofarinacea* Harm.
AUSTRALASIA: Fiji (Dodge, C. W. 1968 *in litt.*).
Ramalina maculata Müll. Arg. var. *tenuis* Müll. Arg.
AFRICA: Principe (Dodge 1971).
Sarcographa labryrinthica (Ach.) Müll. Arg.
AFRICA: Cameroon (S.W.) (Dodge 1953, 1964); Nigeria (Dodge 1953); S. Tomé (Dodge 1964).
Sarcographa thoroldii Dodge
AFRICA: Cameroon (S.W.) (Dodge 1964); Fernando Po (Dodge 1953).
Sticta ambavillaria (Bory) Ach.
see *Stictina ambavillaria* (Bory) Nyl.

Sticta l'herminieri Vain.
see *Stictina ambavillaria* (Bory) Nyl.
Stictina ambavillaria (Bory) Nyl.
   WEST INDIES: Guadeloupe (Duss 1904, as *Sticta ambavillaria*; Vainio 1915, as *Sticta l'herminieri*).
Temnospora fulgens (Hampe) Massal.
   AFRICA: Nigeria (James, P. W. 1970 *in litt.*).
Thelotrema cameroonensis Dodge
   AFRICA: Cameroon (S.W.) (Dodge 1953, 1964).
Thelotrema foratum Nyl.
   AFRICA: S. Tomé (Dodge C. W. 1958 *in litt.*).
Tremotylium africanum Räs.
   AFRICA: Nigeria (Dodge 1953); Principe (Dodge 1964).
Tylophoron ascidioides Vain.
   AFRICA: Nigeria (Dodge 1953).
Usnea lyngei Mot.
   AFRICA: Annobon (Dodge, C. W. 1960 *in litt.*).

Lichens (Foliicolous)
Aspidothelium fugiens (Müll. Arg.) Sant.
   AFRICA: Nigeria (Santesson 1952).
Asterothyrium argenteum Müll. Arg.
   AFRICA: Nigeria (Santesson 1952).
Asterothyrium microsporum Sant.
   AFRICA: Nigeria (Santesson 1952).
Asterothyrium monosporum Müll. Arg.
   AFRICA: Nigeria (Santesson 1952).
Asterothyrium octomerum Sant.
   AFRICA: Nigeria (Santesson 1952).
Asterothyrium pittieri Müll. Arg.
   AFRICA: Cameroon (S.W.) (Santesson 1952); Ghana (Santesson 1952); Nigeria (Santesson 1952); Principe (Santesson, R. 1957 *in litt.*); S. Tomé (Santesson, R. 1957 *in litt.*).
Aulaxina opegraphina Fée
   AFRICA: Fernando Po (Thorold 1955*a*).
Aulaxina quadrangula (Stirt.) Sant.
   AFRICA: Nigeria (Santesson 1952); Principe (Santesson, R. 1957 *in litt.*).
Bacidia apiahica Müll. Arg.
   AFRICA: Cameroon (S.W.) (Santesson 1952); Nigeria (Santesson 1952).
   ASIA: Malaysia (West) (Santesson 1952).
Bacidia rhapidophylli (Rehm) Zahlbr.
   AFRICA: Cameroon (S.W.) (Santesson 1952); Fernando Po (Thorold 1955*a*); Nigeria (Santesson 1952).
Bacidia sublecanorina (Nyl.) Zahlbr.
   AFRICA: Cameroon (S.W.); Fernando Po (Thorold 1955*a*).
Byssolecania deplanata (Müll. Arg.) Sant.
   AFRICA: Nigeria (Santesson 1952).

Byssoloma leucoblepharum (Nyl.) Vain. emend. Sant.
AFRICA: Cameroon (S.W.) (Santesson 1952); Nigeria (Santesson 1952).
Byssoloma rotuliforme (Müll. Arg.) Sant.
AFRICA: Fernando Po (Thorold 1955*a*); Nigeria (Santesson 1952).
Calenia depressa Müll. Arg.
AFRICA: Cameroon (S.W.) (Santesson 1952); Nigeria (Santesson 1952).
Calenia graphidea Vain.
AFRICA: Cameroon (S.W.) (Santesson 1952); Nigeria (Santesson 1952).
Catillaria bouteillei (Desm.) Zahlbr.
AFRICA: Cameroon (S.W.) (Santesson 1952); Fernando Po (Santesson, R. 1953 *in litt.*); Nigeria (Santesson, R., 1957 *in litt.*); S. Tomé (Santesson, R., 1957 *in litt.*).
Catillaria patellarioides (Rehm) Sant.
see *Psorotheciopsis patellarioides* (Rehm) Sant.
Chroodiscus coccineus (Leight.) Müll. Arg.
AFRICA: Nigeria (Santesson 1952).
Dimerella epiphylla (Müll. Arg.) Malme
AFRICA: Fernando Po (Thorold 1955*a*); Nigeria (Santesson 1952).
Echinoplaca diffluens (Müll. Arg.) Sant.
AFRICA: Nigeria (Santesson 1952).
Echinoplaca hymenula (Müll. Arg.) Sant.
see *Echinoplaca pellicula* (Müll. Arg.) Sant.
Echinoplaca leucotrichoides (Vain.) Sant.
AFRICA: Cameroon (S.W.) (Santesson 1952).
Echinoplaca pellicula (Müll. Arg.) Sant.
AFRICA: Fernando Po (Thorold 1955*a*); Nigeria (Thorold 1952, as *E. hymenula*); Principe (Santesson, R. 1957 *in litt.*).
Gyalectidium filicinum Müll. Arg.
AFRICA: Cameroon (S.W.) (Santesson 1952); Nigeria (Santesson 1952).
Gyalectidium rotuliforme Müll. Arg.
AFRICA: Nigeria (Santesson 1952); Principe (Santesson, R. 1957 *in litt.*)
Lasioloma arachnoideum (Kremp.) Sant.
AFRICA: Nigeria (Santesson 1952); S. Tomé (Santesson, R. 1957 *in litt.*).
Lopadium foliicola (Fée) Sant.
AFRICA: Nigeria (Santesson 1952).
Lopadium fuscum Müll. Arg.
AFRICA: Cameroon (S.W.) (Santesson 1952); Nigeria (Santesson 1952).
Lopadium phyllogenum (Müll. Arg.) Zahlbr.
AFRICA: Cameroon (S.W.) (Santesson 1952); Nigeria (Santesson 1952); S. Tomé (Santesson, R. 1957 *in litt.*).
Lopadium puiggarii (Müll. Arg.) Zahlbr.
AFRICA: Nigeria (Santesson 1952).
Mazosia rotula (Mont.) Massal.
AFRICA: Nigeria (Santesson 1952).
Phyllophiale alba Sant.
AFRICA: Cameroon (S.W.) (Santesson 1952); Nigeria (Santesson 1952).

Porina nitidula Müll. Arg.

AFRICA: Nigeria (Santesson 1952). WEST INDIES: Trinidad (Santesson 1952).

Porina pallescens Sant.

AFRICA: Cameroon (S.W.) (Santesson 1952).

Porina tetramera (Malme) Sant.

AFRICA: Cameroon (S.W.) (Santesson 1952); Nigeria (Santesson 1952).

Porina trichothelioides Sant.

AFRICA: Cameroon (S.W.) (Santesson 1952).

Psorotheciopsis patellarioides (Rehm) Sant.

AFRICA: Nigeria (Thorold 1952, as *Catillaria patellarioides*); S. Tomé (Santesson, R. 1957 *in litt.*).

Sporopodium leprieurii Mont.

AFRICA: Nigeria (Santesson 1952).

Strigula complanata (Fée) Mont.

WEST INDIES: Trinidad (Santesson 1952).

Strigula elegans (Fée) Müll. Arg.

AFRICA: Fernando Po (Thorold 1955a); Nigeria (Santesson 1952). CENTRAL AMERICA: Nicaragua (Santesson 1952). WEST INDIES: Trinidad (Santesson 1952). ASIA: Malaysia (West) (Santesson 1952).

Strigula elegans var. *antillarum* (Fée) Sant.

AFRICA: Nigeria (Santesson 1952).

Strigula elegans var. *stellata* (Nyl. and Cromb.) Sant.

AFRICA: Nigeria (Santesson 1952).

Strigula macrocarpa Vain.

AFRICA: Nigeria (Santesson 1952).

Strigular nemathora Mont.

AFRICA: Cameroon (S.W.) (Santesson 1952); Fernando Po (Thorold 1955a); Nigeria (Santesson 1952); Principe (Santesson, R. 1957 *in litt.*); S. Tomé (Santesson, R. 1957 *in litt.*).

Strigula nitidula Mont.

AFRICA: Cameroon (S.W.) (Santesson 1952); Nigeria (Santesson 1952); Principe (Santesson, R. 1957 *in litt.*).

Strigula subelegans Vain.

ASIA: Malaysia (West) (Santesson 1952).

Tapellaria epiphylla (Müll. Arg.) Sant.

AFRICA: Cameroon (S.W.) (Santesson 1952).

Tapellaria molleri (Henr.) Sant.

AFRICA: Nigeria (Santesson 1952).

Tapellaria phyllophila (Stirt.) Sant.

AFRICA: Cameroon (S.W.) (Santesson 1952); Principe (Santesson, R. 1957 *in litt.*).

Tricharia vainioi Sant.

AFRICA: Fernando Po (Thorold 1955a); Nigeria (Santesson 1952); Principe (Santesson, R. 1957 *in litt.*); S. Tomé (Santesson, R. 1957 *in litt.*).

Trichothelium alboatrum Vain.

AFRICA: Cameroon (S.W.) (Santesson 1952); Nigeria (Santesson 1952).

Trichothelium epiphyllum Müll. Arg.
AFRICA: Nigeria (Santesson 1952).

Bryophytes (Hepatics)
Archilejeunea abbreviata (Mitt.) Vand. Bergh.
AFRICA: Cameroon (S.W.) (Jones, E. W. 1953 *in litt.*).
Archilejeunea africana Steph.
AFRICA: Cameroon (S.W.) (Jones, E. W. 1951 *in litt.*); Fernando Po (Jones, E. W. 1953 *in litt.*).
Caudalejeunea hanningtonii (Mitt.) Steph.
AFRICA: Cameroon (S.W.) (Jones 1953*b*); Ghana (Jones, E. W. 1971 *in litt.*); Nigeria (Jones 1953*b*); Principe (Jones, E. W. 1970 *in litt.*); S. Tomé (Jones, E. W. 1957 *in litt.*).
Ceratolejeunea calabariensis Steph.
AFRICA: Fernando Po (Jones, E. W. 1970 *in litt.*).
Ceratolejeunea jungneri Steph.
AFRICA: Fernando Po (Thorold 1955*a*).
Ceratolejeunea umbonata Steph.
AFRICA: Fernando Po (Thorold 1955*a*).
Ceratolejeunea zenkeri Steph.
AFRICA: Fernando Po (Thorold 1955*a*).
Cheilolejeunea africana Steph.
AFRICA: Ghana (Jones, E. W. 1971 *in litt.*); Nigeria (Jones, E. W. 1970 *in litt.*); S. Tomé (Jones, E. W. 1970 *in litt.*).
Cheilolejeunea inflata Steph.
AFRICA: Cameroon (S.W.) (Jones 1954); Nigeria (Jones 1954); S. Tomé (Jones, E. W. 1970 *in litt.*).
Cheilolejeunea principensis Steph.
AFRICA: Annobon (Jones, E. W. 1970 *in litt.*); Cameroon (S. W.) (Jones 1954); Fernando Po (Jones 1954); Ghana (Jones, E. W. 1971 *in litt.*); Principe (Dalby, D. H. 1958 *in litt.*).
Colura digitalis Mitt.
AFRICA: Annobon (Jones, E. W. 1960 *in litt.*).
Frullania nodulosa (Reinw. Blume and Nees) Nees
AUSTRALASIA: Fiji (Jones, E. W. 1969 *in litt.*).
Frullania spongiosa Steph.
AFRICA: Cameroon (S.W.) (Jones, E. W. 1970 *in litt.*); Nigeria (Jones, E. W. 1952 *in litt.*); Principe (Jones, E. W. 1970 *in litt.*).
Frullania squarrosa Nees
AFRICA: Ghana (Jones, E. W. 1971 *in litt.*); Nigeria (Thorold 1952).
Lejeunea acuta Mitt.
AFRICA: Cameroon (S.W.) (Jones, E. W. 1953 *in litt.*).
Lejeunea caespitosa Lindenb. and Gott.
AFRICA: Cameroon (S.W.) (Jones, E. W. 1970 *in litt.*); Fernando Po (Jones, E. W. 1970 *in litt.*); S. Tomé (Jones, E. W. 1970 *in litt.*).
Lejeunea ecklonii Lindenb.
AFRICA: Ghana (Jones, E. W. 1971 *in litt.*).

Lejeunea papilionacea Steph.
AFRICA: Cameroon (S.W.) (Jones, E. W. 1970 *in litt.*); S. Tomé (Jones, E. W. 1970 *in litt.*).
Lejeunea setacea Steph.
AFRICA: Cameroon (S.W.) (Jones 1969); Fernando Po (Jones, E. W. 1970 *in litt.*); Ghana (Jones, E. W. 1971 *in litt.*); Nigeria (Jones 1969); Principe (Jones 1969); S. Tomé (Jones 1969).
Leptocolea africana (Steph.) E. W. Jones
AFRICA: Ghana (Jones, E. W. 1971 *in litt.*).
Leptocolea nigerica E. W. Jones
AFRICA: Nigeria (Jones 1953*a*); Principe (Jones, E. W. 1970 *in litt.*).
Lopholejeunea abortiva (Mitt.) Steph.
AFRICA: Cameroon (S.W.) (Jones, E. W. 1970 *in litt.*); Nigeria (Thorold 1952).
Lopholejeunea fragilis Steph.
AFRICA: S. Tomé (Jones, E. W. 1957 *in litt.*).
Lopholejeunea obtusilacera Herz. ex Vand. Bergh.
AFRICA: Fernando Po (Jones, E. W. 1951 *in litt.*).
Lopholejeunea subfusca (Nees) Steph.
AFRICA: Annobon (Jones, E. W. 1970 *in litt.*); Cameroon (S.W.) (Thorold 1952); Fernando Po (Jones, E. W. 1953 *in litt.*); Ghana (Jones, E. W. 1971 *in litt.*).
Mastigolejeunea carinata (Mitt.) Steph.
AFRICA: Cameroon (S.W.) (Thorold 1952); Fernando Po (Jones, E. W. 1970 *in litt.*); Ghana (Jones, E. W. 1971 *in litt.*); Nigeria (Thorold 1952); Principe (Jones, E. W. 1970 *in litt.*); S. Tomé (Jones, E. W. 1957 *in litt.*).
Mastigolejeunea florea (Mitt.) Steph.
AFRICA: Ghana (Jones, E. W. 1951 *in litt.*); Nigeria (Thorold 1952); Principe (Jones, E. W. 1970 *in litt.*).
Mastigolejeunea turgida Steph.
AFRICA: Nigeria (Jones, E. W. 1952 *in litt.*).
Microlejeunea africana Steph.
AFRICA: S. Tomé (Jones, E. W. 1970 *in litt.*).
Plagiochila moenkemeyeri Steph.
AFRICA: Cameroon (S.W.) (Jones 1962).
Plagiochila pinniflora Steph.
AFRICA: Cameroon (S.W.) (Jones 1962); Nigeria (Jones 1962).
Plagiochila praemorsa Steph.
AFRICA: Cameroon (S.W.) (Jones 1962).
Plagiochila strictifolia Steph.
AFRICA: Cameroon (S.W.) (Jones 1962).
Radula meyeri Steph.
AFRICA: Principe (Jones, E. W. 1957 *in litt.*); S. Tomé (Jones, E. W. 1957 *in litt.*).
Rectolejeunea brittoniae Evans
SOUTH AMERICA: Peru (Jones, E. W. 1965 *in litt.*), associated with *Rodriguezia batemanii* (Orchidaceae).

Bryophytes (Mosses)

Brachymenium speirocladum C. Müll.
  AFRICA: Fernando Po (Eddy, A. 1972 *in litt.*, uncertain determination).
Calymperes dozyanum Mitt.
  AUSTRALASIA: New Guinea (Lae) (Eddy, A. 1972 *in litt.*).
Calymperes gilletii Ren. and Card.
  AFRICA: Nigeria (Dalby, D. H. 1959 *in litt.*).
Calymperes moluccense Schwaegr.
  AUSTRALASIA: New Ireland (Eddy, A. 1972 *in litt.*, uncertain determination).
Calymperes theriotii Ren. and Card.
  AFRICA: Nigeria (Dalby, D. H. 1959 *in litt.*); Principe (Dalby, D. H. 1959 *in litt.*); S. Tomé (Dalby, D. H. 1959 *in litt.*).
Erythrodontium barteri (Mitt.) Broth.
  AFRICA: Cameroon (S.W.) (Dalby, D. H. 1958 *in litt.*).
Fissidens desertorum (C. Müll.) Par.
  AFRICA: Nigeria (Norkett, A. H. 1959 *in litt.*).
Fissidens sciophyllus Mitt.
  AFRICA: Nigeria (Norkett, A. H. 1951 *in litt.*).
Floribundaria floribunda (Dozy and Molk.) Fleisch.
  AFRICA: Cameroon (S.W.) (Eddy, A. 1972 *in litt.*).
Leucodontopsis cameruniae (Broth.) Broth.
  AFRICA: Cameroon (S.W.) (Dalby, D. H. 1958 *in litt.*); Ghana (Dalby, D. H. 1958 *in litt.*); Nigeria (Thorold 1952).
Neckeropsis disticha (Hedw.) Kindb.
  AFRICA: Cameroon (S.W.) (Thorold 1952); Ghana (Dalby, D. H. 1958 *in litt.*); Nigeria (Thorold 1952); Principe (Dalby, D. H. 1958 *in litt.*).
Orthostichidium cameruniae Dus.
  AFRICA: Fernando Po (Dalby, D. H. 1958 *in litt.*); Dalby, D. H. 1958 *in litt.*); S. Tomé (Dalby, D. H. 1958 *in litt.*).
Orthostichidium perpinnatum (Broth.) Dus.
  AFRICA: Ghana (Jones, E. W. 1971 *in litt.*).
Pilotrichella communis C. Müll. ex Dus.
  AFRICA: S. Tomé (Dalby, D. H. 1958 *in litt.*).
Stereophyllum nitens Mitt.
  AFRICA: Cameroon (S.W.) (Thorold 1952); Ghana (Dalby, D. H. 1958 *in litt.*); Nigeria (Thorold 1952).
Thuidium gratum (P. Beauv.) Jaeg.
  AFRICA: Cameroon (S.W.) (Thorold 1952); Ghana (Jones, E. W. 1971 *in litt.*); Nigeria (Thorold 1952).

Ferns and other Pteridophytes

Antrophyum immersum (Bory ex Willd.) Mett.
  AFRICA: S. Tomé (Exell 1959).
Arthropteris monocarpa (Cordem.) C. Chr.
  AFRICA: Cameroon (S.W.) (Thorold 1952).

Arthropteris obliterata (R. Br.) J. Sm.
see *Arthropteris palisotii* (Desv.) Alston
Arthropteris orientalis (Gmel.) Posth.
     AFRICA: Cameroon (S.W.) (Thorold 1952); S. Tomé (Alston, A.H.G. 1957 *in litt.*).
Arthropteris palisotii (Desv.) Alston
     AFRICA: Cameroon (S.W.) (Thorold 1952, incorrectly as *A. obliterata*, terrestrial, climbing on trunk).
Asplenium africanum Desv.
     AFRICA: Fernando Po (Thorold 1955*a*).
Asplenium barteri Hook.
     AFRICA: Cameroon (S.W.) (Thorold 1952); Fernando Po (Thorold 1955*a*); S. Tomé (Alston, A. H. G. 1957 *in litt.*).
Asplenium cancellatum Alston
     AFRICA: Cameroon (S.W.) (Alston 1956, 1959).
Asplenium cuneatum Lam.
     AUSTRALASIA: Fiji (det. R. B. G. Kew, probably terrestrial, climbing on trunk).
Asplenium currori Hook.
     AFRICA: Cameroon (S.W.) (Thorold 1952).
Asplenium dregeanum Kunze
     AFRICA: Cameroon (S.W.) (Thorold 1952).
Asplenium eurysorum Hieron.
     AFRICA: Principe (Alston, A. H. G. 1957 *in litt.*).
Asplenium exhaustum (Christ) Alston
     AFRICA: S. Tomé (Exell 1959).
Asplenium hemitomum Hieron.
     AFRICA: Cameroon (S.W.) (Thorold 1952).
Asplenium vagans Bak.
     AFRICA: Cameroon (S.W.) (Thorold 1952).
Belvisia mucronata (Fée) Copel.
     AUSTRALASIA: Fiji (det., R. B. G. Kew).
Belvisia spicata (L.f.) Mirb.
     AFRICA: Cameroon (S.W.) (Thorold 1952, as *Hymenolepis spicata*); S. Tomé (Exell 1959).
Ctenitis securidiformis (Hook.) Copel. var. *securidiformis*
     AFRICA: Fernando Po (Thorold 1955*a*, as *Dryopteris securidiformis*).
Cyclophorus nummularifolius (Sw.) C. Chr.
see *Pyrrosia nummularifolia* (Sw.) Ching
Davallia feejeensis Hook.
     AUSTRALASIA: Fiji (det. R. B. G. Kew, probably terrestrial, climbing on trunk).
Drynaria laurentii (Christ) Hieron.
     AFRICA: S. Tomé (Alston, A. H. G. 1957 *in litt.*).
Drynaria volkensii Hieron.
     AFRICA: Fernando Po (Thorold 1955*a*); S. Tomé (Exell 1959).
Dryopteris securidiformis (Hook.) C. Chr.
see *Ctenitis securidiformis* (Hook.) Copel. var. *securidiformis*

Hymenoplepis spicata (L.f.) Presl
see *Belvisia spicata* (L.f.) Mirb.
Lemmaphyllum accedens (Blume) Donk
    AUSTRALASIA: Fiji (det. R. B. G. Kew).
Lomariopsis palustris (Hook.) Mett. ex Kuhn
    AFRICA: Cameroon (S.W.) (Thorold 1952).
Loxogramme lanceolata (Sw.) Presl
    AFRICA: Annobon (det. R. B. G. Kew); Cameroon (S.W.) (Thorold 1952).
Lycopodium ophioglossoides Lam.
    AFRICA: Cameroon (S.W.) (Thorold 1952).
Microgramma owariensis (Desv.) Alston
    AFRICA: Cameroon (S.W.) (Thorold 1952, as *Polypodium lycopodioides*);
    Fernando Po (Thorold 1955a); Principe (Alston, A. H. G. 1957 *in litt.*).
Microsorium punctatum (L.) Copel.
    AFRICA: Cameroon (S.W.) (Thorold 1952, as *Polypodium polycarpon*);
    Fernando Po (Thorold 1955a); Principe (Alston, A. H. G. 1957 *in litt.*).
Nephrolepis biserrata (Sw.) Schott.
    AFRICA: Cameroon (S.W.) (Thorold 1952); S. Tomé (Alston, A. H. G. 1957
    in litt.).
Nephrolepis undulata (Afzel. ex Sw.) J. Sm.
    AFRICA: Cameroon (S.W.) (Thorold 1952); Fernando Po (Thorold 1955a);
    Nigeria (Thorold 1952); S. Tomé (Alston, A. H. G. 1957 *in litt.*).
Phymatodes scolopendria (Burm. f.) Ching
    AFRICA: Cameroon (S.W.) (Thorold 1952, as *Polypodium scolopendria*);
    Fernando Po (Thorold 1955a); Principe (Alston, A. H. G. 1957 *in litt.*); S.
    Tomé (Alston, A. H. G. 1957 *in litt.*).
Platycerium stemaria (P. Beauv.) Desv.
    AFRICA: Cameroon (S.W.) (Thorold 1952); Ghana (Adams and Alston
    1955); Nigeria (Thorold 1952).
Pleopeltis percussa Hook. and Grev.
    SOUTH AMERICA: Peru (det. R. B. G. Kew).
Polypodium lycopodioides auct.
see *Microgramma owariensis* (Desv.) Alston
Polypodium polycarpon Cav. ex Sw.
see *Microsorium punctatum* (L.) Copel.
Polypodium scolopendria Burm. f.
see *Phymatodes scolopendria* (Burm. f.) Ching
Pyrrosia lanceolata (L.) Farwell
    AFRICA: Cameroon (S.W.) Alston, A. H. G. 1953 *in litt.*).
Pyrrosia nummularifolia (Sw.) Ching
    ASIA: Indonesia (Java) (Roepke 1917, as *Cyclophorus nummularifolius*).
Selaginella molliceps Spring
    AFRICA: Cameroon (S.W.) (Thorold 1952); Fernando Po (Thorold 1955a;
    Alston 1959).
Selaginella versicolor Spring
    AFRICA: Fernando Po (Alston 1959, associated with *S. molliceps*).
Trichomanes africanum Christ
    AFRICA: Cameroon (S.W.) (Alston, A. H. G. 1953 *in litt.*).

Trichomanes chevalieri Christ
  AFRICA: Cameroon (S.W.) (Alston, A. H. G. 1953 *in litt.*); Fernando Po
  (Thorold 1955*a*).
Trichomanes erosum Willd.
  AFRICA: Cameroon (S.W.) (Alston, A. H. G. 1953 *in litt.*).
Trichomanes liberiense Copel.
  AFRICA: Cameroon (S.W.) (Thorold 1952).
Vaginularia angustissima (Brack.) Mett.
  AUSTRALASIA: Fiji (det. R. B. G. Kew).
Vittaria guineensis Desv.
  AFRICA: Cameroon (S.W.) (Alston, A. H. G. 1953 *in litt.*); Fernando Po
  (Thorold 1955*a*).

Flowering Plants

Acanthosyris paulo-alvinii Barroso (SANTALACEAE)
  SOUTH AMERICA: Brazil (Alvim and Seeschaaf 1968, as *A. paulo-alvimii*).
Aechmea fendleri André (BROMELIACEAE)
  WEST INDIES: Trinidad (Pittendrigh 1950*b*, as *A. porteoides*).
Aechmea nudicaulis (L.) Griseb.
  WEST INDIES: Trinidad (Downs, W. G. 1960 *in litt.*).
Aechmea porteoides Britton
  see *Aechmea fendleri* André
Aërangis megaphylla Summerh. (ORCHIDACEAE)
  AFRICA: Annobon (det. R. B. G. Kew).
Angraecum eichleranum Kraenzl. (ORCHIDACEAE)
  AFRICA: Cameroon (S.W.) (Thorold 1952).
Anthurium gracile (Rudge) Lindl. (ARACEAE)
  WEST INDIES: Trinidad (Simmonds 1949).
Anthurium scandens (Aubl.) Engler
  WEST INDIES: Trinidad (Simmonds 1949, 1950).
Anthurium scolopendrinum (Ham.) Kunth
  SOUTH AMERICA: Peru (det. R. B. G. Kew).
Begonia eminii Warb. (BEGONIACEAE)
  AFRICA: Cameroon (S.W.) (det. R. B. G. Kew).
Begonia polygonoides Hook. f.
  AFRICA: Cameroon (S.W.) (det. R. B. G. Kew).
Begonia prismatocarpa Hook.
  AFRICA: Fernando Po (Thorold 1955*a*).
Beloglottis costaricensis (Rch. f.) Schltr. (ORCHIDACEAE)
  WEST INDIES: Trinidad (Downs, W. G. 1960 *in litt.*).
Bolusiella talbotii (Rendle) Summerh. (ORCHIDACEAE)
  AFRICA: Annobon (det. R. B. G. Kew).
Brassavola nodosa (L.) Lindl. (ORCHIDACEAE)
  CENTRAL AMERICA: Costa Rica (Hansen, A. J. 1960 *in litt.*).
Brassia longissima Schlechter (ORCHIDACEAE)
  CENTRAL AMERICA: Costa Rica (Hansen, A. J. 1960 *in litt.*).
Bulbophyllum calyptratum Kraenzl. (ORCHIDACEAE)
  AFRICA: Cameroon (S.W.) (det. R. B. G. Kew).

Bulbophyllum melanorrhachis (Rchb. f.) Rchb. f. ex De Wild.
  AFRICA: Annobon (det. R. B. G. Kew).
Bulbophyllum pachyrrhachis (A. Rich.) Griseb.
  WEST INDIES: Trinidad (Downs, W. G. 1960 *in litt.*).
Bulbophyllum simonii Summerh.
  AFRICA: Cameroon (S.W.) (det. R. B. G. Kew).
Bulbophyllum tentaculigerum Rchb. f.
  AFRICA: Cameroon (S.W.) (det. R. B. G. Kew).
Cassytha filiformis L. (LAURACEAE)
  AFRICA: Nigeria (Tinsley 1961, used experimentally for attempts to transmit
  viruses (C.S.S.V. and C.M.L.V.) from infected to healthy cocoa).
Catasetum maculatum Kunth (ORCHIDACEAE)
  CENTRAL AMERICA: Costa Rica (Hansen, A. J. 1962 *in litt.*, as *C.
  oerstedii*).
Catasetum oerstedii Rchb. f.
see *Catasetum maculatum* Kunth
Catopsis floribunda (Brongn.) L. B. Smith (BROMELIACEAE)
  WEST INDIES: Trinidad (Downs, W. G. 1960 *in litt.*).
Catopsis sessiliflora (Ruiz and Pav.) Mez
  WEST INDIES: Trinidad (Downs, W. G. 1960 *in litt.*).
Chamaeangis vesicata (Lindl.) Schltr. (ORCHIDACEAE)
  AFRICA: Nigeria (Thorold 1952).
Cryptarrhena lunata R. Br. (ORCHIDACEAE)
  WEST INDIES: Trinidad (Downs, W. G. 1960 *in litt.*).
Culcasia scandens P. Beauv. (ARACEAE)
  AFRICA: Nigeria (det. R. B. G. Kew, terrestrial, climbing on trunk).
Cuscuta americana L. (CONVOLVULACEAE)
  WEST INDIES: Grenada (Morris 1900).
Cuscuta globulosa Bentham
  WEST INDIES: Trinidad (Nowell 1923, probably this species, as 'Love
  Vine').
Dendrophthoë neelgherrensis (Wight and Arn.) van Tiegh. (LORANTHACEAE)
  ASIA: Sri Lanka (Petch 1924, as *Loranthus neelgherrensis*).
Diaphanthe bidens (Sw.) Schltr. (ORCHIDACEAE)
  AFRICA: Cameroon (S.W.) (Thorold 1952).
Diaphananthe rutilis (Rchb. f.) Summerh.
  AFRICA: Nigeria (Thorold 1952, as *Rhipidoglossum rutilum*).
Dichaea picta Rchb. f. (ORCHIDACEAE)
  WEST INDIES: Trinidad (Downs, W. G. 1960 *in litt.*).
Englerina gabonensis (Engler) Balle (LORANTHACEAE)
  AFRICA: Guinea (Spanish) (Nosti 1953, as *Loranthus micrantherus*).
Epidendrum ciliare L. (ORCHIDACEAE)
  WEST INDIES: Trinidad (Downs, W. G. 1960 *in litt.*).
Epidendrum difforme Jacq.
  CENTRAL AMERICA: Costa Rica (Lankester, C. H. 1960 *in litt.*).
Epidendrum fragrans Sw.
  WEST INDIES: Trinidad (Downs, W. G. 1960 *in litt.*).

Epidendrum hartii Rolfe
   WEST INDIES: Trinidad (Downs, W. G., 1960 *in litt.*).
Epidendrum imatophyllum Lindl.
   CENTRAL AMERICA: Costa Rica (Lankester, C. H. 1960 *in litt.*).
Epidendrum moyobambae Kraenzl.
   WEST INDIES: Trinidad (Downs, W. G. 1960 *in litt.*).
Epidendrum nocturnum Jacq.
   CENTRAL AMERICA: Costa Rica (Lankester, C. H. 1960 *in litt.*).
   WEST INDIES: Trinidad (Downs, W. G. 1960 *in litt.*).
Epidendrum ottonis Rchb. f.
   WEST INDIES: Trinidad (Downs, W. G. 1960 *in litt.*).
Epidendrum ramosum Jacq.
   WEST INDIES: Trinidad (Downs, W. G. 1960 *in litt.*).
Epidendrum rigidum Jacq.
   WEST INDIES: Trinidad (Downs, W. G. 1960 *in litt.*).
Epidendrum schomburgkii Lindl.
   CENTRAL AMERICA: Costa Rica (Lankester, C. H. 1960 *in litt.*).
Epidendrum schumannianum Schlechter
   CENTRAL AMERICA: Costa Rica (Lankester, C. H. 1960 *in litt.*).
Epidendrum stamfordianum Batem.
   CENTRAL AMERICA: Nicaragua (Hansen, A. J. 1962 *in litt.*).
Epidendrum stenopetalum Hook.
   WEST INDIES: Trinidad (Downs, W. G. 1960 *in litt.*).
Epidendrum strobiliferum Rchb. f.
   WEST INDIES: Trinidad (Downs, W. G. 1960 *in litt.*).
Epipogium roseum (Don) Lindl. (ORCHIDACEAE)
   ASIA: Sri Lanka (Petch 1925*b*, associated with roots and dead leaves).
Epipremnum pinnatum (L.) Engler (ARACEAE)
   AUSTRALASIA: Fiji (det. R. B. G. Kew).
Eriopsis werckleri Schlechter (ORCHIDACEAE)
   CENTRAL AMERICA: Costa Rica (Lankester, C. H. 1960 *in litt.*).
Globimetula braunii (Engler) van Tiegh. (LORANTHACEAE)
   AFRICA: Nigeria (Keay 1958).
Globimetula dinklagei (Engler) van Tiegh.
   AFRICA: Cameroon (S.W.) (Keay 1958).
Gongora quinquenervis Ruiz and Pav. (ORCHIDACEAE)
   CENTRAL AMERICA: Costa Rica (Lankester, C. H. 1960 *in litt.*).
Graphorkis lurida (Sw.) O. Ktze. (ORCHIDACEAE)
   AFRICA: Cameroon (S.W.) (det. R. B.G. Kew).
Gravisia aquilega (Salisb.) Mez (BROMELIACEAE)
   WEST INDIES: Trinidad (Purseglove, J. W. 1963 *in litt.*).
Guzmania lingulata (L.) Mez (BROMELIACEAE)
   WEST INDIES: Trinidad (Pittendrigh 1950*b*).
Guzmania monostachia (L.) Rusby ex Mez
   WEST INDIES: Trinidad (Pittendrigh 1950*b*).
Hexisea reflexa (Lindl.) Rchb. f. (ORCHIDACEAE)
   WEST INDIES: Trinidad (Downs, W. G. 1960 *in litt.*).

Isochilus linearis (Jacq.) R. Br. (ORCHIDACEAE)
  WEST INDIES: Trinidad (Downs, W. G. 1960 *in litt.*).
Leochilus labiatus (Sw.) O. Ktze. (ORCHIDACEAE)
  WEST INDIES: Trinidad (Downs, W. G. 1960 *in litt.*).
Leochilus scriptus (Scheidw.) Rchb. f.
  WEST INDIES: Trinidad (Downs, W. G. 1960 *in litt.*).
Lockhartia acuta (Lindl.) Rchb. f. (ORCHIDACEAE)
  WEST INDIES: Trinidad (Downs, W. G. 1960 *in litt.*).
Lophophytum mirabile Schott and Endl. (BALANOPHORACEAE)
  SOUTH AMERICA: Brazil (Bondar 1925, root parasite, probably affecting cocoa).
Loranthus bangwensis Engler and K. Krause
see *Tapinanthus bangwensis* (Engler and K. Krause) Danser
Loranthus farmari Sprague
see *Tapinanthus farmari* (Sprague) Danser
Loranthus incanus Schum.
see *Phragmanthera incana* (Schum.) Balle
Loranthus javanicus D. Dietr.
see *Macrosolen formosus* (Blume) Miq.
Loranthus lanceolatus P. Beauv.
see *Tapinanthus belvisii* (DC.) Danser
Loranthus leonensis Sprague
see *Phragmanthera leonensis* (Sprague) Balle
Loranthus leptolobus Bentham
see *Phragmanthera incana* (Schum.) Balle
Loranthus micrantherus Engler ex Th. Dur. and De Wild.
see *Englerina gabonensis* (Engler) Balle
Loranthus neelgherrensis Wight and Arn.
see *Dendrophthoë neelgherrensis* (Wight and Arn.) van Tiegh.
Macrosolen formosus (Blume) Miq. (LORANTHACEAE)
  AFRICA: S. Tomé (de Seabra 1922, as *Loranthus javanicus*, probably wrongly identified).
Maxillaria camaridii Rchb. f. (ORCHIDACEAE)
  WEST INDIES: Trinidad (Downs, W. G. 1960 *in litt.*).
Maxillaria conferta (Griseb.) C. Schweinf.
  WEST INDIES: Trinidad (Downs, W. G. 1960 *in litt.*).
Maxillaria endresii Rchb. f.
  CENTRAL AMERICA: Costa Rica (Lankester, C. H. 1960 *in litt.*).
Maxillaria rufescens Lindl.
  WEST INDIES: Trinidad (Downs, W. G. 1960 *in litt.*).
Maxillaria trinitatis Ames
  WEST INDIES: Trinidad (Downs, W. G. 1960 *in litt.*).
Maxillaria variabilis Bateman ex Lindl.
  WEST INDIES: Trinidad (Downs, W. G. 1960 *in litt.*).
Monstera obliqua (Miq.) Walp. (ARACEAE)
  WEST INDIES: Trinidad (Simmonds 1949, terrestrial, climbing on trunk).

Monstera pertusa (L.) de Vriese
    SOUTH AMERICA: Peru (det. R. B. G. Kew, growing on branch, but probably terrestrial). WEST INDIES: Trinidad (Simmonds 1949, on trunk, terrestrial).

Oncidium iridifolium H. B. and K.
    see *Oncidium pusillum* (L.) Rchb. f.

Oncidium krameranum Rchb. f. (ORCHIDACEAE)
    CENTRAL AMERICA: Costa Rica (Hansen, A. J. 1960 *in litt.*).

Oncidium luridum Lindl.
    WEST INDIES: Trinidad (Downs, W. G. 1960 *in litt.*).

Oncidium papilio Lindl.
    WEST INDIES: Trinidad (Downs, W. G. 1960 *in litt.*).

Oncidium pusillum (L.) Rchb. f.
    CENTRAL AMERICA: Costa Rica (Lankester, C. H. 1960 *in litt.*, as *O. iridifolium*).

Oncidium stenotis Rchb. f.
    CENTRAL AMERICA: Costa Rica (Lankester, C. H. 1960 *in litt.*).

Ornithocephalus gladiatus Hook. (ORCHIDACEAE)
    WEST INDIES: Trinidad (Downs, W. G. 1960 *in litt.*).

Oryctanthus bothryostachys Eichl. (LORANTHACEAE)
    SOUTH AMERICA: Surinam (van Suchtelen 1955*a, b*).

Oryctanthus cordifolius (Presl) Urban
    CENTRAL AMERICA: Costa Rica (Wellman 1964).

Oryctanthus florulentus (Rich.) Urban
    see *Oryctanthus ruficaulis* (Poepp. and Endl.) Eichl.

Oryctanthus ruficaulis (Poepp. and Endl.) Eichl.
    SOUTH AMERICA: Brazil (Amazon) (Weir 1926); Brazil (Rio de Janeiro (Rizzini 1956, as *O. florulentus*).

Peperomia fernandopoiana C. DC. (PIPERACEAE)
    AFRICA: Cameroon (S.W.) (det. R. B. G. Kew).

Peperomia nummularifolia H. B. and K.
    SOUTH AMERICA: Unlocalized (Jumelle 1900).

Peperomia pellucida (L.) H. B. and K.
    AFRICA: Cameroon (S.W.) (Thorold 1952).

Peperomia rotundifolia (L.) H. B. and K.
    AFRICA: Cameroon (S.W.) (Thorold 1952). SOUTH AMERICA: Peru (det. R. B. G. Kew).

Peperomia stuhlmannii C. DC.
    AFRICA: Cameroon (S.W.) (Thorold 1952).

Phoradendron piperoides (H. B. and K.) Trelease (LORANTHACEAE)
    WEST INDIES: Trinidad (Ayliffe, R. S. 1959 *in litt.*).

Phragmanthera incana (Schum.) Balle (LORANTHACEAE)
    AFRICA: Cameroon (S.W.) (det. R. B. G. Kew); Ghana (Dade 1940, as *Loranthus incanus*); Nigeria (Richards 1952, as *Loranthus leptolobus*).

Phragmanthera leonensis (Sprague) Balle
    UNLOCALIZED: (Roger 1954, as *Loranthus leonensis*).

Phragmanthera nigritana (Hook. f. ex Bentham) Balle
   AFRICA: Ghana (Room, P. M. 1970 *in litt.*).
Phthirusa adunca (G. F. W. Meyer) Macguire (LORANTHACEAE)
   SOUTH AMERICA: Brazil (Warburg 1905, as *P. theobromae*); Venezuela
   (Standen 1952). WEST INDIES: Trinidad (Ayliffe, R. S. 1959 *in litt.*).
Phthirusa pyrifolia (H. B. and K.) Eichl.
   SOUTH AMERICA: Brazil (Amazon) (Weir 1926); Brazil (Rio de Janeiro)
   (Rizzini 1956); Surinam (van Suchtelen 1955*a*, *b*). WEST INDIES: Trinidad
   (Ayliffe, R. S. 1959 *in litt.*).
Phthirusa theobromae (Schult. f.) Eichl.
see *Phthirusa adunca* (G. F. W. Meyer) Macguire
Pleurothallis archidiaconi Ames (ORCHIDACEAE)
   WEST INDIES: Trinidad (Downs, W. G. 1960 *in litt.*).
Pleurothallis ciliata Knowles and Westcott
   WEST INDIES: Trinidad (Downs, W. G. 1960 *in litt.*).
Pleurothallis discoidea Lindl.
   WEST INDIES: Trinidad (Downs, W. G. 1960 *in litt.*).
Pleurothallis pruinosa Lindl.
   WEST INDIES: Trinidad (Downs, W. G. 1960 *in litt.*).
Polystachya adansoniae Rchb. f. (ORCHIDACEAE)
   AFRICA: Cameroon (S.W.) (det. R. B. G. Kew).
Polystachya albescens Ridl.
   AFRICA: S. Tomé (det. R. B. G. Kew).
Polystachya extinctoria Rchb. f.
   WEST INDIES: Trinidad (Downs, W. G. 1960 *in litt.*).
Polystachya foliosa (Hook.) Rchb. f.
   WEST INDIES: Trinidad (Downs, W. G. 1960 *in litt.*).
Polystachya fructiflexa Summerh.
   AFRICA: Cameroon (S.W.) (det. R. B. G. Kew).
Polystachya paniculata (Sw.) Rolfe
   AFRICA: Cameroon (S.W.) (det. R. B. G. Kew).
Polystachya ridleyi Rolfe
   AFRICA: Annobon (det. R. B. G. Kew).
Rangaëris rhipsalisocia (Rchb. f.) Summerh. (ORCHIDACEAE)
   AFRICA: Cameroon (S.W.) (det. R. B. G. Kew).
Rhipidoglossum rutilum (Rchb. f.) Schltr.
see *Diaphananthe rutila* (Rchb. f.) Summerh.
Rhipsalis baccifera (J. S. Mill) Stearn (CACTACEAE)
   AFRICA: Cameroon (S.W.) (Thorold 1952, as *R. cassutha*).
   WEST INDIES: Trinidad (Downs, W. G. 1960 *in litt.*).
Rhipsalis cassutha Gaertn.
see *Rhipsalis baccifera* (J. S. Mill) Stearn
Rodriguezia batemanii Poepp. and Endl. (ORCHIDACEAE)
   SOUTH AMERICA: Peru (det. R. B. G. Kew).
Rodriguezia compacta Schlechter
   CENTRAL AMERICA: Costa Rica (Hansen, A. J. 1960 *in litt.*).
Rodriguezia secunda H. B. and K.
   WEST INDIES: Trinidad (Downs, W. G. 1960 *in litt.*).

Scaphyglottis cuneata Schlechter (ORCHIDACEAE)
   WEST INDIES: Trinidad (Downs, W. G. 1960 *in litt.*).
Scaphyglottis fusiformis (Griseb.) R. E. Scheult
   WEST INDIES: Trinidad (Downs, W. G. 1960 *in litt.*).
Scaphyglottis modesta (Rchb. f.) Schlechter
   WEST INDIES: Trinidad (Downs, W. G. 1960 *in litt.*).
Solenangis clavata (Rolfe) Schltr. (ORCHIDACEAE)
   AFRICA: Ivory Coast (Chevalier 1948).
Solenangis scandens (Schltr.) Schltr.
   AFRICA: Nigeria (Thorold 1952).
Solenostemon monostachyus (P. Beauv.) Briq. (LABIATAE)
   AFRICA: Nigeria (det. R. B. G. Kew, occurrence as an 'accidental' epiphyte).
Stanhopea grandiflora (Lodd.) Lindl. (ORCHIDACEAE)
   WEST INDIES: Trinidad (Downs, W. G. 1960 *in litt.*).
Stelis ophioglossoides (Jacq.) Sw. (ORCHIDACEAE)
   WEST INDIES: Trinidad (Downs, W. G. 1960 *in litt.*).
Stenia pallida Lindl. (ORCHIDACEAE)
   WEST INDIES: Trinidad (Downs, W. G. 1960 *in litt.*).
Struthanthus dichotrianthus Eichl. (LORANTHACEAE)
   SOUTH AMERICA: Colombia (Polania 1957). WEST INDIES: Trinidad (Briton-Jones 1934).
Struthanthus phillyraeoides (H. B. and K.) Blume
   UNLOCALIZED: (Nosti 1953).
Tapinanthus bangwensis (Engler and K. Krause) Danser (LORANTHACEAE)
   AFRICA: Ghana (Dade 1940, as *Loranthus bangwensis*); Fernando Po (det. R. B. G. Kew).
Tapinanthus belvisii (DC.) Danser
   AFRICA: Ivory Coast (Mallamaire 1935*b*, as *Loranthus lanceolatus*).
Tapinanthus buntingii (Sprague) Danser
   AFRICA: Ghana (Room, P. M. 1970 *in litt.*).
Tapinanthus farmari (Sprague) Danser
   AFRICA: Ghana (Dade 1940, as *Loranthus farmari*).
Tapinanthus truncatus (Engler) Danser
   AFRICA: Ghana (Room 1971*a*).
Thonningia sanguinea Vahl (BALANOPHORACEAE)
   AFRICA: Ghana (Dalziel 1937).
Tillandsia anceps Lodd. (BROMELIACEAE)
   WEST INDIES: Trinidad (Downs, W. G. 1960 *in litt.*).
Tillandsia bulbosa Hook.
   WEST INDIES: Trinidad (Downs, W. G. 1960 *in litt.*).
Tillandsia fasciculata Sw.
   WEST INDIES: Trinidad (Downs, W. G. 1960 *in litt.*).
Tillandsia flexuosa Sw.
   WEST INDIES: Trinidad (Downs, W. G. 1960 *in litt.*).
Tillandsia usneoides (L.) L.
   SOUTH AMERICA: Brazil (Bondar 1925). WEST INDIES: Trinidad (Downs, W. G. 1960 *in litt.*).

Utricularia striatula Smith (LENTIBULARIACEAE)
  AFRICA: Fernando Po (Thorold 1955*a*).
Vriesia procera (Mart.) Wittm. (BROMELIACEAE)
  WEST INDIES: Trinidad (Downs, W. G. 1960 *in litt.*).
Vriesia splendens (Brong.) Lem. var. *longibracteata* (Baker) L. B. Smith
  WEST INDIES: Trinidad (Downs, W. G. 1960, *in litt.*).

13
NEMATODE ASSOCIATIONS WITH COCOA

Introduction

Ritzema Bos (1900*b*) first reported root-knot nematode (*Meloidogyne* sp.) incidence on cocoa, under the name *Heterodera radicicola*, but he did not give the locality. Goodey (1933) later recorded it as *Heterodera marioni*. Some subsequent reports of nematodes associated with cocoa, with or without root-galling, are likewise referable to *Meloidogyne* spp. Whitehead (1969) explained that galling of roots is not a criterion of infection with *Meloidogyne*, so that some infections may have been overlooked.

Geographical distribution

Nematodes associated with cocoa have been reported from West Africa (Cameroon, Congo, Ghana, Ivory Coast, Nigeria, and S. Tomé), East Africa (Malawi, Zanzibar), South America (Brazil, Venezuela), Central America (Costa Rica, Guatemala), West Indies (Jamaica), and Asia (India, Java, Philippines). These occurrences are detailed, with literature references, on pp. 230–2.

Economic importance

The consequences of nematode attack are imprecisely known for cocoa, so that it is impossible to estimate economic losses. It seems that establishment may be hampered and young cocoa trees may suffer through nematode infestation. Cotterell (1930) reported the belief that difficulties experienced in S. Tomé and the Congo with the establishment of new cocoa on old cocoa-land were due to root-knot nematode infestation. He observed root-galls with nematodes in the Congo but considered that a similar malady in Ghana was due to soil exhaustion with nematodes functioning as a contributory pathological factor. Ghesquière (1921) considered that the disorder in the Congo which he described as dieback or 'coup de soleil' was due to a complex of factors. Root-knot nematode was the important one, but was associated with attack by *Diplodia* sp. (probably *Botryodiplodia theobromae*) and beetle (*Glenea* sp.) damage. Together they caused desiccation of the cocoa tree. Circumstantial evidence from field and greenhouse observations in Bahia, Brazil, suggested that 'sudden death' disease of cocoa with galling of roots, was associated with infestation by nematodes, including *Meloidogyne* sp. (Jiménez 1969).

In Jamaica, where the 'burrowing nematode' *(Radopholus similis)* seriously affected bananas, Dixon (1961) recovered this nematode from cocoa roots shredded in water. The absence of typical lesions on cocoa roots indicated this host's insensibility to attack. Development of *R. similis* was confined to banana. Species of three genera (*Helicotylenchus, Meloidogyne,* and *Pratylenchus*) were common to the roots of cocoa and *Musa* spp. in Ghana, where Gerard (1963) found species of *Helicotylenchus* in large numbers in soil sampled close to banana and plantain (*Musa* spp.). The numbers obtained from the base of a cocoa tree were generally inversely proportional to the distance from the nearest banana or plantain. In Malawi, Corbett (1961) found *Meloidogyne javanica* on roots of unthrifty cocoa trees. There were patches where establishment was difficult and it seemed likely that this was associated with the presence of banana plants (*Musa* sp.) which are known to be hosts of *M. javanica*.

Pot experiments by Thrower (1958) in Papua and New Guinea, showed that cocoa was immune from attack by *M. javanica*, whilst this nematode attacked *Leucaena glauca* (L.) Benth. (Mimosaceae) to an extent which prevented its being satisfactorily established as cocoa shade. He commented that the behaviour of these plants seemed to be different in Ghana where Edwards (1955, 1956) reported that amelonado seedlings were susceptible to root-knot nematodes (*Meloidogyne* sp.), but *L. glauca* remained relatively free from attack.

In Nigeria, when *M. javanica* larvae were added to pasteurized soil in which cocoa seedlings were growing, their height increase after one year was not much less than that of cocoa seedlings grown without nematodes (Caveness 1967a). There were no apparent adverse effects on growth in similar tests with *Hoplolaimus pararobustus, Hemicycliophora oostenbrinki, Xiphinema ifacolum,* or *Helicotylenchus* sp. In pot experiments with cocoa, using soils from sites in Nigeria known to harbour certain nematodes, some nematode populations increased by a factor of 100 to 1,000 in periods of about one year (Caveness 1967b).

Xiphinema spp. seemed more numerous in soil near cocoa trees infected with cocoa necrosis virus (C.N.V.) than in soil near uninfected trees, at Omi Aboderin, near Asalu, Nigeria. In attempts to transmit C.N.V. by *Xiphinema* spp., no symptoms developed on any of the plants tested (Martini 1962). There was no evidence of transmission of cocoa viruses by nematodes in Ghana (Gerard 1963).

Nematode species associated with above-ground *(a)*, and below-ground *(b)*, parts of cocoa

Hooper (1969) summarized and illustrated the principal structures of plant nematodes and outlined their classification. He explained the difficulties in identifying them and stated that this is often done largely by recognition rather than by logical deduction from morphological characters.

Description, and accounts of the biology, pathogenicity, and control of the following nematodes were given by Orton Williams (1972, 1973*a,b*), by Orton Williams and Siddiqi (1973), and by Siddiqi (1972*a,b,c*, 1973): *Helicotylenchus dihystera, Hopolaimus galeatus, Meloidogyne incognita, Meloidogyne javanica, Pratylenchus coffeae, Radopholus similis, Rotylenchulus reniformis, Trophurus imperialis.* These eight species are among the total number of forty-two species reported in association with cocoa, and listed below:

Aphelenchoides bicaudatus (Imamura) Filipjev and Schuurmans Stekhoven (*b*)
    ASIA: Philippines (Timm 1965).
Criconemella goodeyi (de Guiran) De Grisse and Loof (*b*)
    AFRICA: Ivory Coast (de Guiran 1963, as *Criconemoides goodeyi*).
Criconemoides goodeyi de Guiran
see *Criconemella goodeyi* (de Guiran) De Grisse and Loof
Criconemoides limitaneum (Luc) Luc and de Guiran
see *Discocriconemella limitaneum* (Luc) De Grisse and Loof
Discocriconemella limitaneum (Luc) De Grisse and Loof (*b*)
    AFRICA: Ivory Coast (Luc and de Guiran 1960, as *Criconemoides limitaneum*).
Helicotylenchus cavenessi Sher (*b*)
    AFRICA: Nigeria (Caveness 1967*b*).
Helicotylenchus concavus Román (*b*)
    ASIA: Philippines (Timm 1965).
Helicotylenchus dihystera (Cobb) Sher (*b*)
    AFRICA: Nigeria (Entwistle and Caveness 1963, as *H. nannus*). WEST INDIES: Jamaica (Dixon 1961).
Helicotylenchus erythrinae (Zimmermann) Golden (*b*)
    WEST INDIES: Jamaica (Dixon 1961).
Helicotylenchus microcephalus Sher (*b*)
    AFRICA: Nigeria (Caveness 1967*b*).
Helicotylenchus multicinctus (Cobb) Golden (*b*)
    AFRICA: Ghana (Gerard 1963); Ivory Coast (Luc and de Guiran 1960); Nigeria (Entwistle and Caveness 1963). WEST INDIES: Jamaica (Dixon 1961).
Helicotylenchus nannus Steiner
see *Helicotylenchus dihystera* (Cobb) Sher
Hemicriconemoides cocophillus (Loos) Chitwood and Birchfield (*b*)
    AFRICA: Nigeria (Entwistle and Caveness 1963).
Hemicycliophora oostenbrinki Luc (*b*)
    AFRICA: Nigeria (Entwistle and Caveness 1963).
Hemicycliophora paradoxa Luc (*b*)
    AFRICA: Ivory Coast (Luc and de Guiran 1960).
Hoplolaimus galeatus (Cobb) Thorne (*b*)
    CENTRAL AMERICA: Costa Rica (Tarjan 1971).
Hoplolaimus pararobustus (Schuurmans Stekhoven and Teunissen) Sher (*b*)
    AFRICA: Nigeria (Entwistle and Caveness 1963, as *H. proporicus*).

Hoplolaimus proporicus J. B. Goodey
see *Hoplolaimus pararobustus* (Schuurmans Stekhoven and Teunissen) Sher
Hoplolaimus seinhorsti Luc (*b*)
    ASIA: Philippines (Timm 1965).
Isolaimium nigeriense Timm (*b*)
    AFRICA: Nigeria (Timm 1969).
Meloidogyne arenaria (Neal) Chitwood (*b*)
    AFRICA: Nigeria (Caveness 1967*a*).
Meloidogyne incognita (Kofoid and White) Chitwood (*b*)
    AFRICA: Ghana (Gerard 1963, as *M. incognita* var. *acrita*); Ivory Coast (Luc
    and de Guiran 1960); Nigeria (Entwistle and Caveness 1963). ASIA: India
    (Kumar, Viswanathan, and D'Souza 1971).
Meloidogyne javanica (Treub) Chitwood (*b*)
    AFRICA: Malawi (Corbett 1961).
Meloidogyne thamesi Chitwood (*b*)
    SOUTH AMERICA: Brazil (Bahia) (Lordello 1968).
Mesorhabditis graciliformis (Goffart) Dougherty (*a*)
    AFRICA: Cameroon (S.W.) (Goffart 1935, as *Rhabditis gracilis* from decaying
    fruit, attacked by *Phytophthora* (probably *P. palmivora*)).
Neodiplogaster tropica Cobb (*a*)
    CENTRAL AMERICA: Guatemala (Cobb 1924).
Panagrolaimus filiformis de Man (*a*)
    AFRICA: Cameroon (S.E.) (Bouriquet 1954).
Paratylenchus arculatus Luc and de Guiran (*b*)
    AFRICA: Ivory Coast (Luc and de Guiran 1962).
Paratylenchus curvitatus van der Linde (*b*)
    AFRICA: Nigeria (Entwistle and Caveness 1963).
Pratylenchus brachyurus (Godfrey) Filipjev and Schuurmans Stekhoven (*b*)
    AFRICA: Ivory Coast (Luc and de Guiran 1960); Nigeria (Entwistle and
    Caveness 1963).
Pratylenchus coffeae (Zimmermann) Filipjev and Schuurmans Stekhoven (*b*)
    WEST INDIES: Jamaica (Dixon 1961). ASIA: India (Kumar *et al.* 1971);
    Indonesia (Java) (Fluiter and Mulholland 1941, as *Tylenchus coffeae*).
Radopholus similis (Cobb) Thorne (*b*)
    WEST INDIES: Jamaica (Dixon 1961).
Rhabditis gracilis Goffart
see *Mesorhabditis graciliformis* (Goffart) Dougherty
Rotylenchoides intermedius Luc (*b*)
    AFRICA: Nigeria (Caveness 1967*a*).
Rotylenchulus reniformis Linford and Oliveira (*b*)
    WEST INDIES: Jamaica (Dixon 1961).
Scutellonema brachyurus (Steiner) Andrássy (*b*)
    WEST INDIES: Jamaica (Dixon 1961).
Scutellonema clathricaudatum Whitehead (*b*)
    AFRICA: Nigeria (Caveness 1967*b*).
Trophurus imperialis Loof (*b*)
    AFRICA: Ivory Coast (Luc and de Guiran 1960).

Tylenchorhynchus martini Fielding (*b*)
   AFRICA: Nigeria (Caveness 1967*a*).
Tylenchus coffeae Zimmermann
see *Pratylenchus coffeae* (Zimmermann) Filipjev and Schuurmans Stekhoven
Xiphinema attorodorum Luc (*b*)
   AFRICA: Nigeria (Entwistle and Caveness 1963).
Xiphinema ebriense Luc (*b*)
   AFRICA: Ghana (Gerard 1963); Nigeria (Entwistle and Caveness 1963).
Xiphinema elongatum Schuurmans Stekhoven and Tenuissen (*b*)
   ASIA: Philippines (Timm 1965).
Xiphinemaifacolum Luc (*b*)
   AFRICA: Ghana (Gerard 1963); Nigeria (Entwistle and Caveness 1963).
Xiphinema insigne Loos (*b*)
   ASIA: Philippines (Timm 1965).
Xiphinema longicaudatum Luc (*b*)
   AFRICA: Nigeria (Entwistle and Caveness 1963).
Xiphinema nigeriense Luc (*b*)
   AFRICA: Ghana (Gerard 1963); Nigeria (Entwistle and Caveness 1963).
Xiphinema setariae Luc (*b*)
   AFRICA: Nigeria (Entwistle and Caveness 1963).

Control

Cultural methods

Nematode infestation of young or mature cocoa is nowhere severe or widespread enough to require large-scale control or preventive measures. Corbett (1961) noted that if nematodes became a serious obstacle to cocoa culture in Malawi, an alternative to banana as a 'nurse' crop should be sought. No nematodes were associated with *Terminalia ivorensis* A. Chev. (Gerard 1963), which was considered a suitable tree for shading cocoa in Ghana (Benstead 1953).

In Nigeria, soils were sampled during 4 years for estimations of nematode occurrences in plots of amelonado and Amazon cocoa seedlings grown with either grass, natural weeds, mulch, or bare soil. Caveness (1967*a*) summarized the results by stating that 'the cultural practices used had little effect on the plant parasitic nematode populations'.

Chemical methods

Entwistle and Caveness (1963) summarized the procedure and results from a soil fumigation trial in Ghana, using different doses of Nemagon (D.B.C.P.) injected into the soil of a cocoa field and into the soil of pots containing seedlings. Nematodes were controlled by 4 gals. per acre. In Jamaica, 1 or 2 gals. per acre D.B.C.P. sprinkled on the soil and washed in with water reduced numbers of larvae, mainly *M. incognita* (Dixon 1961). In most of the treatment replicates, populations increased 8 to 12 weeks after treatment. In Nigeria, Caveness (1962) tried a range of D.B.C.P.

dosages injected at a depth of 8 in. (20 cm.), in the field and in pots. At 4 gals. per acre D.B.C.P., nematode populations were almost completely eliminated, without the cocoa showing toxic effects. Whitehead (1969) confirmed that Nemagon (D.B.C.P.) injected into the soil around trees can control nematode damage temporarily, and he mentioned other chemicals used to control nematodes in tea and coffee nurseries. Tarjan, Jiménez, and Soria (1971) found species of six nematode genera (*Helicotylenchus, Meloidogyne, Pratylenchus, Trichodorus, Tylenchus*, and *Xiphinema*) associated with roots of 12-year-old cocoa trees in Costa Rica. Numbers of pods were apparently increased through applications of different nematicides, which included Dasanit, Nemacur, and Nemagon (Martin 1971). It seemed that Nemagon (70 lb./acre) may have been somewhat phytotoxic because the weight of produce was apparently diminished.

14

NUTRITIONAL DISORDERS

Introduction

Consideration is given in this chapter to disorders which are not primarily induced by pathogenic organisms or viruses, but are due to impeded uptake, translocation, or metabolism of nutrients, leading to abnormal appearances shown by the cocoa plant above ground.

Terminology

In common with other plants, the chemical composition of the cocoa tree is difficult to define in quantitative terms. It is convenient to group the elements occurring in higher plants, including cocoa, into three categories: indispensable, essential, and non-essential.

Among about sixty different elements known to occur in plants, a few are 'indispensable', whilst the essentiality of some others is uncertain because the distinction between elements which are considered to be 'essential' and those which are believed to be 'non-essential' is sometimes arbitrary. These elements occur in plants in different amounts, the abundant ones being carbon (C), hydrogen (H), and oxygen (O), which are indispensable. C and H are structural units for all organic molecules, whilst O is indispensable for growth processes of higher plants. These three elements are likely to be inadequately available to cocoa plants only in such exceptional circumstances that their further consideration here is unnecessary. Nitrogen (N) should be categorized as indispensable because it is a structural atom in proteins, nucleic acids and many organic molecules. Despite the occurrence of N in the atmosphere, this essential element is not always adequately available for plants.

An 'essential element' may be defined as follows: the plant can neither grow nor complete its life-cycle if the element is supplied in a sufficiently low concentration. Although implicit in this definition, it is worth noting the corollary that an essential element cannot be replaced completely by any other element. This definition of essentiality is largely academic because the criterion of irreplaceability is difficult to verify in practice and is indeterminate for some elements found in cocoa.

It is convenient to classify essential elements as either 'macronutrients' or 'micronutrients'. Bowen (1966) provided an arbitrary but satisfactory basis for these two classes in the statement that 'most macronutrients are needed at concentrations exceeding 1 ppm in the nutrient solution, while micronutrients are needed at lower concentrations'. There is experimental justification for this basic grouping. Lockard, Vamathevan, and Thamboo (1959a) tabulated the concentrations (as p.p.m. = parts per million) of twelve essential elements in the control ('complete') nutrient solution used for their sand-culture experiments with cocoa. There were seven macro-nutrients in the nutrient solution, in amounts greater than 1 p.p.m. (calcium, iron, magnesium, nitrogen, phosphorus, potassium, and sulphur), and five micronutrients, in amounts less than 1 p.p.m. (boron, copper manganese, molybdenum, and zinc).

The above consideration of the essentiality of elements implies their presence in suitable amounts. An essential nutrient-element may induce abnormalities through presence in either insufficient or excessive amount. It is conventional to use the terms 'deficiency' and 'excess' in this connection, but they are not readily defined in words. These concepts are expressed diagrammatically in the form of a 'response curve' (Bowen 1966; Cooke 1967).

Elements occurring in cocoa plants

Apart from C, H, and O, twenty-two other elements have been reported as present in cocoa leaves and/or beans from different countries (Hart 1911; Maskell, Evans, and Murray 1953; Crowther and Raymond 1954; Deschreider and Van Coillie 1956). There are nineteen putatively 'essential' elements: boron (B), barium (Ba), calcium (Ca), chlorine (Cl), cobalt (Co), copper (Cu), fluorine (F), iron (Fe), potassium (K), magnesium (Mg), manganese (Mn), molybdenum (Mo), nitrogen (N), sodium (Na), phosphorus (P), sulphur (S), silicon (Si), strontium (Sr), zinc (Zn): and three supposedly non-essential elements: aluminium (Al), arsenic (As), lead (Pb).

Economic importance

Four centuries ago, Benzoni (1565) depicted the benefit that the young cocoa plant derived from overhead shade. Murray and Nichols (1966) commented that feral cocoa persists as a heavily shaded understorey tree in the tropical rain-forest of the Amazon basin, where the production of only a few pods per tree has sufficed to ensure the survival of the species. In such circumstances, with little or no removal of crop for human consumption, soil fertility has been maintained. In contrast, under conditions of commercial production, soil fertility has been exploited and exported, formerly without replenishment. In tropical countries generally, control of soil fertility has been neglected (Cooke 1967).

Present experience of nutritional ill-health in cocoa comes mainly from Africa, Asia, and Trinidad, where commercial production of cocoa required yields per unit area to exceed those which would have sufficed to maintain the species under 'natural' conditions.

Soil depletion by cropping

Amounts of nutrients removed in harvested cocoa beans vary seasonally and geographically (Haworth 1953; Lockard and Burridge 1965b). The review of geographically widespread fertilizer experiments by Cunningham (1959), showed common expectation that cocoa plantings required chemical elements singly or in combination. Lockard and Burridge (1965a) reviewed occurrences of micronutrient deficiencies in a number of cocoa-growing countries. Cunningham, Smith, and Hurd (1961) discussed the past, present, and possible future drain on the soil's nutrient reserves in relation to a 'mineral nutrient balance sheet', for different cropping conditions. They and others considered amounts of important macronutrients removed from the soil by cocoa crops (Humphries 1943b, 1944; Adams and McKelvie 1955; Havord 1960; Cooke 1967). Since the removal of micronutrients needs consideration with respect to possible depletion through cropping, approximate percentage concentrations of six trace-elements in cocoa beans are given in Table 14.1. Columns (2) and (4) can be used to estimate weights

TABLE 14.1

Average dry weights and nutrient contents of beans and husk comprising a single pod

	Beans		Husk	
	(1) g	(2) %	(3) g	(4) %
Total dry weight	43·25		50·66	
Nutrient				
N	0·9515	2·200	0·8055	1·590
P	0·1720	0·398	0·0797	0·157
K	0·5744	1·328	1·7115	3·378
Mg	0·1722	0·398	0·1588	0·314
Ca	0·0711	0·164	0·2753	0·543
*Zn		0·005		
*Fe		0·003		
*Mn		0·003		
*Cu		0·002		
*Na		0·002		
*B		0·001		

Columns (1) and (3), values given by Humphries (1943b, 1944).
Columns (2) and (4), weights of constituents ((1) and (3)) expressed as percentages of total dry weight (43·25 and 50·66).
* Column (2), values tabulated by Lockard and Burridge (1965b) for micronutrients (as p.p.m.) are given here as percentages (%) to indicate approximate amounts of these elements, as for macronutrients. Elsewhere in this chapter, amounts of micronutrients are expressed as p.p.m. (parts per million).

of nutrients removed per unit weight of cocoa beans, with or without husk material. There is diversity of procedure when pods are opened to remove the beans whilst discarding the husks, the latter may be left *in situ*, but sometimes they are removed, possibly for composting elsewhere (Atanda and Egbe 1966). In circumstances when an estimate of amount of nutrient removed in husks is required in addition to the amount removed in beans, a 1:1 dry weight ratio for husk: beans may be assumed, as was done by Adams and McKelvie (1955), although it may be noted that under the conditions of his observations, Humphries (1943b) found that this ratio was 1·2:1 (e.g. 50·66:43·25).

More information is available and presented in Table 14.1 for beans (column 2) than for husks (column 4). It is worth noting that although nutrients in husks are released slowly, they are not exported from the producing country as are the nutrients in cocoa beans, at the rate of about 4 tons P and 13 tons K per 1,000 tons dry cocoa exported.

Functions of essential elements

Stiles (1946) discussed attempts to classify the essential elements according to supposed function. It was noted that most of them were in the first four periods of the periodic classification and he stated that 'the heavier metals do not figure among elements necessary for plants'. Twenty years later, the role of many elements was still not fully understood. Bowen (1966) stated that 'although a wide range of functions has been established for the essential elements, the knowledge available is manifestly fragmentary and incomplete'.

Symptoms

General consideration

Although the roles of the different essential elements in a multiplicity of metabolic processes are uncertain, it is axiomatic that too much or too little of one or more of these important elements will have far reaching effects. Consequently, visible symptoms will generally be late manifestations of earlier nutrient derangement, as discussed by Epstein (1972).

Nutrient losses through cocoa production discussed by Adams and McKelvie (1955) are widespread. They stated that 'visual assessment of cocoa health and productivity may be grossly misleading'. Less frequently encountered are the starvation symptoms, sometimes referred to as 'hunger signs' (Sauchelli 1969), which are indicative rather than diagnostic for particular nutrient derangements. Because of the time lapse between initiation of such disorders and visible response by the cocoa plant, either deficiency or excess of a particular element may have diverse ultimate manifestations, whilst different nutritional derangements may in various circumstances be ultimately manifested similarly. Although a cocoa-plant abnormality may not necessarily be referable to an original nutritional derangement, it is worth considering some reported manifestations to show that a non-pathogenic cause may be sought.

Leaf chlorosis and necrosis

The phenomena to which these terms have been applied, take many forms in cocoa. Some in Trinidad were illustrated and discussed by Maskell *et al.* (1953) and by Evans and Murray (1953*a*). They observed plants grown in nutrient cultures, each culture lacking one essential element. Their 'provisional key to symptoms of mineral nutrition' showed that for all the fourteen elements considered, the symptoms of deficiency or excess included chlorosis, or necrosis, or both maladies. Under field conditions, chlorosis as a symptom of nutrient imbalance, is dependent on light intensity to an important extent (Evans and Murray 1953*b*). With low light intensity, the colour of leaves tends to be fully green, but gets progressively paler with higher light intensity. Determinations of chlorophyll content showed less chlorophyll (0·13 per cent) in fully exposed leaves (100 per cent sunlight) than in shaded leaves (0·23 per cent chlorophyll with 15 per cent sunlight). The appearance of plants in full sunlight with chlorotic leaves was much improved by applications of 'complete' (N.P.K.) fertilizer, since there is an interaction between light and mineral nutrition of cocoa (Murray and Nichols 1966). The effect of fertilizer is greater at high light intensity than at low light intensity. Cunningham and Burridge (1960) suggested that one function of shade was to permit the use of soils of low nutrient status, through lowering the growth rate and limiting yields.

A particular manifestation of chlorosis and necrosis, referred to as 'marginal leaf-scorch', was studied first in Trinidad (Hardy 1937), and was believed to be due to deficiency or unavailability of K, or unbalanced uptake of Ca, K, or N. On the other hand, Lockard and Asomaning (1965) stated that 'plants supplied with nitrate nitrogen tended to develop leaf-edge scorch whether or not they were deficient in the other major nutrients'.

A characteristic pattern of darker green and lighter green or yellow tissue in the same leaf, was associated with Fe starvation (Greenwood and Djokoto 1952; Maskell *et al.* 1953). Lockard and Asomaning (1963) noted that experimentally produced symptoms of Cu, Fe, Mn, and Zn deficiency might, through inexperience, be confused with virus disease symptoms.

Defoliation and dieback

In cocoa, as in other mesophytic plants, premature leaf fall is a common response to drought. Murray (1964*b*) noted that in the tropics total loss of water per month by evaporation from the soil and transpiration from the plant ('evapotranspiration') may be between 4 and 5 in. (102 and 127 mm.). The rainfall of certain months in cocoa-growing areas may be less than 4 in. (102 mm.), as for example in parts of South America (Erneholm 1948) and in West Africa (Anon. 1949). Cocoa is liable to suffer from water stress, with the response of abnormal leaf shedding, when evapotranspiration exceeds rainfall. Competition from weeds for soil moisture accentuated dry-season leaf fall in Ghana (Brown and Boateng 1972).

In Nigeria and Cameroon, there occurred a characteristic 'paint-brush' appearance of chupons and also of distal branches in the canopy, which Waterston (1954) referred to as 'leafless twig disease'. However, it was previously reported as a physiological disorder in Cameroon by Ludwigs (1934). Affected shoots lose their leaves and buds in the apical region at an early stage, but the leaf stipules persist as a cluster at the end of the shoot, giving the characteristic appearance. Leafless twigs in Cameroon were sometimes somewhat swollen, which was suggestive of witches' broom disease (von Faber 1909). The cause of the 'false witches' brooms' in Cameroon is not known, but it was regarded by Waterston (1954) as an expression of the 'leafless twig syndrome' including the 'paint brush' appearance. Similar symptoms were produced in cocoa grown in nutrient culture with little or no Cu. Lockard, Vamathevan, and Thamboo (1959b) reported the appearance of cocoa seedlings after growing for about 9 months in sand culture deprived of Cu, at Kuala Lumpur, Malaysia. The following abnormalities were noticed: premature leaf-abscission, shortening of internodes in the abscission region, swelling of stems, and loss of apical dominance by shoot tip. Nichols (1961b) observed similar symptoms after 3 to 4 months on cocoa seedlings grown in sand culture with zero or minimal Cu (0·005 p.p.m.), at St. Augustine, Trinidad. The plants were at first normal in appearance despite little or no Cu in the rooting medium, presumably normal cotyledons have much Cu.

Malformation of leaves

In Ghana, a leaf distortion with mottling syndrome, was associated with the presence of heaps of rotting cocoa pods, and Greenwood (1943) termed this disorder 'sickle leaf mosaic' (see p. 79). Later, this name was changed to 'sickle leaf' to avoid possible inference that this nutritional disorder had virus-disease associations (Greenwood and Hayfron 1951). The mottle pattern of sickle leaf was an interveinal chlorosis and distinct from the vein-clearing and vein-banding pattern of the 'mosaic' induced by virus infection. Attempts to transmit sickle leaf by budding or grafting were unsuccessful, but detailed studies of soils showed that this kind of leaf distortion was associated with high pH values (6·9–7·0) and unusually large content of available K or P (Greenwood 1943; Greenwood and Hayfron 1951). Sickle leaf symptoms were induced in normal seedlings when pieces of rotting husk were added to surface soil, or when either alkaline leaf litter or strongly alkaline ash was incorporated in potting soil for seedlings. Seedlings grown in water culture lacking Zn consistently developed mottling and then distortion of leaves in successive flushes (Greenwood and Hayfron 1951). Subsequently, Ahenkorah (1969) in Ghana confirmed symptom production through unavailability of Zn, but considered that this deficiency at Tafo was not induced by excess P.

In Trinidad, with stringently controlled conditions for mineral-nutrition studies, Maskell *et al.* (1953) showed that sickle leaf-shape was not a universal feature of Zn deficiency, but characterized an intermediate range of deficiency. It seemed that the zinc-deficiency symptom described by Greenwood and Hayfron was induced by a culture technique which rendered Zn largely unavailable. Deformed leaves which had marginal indentations were also ascribed to a lime-induced Fe deficiency (Greenwood and Posnette 1947). Abnormally shaped leaves with dentate margins, and one leaf described as 'trilobate in appearance', were produced on plants grown in solutions described by Greenwood and Djokoto (1952) as 'complete nutrient at high pH' (range pH 6·2–6·5). Maskell *et al.* (1953) found that leaves with serrated margins occurred when Fe and Mg, or Fe and Ca, were deficient together. Havord (1955) concluded that lime-induced chlorosis was not due to failure to assimilate Fe from the soil, but was associated with non-availability of Fe within the plant. For pot experiments made in Ghana by Cunningham (1964), each cocoa bean had one cotyledon removed before planting, in order to grow seedlings with lessened micronutrient reserves, in a sandy loam soil from an area where cocoa trees were unhealthy. With or without soil applications of Fe, Mn, and Zn, plants had many abnormal leaves (average 65–68 per cent), including Fe chlorosis symptoms, sickle-shaped leaves, and other mis-shapen leaves (dentate edges and retuse apices). Plants had smaller percentages of abnormal leaves (36 per cent) with soil applications of S alone, or with soil applications of Fe, Mn, S, and Zn (25 per cent). Plants were without abnormal leaves with soil applications of S and foliar spraying with Fe, Mn, and Zn.

Malformation of pods

In both Ecuador (Tollenaar 1966, 1967) and Ghana (Asomaning and Kwakwa 1966, 1968*a*), production of abnormal fruits had been reported as an indication of B deficiency. In addition to the characteristic of seedlessness, these abnormal fruits had a woody core and were generally mis-shapen. Trees bearing such fruits sometimes displayed leaf symptoms considered to be typical of B deficiency (Sauchelli 1969). Only in Ghana, has severe malformation of larger (seeded) pods been reported. The importance of pod damage through B deficiency there is uncertain, because the suspected manifestations of this disorder may be confused with similar symptoms associated with damage to cocoa fruits by a pentatomid (*Bathycoelia thalassina* (Herrich-Schaeffer)), as discussed by Marchart and Lodos (1969). However, one type of pod malformation occurring in the field was produced in an insect-proof greenhouse (Asomaning and Kwakwa 1965). Further confirmatory observations were hampered by limited production of fruits under greenhouse conditions (Asomaning and Kwakwa 1968*b*). Marchart and Lodos (1969) explained that a microscopical search for possible insect punctures is necessary to distinguish between the 'premature ripening' (colour change from green to yellow in immature fruits) which may occur within a week after first attack by *B. thalassina*, and the similar appearance which may occur as a response to B deficiency, with or without pod malformation.

Control

The nature of a supposed nutritional disorder will generally be conjectural, pending experimental investigation. Such studies may proceed through field trials, or pot tests, or both kinds of test in parallel, but results accrue slowly. Certain 'short-cut' methods for diagnosis or treatment, by leaf injection or stem injection techniques were described by Evans and Fennah (1953).

Consideration of cocoa manuring is beyond present scope, this subject has been considered from various viewpoints (Havord 1960; Burle 1961; Urquhart 1961; Smyth 1966; Eernstman 1968; Wessel 1971). The economics of fertilizer applications to cocoa were discussed by Cunningham (1963), and by Quartey-Papafio and Edwards (1961).

REFERENCES

W.A.C.R.I.: West African Cacao/Cocoa Research Institute (1944–March 1954/ April 1954–61).

W.A.C.R.I. (N): West African Cocoa Research Institute (Nigeria) (1962–4)

C.R.I.G.: Cocoa Institute (Ghana Academy of Sciences (1962–9) (Council for Scientific and Industrial Research (1970–2)).

C.R.I.N.: Cocoa Research Institute of Nigeria (1965–72).

C.E.P.L.A.C.: Comissão Executiva do Plano de Recuperação Econômico-Rural da Lavoura Cacaueira.

F.A.O.: Food and Agriculture Organization of the United Nations.

ABRAHAM, E. V. and PADMANABAN, M. D. (1967). Pests that damage cacao in Madras. *Indian Horticulture* **11**, 11–12.

ACQUAYE, D. K. and SMITH, R. W. (1965). Effects of ground covers and fertilizers on establishment and yield of cocoa on clear-felled land in Ghana. *Expl Agric.* **1**, 131–9.

ADAMS, C. D. and ALSTON, A. H. G. (1955). A list of the Gold Coast Pteridophyta. *Bull. Bri. Mus. Nat. His. Bot.* **1**, 143–85.

ADAMS, S. N. and McKELVIE, A. D. (1955). Environmental requirements of cocoa in the Gold Coast. *Rep. Cocoa Conf. Grosvenor House, London, W.1, 13–15 Sept. 1955*, pp. 22–7. Cocoa, Chocolate, and Confectionery Alliance; London.

ADDOH, P. G. (1971). The danger of importing freeze-dried cocoa pollen into Africa. *III Intl. Cocoa Res. Conf.* Accra, Ghana 23–29 Nov. 1969, pp. 538–41.

ADEBAYO, A. A. (1971). A technique of inoculation of fixed cocoa pods with *Phytophthora palmivora* (Butl.) *Turrialba* **21**, 280–2.

ADOMAKO, D. (1972). Studies on mealybug (*Planococcoides njalensis* (Laing)) nutrition: a comparative analysis for the free carbohydrate and nitrogenous compounds in cocoa bark and mealybug honeydew. *Bull ent. Res.* **61**, 523–31.

AHENKORAH, Yaw (1969). A note on zinc deficiency in cacao (*Theobroma cacao* L.). *Ghana J. agric. Sci.* **2**, 3–6.

AINSWORTH, G. C. (1961). The Review of Applied Mycology. *Rep. 6th Commonwealth Mycol. Conf. 1960*, pp. 17–22. Commonwealth Mycological Institute; Kew.

—— (1971). *Ainsworth and Bisby's dictionary of the fungi. 6th ed.* Commonwealth Mycological Institute; Kew.

AKINREFON, O. A. (1967). Root disease of cacao. *Ann. Rep. C.R.I.N.* 1965–6, p. 125.

—— (1968a). Production of extracellular enzymes by *Phytophthora palmivora* (Butl.) Butl. *J. gen. Microbiol.* **51**, 67–74.

—— (1968b). Phenolic fungitoxicity and the possible role of phenolase of *Phytophthora palmivora* (Butl.) Butl. *Phytopath. Z.* **63**, 153–64.

—— (1969). Biochemical studies on plant tissues infected by *Phytophthora palmivora* (Butl.) Butl. *Ann. appl. Biol.* **63**, 303–13.

ALANDIA, S. BORDA and BELL, F. H. (1957). Diseases of warm climate crops in Bolivia. *Pl. Prot. Bull. F.A.O.* **5**, 172–3.

ALEXANDER, J. V., COOK, R. J. and BOURRET, J. A. (1965). Fusarium species associated with cacao galls. *Phytopathology* **55**, 125.

ALI, Faisal M. (1972). Effect of gamma BHC against capsids on cocoa in Ghana. *Expl Agric.* **8**, 73–7.

ALIBERT, H. (1946). Note préliminaire sur une nouvelle maladie du cacaoyer le 'swollen shoot'. *Agron. Trop. Nogent.* **1**, 34–43.

ALLISON, H. W. S. and CUNNINGHAM, R. K. (1959). Preparing land for cacao in Ghana. Land clearance for field experimentation. *Wld Crops* **11**, 311–13.

ALSTON, A. H. G. (1956). New African ferns. *Bol. Soc. broteriana sér. 2A* **30**, 5–27.

—— (1959). *The ferns and fern-allies of West Tropical Africa. A supplement to the second edition of the Flora of West Tropical Africa.* Crown Agents for Overseas Governments and Administrations; London.

ALTSON, R. A. (1926a). Report of the assistant botanist and mycologist. Appendix III, pp. 39–45. In: *Rep. Dept Sci. Agric. Br. Guiana 31 Dec. 1925.*

—— (1926b). Report on a visit to Jamaica, Costa Rica and Trinidad. *J. Bd Agric. Br. Guiana* **18**, 2–19.

ALVAREDO, R., AMPUERO, E. and DOAK, K. D. (1960). Reaccion de diferentes clones y progenies hibridas a la Buba o Cushion Gall del cacao. *VIII Inter-Amer. Cacao Conf. Trinidad and Tobago 15–25 June, 1960. Proc., pp.* 290–300.

ALVIM, P. de T. (1960). Las necesidades de agua del cacao. *Turrialba* **10** (1), 6–16.

——, MACHADO, A. D. and VELLO, F. (1972). Physiological responses of cacao to environmental factors. *4th intl Cocoa Res. Conf. Trinidad and Tobago, Jan. 1972* (mimeograph).

—— and SEESCHAAF, K. W. (1968). Die-back and death of cacao trees caused by a new species of parasitic tree. *Nature, Lond.* **219**, 1386–7.

AMPONSAH, J. D. and ABROKWA, M. O. (1969). Cocoa hybrid seed gardens. *Ann. Rep. C.R.I.G. 1967–8*, pp. 87–9.

AMPUERO, E. (1967). Monilia pod rot of cocoa. *Cocoa Growers' Bull.* **9**, 15–18.

—— and DESROSIERS, R. (1960). Comportamiento en resistencia a la escoba de bruja de los clones Silecia-1 y 5 traidos del oriente Ecuatoriano. *VIII Inter-Amer. Cacao Conf. Trinidad and Tobago 15–25 June, 1960. Proc., pp.* 156–65.

ANCALMO, O. (1959). Lista preliminar de enfermedades parasitarias en las plantas de El Salvador. *Serv. Coop. Agr. Salvadoreno Amer. Bol. Tec., pp.* 1–29. (Cited by B. R. Lipscomb, in: Miller, P. R. (1963 *in litt.*)).

ANONYMOUS (1925). Fungi received at the Imperial Bureau of Mycology. List I, pp. 1–8. Kew; now the Commonwealth Mycological Institute.

—— (1936). A list of the diseases of cultivated plants in Ceylon, compiled by the Division of Mycology. *Bull. Dept Agric. Ceylon* **88**, 1–47.

—— (1945a). Swollen-shoot of Cacao. How to recognize and control. A memorandum prepared by the West African Cacao Research and Survey Advisory Committee, on the symptoms of swollen-shoot disease with an evaluation of the control measures applied between 1940 and 1943 by the Department of Agriculture, Gold Coast, pp. 1–20. (Also issued as Appendix III of Sessional

Paper No. I of 1948 'Interim Report of the Committee of Enquiry to Review Legislation for the Treatment of the Swollen Shoot Disease of Cocoa'. Government Printing Department; Accra. Compiled anonymously by A. F. Posnette and J. Paine, *fide* Posnette, A. F. 1970 *in litt.*).

—— (1945*b*) The organisation of cocoa research in the British West Indies, Memorandum by Colonial Office. *Rep. and Proc. Cocoa Res. Conf. Colonial Office May–June 1945. Colonial* H.M.S.O.; London. **192**, 104–9.

—— (1948). *Ann. Rep. W. Afr. Cacao Res. Inst. 1947–8*, pp. 62–6.

—— (1949). Weather on the West Coast of tropical Africa. *M.O.* **492**, 1–281. H.M.S.O., London.

—— (1950). *Ann. Rep. W. Afr. Cacao Res. Inst. April 1948–March 1949*, pp. 1–64

—— (1951), *Ann. Rep. W. Afr. Cacao Res. Inst. April 1949–March 1950*, 1–84.

—— (1952). Disease problems of cacao in Cuba. *Cacao, Turrialba* **2**, 3.

—— (1953*a*). *Ann. Rep. W. Afr. Cacao Res. Inst. April 1950–March 1951*, pp. 1–63.

—— (1953*b*). *Ann. Rep. W. Afr. Cacao Res. Inst. April 1951–March 1952*, pp. 1–54.

—— (1953)*c*. Rapport annuel pour l'exercice 1952. *Publ. Inst. nat. Étude agron. Congo belge* (*INEAC*) *1952* (*hors. ser.*), (*Brussels*) 1–395.

—— (1956). Juizo agro-pecuário do ano de 1955. *Gazeta Agric. Moçamb.* **8**, 2–6 (abstract in *Rev. appl. Mycol.* **35**, 509 (1956)).

—— (1960). 1. Host List of fungi etc. Recorded in the South East Asia and Pacific Region, *Theobroma cacao*—Cacao. *F.A.O. Plant Prot. Committee for S. E. Asia and Pacific Reg. Tech. Doc.* **11**, 1–2 (mimeograph). 2. Host List of insects recorded in the South East Asia and Pacific Region, *Theobroma cacao*— Cacao. *F.A.O. Plant Prot. Committee for S E Asia and Pacific Reg. Tech. Doc.* **11**, 1–8 (mimeograph).

—— (1961). *Sierra Leone Rep. Dept Agric. 1959.* Government Printing Department; Freetown, Sierra Leone.

—— (1963). Cocoa. *Sabah Malaysia Ann. Rept. Dept Agric. 1963*, pp. 70–3. Sabah Publishing House; Jesselton.

—— (1964*a*). *Catalogue of the culture collection of the Commonwealth Mycological Institute*, 4th ed., pp. 1–135. Commonwealth Mycological Institute; Kew.

—— (1964*b*). Cocoa. *Sabah Malaysia Ann. Rep. Dept Agric. 1964*, pp. 38–53. Sabah Publishing House; Jesselton.

—— (1965). Cocoa. *State of Sabah Ann. Rep. Dept Agric. 1965*, pp. 52–4.

—— (1966). *Sarawak Ministry of Agric. and Forestry Ann. Rep. Res. Branch, Dept. Agric. 1964*, Government Printing Office; Kuching.

—— (1967). Plant Pathology. *State of Sabah Ann. Rep. Dept Agric. 1965*, pp. 44– 56. Sabah Publishing House; Kota Kinabalu, Sabah, Malaysia.

—— (1968). *Catalogue of the culture collection of the Commonwealth Mycological Institute*, 5th ed., pp. 1–162. Commonwealth Mycological Institute; Kew.

—— (1969). *Infestation control in the cocoa, chocolate and confectionery industry*, pp. 1–62. Cocoa, Chocolate, and Confectionery Alliance; London.

—— (1970). Plant pathology. *State of Sabah Ann. Rep. Dept Agric. 1968*, pp. 35–44. Sabah Publishing House; Kota Kinabalu, Sabah, Malaysia.

—— (1971). Plant pathology. *State of Sabah Ann. Rep. Dept Agric. 1969*, pp. 106–20. Sabah Publishing House; Kota Kinabalu, Sabah, Malaysia.

—— (1972a). *IV intl Cocoa Res. Conf. Intl Choc. Rev.* **27**, pp. 34 and 36–7.

—— (1972b). Plant pathology. *State of Sabah Ann. Rep. Dept Agric. 1970*, pp. 78–88. Sabah Publishing House; Kota Kinabalu, Sabah, Malaysia.

—— (1973). *Catalogue of the Culture Collection of the Commonwealth Mycological Institute.* 6th ed., pp. 1–263. Commonwealth Mycological Institute; Kew.

APPEL, O. and LAUBERT, R. (1906). Bamerkenswerte Pilze I. *Arb. biol. Bund Anst. Land- u. Forstw.* **5**, 147.

—— and STRUNK, H. F. (1904). Ueber einige in Kamerun auf Theobroma cacao beobachtete pilze. *Zentbl. Bakt. Parasitkde* **11**, 632–7.

ARBELAEZ, G. E. (1957). La llaga macana del tronco del cacao. *Acta Agron., Palmira* **7**, 71–103.

ARCHIBALD, J. F. (1961). Transmission of gall-diseases of cacao, mango and pigeon pea. *Nature, Lond.* **190**, 284.

ARMSTRONG, K. B. (1962). Joint W.A.C.R.I./Division of Agriculture ant–mealybug control trials (Methods of application and formulation). *Ann. Rep. W. Afr. Cocoa Res. Inst. 1960–1*, pp. 38–9.

—— (1963). Joint W.A.C.R.I./Division of Agriculture ant–mealybug control trials. *Ann. Rep. W. Afr. Cocoa Res. Inst. 1961–2*, pp. 28–9.

ASHBY, S. F. (1915). Notes on diseases of cultivated crops observed in 1913–14. *Bull. Dept Agric. Jamaica, New Ser.* **2**, 299–327.

—— (1922). Oospores in cultures of *Phytophthora faberi. Kew Bull.*, pp. 257–62.

—— (1927). *Macrophomina phaseoli* (Maubl.) comb. nov. The pycnidial state of *Rhizoctonia bataticola* (Taub.) Butl. *Trans. Br. mycol. Soc.* **12**, 141–7.

—— (1929a). Strains and taxonomy of *Phytophthora palmivora* Butler (*P. faberi* Maubl.). *Trans. Br. mycol. Soc.* **14**, 18–38.

—— (1929b). Diseases of limes and sugar-cane in the West Indies. *Kew Bull.* pp. 209–14 (abstract in *Rev. appl. Mycol.* **9**, 20–21 (1930)).

ASOMANING, E. J. A. (1964a). Root infection of cocoa by *Phytophthora palmivora* Butl. *C.R.I.G. Rep. 1st April 1962–30th Sept. 1963*, pp. 23–5.

—— (1964b). Varietal resistance of young clones and seedlings of cocoa (*Theobroma cacao* L.) to root infection by *Phytophthora palmivora. Trop. Agric., Trin.* **41**, 251–6.

—— and KWAKWA, R. S. (1965). Boron deficiency symptoms in cocoa fruits. *Conf. intle Rech. agron. cacaoyères. Abidjan 15–20 nov. 1965*, pp. 39–43.

—— and —— (1966). Parthenocarpic fruit development in the Amazon shade and fertilizer trial (K_2O_1): boron deficiency suspected. *C.R.I.G. Rep. 1st Oct. 1963–31st March 1965*, pp. 89–90.

—— and —— (1968a). Physiology of cocoa. *Ann. Rep. C.R.I.G. 1965–6*, pp. 93–125.

—— and —— (1968b). Physiology of cocoa. *Ann. Rep. C.R.I.G. 1966–7*, pp. 77–95.

—— and LOCKARD, R. G. (1964). Physiology of cocoa. *C.R.I.G. Rep. 1st April 1962–30th Sept. 1963*, pp. 59–89.

——, LOVI, N. K., and BOAFO, E. O. (1964). Effects of arboricides on mealybug migration and virus availability. *C.R.I.G. Rep. 1st April 1962–30th Sept. 1963*, p. 22.

——, QUANSAH, S. T. and LOVI, N. K. (1964). The destruction of virus-infected trees through the use of arboricides. *C.R.I.G. Rep. 1st April 1962–30th Sept. 1963*, pp. 21–2.

ATANDA, O. A. and EGBE, N. E. (1966). Composting with cocoa husks. *Ann. Rep. C.R.I.N. 1964–5*, pp. 89–90.

ATTAFUAH, A. (1960). The host range of cocoa viruses and symptomatology. *Ann. Rep. W. Afr. Cocoa Res. Inst. 1958–9*, p. 17.

—— (1965). Occurrence of cocoa viruses in wild plant species in Ghana. *Ghana J. Sci.* 5, 97–101.

—— and BLENCOWE, J. W. (1960). A virus disease of cocoa in Sierra Leone. *Ann. Rep. W. Afr. Cocoa Res. Inst. 1958–9*, pp. 19–20.

——, —— and BRUNT, A. A. (1963). Swollen-shoot disease of cocoa in Sierra Leone. *Trop. Agric., Trin.* 40, 229–32.

—— and BRUNT, A. A. F. (1959). The host range of cacao viruses. *Ann. Rep. W. Afr. Cocoa Res. Inst. 1957–8*, p. 22.

—— and—— (1960). Classification of isolates. *Ann. Rep. W. Afr. Cocoa Res. Inst. 1958–9*, pp. 16–17.

—— and DALE, W. T. (1958). Classification and comparison of isolates. *Ann. Rep. W. Afr. Cocoa Res. Inst. 1956–7*, pp. 24–7.

—— and GLENDINNING, D. R. (1965a). Studies on resistance and tolerance to cocoa viruses in Ghana I. A survey of the T17 progeny. *Ann. appl. Biol.* 56, 219–25.

—— and —— (1965b). Studies on resistance and tolerance to cocoa viruses in Ghana. II. A survey of breeding material. *Ann. appl. Biol.* 56, 227–30.

—— and TINSLEY, T. W. (1958). Virus diseases of *Adansonia digitata* L. (Bombacaceae) and their relation to cacao in Ghana. *Ann. appl. Biol.* 46. 20–2.

AUCHINLECK, G. G. and EADY, G. M. (1928). Variations in the yields of cacao trees at Aburi Experiment Station, 1914–1926. *Gold Coast Dept Agric. Bull. 13, Year Book 1927*, pp. 74–7.

AVERNA-SACCÁ, Rosario (1920). Molestias cryptogamicas do cacaueiro (*Theobroma cacao*) e do coqueiro (*Cocos nucifera*). 1 Molestias do cacaueiro. *Bolm Agric., S. Paulo,* 21 sér. (1, 2 and 3), pp. 46–147.

—— (1925). Algumas das molestias cryptogamicas que atacam os fructos do cacaueiro no litoral paulista. *Bolm Agric., S. Paulo,* 26 sér. (10, 11 and 12), 518–39.

AVILA, M. H. (1966). *Manual del cacaotero Colombiano*. Federacion Nacional de Cacaoteros (mimeograph); Bogotá.

AYORINDE, J. A. (1966). Historical notes on the introduction and development of the cocoa industry in Nigeria. *Nigerian agric. J.* 3, 18–23.

BAILEY, A. G. (1966). A check-list of plant diseases in Nigeria. *Federal Republic of Nigeria Memorandum* no. 96, 1–33.

(Addendum, pp. 33–7: compiled by D. G. Robertson, Sept. 1969.)

BAKER, Gladys E. (1966). Inadvertent distribution of fungi. *Can. J. Microbiol.* 12, 109–12.

BAKER, R. E. D. (1936). Notes on Trinidad fungi. I. *Phytophthora. Trop. Agric., Trin.* 13, 330–2.

—— (1940). Distribution of fungous diseases of crop plants in the Caribbean region. *Trop. Agric., Trin.* 17, 90–4.

—— (1943a). Witches' broom disease investigations III. Notes on the occurrence of witches' broom disease at River Estate, 1939–1942. *Trop. Agric., Trin.* **20**, 5–12.

—— (1943*b*). Witches' broom disease investigations IV. Further notes on the susceptibility of I.C. Selections at River Estate to witches' broom disease of cacao. *Trop. Agric., Trin.* **20**, 156–8.

—— (1953*a*). Witches' broom disease of cacao (A review). *Rep. Cacao Res. 1945–51*, pp. 116–18. Imperial College of Tropical Agriculture; St. Augustine, Trinidad.

—— (1953*b*). Anglo-Colombian cacao-collecting expedition. *Rep. Cacao Res. 1952*, pp. 8–10. Imperial College of Tropical Agriculture; St. Augustine, Trinidad.

—— and COPE, F. W. (1949). *Report on a visit to Grenada 4th–9th April, 1949 in connetcion with witches' broom disease of cacao*, p. 2. (mimeograph). Imperial College of Tropical Agriculture; St. Augustine, Trinidad.

——, ——, HOLLIDAY, P. C., BARTLEY, B. G. D. and TAYLOR, D. J. (1954). The Anglo-Colombian cacao-collecting expedition. *Rep. Cacao Res. 1953*, pp. 8–29. Imperial College of Tropical Agriculture; St. Augustine, Trinidad.

—— and CROWDY, S. H. (1942). Witches' broom disease investigations II. Notes on the susceptibility of I.C. Selections at River Estate to witches' broom disease of cacao. *Trop. Agric., Trin.* **19**, 207–9.

—— and —— (1943). Studies in the witches' broom disease of cacao caused by *Marasmius perniciosus* Stahel. Part I. Introduction, symptoms and etiology. *Dept Mycol. and Bact. Mem.* **7**, 1–28. Imperial College of Tropical Agriculture; St. Augustine, Trinidad.

—— and—— (1944). Studies in the witches' broom disease of cacao caused by *Marasmius perniciosus* Stahel. Part II. Field studies and control methods. *Dept Mycol. and Bact. Mem.* **8**, 1–28. Imperial College of Tropical Agriculture; St. Augustine, Trinidad.

——, —— and McKEE, R. K. (1940). A review of latent infections caused by Colletotrichum gloeosporioides and allied fungi. *Trop. Agric., Trin.* **17**, 128–32.

——, —— and THOROLD, C. A. (1941). Witches' broom disease investigations. I. Seasonal variations in intensity of infection and their effect on control methods. *Trop. Agric., Trin.* **18**, 107–16.

—— and DALE, W. T. (1944*a*). Witches' broom disease investigations VIII. Observations on fan broom formation and loss of pods at River Estate from September, 1942 to September, 1943. *Trop. Agric., Trin.* **21**, 170–5.

—— and—— (1944*b*). Witches' broom disease investigations IX. Loss of pods at River Estate. Results to April, 1944. *Trop. Agric., Trin.* **21**, 175–6.

—— and —— (1944*c*). Witches' broom disease investigations X. Loss of pods in I.C.S. clones at River Estate during 1943. *Trop. Agric., Trin.* **21**, 196–8.

—— and —— (1947*a*). Notes on a virus disease of cacao. *Ann. appl. Biol.* **34**, 60–5.

—— and —— (1947*b*). Virus diseases of cacao in Trinidad—II. *Trop. Agric., Trin.* **24**, 127–30.

—— and——(1951). Fungi of Trinidad and Tobago. *Mycol. Pap.* **33**, 1–123.

— and HOLLIDAY, P. (1957). Witches' broom disease of cacao (*Marasmius perniciosus* Stahel). *Phytopath. Pap.* **2**.

— and McKEE, R. K. (1943). Witches' broom disease investigations VI. The infection of flower cushions and pods of cacao by *Marasmius perniciosus* Stahel. *Trop. Agric., Trin.* **20**, 188–94.

BALD, J. G. and TINSLEY, T. W. (1967*a*). A quasi-genetic model for plant virus host ranges I. Group reactions within taxonomic boundaries. *Virology* **31**, 616–24.

—— and —— (1967*b*). A quasi-genetic model for plant virus host ranges II. Differentiation between host ranges. *Virology* **32**, 321–7.

—— and —— (1967*c*). A quasi-genetic model for plant virus host ranges III. Congruence and relatedness. *Virology* **32**, 328–36.

—— and —— (1970). A quasi-genetic model for plant virus host ranges IV. Cacao swollen-shoot and mottle-leaf viruses. *Virology* **40**, 369–78.

BALLEYGUIER, A. (1949). Swollen-shoot disease in the Ivory Coast. *Rep. Cocoa Conf., Grosvenor House, London, W.1., 30th August–1st Sept. 1949 : Appendix III*, p. 112. Cocoa, Chocolate, and Confectionery Alliance; London.

BANCROFT. C. K. (1910). *A handbook of the fungus diseases of West Indian plants.* Geo. Pulman and Sons, Ltd; London.

—— (1919). Disease in plants with special reference to fungi parasitic on crops in British Guiana. *J. Bd Agric. Br. Guiana* **11**, 47–57.

BANNISTER, Roger (1972). Recreation in cities. *Letter to the Editor, The Times* 2 Aug. 1972, p. 15.

BARAT, H. (1954). Phytopathologie. In: *Courr. Cherch.* **8**, 159–86. (Abstract in *Rev. appl. Mycol.* **34**, 633 (1955)).

BARBA, C. and HANSEN, A. J. (1962*a*). Un hongo semejante a *Ceratocystis moniliformis* en cacao en Costa Rica. *Turrialba* **12**, 46–7.

—— and —— (1962*b*). *Ceratocystis fimbriata.* Study of the pathogenicity of *Ceratocystis fimbriata* isolated from cacao, coffee, sweet potato, and coconut. *Cacao, Turrialba* **7**, 5.

BARCROFT, A. L. (1961). *Fed. Malay Ann. Rep. Dept Agric. 1959.* Federation of Malaya; Government Printer.

BARNES, J. M. (1951). Method of determining the presence of Hanane in cocoa beans. In discussion of paper by West, J. (1951), pp. 90–2. *Rep. Cocoa Conf. Grosvenor House, London, W.1, 11th–13th Sept. 1951.* Cocoa, Chocolate and Confectionery Alliance; London.

BARNES, R. F. (1963). Myxomycetes from Trinidad. *Trans. Br. mycol. Soc.* **46**, 453–8.

BARRETT, O. W. (1907). Cacao pests of Trinidad, and notes upon miscellaneous crops. *Proc. agric. Soc. Trin.* **7**, 281–304.

BARROSO, G. M. (1968). *Acanthosyris paulo-alvinii*—uma nova espécie de Santalaceae (Universidade de Brasília, Brasil). *Anais do 19° Congresso de Botânica (mimeograph) Fortaleza, Brazil (fide* Alvim and Seeschaaf 1968).

BARTLETT, A. W. (1905). Report by the Government Botanist on the various diseases of the cocao plant on estates in British Guiana. *Br. Guiana official Gazette* **22**, 230–3.

BARTLEY, B. G. D. (1957). Trinitario-Scavina hybrids. New prospects for cocoa improvement. *Rep. Cocoa Conf. Grosvenor House, London, W.1, 10th–12th Sept. 1957*, pp. 36–44. Cocoa, Chocolate and Confectionery Alliance; London.

—— (1959). The efficiency of a test of the resistance of cacao seedlings to *Marasmius perniciosus* Stahel. *Rep. Cacao Res. 1957–8*; pp. 49–52. Imperial College of Tropical Agriculture; St. Augustine, Trinidad.

—— (1960). Summary of discussion. *VIII Inter-Amer. Cacao Conf. Trinidad and Tobago 15–25 June, 1960. Proc.*, p. 301.

—— (1964*a*). Plant breeding. *Ann. Rep. Cacao Res. 1963*, pp. 14–34. Regional Research Centre, Imperial College of Tropical Agriculture, University of the West Indies; St. Augustine, Trinidad.

—— (1964*b*). Notes on the cacao of Maracaibo and the relationship of pod and cotyledon colours. *Cacao, Turrialba* **9**, 8–10.

—— (1965*a*). Plant breeding. *Ann. Rep. Cacao Res. 1964*, pp. 11–34. Regional Research Centre, Imperial College of Tropical Agriculture, University of the West Indies; St. Augustine, Trinidad.

—— (1965*b*). Progress in cacao breeding and genetics. *Conf. intle Rech. agron. cacaoyères. Abidjan 15–20 nov. 1965*, pp. 228–33.

—— (1966). Plant breeding. *Ann. Rep. Cacao Res. 1965*, pp. 10–29. Regional Research Centre, Imperial College of Tropical Agriculture, University of the West Indies; St. Augustine, Trinidad.

—— (1967). A short history of cacao and chocolate 2. Producing new varieties. (With emphasis on disease resistance). *J. agric. Soc. Trin.* **67**, 25–33.

—— (1968). The development of superior varieties (pp. 11–13) Progeny trials (pp. 13–23). Inbreeding and test crossing programme (pp. 23–26). Witches' broom (pp. 28–33). *Ann. Rep. Cacao Res. 1967*. St. Augustine, Trinidad; Regional Research Centre. Imperial College of Tropical Agriculture. University of the West Indies.

—— (1969). Resistência. Discussão. *Mem. da seg. Conf. intl de Pesquisas em Cacau 19 a 26 de nov. de 1967*, p. 186.

—— (1970). The present position in developing cocoa varieties. *J. agric. Soc. Trin.* **70**, 307–20.

—— (1971). First generation inbreds as parents in hybrids of *Theobroma cacao* L. *Trop. Agric., Trin.* **48**, 79–84.

—— and AMPONSAH, J. D. (1967). Witches' broom. *Ann. Rep. Cacao Res. 1966*, pp. 50–4. Regional Research Centre, Imperial College of Tropical Agriculture, University of the West Indies; St. Augustine, Trinidad.

—— and CHALMERS, W. S. (1970). Witches' broom. *Ann. Rep. Cacao Res. 1970*, pp. 38–9. University of the West Indies, St. Augustine, Trinidad.

—— and ITON, E. F. (1959). A note on the infection of *Herrania* species by *Marasmius perniciosus* Stahel. *Rep. Cacao Res. 1957–8*, pp. 53–4. Imperial College of Tropical Agriculture; St. Augustine, Trinidad.

—— and SMALL, L. W. (1966). Chemical control of C. fimbriata–Xyleborus complex. *Ann. Rep. Cacao Res. 1965*, pp. 54–6. Regional Research Centre, Imperial College of Tropical Agriculture, University of the West Indies; St. Augustine, Trinidad.

BARTOLOMÉ, R. (1952). Effect of fertilizer application on the incidence of cherelle wilt of cacao. *Turrialba* **2**, 9–11.

BATES, J. F. (1963). Early records of cushion gall disease of cocoa from British Guiana. *Pl. Prot. Bull. F.A.O.* **11**, 34–5.

BATISTA, A. C. and CIFERRI, R. (1963). *The sooty-molds of the family Asbolisiaceae.*

Quaderno 31, Pavia, Ist. Botanico; Publicação 163, Istituto di Micologia, Universidade do Recife.

—— and GAYÃO, T. de J. (1953). Algunas fungos da família Hemisphaeriaceae. *Ann. IV Congr. nac. Soc. Bot. Brasil*, pp. 114–34.

—— and VITAL, A. F. (1952). Monografia das especes de Phyllosticta em Pernambuco. *Boln. Secr. Agric. Ind. Com. Est. Pernambuco* **19**, 1–80.

BEAKBANE, A. Beryl (1961). Structure of the plant stem in relation to adventitious rooting. *Nature, Lond.* **192**, 954–5.

—— (1969). Relationships between structure and adventitious rooting. *Proc. intl Plant Propagators Soc. ann. Meeting, 1969*, pp. 192–201.

BEDDALL, Barbara G. edit (1969). *Wallace and Bates in the tropics*. Collier-Macmillan Ltd.; London.

BELL, G. D. H. and ROGERS, H. H. (1957). Cacao breeding at WACRI. *Proc. Cacao Breeding Conf. W. Afr. Cocoa Res. Inst. Tafo, Ghana, 1st –3rd Oct. 1956*, pp. 31–49.

BENAVIDES, G. M. (1955). Insectos 'Passadores' del tronco del cacao. *Cacao Colomb.* **4**, 43–5.

BENNETT, F. D. (1955). Encyrtidae from Trinidad, B.W.I. I. Three species of *Pseudaphycus* reared from mealybugs. *Can. Ent.* **87**, 413–16.

—— (1957). Trinidad Encyrtidae II. Some additional mealybug parasites. *Can. Ent.* **89**, 569–72.

—— and SIMMONDS, F. J. (1964). Distribution and host records of Coccinellidae in the Caribbean area. *Commonw. Tech. Bull. Inst. biol. Control.* **4**, 81–94.

BENSTEAD, R. J. (1953). Cacao re-establishment. *Proc. W. Afr. intl Cacao Res. Conf. W. Afr. Cacao Res. Inst., Tafo, Gold Coast, 12th–16th Dec. 1953*, pp. 95–8.

—— (1958). Establishment and maintenance trials. *Ann. Rep. W. Afr. Cocoa Res. Inst. 1956–7*, pp. 47–50.

BENZONI, G. (1565). *La historia del mondo nuovo*. Venice.

BERARD, J. (1956). Territoire du Togo informations sur le cacao. *Proc. of the 6th Inter-American Cacao Conference*. Service de l'Agriculture, Lomé, Territoire du Togo. Salvador-Bahia, Brazil, 397–405.

BERGEY, D. H., BREED, R. S., MURRAY, E. G. D. and HITCHENS, A. P. (1939). *Bergey's manual of determinative bacteriology. A key for the identification of organisms of the class Schizomycetes*, 5th ed.: The Williams and Wilkins Co.; Baltimore.

BERKELEY, G. H., CARTER, W. and VAN SLOGTEREN, E. (1948). Report of the commission of enquiry into the swollen-shoot disease of Cacao in the Gold Coast. *Colonial* **236**, 1–10. H.M.S.O.; London.

BERKELEY, M. J. (1873). In: *Gdnrs' Chron.* **24**, 810–11.

BERTHAULT, P. (1913). Sur une maladie du cacaoyer dans l'Ouest Africain. *Agron. colon.* **1**, 8–14.

BERWICK, E. J. H. (1960). *Colony of N. Borneo Ann. Rep. Dept Agric. 1959*, pp. 1–69. Government Printing Office; Jesselton.

—— (1964). *Sabah Malaysia Ann. Rep. Dept Agric. 1963*. Sabah Publishing House; Jesselton.

—— (1965). *Sabah Malaysia Ann. Rep. Dept Agric. 1964*. Sabah Publishing House; Jesselton.

BHAT, J. V., LIMAYE, Kunda S. and VASANTHARAJAN, V. N. (1971). The effect of the leaf surface microflora on the growth and root exudation of plants. In: Ecology of Leaf Surface Micro-organisms. *Proc. intl Symp. Univ. of Newcastle upon Tyne, Sept. 1970*, ed. T. F. Preece and C. H. Dickinson, pp. 581–95. Academic Press Inc.; London.

BIGGER, M. (1972). Recent work on the mealybug vectors of cocoa swollen-shoot disease in Ghana. *Pest Artic. & News Summ. (PANS)* **18**, 61–70.

BILLES, D. J. (1941). Pollination of *Theobroma cacao* L. in Trinidad, B.W.I. *Trop. Agric., Trin.* **18**, 151–6.

BIMPONG, Christina E. and CLERK, G. C. (1970). Motility and chemotaxis in zoospores of *Phytophthora palmivora* (Butl.) Butl. *Ann. Bot.* **34**, 617–24.

BISESSAR, S. (1965). *A revised list of diseases of economic plants in British Guiana, 1962*. Agricultural Information Division, Ministry of Agriculture, Georgetown. (Mimeograph; issued May 1965.)

BLACKWELL, Elizabeth (1949). Terminology in Phytophthora. With definitions and descriptions. *Mycol. Pap.* **30**, 1–24.

BLENCOWE, J. W. (1961). Future plans for cocoa breeding in Ghana. *Rep. Cocoa Conf. Grosvenor House, London, W.I., 12th–14th Sept. 1961*, pp. 141–5. Cocoa, Chocolate and Confectionery Alliance; London.

—— (1968). Cocoa growing under rubber: the prospects. Cocoa and coconuts in Malaysia. *Proc. Symp. Kuala Lumpur, Sept. 1967*, ed. J. W. Blencowe and P. D. Turner. The Incorporated Society of Planters; Kuala Lumpur, Malaysia.

——, BRUNT, A. A., KENTEN, R. H. and LOVI, N. K. (1963). A new virus disease of cocoa in Sierra Leone. *Trop. Agric., Trin.* **40**, 233–6.

—— and WHARTON, A. L. (1961). Black-pod disease in Ghana: incidence of the disease in relation to levels of productivity. *Rep. 6th Commonwealth mycol. Conf. 1960*, pp. 139–47. Commonwealth Mycological Institute; Kew.

BLOM, F. and LA FARGE, O. (1926). *Tribes and temples. A record of the expedition to Middle America conducted by the Tulane University of Louisiana in 1925.* Vol. I. The Tulane University of Louisiana; New Orleans.

BLOW, R. (1968). Establishment of cocoa under jungle and conversion to planted shade. *Cocoa Growers' Bull.* **11**, 10–12.

BOLTON, B. (1972). Ant studies. *Ann. Rep. C.R.I.G. 1969–70*, pp. 103–5.

BONDAR, G. (1925). *O Cacao Parte II Molestias e inimigos do cacaoeiro no Estado da Bahia-Brasil.* Imprensa Official do Estado, Bahia.

—— (1939). Factores adversos e molestias de cacau. *Boln téc. Inst. Cacau Bahia 2, Ser. Pragas e Molestias*, pp. 73–85. (Cited by Lipscomb, B. R., in: Miller, P. R. 1963 *in litt.*).

BONDARZEWA-MONTEVERDE, V. N., GUTNER, L. S. and NOVOSSELOVA, E. D. (1936). Die parasitären pilze in den Gewächshäusern des botanischen Institutes der Akademie der Wissenschaften der USSR. *Acta Inst. bot. acad. Sci. URSS Ser. II. Fasc.* **3**, 715–802.

BOOTH, C. (1960). Studies of Pyrenomycetes: V. Nomenclature of some Fusaria in relation to their Nectrioid perithecial states. *Mycol. Pap.* **74**, 1–16.

—— (1966). The genus Cylindrocarpon. *Mycol. Pap.* **104**, 1–56.

—— (1971). *The genus Fusarium*, pp. 1–237. Commonwealth Mycological Institute; Kew.

—— and HOLLIDAY, P. (1972). Rosellinia pepo. *C.M.I. Descriptions of pathogenic Fungi and Bacteria* **354**.

—— and Waterston, J. W. (1964*a*). Calonectria rigidiuscula. *C.M.I. Descriptions of Pathogenic Fungi and Bacteria* **21**.

—— and —— (1964*b*). Gibberella fujikuroi var. subglutinans. *C.M.I. Descriptions of pathogenic Fungi and Bacteria* **23**.

BOULARD, M. (1967). Hémiptéroides nuisibles ou associés aux cacaoyers en République Centrafricaine. *Café-Cacao-Thé* **11**, 220–32.

BOURELLY, P. (1966). *Les algues d'eau douce 1. Les algues vertes.* Boubée et Cie; Paris.

BOURIQUET, G. (1946). Les maladies de plantes cultivées à Madagascar. *Encyclopédie mycologique* **12**, Paris; Paul Lechevalier.

—— (1954). L'étude des nématodes nuisibles aux plantes cultivées dans les territoires français d'outre-mer. *Agron. trop., Nogent* **9**, 84.

BOURRET, J. A. and FORD, E. J. (1965). Distribution of *Calonectria rigidiuscula* and other *Fusarium* species in relation to cushion gall of cacao. *Cacao, Turrialba* **10**, 13–15.

BOWEN, H. J. M. (1966). *Trace elements in biochemistry.* Academic Press; London.

BOWMAN, G. F. (1951). The Inter-American Cacao Center at Turrialba, Costa Rica. *Rep. Cocoa Conf. Grosvenor House, London, W.1, 11th–13th Sept. 1951*, pp. 40–54. Cocoa, Chocolate and Confectionery Alliance; London.

BOX, H. E. (1945). Insect transmission of the 'swollen-shoot' virus in West Africa. *Nature, Lond.* **155**, 608–9.

BRASIER, C. M. (1971). Induction of sexual reproduction in single A^2 isolates of *Phytophthora* species by *Trichoderma viride. Nature new Biology* **231**, 283.

—— (1972). Observations on the sexual mechanism in *Phytophthora palmivora* and related species. *Trans. Br. mycol. Soc.* **58**, 237–51.

BRAUDEAU, J. (1969). *Le cacaoyer. Techniques agricoles et productions tropicales XVII.* G.-P. Maisonneuve et Larose; Paris.

BREED, R. S., MURRAY, E. G. D. and SMITH, N. R. (1957). *Bergey's manual of determinative bacteriology,* 7th ed. Baillière, Tindall and Cox, Ltd.; London.

BRESADOLA, G. (1891). Contribution à la flore mycologique de l'Ile de Saint Thomé. *Revue mycol.* **13**, 68.

BRIAN, P. W. (1957). The effects of some microbial metabolic products on plant growth. In: *The biological action of growth substances*, pp. 166–82. Symposia of Society for Experimental Biology 11. Cambridge University Press, London.

BRIANT, A. K. (1959). *Cocoa growing in Zanzibar*, pp. 1–17. Government Printer; Zanzibar.

BRICK, C. (1908). Einige Krankheiten und Schädigungen tropischer Kulturpflanzen. 1. Kakao. Absterben von Kakaozweigen in Bibundi (Kamerun) durch Fusarium, pp. 224–7. 2. Pestalozzia-Krannheit an Kakaosämlingen von Samoa, pp. 228–30. *Jber. Verein. angew. Bot.* **6**, 223–58.

BRITON-JONES, H. R. (1934). *The diseases and curing of cacao.* Macmillan and Co., Ltd; London.

—— and CHEESMAN, E. E. (1931). Witch broom control. A new aspect of witch broom control in Trinidad. *Trop. Agric., Trin.* **8**, 79–89.

BROOKS, A. J. (1916). Work connected with insect and fungus pests and their control. *Rep. agric. Dept St. Lucia*, pp. 7–10.

—— (1918). Algal disease of cacao. *Rep. agric. Dept St. Lucia*, pp. 13–14.

BROOKS, B. R. and GUARD, A. T. (1952). Vegetative anatomy of *Theobroma cacao*. *Bot. Gaz.* **113**, 444–54.

BROWN, D. A. Ll. and BOATENG, B. D. (1972). Weed control in young cocoa: manual methods compared with a paraquat spraying treatment. *Proc. 11th Br. Weed Control Conf.* Brighton, 1972, pp. 466–71. British Crop Protection Council; Droitwich.

BRUNEAU DE MIRÉ, P. (1969). Une fourmi utilisée au Cameroun dans la lutte contre les mirides du cacaoyer, *Wasmannia auropunctata* Roger. *Café-Cacao-Thé* **13**, 209–12.

BRUNT, A. A. (1960). 'Cushion-gall' disease of cocoa. *Ann. Rep. W. Afr. Cocoa Res. Inst. 1958–9*, pp. 20–1.

—— (1963). Cocoa beans as test plants in investigating diseases of cocoa. *Pl. Prot. Bull. F.A.O.* **11**, 73–5.

—— (1970a). Cacao swollen-shoot virus. *Descriptions of Plant Viruses* **10**. Commonwealth Mycological Institute and Association of Applied Biologists; Kew.

—— (1970b). Cacao yellow mosaic virus. *Descriptions of Plant Viruses* **11**. Commonwealth Mycological Institute and Association of Applied Biologists; Kew.

—— and KENTEN, R. H. (1960). Mechanical transmission of cocoa swollen-shoot virus. *Virology* **12**, 328–30.

—— and —— (1962a). Mechanical transmission of cocoa mottle-leaf Virus and three distinct isolates of the cocoa swollen-shoot Virus. *Virology* **16**, 199–201.

—— and—— (1962b). Mechanical transmission of cocoa viruses. *Ann. Rept. W. Afr. Cocoa Res. Inst. 1960–1*, pp. 19–22.

—— and —— (1962c). Mechanical transmission of cocoa swollen-shoot virus to and from cocoa and other hosts. *Ann. appl. Biol.* **50**, 749–54.

—— and —— (1963). The use of protein in the extraction of cocoa swollen-shoot virus from cocoa leaves. *Virology* **19**, 388–92.

—— and —— (1971). Viruses infecting cacao. *Rev. Plant Path.* **50**, 591–602.

——, ——, GIBBS, A. J. and NIXON, H. L. (1965). Further studies on cocoa yellow mosaic virus. *J. gen. Microbiol.* **38**, 81–90.

——, —— and NIXON, H. L. (1964). Some properties of cocoa swollen-shoot virus. *J. gen. Microbiol.* **36**, 303–9.

—— and WHARTON, A. L. (1960). Transmission of a gall disease of cocoa. *Nature, Lond.* **187**, 80–1.

—— and —— (1961a). A gall disease of cocoa (*Theobroma cacao* L.) in Ghana. *Rep. 6th Commonwealth mycol. Conf., 1960*, pp. 148–56. Commonwealth Mycological Institute; Kew.

—— and —— (1961b). Galls of cocoa—a correction. *Commonw. phytopath. News* **7**, 44–5.

—— and —— (1961c). A gall disease of cocoa in Ghana. *Ann. Rep. W. Afr. Cocoa Res. Inst. 1959–60*, pp. 30–4.

—— and —— (1962a). *Calonectria rigidiuscula* (Berk. & Br.) Sacc. in the cause of a gall disease of cocoa in Ghana. *Nature, Lond.* **193**, 903–4.

—— and —— (1962b). Etiology of a gall disease of cocoa in Ghana caused by *Calonectria rigidiuscula* (Berk. & Br.) Sacc. *Ann. appl. Biol.* **50**, 283–9.

—— and —— (1962c). The distribution and importance of a gall disease of cocoa in Ghana. *Commonw. phytopath. News* **8**, 44–6.

—— and —— (1962d). A gall disease of cocoa in Ghana. *Ann. Rep. W. Afr. Cocoa Res. Inst. 1960–1*, pp. 33–5.

BUGNICOURT, F. (1932). Travaux de cryptogamie. *Bull Econ. de l'Indochine* **35** Sect. *B*: pp. 476–514. (Cited by B. R. Lipscomb, in: Miller, P. R. (1963 *in litt.*)).

—— (1939). Les Fusarium et Cylindrocarpon de l'Indochine. *Encyclopédie mycologique* **11**. Paul Lechevalier; Paris.

BULLOCK, A. A. (1948). Thonningia Vahl. *Kew Bull.* 363–7.

BUNTING, R. H. (1927a). Diseases of cocoa and measures for their control. *Proc. 1st W. African agric. Conf. Ibadan, Nigeria, March 1927*, pp. 86–97.

—— (1927b). Extracts from records of the Mycological Division 1926. *Dept Agric., Gold Coast. Year Book 1926. Bull.* **7**, 23–4 and plate VI.

—— and DADE, H. A. (1924). *Gold Coast plant diseases*. Waterlow and Sons Ltd.; London.

BURLE, L. (1961). *Le cacaoyer*. G.-P. Maisonneuve et Larose; Paris. I.

BURT, E. A. (1916). The Thelephoraceae of North America VII. *Ann. Mo. bot. Gdn* **3**, 319–43.

—— (1918). Corticiums causing Pellicularia disease of the coffee plant, Hypochnose of pomaceous fruits, and Rhizoctonia disease. *Ann. Mo. bot. Gdn* **5**, 119–32.

—— (1924). Some wood-destroying fungi of Java. *Ann. Mo. bot. Gdn* **11**, 37–41.

—— (1926). The Thelephoraceae of North America XV. *Ann. Mo. bot. Gdn,* **13**, 173–354.

BUSSE, W. (1905a). Reisebericht der pflanzenpathologischen Expedition des Kolonial-Wirtschaftlichen Komitees nach Westafrika. *Tropenpflanzer* **9**, 25–37.

—— (1905b). Reisebericht III der pflanzenpathologischen Expedition des Kolonial-Wirtschaftlichen Komitees nach Westafrika. *Tropenpflanzer* **9**, 247–58.

BUTLER, E. J. (1907). An account of the genus *Pythium* and some Chytridiaceae. I. *Mem. Dept Agric. India bot. ser* **1**, 1–106.

—— (1910). The bud-rot of palms in India. *Mem. Dept Agric. India bot. ser.* **3**, 221–80.

—— (1920). Report of the Imperial Mycologist, pp. 58–67. In: *Scient. Rep. agric. Res. Inst. Pusa 1919–20.*

—— (1925). Bud-rot of coconut and other palms. *Imp. Bot. Conf., London, July 7–16, 1924. Rep. Proc.,* pp. 145–7. Cambridge University Press; Cambridge.

BUTT, D. J. (1972). Epidemiology of plant diseases. A commentary on the 1971 advanced study institute. *Rev. plant Path.* **51**, 635–8.

BUYCKX, E. (1953). Observations sur le 'faux chancre' des branches du cacaoyer. *Proc. W. Afr. Intl Cacao Res. Conf. W.A.C.R.I., Tafo, Gold Coast, 12th–16th Dec. 1953*, pp. 58–60.

CADBURY, J. (1949). History of the swollen-shoot disease on cocoa up to 1949. *Rep. Cocoa Conf. Grosvenor House, London, W.1, 30th August–1st Sept. 1949*, pp. 34–9. Cocoa, Chocolate and Confectionery Alliance; London.

CADBURY, P. S. (1949). *Rep. to Cadbury Brothers Ltd. on a visit to the Gold Coast and Nigeria (B.W.A.), Nov.-Dec. 1947*, pp. 1–26, Cadbury Brothers Limited, Bournville.

CALLOW, R. K., KLYNE, W. and KURTI, N. (1965). *General notes on the preparation of scientific papers*, 2nd rev. ed. The Royal Society; London.

CARDENAS C., HUGOLINO (1971). Observaciones sobre la tiña (*Tillandsia recurvata* L.) y su control mediante herbicidas. *Revta Fac. Agron. Univ. cent. Venez.* **6**, 45–50 and plates 51–72.

CARDONA, E. (1953). Influencia de siete insecticidas en la polinizacion y la fructificacaion del cacao, y breve estudio de los insectos polinizadores. *Cacao Colomb.* **2**, 41–61.

CARRUTHERS, J. B. (1900). Linnean Society of London Meeting on 15th February, 1900. *Proc. Linn. Soc. Lond.* **112**, 7.

—— (1904). Report for 1903 of Government Mycologist and Assistant Director. *Circ. agric. J., R. bot. Gdns Peradeniya Vol. 2,* **16**, 217–33.

CARTER, W. (1956). Notes on some mealybugs (Coccideae) of economic importance in Ceylon. *Pl. Prot. Bull. F.A.O.* **4**, 49–52.

CAVENESS, F. E. (1962). End of tour progress report on the Nematology Project. *Ibadan; Min. Agric. and nat. Resources, W. Reg., Nigeria and U.S.A. Agency for intl Development, Project 61-13-050*: (mimeograph).

—— (1967a). Nematology studies 1960–5. End of tour progress report on the nematology project. *Lagos; Min. Agric. and natl Resources, W. Reg., Nigeria and U.S.A. Agency for Intl Development, Project 620-11-110-050*. Rev. ed., Lagos, Sept. 1967 (original issue, Ibadan, May 1965, as referred to in Caveness (1967b)).

—— (1967b). Shadehouse host ranges of some Nigerian nematodes. *Pl. Dis. Reptr* **51**, 33–7.

CEJP, K. (1930). *Fusarium allescherianum* P. Henn., parasit nekterých skleníkových rostlin. *Ochr. Rost.* **10**, 75–7. (Abstract in *Rev. appl. Mycol.* **10**, 100–1 (1931)).

CHALMERS, W. S. (1969). Trinidad–Ecuador co-operative programme. *Ann. Rep. Cacao Res. 1968*, pp. 23–6. Regional Research Centre, Imperial College of Tropical Agriculture, University of the West Indies; St. Augustine, Trinidad.

—— (1970a). Trinidad–Ecuador co-operative programme. *Ann. Rep. Cacao Res. 1969*, pp. 23–6. Regional Research Centre, Imperial College of Tropical Agriculture, University of the West Indies; St. Augustine, Trinidad.

—— (1970b). Witches' broom inoculations. *Ann. Rep. Cacao Res. 1969*, pp. 26–7. Regional Research Centre, Imperial College of Tropical Agriculture, University of the West Indies; St. Augustine, Trinidad.

—— (1970c). U.W.I.–I.N.I.A.P. Ecuador co-operative programme. *Ann. Rep. Cacao Res. 1970*, pp. 33–7. Regional Research Centre, Imperial College of Tropical Agriculture, University of the West Indies. St. Augustine, Trinidad.

—— (1972a). Las Hermanas Progeny Trials. *Ann. Rep. Cacao Res. 1971*, pp. 7–12. Regional Research Centre, Imperial College of Tropical Agriculture, University of the West Indies; St. Augustine, Trinidad.

—— (1972b). U.W.I.–I.N.I.A.P. Ecuador co-operative programme. *Ann. Rep.*

Cacao Res. 1971, pp. 25–7. Regional Research Centre, Imperial College of Tropical Agriculture, University of the West Indies; St. Augustine, Trinidad.

CHALOT, C. and LUC. M. (1906). *Le cacaoyer en Congo Français*, pp. vii and 59. Bibliothèque d'agriculture coloniale. Libraire Maritime et Coloniale, Paris.

CHANDRASRIKUL, A. (1962). A preliminary host list of plant diseases in Thailand. *Tech. Bull. Agric., Bangkok, Thailand.* **6**, 1–23.

CHAPMAN, Anne C. (1957). Port of trade enclaves in Aztec and Maya civilizations. In: *Trade and market in the early empires,* Ed. Karl Polanyi, Conrad M. Arensberg, and Harry W. Pearson, pp. 114–53. The Free Press; Glencoe, Illinois, U.S.A.

CHARDON, C. E. and TORO, R. A. (1930). Mycological explorations of Colombia. *J. Dept. Agric. P. Rico* **14**, 195–369.

—— and —— (1934). Mycological explorations of Venezuela. *Monogr. Univ. P. Rico, phys. biol. Sci.* **2**, 1–353.

CHARLES, L. J. (1959). Observations on *Anopheles (Kertezia) bellator* D. and K. in British Guiana. *Am. J. trop. Med. Hyg.* **8**, 160–7.

CHEE, K. H. (1969a). Variability of *Phytophthora* species from *Hevea brasiliensis.* *Trans. Br. mycol. Soc.* **52**, 425–36.

—— (1969b). Cocoa seedling dieback caused by *Phytophthora palmivora. Pl. Prot. Bull. F.A.O.* **17**, 140.

—— (1969c). Hosts of *Phytophthora palmivora. Rev. appl. Mycol.* **48**, 337–44.

—— (1971). Host adaptability to strains of *Phytophthora palmivora. Trans. Br. mycol. Soc.* **57**, 175–8.

CHEESMAN, E. E. (1927). Fertilization and embryogeny in *Theobroma cacao* L. *Ann. Bot.* **41**, 107–26.

—— (1932a). The economic botany of cacao. A critical survey of the literature to the end of 1930. *Trop. Agric., Trin. Suppl.*, pp. 1–16.

—— (1932b). The botanical programme of 1931. *1st ann. Rep. Cacao Res. 1931,* pp. 2–3. Imperial College of Tropical Agriculture; St. Augustine, Trinidad.

—— (1933). The botanical programme of 1932. *2nd ann. Rep. Cacao Res. 1932,* pp. 1–3. Imperial College of Tropical Agriculture; St. Augustine, Trinidad.

—— (1934). The botanical programme of 1933. *3rd ann. Rep. Cacao Res. 1933,* pp. 3–4. Imperial College of Tropical Agriculture; St. Augustine, Trinidad.

—— (1936). The vegetative propagation of cacao. VII. Root systems of cuttings. *5th ann. Rep. Cacao Res. 1935,* p. 7. Imperial College of Tropical Agriculture; St. Augustine, Trinidad.

—— (1938). Recent botanical researches in cacao. *Emp. J. exp. Agric.* **6**, 219–24.

—— (1941a). The botanical programme of 1940. *10th ann. Rep. Cacao Res. 1940,* p. 2. Imperial College of Tropical Agriculture; St. Augustine, Trinidad.

—— (1941b). Field experiments of the Botanical Section. *10th ann. Rep. Cacao Res. 1940,* pp. 2–11. Imperial College of Tropical Agriculture; St. Augustine, Trinidad.

—— (1944a). The botanical programme, 1941–3. *11th Rep. Cacao Res. 1941–3,* pp. 3–4. Imperial College of Tropical Agriculture; St. Augustine, Trinidad.

—— (1944b). Progress report on field experiments of the botanical section to August, 1943. *11th Rep. Cacao Res. 1941–3,* pp. 4–15. Imperial College of Tropical Agriculture; St. Augustine, Trinidad.

—— (1944c). Notes on the nomenclature, classification and possible relationships of cacao populations. *Trop. Agric., Trin.* **21**, 144–59.

—— (1945). Field experiments in cacao research, 1943–4. In: Interim Report on Cacao Research 1943–4. *Trop. Agric., Trin.* **22**, 64–8.

—— (1946). Results of cacao experiments in 1944–5. In: Interim Report on Cacao Research 1944–5. *Trop. Agric., Trin.* **23**, 63–5.

—— (1953). Discussion. The results of the Colombian Expedition. *Rep. Cocoa Conf. Grosvenor House, London, W.1, 15th–17th Sept. 1953*, pp. 63–4. Cocoa, Chocolate and Confectionery Alliance; London.

—— and POUND, F. J. (1934). Further notes on criteria of selection in cacao. *3rd ann. Rep. Cacao Res. 1933*, pp. 21–4. Imperial College of Tropical Agriculture; St. Augustine, Trinidad.

CHEVALIER, A. (1946). Un proche parent des Theobroma spontané en Cote-d'Ivoire et Gold Coast pays de grande culture du cacaoyer. *Revue int. Bot. appl. Agric. trop.* **26**, 304–6.

—— (1948). Une Orchidée nuisible aux caféiers et aux cacaoyers cultivées à la Côte d'Ivoire. *Revue int. Bot. appl. Agric. trop.* **28**, 463–4.

CHRISTALLER, J. G. (1881). *Dictionary of the Asante and Fante language.* Evangelical Missionary Society; Basel.

CIFERRI, R. (1927a). Studien über Kakao. I. Untersuchungen über den mussigen Gerüch der Kakaobohnen. *Zentbl. Bakt. Parasitkde Abt. 2* (71), 80–93.

—— (1927b). Notae mycologicae et phytopathologicae (Serie II, N. 1–15). *Revta Patologia vegetale, Pavia* **17**, 209–89.

—— (1929a). Phytopathological survey of Santo Domingo, 1925–9. *J. Dept Agric. P. Rico* **14**, 5–44.

—— (1929b). Microflora Domingensis, Lista de los hongos hasta la fecha indicados en Santo Domingo. *Estación Agron. Moca, Ser. B—Bot.* **14**, 1–261.

—— (1930a). Contribuzioni alla sistematica della Torulopsidaceae II–XIV. *Arch. Protistenk.* **71**, 404–52.

—— (1930b). Informe general sobre la Industria Cacaotera de Santo Domingo. Republica Dominicana. *Estación Agron. Moca, Ser. B—Bot.* **16**, 1–190.

—— (1942). Relazione sull'attivata del R. Laboratorio crittogamico e del R. Osservatorio di Fitopatologia di Pavia durante l'anno 1942(b) Il 'carbono' del dattero e del cacao. *Atti Ist. Bot. Univ. Lab. crittogam. Pavia, Ser.* **5**, 70–6.

—— (1948). Una virosis del cacao en Colombia y en la Republica Dominicana. *Revta Fac. nac. Agron., Colombia* **8**, 79–84.

—— (1961). Mycoflora Domingensis integrata. *Quad. Lab. crittogam., Pavia* **19**, 1–539.

—— and BATISTA, A. C. (1957). A Dothideaceous species on cacao leaves. *Atti Ist. bot. Univ. Lab. crittogam Pavia, Ser.* **5**, **14**, 232–6.

—— and PARODI, E. (1933). Descrizione del fungo che cause la 'Moniliasi' del cacao. *Phytopath. Z.* **6**, 539–42.

CLAESSENS, J. (1914). Note relative à la culture du Cacaoyer au Mayumbe (Congo belge). *Bull. agric. Congo Belge* **5**, 215–46.

CLERK, G. C. (1972). Germination of sporangia of *Phytophthora palmivora* (Butl.) Butl. *Ann. Bot.* **36**, 801–7.

COBB, N. A. (1924). *Neodiplogaster tropica* n.g. (?) n. sp. *J. Parasit.* **11**, 105.

COHIC, F. (1953). Extract from a report made in the New Hebrides (Efate-

Mallikolo–Espiritu Santo) from 13th January to 2nd February, 1949. Appendix 3, pp. 19–23 in: Urquhart, D. H. Cocoa growing in the New Hebrides. *Tech. Pap. S. Pacif Commn.* **40.**

COLEMAN, L. (1910*a*). Diseases of the Areca Palm I. *Bull. Dept Agric. Mysore, Ser.* **2**, pp. 1–92.

—— (1910*b*). Diseases of the Areca Palm (*Areca catechu* L.) I. Koleroga or rot-disease. *Annls mycol.* **8**, 591–631.

COLLENS, A. E. (1909). Cacao pests. *Bull. Dept Agric. Trin. Tobago, No. 61, New Ser.,* Section **11**, 34–8.

COLLINGWOOD, C. A. (1971*a*). International Capsid Research Team. *Cocoa Growers' Bull.* **17**, 11–19.

—— (1971*b*). Cocoa capsids in West Africa. *Rep. intl Capsid Res. Team 1965–71.* Cocoa, Chocolate and Confectionery Alliance, for International Office of Cocoa and Chocolate; London.

—— (1972). Cocoa in West Africa: the economics of pest control. *Span* **15**, 74–7.

COMTE, Auguste (1852). *Catéchisme positiviste, ou Sommaire exposition de la religion universelle, en onze entretiens systématiques entre une femme et un prêtre de l'humanité.* Paris; chez l'auteur.

CONWAY, G. R. (1964). A note on mirid bugs (Hemiptera: Miridae) and some other insect pests of cocoa in Sabah, Malaysia. *Proc. Conf. mirids and other pests of cacao, W.A.C.R.I. (N) 24th–27th March 1964,* pp. 80–84.

—— (1971). *Pest of cocoa in Sabah and their control (with a list of the cocoa fauna).* State Ministry of Agriculture and Fisheries, with Publications Branch, Ministry of Agriculture and Lands; Sabah, Malaysia.

COOK, M. T. and OTERO, J. I. (1939). Enfermedades del cacao: pp. 281–96. In: *Enfermedades de las plantas economicas de las Antilles. Monogr. Univ. P. Rico phys. biol. Sci.* **4.**

COOKE, G. W. (1967). *The control of soil fertility.* Crosby Lockwood; London.

COOKE, W. B. (1961). The genus Schizophyllum. *Mycologia* **53**, 574–99.

COPE, F. W. (1939*a*). Some factors controlling the yield of young cacao. II. *8th ann. Rep. Cacao Res. 1938,* pp. 4–15. Imperial College of Tropical Agriculture; St. Augustine, Trinidad.

—— (1939*b*). Studies in the mechanism of self-incompatibility in cacao. *8th ann. Rep. Cacao Res. 1938,* pp. 20–1. Imperial College of Tropical Agriculture; St. Augustine, Trinidad.

—— (1940). Studies in the mechanism of self-incompatibility in cacao—II. *9th ann. Rep. Cacao Res. 1939,* pp. 19–23. Imperial College of Tropical Agriculture; St. Augustine, Trinidad.

—— (1953*a*). An interim report on the Anglo-Colombian cocoa-collecting expedition. *Rep. Cocoa Conf. Grosvenor House, London, W.1, 15th–17th Sept. 1953,* pp. 57–63. Cocoa, Chocolae and Confectionery Alliance; London.

—— (1953*b*). Statistical studies in the effects of virus infection upon yield in clonal cacao. *Rep. Cacao Res. 1945–51,* pp. 126–9. Imperial College of Tropical Agriculture; St. Augustine, Trinidad.

—— (1959). Incompatibility in *Theobroma cacao. Rep. on Cacao Res. 1957–8,* pp. 7–17. Imperial College of Tropical Agriculture; St. Augustine, Trinidad.

—— (1962*a*). The mechanism of pollen incompatibility in *Theobroma cacao* L. *Heredity, Lond.* **17**, 157–82.

—— (1962b). The effects of incompatibility and compatibility on genotype proportions in populations of *Theobroma cacao* L. *Heredity, Lond.* **17**, 183–95.

CORBETT, D. C. M. (1961). Extract from report of the plant pathologist. In: *Nyasaland Protect. ann. Rep. Dept Agric. 1959/60 (Part II)*, pp. 157–8. Government Printer; Zomba, Nyasaland.

—— (1964). A supplementary list of plant diseases in Nyasaland. *Mycol. Pap.* **95**, 1–16.

—— (1965). Plant pathology. In: *Malawi Min. nat. Resources, ann. Rep. Dept Agric. 1962/63 (Part II)*, pp. 135–6.

CORNER, E. J. H. (1952). Addenda Clavariacea I. Two new Pteruloid genera and *Deflexula*. *Ann. Bot.* **16**, 269–91.

CORNWELL, P. B. (1956). Some aspects of mealybug behaviour in relation to the efficiency of measures for the control of virus diseases of cacao in the Gold Coast. *Bull. ent. Res.* **47**, 137–66.

—— (1957). An investigation into the effect of cultural conditions on populations of the vectors of virus diseases of cacao in Ghana with an evaluation of seasonal population trends. *Bull. ent. Res.* **48**, 375–96.

—— (1958). Movements of the vectors of virus diseases of cacao in Ghana. I. Canopy movements in and between trees. *Bull. ent. Res.* **49**, 613–30.

—— (1960). Movements of the vectors of virus diseases of cacao in Ghana. II. Wind movements and aerial dispersal. *Bull. ent. Res.* **51**, 175–201.

COSTANTIN, J. and GALLAUD, M. (1903). Sur la 'Mancha' maladie du cacaoyer. *Revue Cult. colon.* **13**, 33–7 (part iv); **13**, 65–9 (part v); **13**, 97–101 (part vi).

COTTERELL, G. S. (1928). Minor pests of cacao. *Dept Agric. Gold Coast. Year Book 1927. Bull.* **13**, 100–6.

—— (1930). Report on the occurrence of Sahlbergella spp. and other insect pests of cacao in Fernando Poo, San Thomé and the Belgian Congo. *Dept Agric., Gold Coast. Year Book 1929. Bull.* **22**, 112–33.

—— (1943). Entomology. *Rep. cent. Cocoa Res. Stn, Tafo, Gold Coast, 1938–42*, pp. 46–55.

COUPRIE, F. (1972). Étude de certains aspects de l'écophysiologie du cacaoyer liés a sa productivité en Ouganda. *Café-Cacao-Thé* **16**, 31–43.

COUTINHO, A. X. P. (1925). Florae mycologicae Insulae St. Thomae (sinu guineensi) contributio, Anais do Instituto de Agronomia Coimbra **1925**. *Anais Inst. sup. Agron., Ano* **2**, 1–26. Imprensa da Universidade; Coimbra.

CRANDALL, B. S. and JAVIER DIEGUEZ, C. (1948). A check list of the diseases of economic plants in the Tingo Maria zone of the Peruvian montana. *Pl. Dis. Reptr* **32**, 20–7.

CROWDY, S. H. (1947). Observations on the pathogenicity of *Calonectria rigidiuscula* (Berk. & Br.) Sacc. on *Theobroma cacao* L. *Ann. appl. Biol.* **34**, 45–59.

—— and POSNETTE, A. F. (1947). Virus diseases of cacao in West Africa II. Cross-immunity experiments with viruses 1A, 1B and 1C. *Ann. appl. Biol.* **34**, 403–11.

CROWTHER, P. C. and RAYMOND, W. D. (1954). The analysis of soil and foliage material in connection with sickle leaf disease of cacao in Ceylon. *Colon. Pl. Anim. Prod.* **4**, 257–9.

CRUICKSHANK, A. M. (1970). Cocoa in Grenada. *Cocoa Growers' Bull.* **15**, 4–11.

CUATRECASAS, J. (1964). Cacao and its allies. A taxonomic revision of the genus *Theobroma*. *Contr. U.S. nat. Herb.* **35**, 379–614.

CULBERSON, Chicita F. (1969). *Chemical and botanical guide to lichen products.* The University of North Carolina Press; Chapel Hill.

—— (1970). Supplement to 'Chemical and botanical guide to lichen products'. *Bryologist* **73**, 177–377.

CUNNINGHAM, R. K. (1959). A review of the use of shade and fertilizer in the culture of cocoa. *Tech. Bull. W. Afr. Cocoa Res. Inst.* **6**, 1–15.

—— (1963). What shade and fertilizers are needed for good cocoa production? *Cocoa Growers' Bull.* **1**, 11–16.

—— (1964). Micro-nutrient deficiency in cacao in Ghana. *Emp. J. exp. Agric.* **32**, 42–50.

—— and BURRIDGE, J. C. (1960). The growth of cacao (*Theobroma cacao*) with and without shade. *Ann. Bot. New Ser.* **24**, 458–62.

——, SMITH, R. W. and HURD, R. G. (1961). A cocoa shade and manurial experiment at the West African Cocoa Research Institute, Ghana. II. Second and third years. *J. hort. Sci.* **36**, 116–25.

DA CAMARA, E. de S. (1920). Mycetes aliquot novi alique in mycoflora Azorica et Africana ignoti. Seen as '*separata da Revta agron. Lisb.*

—— (1925). Minutissimum mycoflorae subsidium Sancti Thomensis Insula I. Mycetas. *Anais Inst. sup. Agron. Coimbra* **2**, 135–7.

—— (1929). Minutissimum mycoflorae subsidium Sancti Thomenses Insulae. II. Mycetes. *Revta Agron., Lisb.* **1**, 13–24.

DA CAMARA, M. de S. and CANNAS MENDES, A. (1910). *Mycetae aliquot et insecta pauca Theobromae cacao in Sancti Thomensis Insula*, p. 8 and Table VI. F. Carneiro & Ca; Lisboa.

—— and COUTINHO, D. M. de F. P. (1925). O presente e o futuro das plantações em S. Tomé. *An. Inst. Sup. Agron. Coimbra* **2** (2), 138–96.

DADANT, R. (1953). Phytopathology of the cocoa tree in the New Hebrides. Appendix 2, pp. 15–18. In Urquhart, D. H. (1953) 'Cocoa growing in the New Hebrides'. *Tech. Pap. S. Pacif. Commn.* **40**.

—— (1954). Contribution à l'étude des maladies du cocotier, du cacaoyer et du cafeier aux Nouvelles-Hebrides. *Agron. trop., Nogent* **9**, 41–8.

DADE, H. A. (1927*a*). 'Collar Crack' of cacao. (*Armillaria mellea* (Vahl.) Fr.). *Dept Agric., Gold Coast. Bull.* **5**, 1–21.

—— (1927*b*). Economic significance of cacao pod diseases and factors determining their incidence and control. *Dept Agric., Gold Coast. Bull.* **6**.

—— (1928*a*). The relation between diseased cushions and the seasonal outbreak of 'black pod' disease of cacao. *Dept Agric., Gold Coast. Year Book 1927. Bull.* **13**, 85–8.

—— (1928*b*). Dissemination of cacao pod diseases by invertebrates. *Dept Agric., Gold Coast. Year Book 1927. Bull.* **13**, 93.

—— (1928*c*). Ceratostomella paradoxa, the perfect stage of Thielaviopsis paradoxa (De Seynes) von Höhnel. *Trans. Br. Mycol. Soc.* **13**, 184–93.

—— (1929*a*). Further notes on cushion canker of cacao. *Dept Agric., Gold Coast. Year Book 1928. Bull.* **16**, 135–8.

—— (1929*b*). Origin and spiral arrangement of cushions in cacao. *Dept Agric., Gold Coast. Year Book 1928. Bull.* **16**, 147–50.

—— (1929c). Minor records, Division of Mycology 1928. *Dept Agric., Gold Coast. Year Book 1928. Bull.* **16**, 250–3.

—— (1930). Further observations on cacao pod diseases in the Gold Coast. *Dept Agric., Gold Coast. Year Book 1930. Bull.* **23**, 109–21.

—— (1940). A revised list of Gold Coast fungi and plant diseases. *Kew Bull.*, 205–47.

—— and PATTERSON, W. H. (1922). Some causes of cocoa 'die-back'. *J. Gold Cst agric. comml Soc.* **1**, 137–40.

DAKWA, J. T. (1968). Minor diseases. *Ann. Rep. C.R.I.G. 1966–7*, p. 38.

DALE, W. T. (1946). Witches' broom disease investigations XII. Further studies on the infection of cacao pods by *Marasmius perniciosus* Stahel. *Trop. Agric., Trin.* **23**, 217–21.

—— (1953). *Plant pathology : a progress report. Rep. Cacao Res. 1952*, pp. 60–1. Imperial College of Tropical Agriculture; St. Augustine, Trinidad.

—— (1955a). Optimum conditions for transmission. *Ann. Rep. W. Afr. Cocoa Res. Inst. 1954–5*, pp. 33–5.

—— (1955b). Resistance and tolerance. *Ann. Rep. W. Afr. Cocoa Res. Inst. 1954–5*, pp. 41 and 44–5.

—— (1956). Studies on resistance and tolerance to cacao viruses. *Proc. Cacao Breeding Conf. WACRI, Tafo, Ghana 1st–3rd Oct. 1956*, pp. 3–6.

—— (1957a). Insect-transmission studies. *Ann. Rep. W. Afr. Cocoa Res. Inst. 1955–6*, pp. 30–1.

—— (1957b). Resistance and tolerance. *Ann. Rep. W. Afr. Cocoa Res. Inst. 1955–6*, pp. 35–8.

—— (1958). Resistance and tolerance. *Ann. Rep. W. Afr. Cocoa Res. Inst. 1956–7*, pp. 27–30.

—— (1962). Diseases and pests of cocoa A. Virus diseases. In: *Agriculture and land use in Ghana,* ed. J. B. Wills, pp. 286–316. Oxford University Press; London.

—— and ATTAFUAH, A. (1957). The host range of cacao viruses. *Ann. Rep. W. Afr. Cocoa Res. Inst. 1955–6*, pp. 28–30.

—— and —— (1958). The host range of cacao viruses. *Ann. Rept. W. Afr. Cocoa Res. Inst. 1956–7*, pp. 20–2.

D'ALMEIDA, J. V. and DA CAMARA, M. de S. (1903). Trabalhos do laboratorio de nosolgia vegetal. *Revta agron., Lisb.* **1**, 89.

—— and —— (1909). Plantas Insulae St. Thomae. *Bolm Soc. broteriana* **24**, 240.

DALZIEL, J. M. (1937). *The useful plants of West Tropical Africa.* An Appendix to 'the Flora of West Tropical Africa', by J. Hutchinson and J. M. Dalziel. Crown Agents for the Colonies; London.

DASH, J. S. (1931). *Report of the Director of Agriculture for the year 1930,* pp. 1–37. British Guiana, Administration.

DAVIS, R. A. (1970). Control of rats and mice. *Min. of Agric., Fisheries and Food Bull.* **181**. H.M.S.O.; London.

DE GUIRAN, G. (1963). Quatre espèces nouvelles du genre *Criconemoides* (Taylor) (*Nematoda-Criconematidae*). *Revue Path. Vég. Ent. agric. Fr.* **42**, 1–11.

DEIGHTON, F. C. (1930). Annual Report of the Mycological Section for the year 1929. In: *Ann. Rep. agric. dept Sierra Leone 1929*, pp. 20–3. (Abstract in *Rev. appl. Mycol.* **10**, 80 (1930)).

—— (1945). *Cacao in Sierra Leone*, Agricultural Department; Government Printer; Freetown, Sierra Leone.

—— (1956). *Diseases of cultivated and other economic plants in Sierra Leone*. Government Printing Department, Sierra Leone.

—— and PIROZYNSKI, K. A. (1972). Microfungi. V. More hyperparasitic hyphomycetes. *Mycol. Pap.* **128**, 1–110.

DELACROIX, G. (1897). Quelques espèces nouvelles. *Bull. Soc. mycol. Fr.* **13**, 114–27.

—— (1905). Champignons parasites de plantes cultivées dans les régions chaudes. *Bull Soc. mycol. Fr.* **21**, 191–204.

DELANY, M. J. (1972). The ecology of small rodents in tropical Africa. *Mammal Rev.* **2**, 1–42.

DELGADO, J. C., AMPUERO, E. and DOAK, K. D. (1960). Posible evidencia de resistencia a la Monilia roreri Cif. y Par. en algunos clones de la Estacion Experimental Tropical de Pichilingue. *Rep. VIII Inter-Amer. Cacao Conf., Trinidad*, pp. 184–92.

—— and ECHANDI, E. (1965). Evaluacion de la resistencia do especies y clones de cacao al mal del machete provocado por *Ceratocystis fimbriata*. *Turrialba* **15**, 286–9.

DE LOTTO, G. (1958). The Pseudococcidae (Hom.: Coccoidea) described by C. K. Brain from South Africa. *Bull. Br. Mus. nat. Hist. Ent.* **7**, 77–120.

—— (1964). Observations on African mealybugs (Hemiptera: Coccoidea) *Bull. Br. Mus. nat. Hist. Ent.* **14**, 341–97.

—— (1965). The nomenclatural status of the common long tailed mealybug (Homoptera: Pseudococcidae). *J. ent. Soc. Sth Afr.* **27**, 226–9.

—— (1967). A contribution to the knowledge of the African Coccoidea (Homoptera). *J. ent. Soc. Sth Afr.* **29**, 109–20.

DEMOULIN, V. (1973). Phytogeography of the fungal genus *Lycoperdon* in relation to the opening of the Atlantic. *Nature, Lond.* **242**, 123–5.

DENNIS, R. W. G. (1950). New Fungi. *Kew Bull.*, p. 170.

—— (1951). Some Agaricaceae of Trinidad and Venezuela. Leucosporae: Part I. *Trans. Br. mycol. Soc.* **34**, 411–82.

—— (1952). Some American Agaricaceae referred by Berkeley and Montagne to Marasmius, Collybia or Heliomyces. *Kew Bull.*, pp. 387–410.

—— (1957). Some Xylarias of Tropical America. *Kew Bull.*, pp. 401–44.

—— (1970). Fungus flora of Venezuela and adjacent countries. *Kew Bull. add. Ser. III.*

—— and REID, D. A. (1957). Some Marasmioid fungi allegedly parasitic on leaves and twigs in the tropics. *Kew Bull.* pp. 287–92.

DE PONS, F. R. J. (1806). *Voyage a la partie orientale de la terre-ferme, dans l'Amerique Meridionale, fait pendant les années 1801, 1802, 1803, et 1804*. Vol. 2, pp. 1–469. F. Buisson; Paris.

DE REYES, Lilian C. and REYES, E. H. (1971). Obtencion de cultivares de cacao resistentes al hongo *Ceratocystis fimbriata* Ellis & Halsted. *III Intl Cocoa Res. Conf. Accra, Ghana 23–29 Nov. 1969*, pp. 499–502.

——, —— and ESCOBAR, F. (1972). Etiologia de una nueva enfermedad del fruto de cacao en Venezuela. *4th Intl Cocoa Res. Conf., Trinidad and Tobago 9th–18th Jan. 1972*, pp. 1–5 (mimeograph).

DES ABBAYES, H. (1955). Lichens récoltés en Guinée Française et en Côte-d'Ivoire (Missions H. des Abbayes, 1948 et 1951). VIII. Arthoniacées, Graphidacées, Chiodectonacées, Thélotrémacées, Diploschistacées, Lécidéacées Lécanoracées, Caloplacacées. *Bull. Inst. français Afrique noire* **17**, 973–88.

—— (1958). Lichens récoltés en Guinée Française et en Côte d'Ivoire (Missions H. des Abbayes 1948, 1951, et 1954). IX. Supplément aux Parméliacées. *Bull. Inst. fr. Afr. noire* **20**, 1–27.

DESCHREIDER, A. R. and VAN COILLIE, L. (1956). Les oligoélements dans les fèves de cacao. *Intl Choc. Rev.* **11**, 374–84.

DE SEABRA, A. F. (1922). Note préliminaire sur la maladie des cacaoyers connue à S. Thomé sous la désignation de 'seca dos ramos'. In: Études sur les maladies et les parasites du cacaoyer et d'autres plantes cultivées à S. Thomé. *Mém. Soc. port. Sci. nat. Sér. zool.* **2**, 70–116.

DE SILVA, M. D. (1957). A new species of Helopeltis (Hemiptera–Heteroptera, Miridae) found in Ceylon. *Bull. ent. Res.* **48**, 459–61.

DESJARDINS, P. R., ZENTMYER, G. A. and REYNOLDS, D. A. (1969). Electron microscopic observations of the flagellar hairs of *Phytophthora palmivora* zoospores. *Can. J. Bot.* **47**, 1077–9.

——, —— and —— (1970). On the binucleate condition of the quadriflagellated zoospores of *Phytophthora palmivora. Mycologia* **62**, 421–7.

DESLANDES, J. A. (1944). Observações fitopatologicos na Amazônia. *Bolm fitossanit.* **1**, 197–242. (Abstract in *Rev. appl. Mycol.* **26**, 333–5 (1947)).

DESROSIERS, R. (1957). Developments in the control of witches broom, Monilia pod rot and Ceratostomella diseases of cacao. *Reuniao do Comite Tecnico Interamer. de Cacau. Bahia, 20–27 May, 1956*, pp. 73–82.

—— (1960). Fungus diseases of cacao and their control. In: Hardy 1960a, pp. 231–59.

—— and BOLAÑOS, C. W. (1955). Inhibition of sporophore development of *Marasmius perniciosus* (Stahel) on cocoa. *Turrialba* **5**, 28–32.

——, —— and VARGAS, J. (1955). Evaluación de clones de cacao en relación con au resistencia a la escoba de bruja (*Marasmius perniciosus*, Stahel). *Turrialba* **5**, 78–82.

—— and DIAZ, J. (1956a). Enfermedades del cacao y su control. *Boln Ext. Ecuador Ministerio de Economia* **1**, 1–29.

—— and —— (1956b). The world distribution of diseases of cacao. *Separate da VI Reunião do Comité Técnico Interamer. de Cacau. Realizada de 20 a 27 de Maio de 1956*, pp. 331–41.

—— and VON BUCHWALD, A. (1949). Report of a trip to the Napo River (December 1949). *Annex to ann. Rep., Estacion exp. trop. Agricola, Hacienda Pichilingue* pp. 1–11.

——, —— and BOLAOÑS, C. (1955). Effect of rainfall on the incidence of Monilia pod rot of cacao in Ecuador. *Pl. Prot. Bull. F.A.O.* **3**, 162–7.

DESSART, P. (1961). Contribution à l'étude des Ceratopogonidae (Diptera). Les *Forcipomyia* pollinisateurs du cacaoyer. *Bull. agric. Congo* **52**, 525–40.

—— (1963). Contribution a l'etude des Ceratopogonidae (Diptera) (VII). Tableaux dichotomiques illustrés pour la determination des Forcipomyia Africains. *Mem Inst. R. Sci. nat. Belg. deuxième Ser., Fasc.*, **72**, 1–151.

DE VERTEUIL, L. L. (1959). Annual report—cocoa agronomy—1957. In: *Trinidad and Tobago Admin. Rep. Affairs of Cocoa Board 1957*, pp. 31–42. Government Printing Office; Trinidad.

—— and MOLL, E. R. (1960). Rehabilitation for the future. *VIII Inter-Amer. Cacao Conf., Trinidad and Tobago 15–25 June, 1960, Proc.*, pp. 42–8.

DIAS, Maria R. de S., LUCAS, Maria T., DE VASCONCELOS, A. T., and DA CAMARA, E. de S. (1953). Minutissimum mycoflorae subsidium, Sancti Thomensis et Prinsipis Insulae. Part III. *Agronomia lusit.* **15**, 5–14.

DICKINSON, C. H. (1968). Gliomastix Guéguen. *Mycol. Pap.* **115**, 1–24.

DICKSON, K. B. (1964). The agricultural landscape of Southern Ghana and Ashanti-Brong Ahafo: 1880 to 1850. *Bull. Ghana geogr. Ass.* **9**, 25–35.

—— (1969). *A historical geography of Ghana.* University Press; Cambridge.

DIXON, W. B. (1961). Nematological investigations 1958–61. *Bull. Minist. Agric. Lds Jamaica* **59** (New Ser.), 1–35.

DODGE, C. W. (1953). Some lichens from Tropical Africa. *Ann. Mo. bot. Gdn* **40**, 271–401.

—— (1964). Some lichens of Tropical Africa IV. Dermatocarpaceae to Pertusariaceae. *Nova Hedwigia* **12**, 1–282.

—— (1971). Some lichens of Tropical Africa V: Lecanoraceae to Physciaceae. *Nova Hedwigia* **38**, 1–225.

DOMÍNGUEZ, P. F. (1971). Advance del trabajo sobre selección de plantas de cacao (*Theobroma cacao* L.) por resistencia al hongo *Ceratocystis fimbriata. Revta. Fac. Agron. Univ. cent. Venez.* **6**, 5–29.

DONALD, R. G. (1953). Coccid collections. *Ann. Rep. W. Afr. Cacao Res. Inst. 1952–3*, pp. 22–3.

—— (1955). Mealybug studies. *Ann. Rep. W. Afr. Cocoa Res. Inst. 1954–5*, pp. 101–4.

—— (1956). The natural enemies of some Pseudococcidae in the Gold Coast. *Jl W. Afr. Sci. Ass.* **2**, 48–59.

—— (1957). Mealybug studies. *Ann. Rep. W. Afr. Cocoa Res. Inst. 1955–6*, p. 88.

—— (1959). Mealybug studies. *Ann. Rep. W. Afr. Cocoa Res. Inst. 1957–8*, pp. 75–6.

DUDGEON, G. C. (1910a). Notes on two West African Hemiptera injurious to cocoa. *Bull. ent. Res.* **1**, 59–61.

—— (1910b). West African Hemiptera injurious to cocoa. *Bull. ent. Res.* **1**, 177.

DUDMAN, W. F. and NICHOLS, R. (1959). Absence of gibberellin-like substances in filtrates of *Marasmius perniciosus* Stahel (witch broom disease of cacao). *Nature, Lond.* **183**, 899–900.

DUMBLETON, L. J. (1954). A list of plant diseases recorded in South Pacific Territories. *Tech. Pap. S. Pacif. Commn* **78**.

DUN, G. S. (1954). Notes on cacao capsids in New Guinea. *Papua New Guin. agric. Gaz.* **8**, 7–11.

DUSS, R. P. (1903). *Énumération méthodique des champignons recueillis à la Guadeloupe et à la Martinique*, Lons-le-Saunier.

—— (1904). *Les principaux lichens de la Guadeloupe.* Lons-le-Saunier.

ECKERT, J. W. and TSAO, P. H. (1960). A preliminary report on the use of pimaricin in the isolation of Phytophthora spp. from root tissues. *Pl. Dis. Reptr* **44**, 660–1. (Abstract in *Rev. appl. Mycol.* **40**, 80 (1961)).

—— and —— (1962). A selective antibiotic medium for isolation of Phytophthora and Pythium from plant roots. *Phytopathology* **52**, 771–7. (Abstract in *Rev. appl. Mycol.* **42**, 251 (1963)).

EDWARD, I. L. (1961). Clonal cacao at Keravat II. *Papua New Guin. Agric. J.* **14**, 16–37.

EDWARDS, D. F. (1969). Hybrid seed-gardens. *Cocoa Growers' Bull.* **13**, 14–19.

—— (1972a). Seed production methods, *C.R.I.G. Ann. Rep. 1969–70*, pp. 147 and 150–4.

—— (1972b). Some notes on the development and management of hybrid cocoa varieties. Cocoa and Coconuts in Malaysia. *Proc. Conf. Kuala Lumpur 25–27 Nov. 1971*, pp. 13–21. The Incorporated Society of Planters; Kuala Lumpur, Malaysia.

EDWARDS, E. E. (1955). Further observations on the occurrence of nematodes of the genus *Meloidogyne* in the Gold Coast. *J. Helminth.* **29**, 153–70.

—— (1956). Studies on resistance to the root-knot nematode of the genus *Meloidogyne* Goeldi, 1887. *Proc. helminth. Soc. Wash.* **23**, 112–18.

EERNSTMAN, T. (1968). Chemical analysis of leaves and other organs of *Theobroma cacao* L. as a means of diagnosing fertilizer requirements. A critical analysis of the literature (Summary of a fuller report). Literatuuroverzicht nr. 34: Centrum voor Landbouwpublikaties en Landbouwdocumentatie Wageningen.

EKUNDAYO, J. A. (1970). Pycnidium production by *Botryodiplodia theobromae*. III. Germination of pycnidiospores. *Can. J. Bot.* **48**, 67–70.

—— and HASKINS, R. H. (1969a), Pycnidium production by *Botryodiplodia theobromae*. I. The relation of light to the induction of pycnidia. *Can. J. Bot.* **47**, 1153–6.

—— and —— (1969b). Pycnidium production by *Botryodiplodia theobromae*. II. Development of the pycnidium and fine structure of the maturing pycnospore. *Can. J. Bot.* **47**, 1423–4.

ELLIS, M. B. (1958). Clasterosporium and some allied Dematiaceae Phragmosporae. I. *Mycol. Pap.* **70**, 1–89.

—— (1961). Dematiaceous Hyphomycetes. III. *Mycol. Pap.* **82**, 1–55.

—— (1963). Dematiaceous Hyphomycetes. V. *Mycol. Pap.* **93**, 1–33.

—— (1965). Dematiaceous Hyphomycetes. VI. *Mycol. Pap.* **103**, 1–46.

—— (1971). *Dematiaceous Hyphomycetes*. Commonwealth Mycological Institute, Kew.

ELOJA, A. L. and GANDIA, I. M. (1963). A new threat to cacao. *Coffee, Cacao J., Philippines* **6**, 40.

EMECHEBE, A. and LEAKEY, C. L. A. (1968). *Verticillium dahliae* established as the cause of sudden death of cocoa. *Pl. Prot. Bull. F.A.O.* **16**, 13.

——, —— and BANAGE, W. B. (1971). *Verticillium* wilt of cacao in Uganda: symptoms and establishment of pathogenicity. *Ann. appl. Biol.* **69**, 223–7.

——, —— and —— (1972). *Verticillium* wilt of cacao in Uganda: the relationship between *Verticillium dahliae* and cacao roots. *Ann. appl. Biol.* **70**, 157–62.

ENRIQUEZ, G. A. and SORIA, J. V. (1967). *Cacao cultivars register*, pp. 1–12, and cultivar no. 1–67. Inter-American Institute of Agricultural Research (Turrialba, Costa Rica).

ENTWISTLE, Helen (1957). Cacao pollination. *Proc. Cacao Breeding Conf. W. Afr. Cocoa Res. Inst. Tafo, Ghana, 1st–3rd Oct. 1956*, pp. 19–21.

—— and HURD, Joyce (1959). Pollination studies. *Ann. Rep. W. Afr. Cocoa Res. Inst. 1957–8*, pp. 42–4.

ENTWISTLE, P. F. (1959). Joint W.A.C.R.I.–Department of Agriculture mealybug control trials. *Ann. Rep. W. Afr. Cocoa Res. Inst. 1957–8*, pp. 31–6.

—— (1960a). A review of the problem of shot hole borer (Coleoptera, Scolytidae and Platypodidae) attack on cocoa in West Africa. *VIII Inter-Amer. Cacao Conf., Trinidad and Tobago, 15–25 June, 1960 Proc.*, pp. 208–23.

—— (1960b). Joint W.A.C.R.I.–Division of Agriculture mealybug control trials. *Ann. Rep. W. Afr. Cocoa Res. Inst. 1958–9*, pp. 30–2.

—— (1961a). Joint W.A.C.R.I.–Division of Agriculture mealybug control trial. *Ann. Rep. W. Afr. Cocoa Res. Inst. 1959–60*, pp. 34–5.

—— (1961b). The increase of minor pests of cocoa following application of dieldrin. *Ann. Rep. W. Afr. Cocoa Res. Inst. 1959–60*, pp. 36–7.

—— (1972). *Pests of cocoa*. Longman Group Ltd.; London.

—— and ARMSTRONG, K. B. (1961). Joint W.A.C.R.I.–Division of Agriculture ant control trials: methods of application and formulation. *Ann. Rep. W. Afr. Cocoa Res. Inst. 1959–60*, pp. 37–9.

—— and CAVENESS, F. E. (1963). Nematology. *Ann. Rep. W. Afr. Cocoa Res. Inst. 1961–2*, pp. 113–14.

—— and LONGWORTH, J. F. (1963). The relationships between cacao viruses and their vectors: the feeding behaviour of three mealybug (Homoptera: Pseudococcidae) species. *Ann. appl. Biol.* **52**, 387–91.

—— and —— (1964). The feeding behaviour of three mealybugs. *Ann. Rep. W. Afr. Cocoa Res. Inst. (Nigeria) 1962–3*, pp. 28–9.

—— and YOUDEOWEI, A. (1964). A preliminary world review of cacao mirids. *Proc. Conf. on Mirids and other pests of cacao, W.A.C.R.I. (N.) 24th –27th March 1964*, pp. 71–9.

——, —— and EGUAGIE, W. (1964). Field experiments in the control of *Sahlbergella singularis* Hagl. (Hemiptera: Miridae) with Sevin and Sumithion in Nigeria. *Proc. Conf. on mirids and other pests of cacao, W.A.C.R.I. (N.) 24th–27th March 1964*, pp. 26–34.

EPSTEIN, E. (1972). *Mineral nutrition of plants: principles and perspectives*, John Wiley and Sons, Inc.; New York.

ERNEHOLM, I. (1948). *Cacao production of South America. Historical development and present geographical distribution*, C. R. Holmquists Boktryckeri AB:; Gothenburg, Sweden.

ESCAMILLA, S. (J.G.) (1960). *La buba del cacao*, pp. 1–16. Institute de Investigaciones Agricolas, Mexico.

ESENAM, E. U. (1971). Banana as an important host for the black pod disease pathogen. *Jl W. Afr. Sci. Ass.* **16**, 13–16.

—— and LADIPO, J. L. (1967). Cross infection trials with swollen-shoot virus of cacao on cultivated Kola seedlings. *Nigerian agric. J.* **4**, 64–5.

EVANS, G. (1932). Preface. *1st ann. Rep. Cacao Res. 1931*, pp. 1–2. Imperial College of Tropical Agriculture; St. Augustine, Trinidad.

——, MITCHELL, K., GREENIDGE, C. W. W., HARKNESS, J. W. P., BEASLEY, C. G., GREGORY-SMITH, H. G. and MARNHAM, J. E. (1948). Report of the British Guiana and British Honduras settlement Commission. *Colonial Office Cmd. 7533*, H.M.S.O.; London.

EVANS, H. and FENNAH, R. G. (1953). Investigations on the mineral nutrition of cacao. *Rep. Cacao Res. 1945–51*, pp. 38–52. Imperial College of Tropical Agriculture; St. Augustine, Trinidad.

—— and MURRAY, D. B. (1953*a*). A colour-illustrated guide to the diagnosis of mineral deficiencies in cacao. *Rep. Cacao Res. 1945–51*, pp. 65–6. Imperial College of Tropical Agriculture; St. Augustine, Trinidad.

—— and —— (1953*b*). A shade and fertilizer experiment on young cacao. Progress Report. *Rep. Cacao Res. 1945–51*, pp. 67–78. Imperial College of Tropical Agriculture; St. Augustine, Trinidad.

EVANS, H. C. (1971). Transmission of *Phytophthora* pod rot of cocoa by invertebrates. *Nature, Lond.* **232**, 346–7.

—— (1973). New developments in black pod epidemiology. *Cocoa Growers' Bull.* **20**, 10–16.

—— and LESTON, D. (1971). A Ponerine ant (Hym., Formicidae) associated with Homoptera on cocoa in Ghana. *Bull. ent. Res.* **61**, 357–62.

EVERARD, C. O. R. (1964). Some aspects of vertebrate damage to cocoa in West Africa. *Proc. Conf. on Mirids and other pests of cacao at W.A.C.R.I. (N.), 24th–27th March 1964*, pp. 114–19.

—— (1968). *A report on the rodent and other vertebrate pests of cocoa in Western Nigeria*. Western State of Nigeria. Research Division, Ministry of Agriculture and Natural Resources, Moor Plantation, Ibadan, Nigeria (mimeograph).

EXELL, A. W. (1959). Additions to the Flora of S. Tomé and Principe. *Bull. Inst. fr. Afri. noire* **21**, 439–76.

FARQUHARSON, C. O. and LISTER, G. (1916). Notes on South Nigerian Mycetozoa. *J. Bot., Lond.* **54**, 121–33.

FARR, Marie L. (1969). Bredin–Archbold–Smithsonian biological survey of Dominica. Myxomycetes from Dominica. *Contr. U.S. natn. Mus.* **37**, 397–440.

FAWCETT, G. L. (1914). Cacao diseases. *Rep. P. Rico fed. agric. exp. Stn 1914*, p. 29. (Cited by Rorer, J. B. (1916).) The pink disease of cacao (*Bull. Dept Agric. Trin. Tobago* **15**, 86–9).

FENNAH, R. G. (1959). Nutritional factors associated with the development of mealybugs on cacao. *Rep. Cacao Res. 1957–8*, pp. 18–28. Imperial College of Tropical Agriculture; St. Augustine, Trinidad.

FERDINANDSEN, C. C. F. and WINGE, O. (1910). Fungi from Prof. Warming's expedition to Venezuela and the West Indies. *Bot. Tidssk.* **30**, 208–22.

FERREIRA, E., CORRÊA, R. R., TOMICH, A. and DE SÁ, F. T. (1969). Estudi sôbre o raio de vôo do *Anopheles* (*Kerteszia*) *cruzii* e do *Anopheles* (*Kerteszia*) *bellator* em Guaratuba, Litoral do Estado do Paraná, Brasil. *Revta bras. Malar. Doenc. trop.* **21**, 819–22.

FIDALGO, O. and FIDALGO, Maria E. P. K. (1966). Polyporaceae from Trinidad and Tobaco. I. *Mycologia* **58**, 862–904.

FIRMAN, I. D. (1972). A list of fungi and plant parasitic bacteria, viruses and nematodes in Fiji. *Phytopath. Pap.* **15**, 1–36.

—— and SUNDARAM, S. (1970). Reaction of cocoa cultivars to canker caused by *Phytophthora palmivora*, in Fiji. *Pl. Dis. Reptr* **54**, 1035–7.

—— and VERNON, A. J. (1970). Cocoa canker caused by *Phytophthora palmivora*. *Ann. appl. Biol.* **65**, 65–73.

FISHER, H. H., SODERHOLM, P. K. and KAHN, R. P. (1967). U.S. Department of

Agriculture cacao clone collection. *U.S. Dept Agric., Crops Research* (ARS 34–37–4), pp. 1–31.

FLUITER, H. J. de and MULHOLLAND, J. J. (1941). Gegevens, verkregen bij het onderzoek naar de waardplanten van *Tylenchus coffeae*. *Bergcultures* **15**, 1588–93.

FONAROFF, L. S. (1966). *Biogeographic aspects of malaria in Trinidad*. Berkeley, California; University of California, Department of Geography.

FONTANILLA-BARROGA, S. (1965). A progress report on the study of insects associated with pollination of *Theobroma cacao* with special emphasis on midges. *Philipp. J. Agric.* **27**, 147–59.

FORD, E. J., BOURRET, J. A. and SNYDER, W. C. (1967). Biologic specialization in Calonectria (Fusarium) rigidiuscula in relation to green point gall of cocoa. *Phytopathology* **57**, 710–12.

FORDHAM, R. (1972). Plant physiology. *Ann. Rep. Cacao Res. 1971*, pp. 28–48. Regional Research Centre, Imperial College of Tropical Agriculture, University of the West Indies; St. Augustine, Trinidad.

FORSYTH, J. (1966). *Agricultural insects of Ghana*. Ghana Universities Press; Accra.

FOUGEROUZE, J. (1966). Quelques problèmes de bioclimatologie en Guyane Française. *Agron. trop., Nogent* **21**, 291–346.

FOWLER, R. L., DESROSIERS, R. and HOPP, H. (1956). Evaluation of certain factors affecting the yield of cacao in Ecuador. *Ecology* **37**, 75–81.

—— and LÓPEZ, G. H. R. (1949). The cacao industry of Ecuador. *Foreign Agric. Rep.* **34**, 1–48. U.S. Dept Agric., Office of Foreign Agricultural Relations, Washington, D.C.

FOX, R. A. (1964). A report on a visit to Nigeria (9th–30th May, 1963) undertaken to make a preliminary study of root diseases of rubber. *Res. Arch. rubber Res. Inst. Malaya, Document 27*. (Mimeograph.)

—— (1967). The role of biological eradication in root-disease control in replantings of *Hevea brasiliensis*. Plant Prot. Committee for S.E. Asia and Pacific Reg. *Tech. Doc.* **54**, 1–4. (Extracts by Fox published in *Ecology of soil-borne plant pathogens*, University of California Press, 1965).

FRAENKEL-CONRAT, H. (1969). *The chemistry and biology of viruses*. Academic Press, Inc.; New York.

FRAGOSO, R. G. and CIFERRI, R. (1928). Hongos parasitos y saprofitos de la Republica Dominicana. *Bol. R. Soc. esp. Hist. nat.*, vol. **25–28**, Serie *1a–15a* (1925–7). Reprinted in: *Estación agron. Moca, Ser. B, Bot.* (Nos. **8, 11, 13**).

FRASELLE, J. (1962). Maladies parasitaires; maladies non parasitaires. In: BUYCKX, E. (1962). Précis des maladies et des insectes nuisibles rencontrés sur les plantes cultivées au Congo, au Rwanda et au Burundi. *Inst. nat. pour l'Étude agron. du Congo (I.N.E.A.C.) Publ. Hors Sér. 1962*, pp. 143–50, 169–70, 170–1.

FREE, J. B. (1970). *Insect pollination of crops*. Academic Press Inc.; London.

FREEMAN, W. E. (1967). The new clones. *J. agric. Soc., Trin.* **67**, 113–23.

FREEMAN, W. G. (1925). *Administration Report of the Director of Agriculture for the year 1924*, pp. 1–26. Trinidad and Tobago Department of Agriculture.

FRIEND, D. (1971). Rat damage to cocoa in the Solomons. *S. Pac. Bull.* **21**, 19–22.

—— and BROWN, J. F. (1971). The incidence and importance of diseases of cacao in the British Solomon Islands Protectorate. *Pl. Dis. Reptr* **55**, 885–8.

FRITSCH, F. E. (1965). *The structure and reproduction of the algae.* Vol. I (repr. 1965). The Syndics of the Cambridge University Press; London.

GADD, C. H. (1924). *Phytophthora faberi* Maubl. *Ann. R. bot. Gdns Peradeniya* 9, 47–89.

—— (1928). *Sphaerostilbe repens. Tea Q.* 1, 16.

GALLEGLY, M. E. (1970). Genetical aspects of pathogenic and saprophytic behaviour of the Phycomycetes with special reference to *Phytophthora.* In *Root diseases and soil-borne pathogens* (ed. T. A. Toussoun, R. V. Bega and P. A. Nelson), pp. 50–4. 2nd Intl Symp. factors Determining behaviour of Plant Pathogens in Soil, Imperial Coll., Lond., July 14–28, 1968 in Conjunction with 1st intl Cong. of Plant Pathology. University of California Press.

GANDIA, I. M. (1962). Brown bark rot of cacao trunk. *Coffee Cacao J., Philippines,* 5, 133 and 144.

—— (1963). Laboratory screening of some commercial fungicides against some cacao pod rot organisms. *Pl. Ind. Dig.* 26, 8–9 and 25–7.

GARCÉS, C. O. (1940). *Enfermedades del cacao en Colombia.* Republica de Colombia Ministerio de la Economia Nacional: Imprenta Nacional; Bogota.

—— (1941). Informe sobre la situación patológica de los cacaotales en los Departmentos de Valle y Cauca. *Revta Fac. nac. Agron. Colombia* 4, 1280–300.

GARCIA, C. B. and NAUNDORF, G. (1952). Un año de experimentos sobre control de la Moniliasis en el cacao. *Cacao Colomb.* 1, 31–40.

GARCÍA PAYÓN, J. (1936). *Amaxocoatl o libro del chocolate,* pp. 1–124. Toluca, Mexico.

GARJEANNE, A. J. M. (1932). Physiology. In: *Manual of Bryology,* ed. Fr. Verdoorn, pp. 207–32. Martinus Nijhoff; The Hague.

GARRETT, S. D. (1938). Soil conditions and the root-infecting fungi. *Biol. Rev.* 13, 159–85.

—— (1944). *Root disease fungi, a treatise on the epidemiology of soil-borne disease in crop plants, and a first exposition of the principles of root disease control.* Chronica Botanica Company; Waltham, Mass.

—— (1956). Rhizomorph behaviour in *Armillaria mellea* (Vahl.) Quel. II. Logistics of infection. *Ann. Bot.* 20, 193–209 (abstract in *Rev. appl. Mycol.* 35, 706 (1956)).

—— (1960). *Biology of root-infecting fungi,* Cambridge University Press; London. (Reprint.)

—— (1970). *Pathogenic root-infecting fungi,* Cambridge University Press; London.

GEHRMANN, K. (1913). Krankheiten und Schädlinge der Kulturpflanzen auf Samoa. Bericht an das Reichskolonialamt über pflanzenpathologische Untersuchungen im Jahre 1910. *Arb. biol. (Bund Anst. Land-u. Forstw.)* 9, 1–72.

GEORGHIOU, G. P. (1972). The evolution of resistance to pesticides. In: *Ann. rev. of ecology and systematics,* ed. R. F. Johnston, P. W. Frank and C. D. Michener, pp. 133–68. Annual Reviews Inc.; Palo Alto, California.

GERARD, B. M. (1964). Side-effects of insecticides. *C.R.I.G. Rep. 1st April 1962–30th Sept. 1963,* p. 30.

—— (1966). Pollination studies. *C.R.I.G. Rep. 1st Oct. 1963–31st March 1965,* pp. 46–7.

—— (1967). A review of 50 years applied entomology in Nigeria: Tree Crops. *Proc. entomol. Soc. Nigeria*, **1967**, 25–38.

GERARD, P. M. (1963). Nematode studies. *Ann. Rep. W. Afr. Cocoa Res. Inst. 1961–2*, pp. 32–3.

GHESQUIÈRE, J. (1921). Nouveaux parasites du cacaoyer. Maladie vermiculaire du cacaoyer (*Tylenchus (Heterodera) radicicola* Greef) et sa relation avec la maladie du *Diplodia* (Coup de soleil, Die back). *Bull. agric. Congo belge* **12**, 709–18.

GIBBS, D. G. and PICKETT, A. D. (1966). Feeding by *Distantiella theobroma* (Dist.) (Heteroptera, Miridae) on cocoa. I. The effects of water stress in the plant. *Bull. ent. Res.* **57**, 159–69.

GIBBS, J. N. and BRASIER, C. M. (1973). Correlation between cultural characters and pathogenicity in *Ceratocystis ulmi* from Britain, Europe and America. *Nature, Lond.* **241**, 381–3.

GIBSON, I. A. S. (1961). A note on variation between isolates of *Armillaria mellea* (Vahl. ex Fr.) Kummer. *Trans. Br. mycol. Soc.* **44**, 123–8.

—— and CORBETT, D. C. M. (1964). Variation in isolates from Armillaria root disease in Nyasaland. *Phytopathology* **54**, 122–3.

—— and GOODCHILD, N. A. (1961). *Armillaria mellea* in Kenya tea plantations. *Rep. 6th Commonwealth mycol. Conf. 1960*, pp. 39–40. Commonwealth Mycological Institute; Kew.

GILLETT, J. B. (1962). Pest Pressure, an underestimated factor in evolution. *Publs Syst. Ass.* **4**. *Taxonomy and geography*, pp. 37–46.

—— (1963). Pest Pressure: a solution to some botanical problems. *The Times Science Rev. Q.* **50**, 4–6.

GILMOUR, J. S. L., HORNE, F. R., LITTLE, E. L., STAFLEU, F. A. and RICHENS, R. H. (1969). *International code of nomenclature of cultivated plants—1969* (from *Regnum Vegetabile* vol. 64), pp. 1–32. International Bureau for Plant Taxonomy and Nomenclature of the International Association for Plant Taxonomy; Utrecht, Netherlands.

GLENDINNING, D. R. (1962). Natural pollination of cocoa. *Nature, Lond.* **193**, 1305.

—— (1963*a*). The inheritance of bean size, pod size and number of beans per pod in cocoa (*Theobroma cacao* L.), with a note on bean shape. *Euphytica* **12**, 311–22.

—— (1963*b*). The C.R.I. cocoa varieties. *Ghana J. Sci.* **3**, 111–19.

—— (1967). New cocoa varieties in Ghana. *Cocoa Growers' Bull.* **8**, 19–24.

—— and EDWARDS, D. F. (1961). The development and production of the new W.A.C.R.I. hybrid varieties. *Rep. Cocoa Conf. Grosvenor House, London, W.1, 12th–14th Sept. 1961*, pp. 137–40. Cocoa, Chocolate and Confectionery Alliance; London.

——, LEGG, J. T., LOVI, N. K. and MARTINSON, V. A. (1966). A field experiment in Ghana on the tolerance of cocoa seedlings to cocoa swollen-shoot and cocoa mottle-leaf viruses. *Ann. appl. Biol.* **57**, 389–96.

—— and MARTINSON, V. A. (1966). Plant breeding and selection. *C.R.I.G. Rep. 1st Oct. 1963–31st March 1965*, pp. 52–75.

GOBERDHAN, L. and GANPAT, D. (1960). Cushion gall of cocoa in Trinidad. *VIII Inter-Amer. Cacao Conf. Trinidad and Tobago 15–25 June, 1960. Proc.*, pp. 270–80.

GOFFART, H. (1935). *Rhabditis gracilis* n. sp. (Rhabditidae, Nematoda) als bewohner faulender Kakaofrüchte. *Zool. Anz.* **109**, 134–8.

GONÇALVES, J. R. C. (1965). *Theobroma grandiflorum* (Spreng.) Schum. as source of inculum of witch-broom disease of *Theobroma cacao* L. *Trop. Agric., Trin.* **42**, 261–3.

GOODALL, D. W. (1949). Virus diseases of cacao in West Africa. IV. Effect of virus infection on growth and water content of cacao seedlings. *Ann. appl. Biol.* **36**, 440–7.

GOODCHILD, A. J. P. (1952). A study of the digestive system of the West African cacao capsid bugs (Hemiptera, Miridae). *Proc. zool. Soc. Lond.* **122**, 543–72.

GOODEY, T. (1933). *Plant parasitic nematodes and the diseases they cause.* Methuen and Co. Ltd.; London.

GORDON, W. L. (1956). The taxonomy and habitats of the Fusarium species of Trinidad, B.W.I. *Can. J. Bot.* **34**, 847–64.

GORENZ, A. M. (1960). Transmission of the cushion gall disease of cacao. *VIII Inter-Amer. Cacao Conf. Trinidad and Tobago 15–25 June, 1960. Proc.*, 249–54.

—— (1969). Green-point cushion gall. *Ann. Rep. C.R.I.N. 1967–8*, pp. 94–5.

—— (1970). Spread of Phytophthora pod rot from the tree base to pods in the canopy. *Ann. Rep. C.R.I.N. 1968–9*, 53–4.

—— (1972a). Dissemination of *P. palmivora* by rodents. *Ann. Rep. C.R.I.N. 1970–1*, pp. 126–7.

—— (1972b). The occurrence of Thielaviopsis pod rot in Nigeria. *Ann. Rep. C.R.I.N. 1970–1*, pp. 128–9.

GRAHAM, K. M. (1964). New records for Fiji. In: F.A.O. *Plant Prot. Committee for S E Asia and Pacific Reg. 3rd Q. Rep. 1964 July–Sept.*, ed. A. Johnson, p. 5.

—— (1965). In Johnston (1965b). *F.A.O. Plant Prot. Committee for SE Asia and Pacific Reg. Q. Newsletter* **8**, 6. (Mimeograph.)

GRAVIER, C. (1907). Les maladies de cacaoyers a San-Thomé. *Bull. Mus. d'Hist. nat.* **2 and 3**, 130–41.

GREATHEAD, D. J., LIONNET, J. F. G., LODOS, N. and WHELLAN, J. A. (1971). A review of biological control in the Ethiopian Region. *Commonwealth Inst. Biol. Control Tech. Comm.* **5**, 1–162. Commonwealth Agricultural Bureaux; Farnham Royal, Slough.

GREATHOUSE, D. C., LAETSCH, W. M. and PHINNEY, B. O. (1971). The shoot-growth rhythm of a tropical tree, *Theobroma cacao*. *Amer. J. Bot.* **58**, 281–6.

GREEN, E. E. (1901). Helopeltis. 'What we know and what we want to know about it.' *Royal Botanic Gardens, Ceylon, Circular Ser. I*, **21**, 277–83.

GREENWOOD, M. (1943). Chemistry, pp. 31–45. *Gold Coast Colony Dept Agric. Rep. on Central Cocoa Res. Stn, Tafo, Gold Coast, 1938–42* (compiled and edited by M. Greenwood).

—— and DJOKOTO, R. K. (1952). Symptoms of mineral deficiency in cacao. *J. hort. Sci.* **27**, 223–36.

—— and HAYFRON, R. J. (1951). Iron and zinc deficiencies in cacao in the Gold Coast. *Emp. J. exp. Agric.* **19**, 73–86.

—— and POSNETTE, A. F. (1947). A morphological change induced in leaves of *Theobroma cacao* by mineral deficiency. *Nature, Lond.* **159**, 542.

GREGORY, J. L. (1954). Review of work done by the Entomological Section, Department of Agriculture, 1948–54. *Rep. 6th Commonwealth ent. Conf. 7th–16th July 1954*, pp. 290–302. Commonwealth Institute of Entomology; London.

GREGORY, P. H. (1948). The multiple-infection transformation. *Ann. appl. Biol.* **35**, 412–17.

—— (1968). Interpreting plant disease dispersal gradients. In: *Annual Review of Phytopathology*, ed. J. G. Horsfall and K. F. Baker; vol. 6, pp. 189–212. Annual Reviews Inc.; Palo Alto, California.

—— (1969). *Black pod disease project report*. Cocoa, Chocolate and Confectionery Alliance; London.

—— (1971). Black pod disease: the future. *III intl Cocoa Res. Conf., Accra, Ghana 23–29 Nov. 1969*, pp. 365–9. Cocoa Research Institute; Tafo, Ghana.

—— (1972). Cocoa: the importance of black pod disease. *Span* **15**, 30–1.

GRIMALDI, J. (1952). Contribución al estudio de las criptógamas parásitas y saprofitas del cacaotal en el Cameroun. *Trabajo pres. a la Cuarta Conf. Comité téc. Interamer. del Cacao celebrada en Guayaquil, Ecuador durante Junio 9–16 de 1952* (mimeograph), pp. 1–23.

—— (1954a). Les maladies cryptogamiques du cacaoyer au Cameroun. *Agron. trop., Nogent* **9**, 544–62.

—— (1954b). Les principaux cryptogames observés sur *Theobroma cacao* au Cameroun. *5th Reunion del Comité tecnico Interamer. del Cacao, vol. I, trabajos pres., Turrialba*, pp. 1–36.

GRUBB, P. J., FLINT, O. P. and GREGORY, S. C. (1969). Preliminary observations on the mineral nutrition of epiphytic mosses. *Trans. Br. bryol. Soc.* **5**, 802–7.

GUBA, E. F. (1961). *Monograph of Monochaetia and Pestalotia*, pp. vi and 342. Harvard University Press; Cambridge, Mass.

GUILLAUMIN, J. J. (1971). Contribution à l'étude des 'maladies à filaments blancs' en basse Côte-d'Ivoire. *Annals Phytopathologie 3*, 143–9 (abstract in *Hort. Abstr.* **43**, 100 (1973)).

GUMILLA, J. (1791). *Historia natural, civil y geográfica de las naciones situadas en las riveras del Rio Orinoco*. Vol. 1 (Nueva Impresion): Barcelona.

HADLAND, J. R. G. (1957). A further report on the control of black pod disease in the Western Region of Nigeria. *Rep. Cocoa Conf. Grosvenor House, London, W.1, 10th–12th Sept. 1957*, pp. 118–19. Cocoa, Chocolate and Confectionery Alliance; London.

—— and REEVES, H. W. (1955). The development of fungicidal spraying in Nigeria against black pod disease in cocoa. *Rep. Cocoa Conf. Grosvenor House, London, W.1, 13th–15th Sept. 1955*, pp. 96–9. Cocoa, Chocolate and Confectionery Alliance; London.

HALE, M. E. (1967). *The biology of lichens*, Edward Arnold Ltd.; London.

HALL, W. J. (1945). The identity of a mealybug vector of 'swollen-shoot' virus disease of cacao in West Africa. *Bull. ent. Res.* **36**, 305–13.

HAMILTON, R. A. and ARCHBOLD, J. W. (1945). Meteorology of Nigeria and adjacent territory. *Q. Jl R. met. Soc.* **71**, 231–62.

HANCOCK, B. L. (1949). A laboratory colour test for the diagnosis of swollen-shoot of *Theobroma cacao*. *Trop. Agric., Trin.* **26**, 54–6.

HANNA, A. D. and HEATHERINGTON, W. (1957). Arrest of the swollen-shoot virus disease of cacao in the Gold Coast by controlling the mealybug vectors with the systemic insecticide, Dimefox. *Ann. appl. Biol.* **45**, 473–80.

——, Judenko, E. and Heatherington, W. (1955). Systemic insecticides for the control of insects transmitting swollen-shoot virus disease of cacao in the Gold Coast. *Bull. ent. Res.* **46**, 669–710.

Hansen, A. J. (1963a). The role of *Fusarium decemcellulare* and *Fusarium roseum* in the green-point cushion gall complex of cacao. *Turrialba* **13**, 80–7.

—— (1963b). Pathology. In: Cacao Program Annual Report 1962–3. *Cacao, Turrialba* **8**, 3–6.

—— (1964). Role of the brown jay in epiphytotics of Thielaviopsis pod rot of cacao. *Phytopathology* **54**, 894–5.

—— (1966). Fusaria as agents of cacao green-point cushion gall in the Caribbean and in Latin America. *Pl. Dis. Reptr* **50**, 229–33.

—— and de Reyes, Lilian (1963). Agalla de puntos verdes en el cacao de Venezuela y Costa Rica. *Turrialba* **13**, 128–30.

Hansford, C. G. (1926). The Fusaria of Jamaica. *Kew Bull.,* pp. 257–88.

—— (1937). Annotated host list of Uganda parasitic fungi and plant diseases, Part II. *E. Afr. agric. J.* **2**, 498–504.

—— (1943a). Host list of the parasitic fungi of Uganda. *E. Afr. agric. J.* **8**, 248–52

—— (1943b). Contributions towards the fungus flora of Uganda. V. *Fungi imperfecti. Proc. Linn. Soc., Lond. 1942–3* **155**, 34–67.

—— (1957). Australian fungi. IV. New records and revisions (continued). *Proc. Linn. Soc. N.S.W.* **82**, 209–29.

Hardy, F. (1937). Marginal leaf-scorch of cacao. Its relationship to soil potash deficiency. (With a note on the ecology of cacao thrips.) *6th ann. Rep. Cacao Res. 1936,* pp. 13–24. Imperial College of Tropical Agriculture; St. Augustine, Trinidad.

—— (1953). The productivity of cacao soils and its improvement. *Trop. Agric., Trin.* **30**, 135–8.

—— (1957). *Future prospect of cacao-growing in Panama (Observations based on an 11 days' visit, 18th–28th Jan. 1957).* Inter-American Institute of Agricultural Sciences; Report 12 (mimeograph); Turrialba, Costa Rica.

—— (1958). The effects of air temperature on growth and production in cacao. *Cacao, Turrialba* **3**, 1–14.

—— (1960a). *Cacao manual (English ed.)* compiled and ed. F. Hardy. Inter-American Institute of Agricultural Sciences; Turrialba, Costa Rica.

—— (1960b). Editor's footnote, to Soria (1960a), p. 329.

Harland, S. C. (1925). Studies in cacao Part I. The method of pollination. *Ann. appl. Biol.* **12**, 403–9.

Harper, J. L., Lovell, P. H. and Moore, K. G. (1970). The shapes and sizes of seeds. In: *Annual review of ecology and systematics,* ed. R. F. Johnston, P. W. Frank and C. D. Michener, Vol. 1, pp. 327–56. Annual Reviews Inc.; Palo Alto, California.

Harper, S. H. and Letcher, R. M. (1966). Chemistry of lichen constituents. Part I. Some constituents of *Acarospora schleicheri, Buellia rhodesiaca, Caloplaca cinnabarium, Dermatiscum thunbergii, Parmelia dilatata, Parmelia gossweileri, Pertusaria* species (L 19), *Temnospora fulgens* and *Usnea implicita. Proc. Trans. Rhod. Sci. Ass.* **51**, 156–84.

HARRIS, D. R. (1972). The origins of agriculture in the tropics. *Am. Scient.* **60**, 180–93.

HARRIS, K. M. (1968). A systematic revision and biological review of the cecidomyiid predators (Diptera: Cecidomyiidae) on world Coccoidea (Hemiptera–Homoptera). *Trans. R. ent. Soc. Lond.* **119**, 401–94.

HART. J. H. (1911). *Cacao. A manual on the cultivation and curing of cacao.* Duckworth and Co.; London.

HARWOOD, L. W. (1959). Diseases of cocoa. *Agric. J. Fiji* **29**, 96–8.

HASSELO, H. N. and PRICE, D. (1961). The assessment of black pod disease control in cocoa by mistblowing. *Trop. Agric., Trin.* **38**, 133–44.

HAVORD, G. (1955). Lime-induced chlorosis in cacao seedlings. *Rep. Cacao Res. 1954*, pp. 72–6. Imperial College of Tropical Agriculture; St. Augustine, Trinidad.

—— (1960). Fertilizer usage in cacao growing. In: *Cacao manual*, compiled and ed. F. Hardy, pp. 207–12. Inter-American Institute of Agricultural Sciences; Turrialba, Costa Rica.

HAWKSWORTH, D. L. (1972). *Ustulina deusta. C.M.I. Descriptions of pathogenic Fungi and Bacteria* **360**.

—— and TALBOYS, P. W. (1970). *Verticillium dahliae. C.M.I. Descriptions of pathogenic Fungi and Bacteria* **256**.

HAWORTH, F. (1953). The effect of age, season and environment on the nitrogenous components of cacao beans. *Rep. Cacao Res. 1945–51*, pp. 92–7. Imperial College of Tropical Agriculture; St. Augustine, Trinidad.

HEARLE, J. W. S., SPARROW, J. T. and CROSS, P. M. (1972). *The use of the scanning electron microscope.* Pergamon Press Ltd.; Oxford.

HEATH, R. G. (1958). *Ann. Rep. Dept Agric., Fed. Malaya, 1957*, Government Printer, Federation of Malaya.

HEINZE, K. (1959). *Phytopathogens Viren und ihre Überträger.* Duncker and Humblot; Berlin.

HELFENBERGER, A. and HUTCHINS, L. M. (1966). Control of green-point gall of cacao on artificially inoculated cacao seedlings under greenhouse conditions. *Cacao, Turrialba* **11**, 1–7.

HEMPEL, A. (1904). Uma nova especie de fungo que produz o cancro no cacaoeiro, *Calonectria bahiensis* n. sp. *Bolm Agric. S. Paulo*, **5**, 22–4.

HENDERSON, F. C. (1954). Cacao as a crop for the owner-manager in Papua and New Guinea. *Papua New Guin. agric. J.* **9**, 45–74.

HENDRICKX, F. L. (1948). Sylloge fungorum congensium. *Catalogue des champignons signalés au Congo Belge et au Ruanda-Urundi. L'Inst. national pour l'Étude agron. Congo Belge (I.N.É.A.C.). Sér. sci.* **35**, pp. 1–216.

HENNINGS, P. (1895). Fungi camerunenses. I. *Engler's botanischen Jahrbüchern* **22**, 72–111.

HENRIQUES, J. A. (1917). Ilha de S. Tomé, sob o ponto de vista historico-natural e agricola. *Bolm Soc. broteriana* **27**, 1–216.

HERKLOTS, G. A. C. (1961). *The birds of Trinidad and Tobago.* Collins; London.

HERNANDEZ, S. A. (1968). El cacao. *Agronomia Venezuela* **9**, 8–28.

HEWISON, H. K. and ABABIO, N. K. (1930). Flower and fruit production of *Theobroma cacao. Dept Agric. Gold Coast Year Book 1929. Bull.* **22**, 87–94.

HICKS, P. G. (1967). Observations on the diseases and conditions of cacao pods in

Papua and New Guinea—pod losses 1962–65. *Papua New Guin. Agric. J.* **19**, 5–9.

HISLOP, E. C. (1963*a*). Studies on the chemical control of *Phytophthora palmivora* (Butl.) Butl. on *Theobroma cacao* L. in Nigeria. IV. Further laboratory and field trials of fungicides. *Ann. appl. Biol.* **52**, 465–80.

—— (1963*b*). Studies on the chemical control of *Phytophthora palmivora* (Butl.) Butl. on *Theobroma cacao* L. in Nigeria. V. Comparisons of three spraying machines for applying fungicides. *Ann. appl. Biol.* **52**, 481–92.

—— (1964). Black pod disease. *Cocoa Growers' Bull.* **2**, 4–9.

—— and PARK, P. O. (1962*a*). Studies on the chemical control of *Phytophthora palmivora* (Butl.) Butl. on *Theobroma cacao* L. in Nigeria. I. Laboratory bio-assay of fungicides on detached pods. *Ann. appl. Biol.* **50**, 57–65.

—— and —— (1962*b*). Studies on the chemical control of *Phytophthora palmivora* (Butl.) Butl. on *Theobroma cacao* L. in Nigeria. II. Persistence of fungicides on pods. *Ann. appl. Biol.* **50**, 67–76.

—— and —— (1962*c*). Studies on the chemical control of *Phytophthora palmivora* (Butl.) Butl. on *Theobroma cacao* L. in Nigeria. III. Field Trials. *Ann. appl. Biol.* **50**, 77–88.

HOLDEN, M. (1957). An investigation on polyphenolic compounds of the cacao leaf in connexion with chemical method for detecting virus infection. *J. Sci. Fd Agric.* **8**, 553–61.

HOLLIDAY, P. (1952). Witches' broom disease of cacao (*Marasmius perniciosus* Stahel). *Colonial* **286**, 1–8. H.M. S. O.; London.

—— (1953). The cultivated cacao of Colombia. *J. agric. Soc. Trin.* **53**, 397–406.

—— (1954*a*). The susceptibility of some Imperial College Selections to witches' broom disease. *Rep. Cacao Res. 1953*, pp. 58–63. Imperial College of Tropical Agriculture; St. Augustine, Trinidad.

—— (1954*b*). Spraying against witches' broom disease. *Rep. Cacao Res. 1953*, pp. 64–6. Imperial College of Tropical Agriculture; St. Augustine, Trinidad.

—— (1954*c*). Control of witches' broom disease of cacao in Trinidad. *Trop. Agric., Trin.* **31**, 312–17.

—— (1955). A test for resistance to *Marasmius perniciosus* Stahel. *Rep. Cacao Res. 1954*, pp. 50–5. Imperial College of Tropical Agriculture; St. Augustine, Trinidad.

—— (1957*a*). Further observations on the susceptibility of Imperial College Selections to witches' broom disease. *Rep. Cacao Res. 1955–6*, pp. 48–53. Imperial College of Tropical Agriculture; St. Augustine, Trinidad.

—— (1957*b*). Spread of pod rot of cacao. *Commonw. phytopath. News* **3**, 12.

—— (1960). A spraying and harvesting trial in Trinidad against cocoa pod diseases. *Trop. Agric., Trin.* **37**, 235–42.

—— (1962). The spread of witches' broom disease of cacao. *Trans. Br. mycol. Soc.* **45**, 281.

—— (1970*a*). Crinipellis perniciosa. *C.M.I. Descriptions of pathogenic Fungi and Bacteria*, **223**.

—— (1970*b*). Monilia roreri. *C.M.I. Descriptions of pathogenic Fungi and Bacteria*, **226**.

—— (1970*c*). Trachysphaera fructigena. *C.M.I. Descriptions of Pathogenic Fungi and Bacteria*, **229**.

—— (1971). Some tropical plant pathogenic fungi of limited distribution. *Rev. Plant Path.* **50**, 337–48.

—— and BAKER, R. E. D. (1953). The susceptibility of the ICS clones to witches' broom disease at River Estate, Trinidad. *Rep. Cacao Res. 1945–51*, pp. 119–21. Imperial College of Tropical Agriculture; St. Augustine, Trinidad.

—— and MOWAT, W. P. (1963). Foot rot of *Piper nigrum* L. (*Phytophthora palmivora*). *Phytopath. Pap.* **5**.

—— and PUNITHALINGAM, E. (1970). Macrophomina phaseolina. *C.M.I. Descriptions of pathogenic Fungi and Bacteria* **275**.

HOOPER, D. J. (1969). Identification of plant and soil nematodes. In: Nematodes of tropical crops, ed. by J. Peachey. *Tech. Commun. Commonw. Bur. Helminth.* **40**, 37–66.

HOPKINS, J. C. F. (1933). *Rhizoctonia lamellifera* Small: a distinct species of the *Rhizoctonia bataticola* group of fungi. *Proc. Rhod. Sci. Ass.* **32**, 65–79.

—— (1960). Plant diseases in the British Colonial Dependencies. *Pl. Prot. Bull. F.A.O.* **8**, 109.

HOWARD, A. (1901*a*). The fungoid diseases of cacao in the West Indies. *W. Indian Bull.* **2**, 190–211.

—— (1901*b*). On *Diplodia cacaoicola*, P. Henn.; a parasitic fungus on sugar-cane and cacao in the West Indies. *Ann. Bot.* **15**, 683–702.

HOWES, F. N. (1947) The early introductions of cocoa to West Africa. *Trop. Agric., Trin.* **23**, 172 (reprinted from 'African Affairs' July 1946).

HUBERT, F. P. (1957). Diseases of some export crops in Indonesia. *Pl. Dis. Reptr*, **41**, 55–63.

HUGHES, S. J. (1952). Fungi from the Gold Coast. I. *Mycol. Pap.* **48**, 1–91.

—— (1953) Fungi from the Gold Coast. II. *Mycol. Pap.* **50**, 1–104.

HUGUENIN, B. (1964). In: Johnston, A. (1964*a*). F.A.O. *Plant Prot. Committee SE Asia and Pacific Reg. 1st Q. Rep. 1964 Jan.–March.*, pp. 8–9.

HUMPHRIES, E. C. (1940). Studies in the physiology of *Theobroma cacao*, with special reference to cherelle wilt. I. Preliminary investigation of the factors concerned in wilt. *9th ann. Rep. Cacao Res. 1939*, 33–42. Imperial College of Tropical Agriculture; St. Augustine, Trinidad.

—— (1943*a*). Wilt of cacao fruits (*Theobroma cacao*) I. An investigation into the causes. *Ann. Bot.*, N.S., **7**, 31–44.

—— (1943*b*). Wilt of cacao fruits (*Theobroma cacao*) II. A preliminary survey of the carbohydrate metabolism with special reference to wilt susceptibility. *Ann. Bot.*, N.S. **7**, 45–61.

—— (1944). Wilt of cacao fruits (*Theobroma cacao*) III. Changes in mineral content during development. *Ann. Bot.* **8**, 57–70.

HUNTER, J. R. (1958). Report on consultation visit to Peru. *Inter-Amer. Inst. Agric. Sci, Turrialba, Costa Rica, Rep.* **28**, 1–10 (mimeograph).

HURD, R. G. (1961). Plant physiology. *Ann. Rep. W. Afr. Cocoa Res. Inst. 1959–60*, pp. 57–60.

HURTADO, C. A. (1960). Efectos de la polinizacion controlada sobre la produccion del cacao. *VIII Inter-American Cacao Conference, Trinidad and Tobago 15–25 June, 1960, Proceedings*, pp. 109–15.

HUTCHINS, L. M. (1958*a*). Report on cushion gall of cacao in Nicaragua as observed in recent surveys. *Inter-Amer. Inst. Agric. Sci., Turrialba, Costa Rica Rep.* **29**, 1–4.

—— (1958*b*). Current surveys for cushion gall. *7th Inter-Amer. Cacao Conf. Palmira–Colombia July 13–19, 1958*, pp. 1–9. Inter-American Cacao Center, Turrialba, Costa Rica.

—— (1959*a*). Cushion gall of cacao and disease-free propagating material, Inspection of plantings at Quepos, Costa Rica. *Inter-Amer. Inst. Agric. Sci., Turrialba, Costa Rica, Rep.* **31**, 1–9.

—— (1959*b*). Transmission of cushion gall of cacao by means of tissue transplantation. *Comun. Turrialba* **66**, 1–6.

—— (1960). Cushion gall. In: *Cacao manual* (English ed.). Compiled and ed. F. Hardy, pp. 260–8. Inter-American Institute of Agricultural Sciences; Turrialba, Costa Rica.

—— (1963). Recent advances in cushion gall research. *Phytopathology* **53**, 25.

—— (1964). Predisposition to cacao knob gall in wounds where flowery gall has been excised. *Phytopathology* **54**, 499.

—— (1965). Loss of gall-inducing capacity of cacao, when Calonectria rigidiuscula passes from the conidial (Fusarium) stage through the perfect (ascospore) stage. *Pl. Dis. Reptr* **49**, 564–5.

—— (1966). Loss of gall-inducing capacity of Fusarium rigidiuscula on cacao by interference from another Fusarium clone. *Pl. Dis. Reptr* **50**, 219–22.

——, DESROSIERS, R. and MARTIN, E. (1959). Varietal susceptibility to flowery cushion gall of cacao. *Inter-Amer. Inst. agric. Sci., Turrialba, Costa Rica, Rep.* **33**, 1–10.

—— and SILLER, L. R. (1960). Cushion gall types in cacao. *VIII Inter-Amer. Cacao Conf. Trinidad and Tobago 15–25 June, 1960. Proc.*, pp. 281–9.

——, SORIA, J. and SILLER, L. R. (1964). Partial resistance to green-point cushion gall in cacao clones completely resistant to flowery gall. *Phytopathology* **54**, 499.

HUTCHINSON, J. (1969). *Evolution and phylogeny of flowering plants. Dicotyledons; facts and theory.* Academic Press Inc.; London.

IDROBO, S. M. (1958*a*). El complejo Xyleborus-Ceratostomella en Colombia. *Sépt. Conf. interamer. de Cacao, Palmira, Colombia, 13–19 de julio de 1958.* pp. 73–9.

—— (1958*b*). Una prueba de resistencia a *Ceratostomella fimbriata* (E. and H.) Elliott. *Sépt. Conf. interamer. de Cacao, Palmira, Colombia, 13–19 de julio de 1958.* pp. 149–51.

—— and NAUNDORF, G. (1956). Produccion de toxinas por el *Ceratostomella fimbriata* en cacao. *Cacao Colomb.* **5** 37–9.

IGWEGBE, E. C. K. (1966*a*). The preferences shown by *Planococcoides njalensis* (Laing) and *Ferrisiana virgata* (Ckll.) for different feeding sites and its effect on their efficiency as vectors. *Ann. Rep. C.R.I.N. 1964–5*, pp. 60–2.

—— (1966*b*). Availability of C.S.S.V. in different cocoa clones to *Planocococcoides njalensis* (Laing). *Ann. Rep. C.R.I.N. 1964–5*, pp. 62–5.

IMLE, B. P. and CUATRECASAS, J. (1967). Plant introduction with *Theobroma cacao*. *Proc. internatl Symp. on Plant Introduction, Escuela Agricola Panamericana, Tegucigalpa, Honduras Nov. 30–Dec. 2, 1966*, pp. 137–45.

INGOLD, C. T. (1967). Liberation mechanisms of fungi. In: *Airborne microbes*;

ed. P. H. Gregory and J. L. Monteith, pp. 102–15. Society for General Microbiology; Cambridge University Press.

ITON, E. F. (1959). Studies on a wilt disease of cacao at River Estate. *Rep. Cacao Res. 1957–8*, pp. 55–64. Imperial College of Tropical Agriculture; St. Augustine, Trinidad.

—— (1960). Ceratostomella wilt in cacao in Trinidad. *VIII Inter-Amer. Cacao Conf., Trinidad and Tobago 15–25 June, 1960. Proc.*, pp. 201–7.

—— (1961). Studies on a wilt disease of cacao at River Estate II. Some aspects of wind transmission. *Rep. Cacao Res. 1959–60*, pp. 47–58. Imperial College of Tropical Agriculture; St. Augustine, Trinidad.

—— (1966). Ceratocystis wilt. *Ann. Rep. Cacao Res. 1965*, pp. 44–50. Regional Research Centre, Imperial College of Tropical Agriculture, University of the West Indies; St. Augustine, Trinidad.

—— (1968). A basis for the control of *Ceratocystis* wilt of cacao. *First intl Cong. Plant Pathology, London 14–26 July 1968. Abstr. of papers (unpublished)*. p. 95.

—— and CONWAY, G. R. (1961). Studies on a wilt disease of cacao at River Estate III. Some aspects of the biology and habits of *Xyleborus* spp. and their relation to disease transmission. *Rep. Cacao Res. 1959–60*, pp. 59–65. Imperial College of Tropical Agriculture; St. Augustine, Trinidad.

JACQUET, J. H. (1929). Les balais de sorcière du cacaoyer et les moyens de les éviter. *Agron. colon.* **18**, 129–33.

JAMES, H. C. (1957). Plant Pathology. Investigations 1955; *Bull. Dept Agric. Jamaica* **55** (New Ser.), 25–7.

JENMAN, G. S. and HARRISON, J. B. (1897). Pests affecting cacao plantations. *Br. Guiana Rep. on agric. work in bot. Gardens for 1893–4–5*, pp. 120–1. Georgetown; Demerara.

JIMÉNEZ, Sáenz E. (1969). Relación entre el ataque de nemátodos y la muerte súbita del cacao (*Theobroma cacao* L.) en Bahia, Brasil. *Turrialba* **19**, 255–60.

—— LLANO, G. A. and HUTCHINS, L. M. (1966). Efecto del nitrogeno, potasio y boro en el crecimiento de la buba de puntos verdes en cacao *Proc Amer. Soc. hort. Sci. Caribbean Reg. XIII ann. Meeting, Kingston, Jamaica, July 5–11, 1965*, pp. 9 and 214–23.

JOHNS, R. and GIBBERD, A. V. (1950). An assessment of swollen-shoot disease in Nigeria and an outline of some problems in connection with the rehabilitation of the cocoa industry. *Rep. Cocoa Conf., Grosvenor House, London, W.1, 13th–14th Sept. 1950*, pp. 14–18. Cocoa, Chocolate and Confectionery Alliance; London.

JOHNSON, C. G. (1962a). Capsids: A review of current knowledge. In: *Agriculture and land use in Ghana,* ed. J. B. Wills, pp. 316–31. Oxford University Press.

—— (1962b). The ecological approach to cocoa disease and health. In: *Agriculture and land use in Ghana*; ed. J. B. Wills, pp. 348–52. Oxford University Press.

—— (1969). *Migration and dispersal of insects by flight.* Methuen and Co. Ltd.; London.

JOHNSON, W. H. (1912). *Cocoa, its cultivation and preparation.* Imperial Institute Handbooks, John Murray; London.

JOHNSTON, A. (1959). Plant disease investigation in the Federation of Malaya. *Pl. Prot. Bull. F.A.O.* **8**, 1–4.

REFERENCES

—— (1960a). A supplement to a Host List of Plant Diseases in Malaya. *Mycol. Pap.* **77**, 1–30.

—— (1960b). *A preliminary plant disease survey in the British Solomon Islands Protectorate.* F.A.O. Rome Plant Production and Protection Division, 1–36 (mimeograph).

—— (1960c). *A preliminary plant disease survey in North Borneo.* F.A.O. Rome Plant Production and Protection Division, 1–43 (mimeograph).

—— (1960d). *A preliminary plant disease survey in Sarawak.* F.A.O. Rome Plant Production and Protection Division, 1–17 (mimeograph).

—— (1961). *A preliminary plant disease survey in Netherlands New Guinea. Netherlands New Guinea Dept of economic Affairs, agric. Ser. 1961* **4**, 1–55.

—— (1963a). Plant Protection Committee for the South East Asia and Pacific Region. *Commonw. phytopath. News* **9**, 19–20.

—— (1963b). Host list of plant diseases in the New Hebrides. *F.A.O. Plant Prot. Committee for SE Asia and Pacific Reg. tech. Doc.* **27**, 1–9 (mimeograph).

—— (1963c). Host list of plant diseases in Samoa. *F.A.O. Plant Prot. Committee for SE Asia and Pacific Reg., Tech. Doc.* **35**, 1–5 (mimeograph).

—— (1964a). *F.A.O. Plant Prot. Committee for SE Asia and Pacific Reg., 1st Q. Rep. 1964 Jan.–March,* pp. 1–18 (mimeograph).

—— (1964b). *F.A.O. Plant Prot. Committee for SE Asia and Pacific Reg. 3rd Q. Rep. 1964 July–Sept.,* pp. 1–15 (mimeograph).

—— (1965). *F.A.O. Plant Protection Committee for the SE Asia and Pacific Reg. 4th Q. Rep. 1964 Oct.–Dec.,* pp. 1–17 (mimeograph).

JOLY, P. (1964). *Le genre Alternaria.* Paul Lechevalier; Paris.

JONES, E. (1971). Control of black pod disease of cocoa in Trinidad: Preliminary report. *III intl Cocoa Res. Conf., Accra, Ghana 23–9 Nov. 1969,* pp. 447–51. Cocoa Research Institute; Tafo, Ghana.

JONES, E. W. (1953a). African Hepatics II. *Leptocolea* with hyaline-margined leaves. *Trans. Br. bryol. Soc.* **2**, 144–57.

—— (1953b). African Hepatics IV. The genus *Caudalejeunea. Trans. Br. bryol. Soc.* **2**, 164–71.

—— (1954). African Hepatics VII. The genus *Cheilolejeunea. Trans. Br. bryol. Soc.* **2**, 380–92.

—— (1962). African Hepatics XV. *Plagiochila* in Tropical Africa. *Trans. Br. bryol. Soc.* **4**, 254–325.

—— (1969). African Hepatics XXI. *Microlejeunea, Chaetolejeunea, Pleurolejeunea. Trans. Br. bryol. Soc.* **5**, 775–89.

JONES, T. S. (1970). *Mammalian cocoa pests in Sierra Leone.* Mimeograph report; pp. 1–3.

JOUBERT, J. J. and RIJKENBERG, F. H. J. (1971). Parasitic green algae. *Annual Rev. Phytopath.* **9**, 45–64. Annual Reviews Inc.; Palo Alto, California.

JUMELLE, H. (1900). *Le Cacaoyer, sa culture et son exploitation dans tous les pays de production.* Paris.

KADEN, O. F. (1933). Untersuchungsergebnisse über nichparasitäre kakaokrankheiten in San Tomé und Principe. *Tropenpflanzer* **36**, 321–40.

KAMPEN, M. D. (1972). *The sculptures of El Tajin Veracruz, Mexico.* University of Florida Press; Gainesville, U.S.A.

KAPLAN, L., LYNCH, T. F. and SMITH, C. E. (1973). Early cultivated beans

(*Phaseolus vulgaris*) from an intermontane Peruvian valley. *Science, N.Y.* **179**, 76–7.

KAY, D. (1959). Studies on 'dieback' of cacao. *Ann. Rep. W. Afr. Cocoa Res. Inst. 1957–8*, pp. 69–73.

—— (1961). Dieback of cocoa. *Tech. Bull. W. Afr. Cocoa Res. Inst.* **8**, 1–20.

KEANE, P. J. (1971). Vascular-streak dieback of cocoa in West Malaysia. *Rep. of Visit to W. Malaysia 26/9/71–6/10/71* (mimeograph), pp. 1–4.

——, FLENTJE, N. J. and LAMB, K. P. (1971). Vascular-streak dieback of cocoa in Papua, New Guinea. *Univ. Papua and New Guinea Dept Biol. Occasional Papers* **1**, 1–13.

——, —— and —— (1972). Investigation of vascular-streak dieback of cocoa in Papua. New Guinea. *Aust. J. biol. Sci.* **25**, 553–64.

—— and TURNER, P. D. (1972). Vascular-streak dieback of cocoa in West Malaysia. In: Cocoa and Coconuts in Malaysia. *Proc. Conf. Kuala Lumpur 25–7 Nov. 1971*, ed. R. L. Wastie and D. A. Earp, pp. 50–7. The Incorporated Society of Planters; Kuala Lumpur, Malaysia.

KEAY, R. W. J. (1958). *Flora of West Tropical Africa* vol. I. Part 2 (rev. 2nd ed.). Crown Agents; London.

KENTEN, R. H. (1972a). Virus diseases of tropical crops. Cocoa necrosis virus (CNV). *Rothamsted exp. Stn Rep 1971. Part I*, p. 130.

—— (1972b). The purification and some properties of cocoa necrosis virus, a serotype of tomato black ring virus. *Ann. appl. Biol.* **71**, 119–26.

—— and LEGG, J. T. (1965). Observations on the purification and properties of cocoa swollen-shoot virus. *Ghana J. Sci.* **5**, 221–5.

—— and —— (1967). Some properties of cocoa mottle-leaf virus. *Jnl gen. Virol.* **1**, 465–70.

—— and —— (1968a). Purification and properties of cocoa swollen-shoot virus (CSSV) and cocoa mottle-leaf virus (CMLV). *Ann. Rep. C.R.I.G. 1965–6*, pp. 23–4.

—— and —— (1968b). Purification and properties of cocoa virus. *Ann. Rep. C.R.I.G. 1966–7*, p. 22.

—— and —— (1971a). Varietal resistance of cocoa to swollen-shoot disease in West Africa. *Pl. Prot. Bull. F.A.O.* **19**, 1–11.

—— and —— (1971b). Serological relationships of some viruses from cocoa (*Theobroma cacao* L.) in Ghana. *Ann. appl. Biol.* **67**, 195–200.

—— and OWUSU, G. K. (1970). Cocoa necrosis virus. *Ann. Rep. C.R.I.G. 1968–9*, p. 35.

KERRICH, G. J. (1953). Report on Encyrtidae associated with mealybugs on cacao in Trinidad and on some other species related thereto. *Bull. ent. Res.* **44**, 789–810.

—— (1967). On the classification of the Anagyrine Encyrtidae, with a revision of some of the genera (Hymenoptera: Chaloidoidea). *Bull. Br. Mus. nat. Hist. Ent.* **20**, 141–250.

KEVORKIAN, A. G. (1951). The cushion-gall disease of cacao. *Phytopathology* **41**, 562–3.

KING, B. and EGGINS, H. O. W. (1972). Some observations on decay mechanisms of microfungi deteriorating wood. In: *Biodeterioration of materials* ed. A. H.

Walters and E. H. Hueck-van der Plas, Vol. 2: pp. 145–51. Applied Science Publishers Ltd; London.

KING, J. L. (1971). *Cihuatlán y Tepecoacuilco; provincias tributarias de México en el siglo XVI*. Universidad Nacional Autónoma de México, Institute de Investigaciones Históricas; México.

KIRBY, A. H. M. (1973). Progress in the control of orchard pests by integrated methods. *Hort. Abstr.* **431**, 1–16.

KIRKPATRICK, T. W. (1950). Insect transmission of cacao virus disease in Trinidad. *Bull. ent. Res.* **41**, 99–117.

—— (1953*a*). Insect pests of cacao and insect vectors of cacao virus disease. *Rep. Cacao Res. 1945–51*, pp. 122–5. Imperial College of Tropical Agriculture; St. Augustine, Trinidad.

—— (1953*b*). Notes on minor insect pests of cacao in Trinidad. *Rep. Cacao Res. 1952*, pp. 62–71. Imperial College of Tropical Agriculture; St. Augustine, Trinidad.

KITCHING, R. A. (1954). Cocoa in British Guiana. *Fm Jl. Br. Guiana* **17**, 47–51.

KNIGHT, R. and ROGERS, H. H. (1955). Recent introductions to West Africa of *Theobroma cacao* and related species. I. A review of the first ten years. *Emp. J. exp. Agric.* **23**, 113–25.

—— and TINSLEY, T. W. (1958). Some histological observations on virus-infected *Theobroma cacao* L. *Ann. appl. Biol.* **46**, 7–10.

KNOKE, J. K. (1965). Relatório sobre uma viagem de estudos entomológicos realizada à regiao cacaueira de Bahia-Brasil. *CEPLAC Comunicado ao pessoal técnico* **12**, 1–12.

—— and SAUNDERS, J. L. (1966). Induced fruit set of *Theobroma cacao* by mist-blower application of insecticides. *J. econ. Ent.* **59**, 1427–30.

KRUG, C. A. and QUARTEY-PAPAFIO, E. (1964). World cocoa survey. *F.A.O. agric. Stud.* **63**, 1–242.

KRUPASAGAR, V. and SEQUEIRA, L. (1969). Auxin destruction by *Marasmius perniciosus*. *Am. J. Bot.* **56**, 390–7.

KUIJT, J. (1969). *The biology of parasitic flowering plants*. University of California Press; Berkeley, California.

KUMAR, A. C., VISWANATHAN, P. R. K. and D'SOUZA, G. I. (1971). A study on plant parasitic nematodes of certain commercial crops in coffee tracts of South India. *Indian Coff.* **35**, 222–4.

LAMB, J. (1957). In discussion of the effect of BHC on the heleid midge. *Rep. Cocoa Conf. Grosvenor House, London, W.1, 10th–12th Sept. 1957*, p. 69. Cocoa, Chocolate and Confectionery Alliance; London.

LARTER, L. N. H. and MARTYN, E. B. (1943). Preliminary list of plant diseases in Jamaica. *Mycol. Pap.* **8**, 1–16.

LASS, R. A. (1970). Cocoa in Ecuador. *Cocoa Growers' Bull.* **14**, 8–15.

—— and EGBE, N. E. (1972). Cocoa in Nigeria. *Cocoa Growers' Bull.* **18**, 5–13.

LAST, F. T. and DEIGHTON, F. C. (1965). The non-parasitic microflora on the surfaces of living leaves. *Trans. Br. mycol. Soc.* **48**, 83–99.

LAVABRE, E. M., PIART, J. and NGUYEN BAN, J. (1965). Résultats des essais d'insecticides en laboratoire et en plein champ contre les mirides des cacaoyers. *Conf. intle Rech. agron. cacaoyères Abidjan 15–20 nov. 1965*, pp. 143–8.

LAVIOLA, Cesare (1972). Discussion group 'Cytology and Genetics of the genus Phytophthora'. *Int. Newsletter Pl. Path.* **2**.

LAYCOCK, D. H. (1945). Preliminary investigations into the endotropic mycorrhiza of *Theobroma cacao* L. *Trop. Agric., Trin.* **22**, 77–80.

LEACH, J. R., SHEPHERD, R. and TURNER, P. D. (1971). Underplanting coconuts with cocoa in West Malaysia. Part 2—Maintenance. *Cocoa Growers' Bull.* **17**, 5–10.

LEACH, R. (1937). Observations on the parasitism and control of *Armillaria mellea. Proc. R. Soc. B,* **121**, 561–73.

—— (1939). Biological control and ecology of *Armillaria mellea* (Vahl.) Fr. *Trans. Br. mycol. Soc.* **23**, 320–29.

LEAKEY, C. L. A. (1965). Sudden death disease of cacao in Uganda associated with Verticillium dahliae Kleb. *E. Afr. agric. For. J.* **31**, 21–4.

LEATHER, R. I. (1961). Plant pathology. *Bull. Minist. Agric. Lds Jamaica 1960–1* **60** (new Ser.), 42–8.

—— (1967). A catalogue of some plant diseases and fungi in Jamaica. *Bull. Minist. Agric. Lds Jamaica* **61** (New Ser.), 1–92.

LEBEN, C. (1965). Epiphytic microorganisms in relation to plant disease. In: *Annual Review of Phytopathology* vol. 3, ed. J. G. Horsfall and K. F. Baker, pp. 209–30. Annual Reviews, Inc.; Palo Alto, California.

LEFTWICH, A. W. (1973). *A dictionary of zoology.* 3rd ed. Constable and Co. Ltd.; London.

LEGG, J. T. (1972). Measures to control spread of cocoa swollen-shoot disease in Ghana. *Pest Artic. & News Summ.* (PANS) **18**, 57–60.

—— and AGBODJAN, F. X. (1969). Swollen-shoot disease. *Ann. Rep. C.R.I.G. 1967–8,* pp. 23 and 25.

—— and BONNEY, J. K. (1966). Classification and comparison of isolate. *C.R.I.G. Rep. 1963–5,* pp. 27–9.

—— and —— (1967). The host range and vector species of viruses from *Cola chlamydantha* K. Schum., *Adansonia digitata* L., and *Theobroma cacao* L. *Ann. appl. Biol.* **60**, 399–403.

—— and —— (1968a). Classification and comparison of isolates. *Ann. Rep. C.R.I.G. 1965–6,* p. 30.

—— and —— (1968b). Insect transmission studies. *Ann. Rep. C.R.I.G. 1965–6,* pp. 30–1.

—— and —— (1968c). Classification and comparison of isolates. *Ann. Rep. C.R.I.G. 1966–7,* p. 27.

—— and KENTEN, R. H. (1968). Some observations on cocoa trees tolerant to cocoa swollen-shoot virus. *Trop. Agric., Trin.* **45**, 61–5.

—— and —— (1971a). Selection of cocoa progenies resistant to and tolerant of cocoa swollen-shoot virus. III *Intl Cocoa Res. Conf. Accra, Ghana 23–9 Nov. 1969,* pp. 503–11.

—— and —— (1971b). Field experiments on the resistance of cocoa to cocoa swollen-shoot virus. *Ann. appl. Biol.* **67**, 369–75.

—— and LOVI, N. K. (1968). Search for local lesion host of swollen-shoot virus. *Ann. Rep. C.R.I.G. 1966–7,* pp. 22–4.

—— and —— (1969). Search for local lesion host of swollen-shoot virus. *Ann. Rep. C.R.I.G. 1967–8,* p. 29.

LELLIS, W. T. (1952). *Temperaturas como factor limitante 'podriadão parda' dos frutos do cacaueiro*, pp. 1–14. *Instituto de Cacau de Bahia*; Brasil.

—— and FILHO, O.P. (1957). Comparison between fungicides in the control of cocoa brown pod rot (black pod disease). *Rep. Cocoa Conf. Grosvenor House, London, W.1, 10th–12th Sept. 1957*, pp. 78–80. Cocoa, Chocolate and Confectionery Alliance; London.

LEMS, G. (1965). Cacao selection and breeding in Suriname. *Proc. Cong. agric. Res. in the Guianas Paramaribo Nov. 27th–Dec. 3rd 1963*, pp. 27–37. (Bull. **82**, Agricultural Experiment Station, Paramaribo, Surinam.)

—— (1967). Gegevens over drie legitieme cacao families. *Surin. Landb.* **15**, 11–22.

LENT, R. (1966). The origin of the cauliflorous inflorescence of *Theobroma cacao*. *Turrialba* **16**, 352–8.

LE PELLEY, R. H. (1943). An oriental mealybug (*Pseudococcus lilacinus* Ckll.) (Hemiptera) and its insect enemies. *Trans. R. ent. Soc. Lond.* **93**, 73–93.

—— (1968). *Pests of coffee*, Longmans, Green and Co. Ltd.; London.

LEPPIK, E. E. (1970). Gene centers of plants as sources of disease resistance. In: *Annual Review of Phytopathology*, ed. J. G. Horsfall and K. F. Baker; vol. 8, pp. 323–44. Annual Reviews Inc.; Palo Alto, California.

LESTON, D. (1970*a*). Entomology of the cocoa farm. *Annual Review of Entomology* **15**, 273–94. Annual Reviews Inc.; Palo Alto, California.

—— (1970*b*). Incidence of thread blights on cocoa in Ghana. *Pest Artic. & News Summ.* (PANS) **16**, 516–17.

—— (1971). Ants, capsids and swollen-shoot in Ghana: Interactions and the implications for pest control. *III intl Cocoa Res. Conf., Accra, Ghana 23–9 Nov. 1969*, pp. 205–21.

—— and GIBBS, D. G. (1969). Seasons and cocoa insect cycles. *C.R.I.G. Ann. Rep. 1967–8*, pp. 61–3.

LEWTON-BRAIN, L. (1905). Fungoid diseases of cacao. *Trop. Agric. Mag. Ceylon agric. Soc.* **25**, 470–3.

LIEFSTINGH, G. (1966). Is chemical clearing a possibility? *Cocoa Growers' Bull.* **6**, 12–16.

LIMÓN, B. (1945). Algunas enfermedades fungosas del cacaotero en Tabasco. *Fitofilo* **4**, 193–239.

LINDEBERG, G. (1948*a*). On the occurrence of polyphenol oxidases in soil-inhabiting Basidiomycetes. *Physiol. Plant.* **1**, 196–205.

—— (1948*b*). Some properties of the catecholases of litter-decomposing and parasitic Hymenomycetes. *Physiol. Plant.* **1**, 401–9.

—— and MOLIN, K. (1949). Notes on the physiology of the cacao parasite *Marasmius perniciosus*. *Physiol. Plant.* **2**, 138–44.

LINTON, R. D. (1950). Swollen-shoot control in other areas and rehabilitation progress in general. *Rep. Cocoa Conf. Grosvenor House, London, W.1, 13th–14th Sept. 1950*, pp. 11–13. Cocoa, Chocolate and Confectionery Alliance; London.

LISTER, R. M. (1953). Search for new vectors. *Ann. Rep. W. Afr. Cacao Res. Inst. 1952–3*, pp. 9–10.

—— and THRESH, J. M. (1954). Mealybug vectors. *Ann. Rep. W. Afr. Cacao Res. Inst. 1953–4*, p. 13.

LITZENBERGER, S. C. and STEVENSON, J. A. (1957). A preliminary list of Nicaraguan plant diseases. *Pl. Dis. Reptr Suppl.* **243**, 1–19.

LIZER, C. (1914). Quelques notes por servir de complément au recueil de Mr. L. Herman-Merck sur 'Les parasites végétaux des plantes cultivées en Argentine et dans les regions limitrophes'. *An. Soc. cient. Argent.* **78**, 5–17. (Footnote to title, on p. 5: 'Extrait des Anales del Museo de historia natural de Buenos Aires tome XXVI pp. 163–225 Aout. 1914'.)

LOCK, R. H. (1904). On the varieties of cacao existing in the Royal Botanic Gardens and Experiment Station at Peradeniya. *Circ. agric. J. R. bot. Gdns Peradeniya* **2**, 385–406.

—— (1911). Report on experiments in manuring old cacao, carried out at the Experiment Station, Peradeniya, between 1903 and 1911. *Circ. agric. J.R. bot. Gdns Peradeniya* **6**, 51–82.

LOCKARD, R. G. and ASOMANING, E. J. A. (1963). Physiology of cocoa. *Ann. Rep. W. Afr. Cocoa Res. Inst. 1961–2*, pp. 54–67.

—— and —— (1965). Mineral nutrition of cacao (*Theobroma cacao* L.) IV. Effects of nitrate and urea nitrogen on deficiency symptoms of phosphorus, potassium, calcium and magnesium in sand culture. *Trop. Agric., Trin.* **42**, 55–62.

—— and BURRIDGE, J. C. (1965a). The levels of manganese, sodium, aluminium, iron, boron, zinc and copper in the leaves of cacao (*Theobroma cacao* L.) as affected by shade, fertilizer, irrigation and season. *Ann. Bot. N.S.*, **29**, 283–92.

—— and —— (1965b). The levels of macro- and micro-nutrients in the beans of cacao (*Theobroma cacao* L.) in relation to shade, fertilizer, irrigation and season. *Ann. Bot. N.S.* **29**, 377–82.

——, VAMATHEVAN, P. and THAMBOO, S. (1959a). Mineral deficiency symptoms of cacao grown in sand-culture. *Bull. Dept Agric. F.M.S.* **107**.

——, —— and —— (1959b). Swellings on the shoots of cacao plants deficient in copper. *Nature, Lond.* **184**, 75–6.

LOCKWOOD, G. (1971). Incidence of cacao black pod disease (*Phytophthora palmivora*) in relation to time of crop maturity in the Eastern Region of Ghana. *J. hort. Sci.* **46**, 185–93.

—— (1973). Effects of Ghanaian cocoa swollen-shoot virus on young bearing trees of a range of varieties. *Ex. Agric.* **9**, 31–9.

LODOS, N. and BOAFO, E. O. (1968). Studies of ants associated with mealybugs and virus vector investigations. *Ann. Rep. C.R.I.G. 1966–7*, p. 38.

LONGWORTH, J. F. (1960). Cushion gall. *Ann. Rep. W. Afr. Cocoa Res. Inst. 1958–9*, pp. 77–8.

—— (1961). Tolerance of cocoa to swollen-shoot disease in Nigeria. *Rep. Cocoa Conf. Grosvenor House, London, W.1, 12th–14th Sept. 1961*, pp. 145–7. Cocoa, Chocolate and Confectionery Alliance; London.

—— (1963). The effect of swollen-shoot disease on mature cocoa in Nigeria. *Trop. Agric. Trin.* **40**, 275–83.

—— (1964a). Virus tolerance. *Ann. Rept. W. Afr. Cocoa Res. Inst. (Nigeria) 1962–3*, pp. 26–7.

—— (1964b). The preference shown by *P. njalensis* and *F. virgata* for different sites, and its effect on their efficiency as vectors. *Ann. Rep. W. Afr. Cocoa Res. Inst. (Nigeria) 1962–3*, pp. 29–30.

—— (1965). The effect of light on transmission of cocoa swollen-shoot virus by insects and by mechanical methods. *Ann. Rep. W. Afr. Cocoa Res. Inst. (Nigeria) 1963–4*, p. 46.

——, ARE, L. A. and FREEMAN, G. H. (1965). Problems in assessment of the response of cacao progenies (*Theobroma cacao* L.) to infection with swollen-shoot virus in Nigeria. *Nigerian agric. J.* **2**, 1–6.

—— and ENTWISTLE, P. F. (1965). Virus/vector relationships. *Ann. Rep. W. Afr. Cocoa Res. Inst. (Nigeria) 1963–4*, pp. 40–3.

—— and THRESH, J. M. (1963a). The reaction of different cacao types to infection with swollen-shoot virus. *Ann. appl. Biol.* **52**, 117–124.

—— and —— (1963b). Field trials on the effect of a Nigerian swollen-shoot virus on the growth of different cacao types. *Ann. appl. Biol.* **52**, 217–24.

—— and —— (1964). Supplementary note on tolerance to cacao swollen-shoot virus in Nigeria. *Ann. appl. Biol.* **53**, 343–4.

LÓPEZ, R. F. (1954). Fisiologia de la germinación de esporos de Monilia sp. *Cacao Colomb.* **3**, 183–207.

LORDELLO, L. G. E. (1968). Nematóides associados a uma doença do cacaueiro. *Revta Agric. S. Paulo* **43**, 154.

LOSADA, S. B. (1958). Agallas hiperplasias en los meristemos florales del cacao. *Sépt. Conf. interamer. de Cacao, Palmira, Colombia 13–19 de Julio de 1958*, pp. 159–62. Ministerio de Agricultura de Colombia Division de Investigaciones Agropecuarias (D.I.A.).

LOTHROP, S. K. (1927). The word 'Maya' and the fourth voyage of Columbus. *Indian Notes* **4**, 350–63.

—— (1952). Metals from the Cenote of Sacrifice Chichen Itza, Yucatan. *Mem. Peabody Mus. Harv. U.* **10**.

LOWY, B. (1952). The genus Auricularia. *Mycologia* **44**, 656–92.

LUC, M. (1952). Ophiostoma moniliforme (Hedgc.) H. & P. Syd. et ses diverses formes. *Rev. Mycol. 17 Suppl. Coloniale* **1**, 10–16.

—— and DE GUIRAN, G. (1960). Les nématodes associés aux plantes de l'Ouest Africain. Liste préliminaire. *Agron. trop., Nogent* **15**, 434–49.

—— and —— (1962). Deux nouveaux *Paratylenchus* (*Nematoda-Criconematidae*) de Côte d'Ivoire. *Nematologica* **7**, 133–8.

LUDWIGS, K. (1920). Wurzelpilze an Kakao.-Kakaoverjüngung. *Tropenpflanzer* **23**, 167–73.

—— (1934). Hexenbesen an kakaobäumen. *Tropenpflanzer* **37**, 198–203.

LUTZ, L. (1906). Trois champignons nouveaux de l'Afrique Occidentale. *Bull. Soc. bot. Fr.* **53**, 48–52 (as xlviii–lii).

MACFARLANE, Helen, H. (1968). Review of Applied Mycology. Compiled from world literature on plant pathology. Plant Host—Pathogen Index to Volumes 1–40 (1922–61). Commonwealth Mycological Institute; Kew.

MACFIE, J. W. S. (1944). Ceratopogonidae collected in Trinidad from cacao flowers. *Bull. ent. Res.* **35**, 297–300.

MACKENZIE, A. F. (1952). Proceedings of the Scientific Meeting held on Tuesday, June 10th, 1952. *Agenda Abst. of sci. Meetings of Zool. Soc. Lond. 1952*; **5**, 1–2.

MALAGUTI, G. (1952). *Ceratostomella Fimbriata* en el cacao de Venezuela. *Acta cient. venez.* **3**, 94–7.

—— (1958a). Observaciones sobre la enfermedad necrosis del tronco de cacao por *Ceratostomella fimbriata* en Venezuela. *Sépt. Conf. Interamer. de Cacao, Palmira, Colombia, 13–19 de julio de 1958*, pp. 80–5.

—— (1958*b*). Primeras observaciones sobre la 'buba' o 'agallas' del cacao en Venezuela. *Agronomía trop. Venezuela*, **8** 115–20.

—— (1959). La buba o 'agallas' de cacao. *Agricultura venez.* **23**, 8–9.

—— (1963). Plant disease situation in Venezuela during 1962. *Pl. Prot. Bull. F.A.O.* **11**, 43–5.

—— and DE REYES, Lilian C. (1964). A gall disease of cacao and mango in Venezuela caused by Calonectria rigidiuscula. *Phytopathology* **54**, 499.

—— and SIROTTI, L. (1952). Podredumbre de la corteza de los bucares (Erythrina spp.) y del cacao (Theobroma cacao) en Venezuela. *Agronomía trop. Venezuela* **2**, 41–53.

MALLAMAIRE, A. (1935*a*). Sur quelques pourridiés en Côte d'Ivoire. *Revue Bot. appl. Agric. trop.* **15**, 603–8.

—— (1935*b*). French West Africa: diseases of plants cultivated in the Ivory Coast. *Intl Bull. Plant Prot.* **9**, 198–200.

MANÇO, G. R. and MEDEIROS, A. G. (1969). Considerações sôbre a 'morte súbita' do cacaueiro na Bahia. *Mem. sec. Conf. Intl de Pesquisas em Cacau 19 a 26 de Nov. de 1967*, pp. 237–40. São Paulo, Brazil.

MANGENOT, G., ALIBERT, H. and BASSET, A. (1946*a*). Sur les caracteres du 'swollen-shoot' en Côte-d'Ivoire. *Revue int. Bot. appl. Agric. trop.* **26**, 173–84.

——, —— and —— (1946*b*). Sur les lesions caracteristiques du 'swollen-shoot' en Côte d'Ivoire. *C.R. hebd. Séanc. Acad. Sci., Paris* **222**, 749–51.

MANN, H. H. and HUTCHINSON, C. M. (1904). Red rust: A serious blight of the tea plant. *Indian Tea Ass. 1904*, **4** (2nd ed.), pp. 1–26.

—— and —— (1907). *Cephaleuros virescens*, Kunze: The 'red rust' of tea. *Mem. Dept Agric. India, Bot. Ser.* **1**, 1–35.

MAPOTHER, H. R. (1955). Arboricides. *Ann. Rep. W. Afr. Cocoa Res. Inst. 1954–5*, pp. 88–9.

MARAITE, H. (1972). Qualitative and quantitative changes induced in the polyphenoloxidases and peroxidases of plants by several ecological factors. In: *Phytotoxins in plant diseases*, ed. R. K. S. Wood, A. Ballio and A. Graniti, pp. 479–80. Academic Press Inc.; London.

MARCHART, H. (1969*a*). Field trials with Baygon. *Ann. Rep. C.R.I.G. 1967–8*, p. 74.

—— (1969*b*). Side effects of Baygon (arprocarb). *Ann. Rep. C.R.I.G. 1967–8*, 74–5.

—— (1971*a*). Chemical control of cocoa capsids: Alternatives to lindane. *III intl Cocoa Res. Conf., Accra, Ghana 23–9 Nov. 1969*, pp. 173–85.

—— (1971*b*). Ants, capsids and swollen-shoot: a reply to D. Leston. *III intl Cocoa Res. Conf., Accra, Ghana 23–9 Nov. 1969*, 235–6.

—— and LESTON, D. (1968). Radioisotope tagging experiments. *Ann. Rep. C.R.I.G. 1965–6*, pp. 52–4.

—— and —— (1969). Predators of *Distantiella theobroma*. *Ann. Rep. C.R.I.G. 1967–8*, pp. 63–5.

—— and LODOS, N. (1969). The biology and insecticidal control of the cocoa pod pentatomid *Bathycoelia thalassina* (Herrich-Schaeffer) (Hemiptera, Pentatomidae). *Ghana J. Agric. Sci.* **2**, 31–7.

MARQUINA, I. (1964). *Arquitectura prehispanica. Memorias del I.N.A.H. I*, 2nd ed. Instituto Nacional de Antropologia e Historia; Mexico.

MARTIN, H., ed. (1971). *Pesticide manual. Basic information on the chemicals used as active components of pesticides.* 2nd ed., pp. 1–495. British Crop Protection Council; Droitwich.

MARTIN, P. S. (1973). The discovery of America. *Science, N.Y.* **179**, 969–74.

MARTINI, C. K. H. (1959a). Insect transmission of cacao viruses. *Ann. Rept. W. Afr. Cocoa Res. Inst. 1957–8*, 68–9.

—— (1959b). Observations on 'chlorosis', 'leafless twig' and 'Paint brush' diseases in the British Cameroons. *Ann. Rep. W. Afr. Cocoa Res. Inst. 1957–8*, pp. 73–4.

—— (1960). Cocoa necrosis virus. *Ann. Rep. W. Afr. Cocoa Res. Inst. 1958–9*, pp. 67–8.

—— (1961). Transmission of Nigerian cocoa viruses. *Ann. Rep. W. Afr. Cocoa Res. Inst. 1959–60*, pp. 68–9.

—— (1962). Vectors of Nigerian cocoa viruses. *Ann. Rep. W. Afr. Cocoa Res. Inst. 1960–1*, pp. 75–6.

MARTYN, E. B. (1933). Preliminary list of diseases of economic plants in British Guiana. *Kew Bull.*, pp. 107–10.

—— (1968). Plant Virus Names. An annotated list of names and synonyms of plant viruses and diseases. *Phytopath. Pap.* **9**.

MARTYR, Peter (1612). *De novo orbe, or the historie of the West Indies.* London.

MASKELL, E. J., EVANS, H. and MURRAY, D. B. (1953). The symptoms of nutritional deficiencies in cacao produced in sand and water cultures. *Rep. Cacao Res. 1945–51*, 53–64. Imperial College of Tropical Agriculture; St. Augustine, Trinidad.

MASON, E. W. (1933). *Annotated account of fungi received at the Imperial Mycological Institute* list II (fasc. 2), pp. 1–67. Imperial Mycological Institute (now Commonwealth Mycological Institute); Kew.

MASSEE, G. (1899). Cacao disease in Trinidad. *Kew Bull.*, pp. 1–6.

—— (1906). *Fungi exotici* V. *Kew Bull.*, pp. 255–8.

—— (1907). Additions to the wild fauna and flora of the Royal Botanic Gardens Kew: IV. New and additional species of fungi. *Kew Bull.*, pp. 238–44.

—— (1908). *Fungi exotici* VIII. *Kew Bull.*, pp. 216–19.

—— (1910). *Fungi exotici* X. *Kew Bull.*, pp. 1–6.

MASSIGLI, R. and CADOGAN, A. (1930). Exchange of notes between His Majesty's Government in the United Kingdom and the French Government regarding the boundary between the British and French Mandated Territories of Togoland. *Treaty Ser.* **45** (*1930*) *Cmd. 3713*, pp. 1–62 and map. H.M.S.O.; London.

MAUBLANC, C. (1909). Les maladies des plantes cultivées dans les pays chauds. Maladies du Cacaoyer. *Agriculture prat. Pays chauds 9ᵉ Année* **79**, 314–24.

MAUNY, R. (1953). Notes historiques autour des principales plantes cultivées d'Afrique occidentale. *Bull. Inst. fr. Afr. noire* **15**, 684–730.

MAYNÉ, R. (1917). Insectes et autres animaux attaquant le cacaoyer au Congo Belge. *Étud. Biol. agric.*, **3**, 1–80. Royaume de Belgique. Ministère des Colonies. Service de l'Agriculture.

—— and VERMOESEN, C. (1914). Le 'Sahlbergella singularis' et le chancre du cacaoyer au Mayumbe. *Bull. Agric. Congo Belge* **5**, 261–81.

McCREARY, C. W. R., McDONALD, J. A., MULLOON, V. I. and HARDY, F. (1943). The root system of cacao. *Trop. Agric., Trin.* **20**, 207–20.

McINTOSH, A. E. S. (1951). *Ann. Rep. Dept Agric. Malaya 1949*, pp. 1–87.

McKELVIE, A. D. (1955). Cherelle wilt. *Ann. Rep. W. Afr. Cocoa Res. Inst. 1954–5*, pp. 89–90.

—— (1956). Cherelle wilt of cacao I. Pod development and its relation to wilt. *J. exp. Bot.* **7**, 252–63.

—— (1957a). Physiology of fruiting. *Ann. Rep. W. Afr. Cocoa Res. Inst. 1955–6*, pp. 71–6.

—— (1957b). W.A.C.R.I. breeding material. *Proc. Cacao Breeding Conf. W.A.C.R.I., Tafo, Ghana, 1st–3rd Oct. 1956*, pp. 10–15.

—— (1960). Cherelle wilt of cacao II. Wilt in relation to yield. *J. exp. Bot.* **11**, 413–24.

McKENZIE, H. L. (1967). *Mealybugs of California with taxonomy, biology and control of North American species (Homoptera: Coccoidea: Pseudococcidae)*. University of California Press; Berkeley.

McLAUGHLIN, J. H. (1950a). Observations on cacao in Ecuador. *Cacao Inf. Bull.* **2**, 1–5.

—— (1950b). Observations on cacao in Peru. *Cacao Inf. Bull.* **2**, 3–4.

—— (1956). El *Phytophthora palmivora* Butl. y un insecto membrácido como causantes del cherelle wilt en Costa Rica. *Suelo tico* **9**, 167–75 (abstract in *Rev. appl. Mycol.* **35**, 753 (1956)).

MEDEIROS, A. G. (1965). Methodology of research to study resistance of cacao to *Phytophthora palmivora* (Butl.) Butl. *Conf. intle Rech. agron. cacaoyères. Abidjan 15–20 nov. 1965*, pp. 205–11.

—— and DE MELLO, J. W. (1969). Ocorréncia de *Phytophthora palmivora* (Butl.) Butl. em cacaueiros, no Espirito santo. *Mem. seg. Conf. intl de Pesquisas em Cacau 19–26 de Nov. de 1967*, pp. 246–8 São Paulo, Brazil.

MEIFFREN, M. (1949). 'Swollen-shoot', maladie du cacaoyer. *Agron. trop., Nogent* **4**, 563–78.

—— and BRAUDEAU, J. (1963). Contribution a l'étude des cacaoyers de Guyane française. Essais d'inoculation de cabosses par *Phytophthora palmivora* Butl. *Café-Cacao-Thé* **7**, 113–18.

MEIKLEJOHN, Jane (1962). Microbiology of the nitrogen cycle in some Ghana soils. *Emp. J. exp. Agric.* **30**, 115–26.

METCALFE, C. R. and CHALK, L. (1950). *Anatomy of the dicotyledons.* Vol. I. Clarendon Press; Oxford.

MILNE, R. G. and KENTEN, R. H. (1970). Cocoa swollen-shoot virus. *Rep. Rothamsted exp. Stn. 1969*, Part 1, p. 146.

MIRANDA, F. (1962). Wild cacao in the Lacandona Forest, Chiapas, Mexico. *Cacao, Turrialba* **7**, 8.

MIRANDA, S. and DA CRUZ, H. M. (1953). Fighting brown pod rot disease in Bahia. *Rep. Cocoa Conf. Grosvenor House, London, W.1, 15th–17th Sept. 1953*, pp. 120–2. Cocoa, Chocolate and Confectionery Alliance; London.

MITCHELL, J. W., HUTCHINS, L. M. and MARTH, P. C. (1965). Effect of green-point gall extracts and some regulating substances on vegetative buds of cocoa plants. *Proc. Am. Soc. hort. Sci.* **87**, 187–93.

MOLINA, A. and DESROSIERS, R. (1965). La buba floral como factor limitante en la produccion de cacao cultivado a pleno sol. *Proc. Caribbean Reg. Amer. Soc. hort. Sci. XII ann. Meeting, Cagua, Venezuela, Oct. 25–31, 1964*, pp. 203–8.

MONOD, T. (1951). Un catalogue des plantes de Richard-Toll (Sénégal) en 1824. *Bull. Inst. fr. Afr. noire* **13**, 1281–98.

MONTSERIN, B. G. (1950). Subsidized rehabilitation with clonal cocoa. *Rep. Cocoa Conf. Grosvenor House, London, W.1, 13th–14th Sept. 1950*, pp. 31–7. Cocoa, Chocolate and Confectionery Alliance; London.

—— (1966). *Trinidad and Tobago administration report of the affairs of the Cocoa Board for the year 1962*, pp. 1–27. Government Printery; Trinidad and Tobago.

MORALES, M. E. and MATARRITA, A. A. (1961). El capsido del cacao y su importancia en el cultivo del cacao en Costa Rica. *El Cacaotero* **3**, 11–14.

MOREAU, C. and MOREAU, Mireille (1951). Sur quelques Hyphomycetes. *Bull. Soc. linn. Normandie, Sér.* **9**, 71–82.

MORENO, L. J. P., ZULETA, L. C. and LAURENT, A. (1968). *Manual para el cultivo del cacao*. Compania Nacional de Chocolates S.A., Cali; Colombia.

MORGAN-JONES, G. (1967a). *Ceratocystis fimbriata. C.M.I. Descriptions of pathogenic Fungi and Bacteria* **141**.

—— (1967b). *Ceratocystis moniliformis. C.M.I. Descriptions of pathogenic Fungi and Bacteria* **142**.

MORRIS, D. (1887). *Cacao : how to grow it and how to cure it*, pp. 1–42. Aston W. Gardner and Co; Kingston, Jamaica.

—— (1900). Cacao industry in Grenada. *W. Indian Bull.* **1**, 415–22.

MORTON, F. J. and SMITH, G. (1963). The genera *Scopulariopsis* Bainier, *Microascus* Zukal and *Doratomyces* Corda. *Mycol. Pap.* **86**, 1–96.

MORWOOD, R. B. (1956). A preliminary list of plant diseases in Fiji. *Agric. J. Colony of Fiji* **27**, 51–4.

MUIR, J. C. (1948). *Trinidad and Tobago administration report of the Director of Agriculture for the year 1946*, pp. 1–28.

MÜLLER, A. S. (1941). El reconocimiento de las enfermedades de las plantas cultivadas en Venezuela. *Boln Soc. venez. Cienc. nat.* **7**, 99–112.

—— (1950). A preliminary survey of plant diseases in Guatemala. *Pl. Dis. Reptr* **34**, 161–4.

MULLER, H. A. and NJOMOU, S. E. (1970). Contribution a la mise au point de la lutte chimique contre la pourriture brune des cabosses du cacaoyer (*Phytophthora palmivora* (Butl.) Butl.) au Cameroun. *Café-Cacao-Thé* **14**, 209–20.

MULLER, H. R. A. (1936). Het Phytophthora-voetrot van Peper (Piper nigrum L.) in Nederlandsche-Indië. *Meded. Inst. PlZiekt., Batavia* **88**, 73 (abstract in *Rev. appl. Mycol.* **16**, 559 (1937)).

MURRAY, D. B. (1953). The effect of mineral injections and hormone sprays on flower setting and fruit development in cacao. I. *Rep. Cacao Res. 1952*, pp. 22–6. Imperial College of Tropical Agriculture; St. Augustine, Trinidad.

—— (1959). Las Hermanas—the new sub-station. *Rep. Cacao Res. 1957–8*, pp. 36–8. Imperial College of Tropical Agriculture; St. Augustine, Trinidad.

—— (1964a). Administration. *Ann. Rep. Cacao Res. 1963*, pp. 9–14. Regional Research Centre, Imperial College of Tropical Agriculture, University of the West Indies. St. Augustine, Trinidad.

—— (1964b). Environmental factors and the growth of cocoa. *Cocoa Growers' Bull.* **3**, 8–11.

—— (1966). River Estate and Las Hermanas. *Ann. Rep. Cacao Res. 1965*, pp. 8–9; Regional Research Centre, Imperial College of Tropical Agriculture, University of the West Indies; St. Augustine, Trinidad.

—— (1967). Administration. *Ann. Rep. Cacao Res. 1966*, pp. 7–9. Regional Research Centre, Imperial College of Tropical Agriculture, University of the West Indies; St. Augustine, Trinidad.

—— (1968). *Report on a visit to Bolivia in April–May 1968*, pp. 1–21, mimeograph.

—— and NICHOLS, R. (1966). Light, shade and growth in some tropical plants. In *Light as an ecological factor, Symp. Br. ecol. Soc. Cambridge 30th March–1st April 1965*. Ed. R. Bainbridge, G. C. Evans and O. Rackham. pp. 249–61. Vol. 6, Blackwell Scientific Publications; Oxford.

—— and SWARBRICK, J. T. (1959). Heat treatment of cacao budwood with reference to cacao virus. *Rep. Cacao Res. 1957–8*, pp. 65–6. Imperial College of Tropical Agriculture. St. Augustine, Trinidad.

MYERS, J. G. (1930). Notes on wild cacao in Surinam and British Guiana. *Kew Bull.*, pp. 1–10.

—— (1934). Observations on wild cacao and wild bananas in British Guiana. *Trop. Agric., Trin.* **11**, 263–7.

NAUNDORF, G. (1952). Influencia de algunos fungicidas sobre fecundacion en el cacao. *Cacao Colomb.* **1**, 71–82.

—— (1954). Contribuciones el problema de la Moniliasis en cacao. *Cacao Colomb.* **3**, 35–61.

—— (1956). La relacion entre *Phytophthora faberi, Ophiostoma fimbriata, y Xyleborus* sp. *Cacao Colomb.* **5**, 35–6.

—— and MILLER, M. R. (1952). Influencia de algunos insecticidas sobre la fecundacion de cacao. *Cacao Colomb.* **1**, 87–8.

NAVEL, H. C. (1921). Les principaux ennemis du cacaoyer aux Iles de Sãn-Thomé et de Principe. *Rapp. sur une Miss. d'Étude agric. et phytopath.*, pp. 1–135. Émile Larose; Paris.

NEWHALL, A. G. (1948). Research at Turrialba on cacao diseases. *Cacao Inf. Bull.* **1**, 1–7.

—— (1969). Copper fungicides for the control of *Phytophthora* pod rot of cacao. *Mem. seg. Conf. intl de Pesquisas em Cacau 19–26 de Nov. 1967*, pp. 219–26, São Paulo, Brazil.

——, PAREDES, A. and SALAZAR, L. G. (1968). Control of *Phytophthora* pod rot on cacao with fungicides. Results of three experiments. *Cacao, Turrialba* **13**, 3–13.

NICHOLS, R. (1957). The growth substances of *Theobroma cacao*. I. *Rep. Cacao Res. 1955–6*, pp. 33–40. Imperial College of Tropical Agriculture; St. Augustine, Trinidad.

—— (1959a). The effect of gibberellic acid on cacao seedlings. *Rep. Cacao Res. 1957–8*, pp. 41–3. Imperial College of Tropical Agriculture; St. Augustine, Trinidad.

—— (1959b). The growth substances of *Theobroma cacao*. II. *Rep. Cacao Res. 1957–8*, pp. 44–7. Imperial College of Tropical Agriculture; St. Augustine, Trinidad.

—— (1960). Auxins of cacao and cherelle wilt. *VIII Inter-Amer. Cacao Conf., Trinidad and Tobago 15–25 June, 1960, Proc.,* pp. 100–8.

—— (1961*a*). Auxins of cacao and the mechanism which causes the physical symptoms of cherelle wilt. *Rep. Cacao Res. 1959–60,* pp. 14–17. Imperial College of Tropical Agriculture; St. Augustine, Trinidad.

—— (1961*b*). Copper and cacao I. Sand culture studies. *Rep. Cacao Res. 1959–60,* pp. 23–7. Imperial College of Tropical Agriculture; St. Augustine, Trinidad.

—— (1961*c*). Low-volume spraying experiments with copper on cocoa. *Rep. Cocoa Conf. Grosvenor House, London, W.1, 12th–14th Sept. 1961,* pp. 111–15. Cocoa, Chocolate and Confectionery Alliance; London.

—— (1961*d*). Xylem occlusions in the fruit of cacao (*Theobroma cacao*) and their relation to cherelle wilt. *Ann. Bot. N.S.* **25,** 463–75.

—— (1963). Effect of copper on cacao (*Theobroma cacao*). *XVIth internl Horticultural Cong., 1962; Brussels, Belgium; Aug. 31–Sept. 8,* pp. 497–507. Editions J. Duculot S.A., Gembloux, Belgium.

—— (1964*a*). Studies of fruit development of cacao (*Theobroma cacao*) in relation to cherelle wilt. I. Development of the pericarp. *Ann. Bot. N.S.,* **28,** 619–35.

—— (1964*b*). Plant physiology—development of the fruit; fruit thinning experiments. *Ann. Rep. Cacao Res. 1963,* pp. 36–42. University of the West Indies; Imperial College of Tropical Agriculture, Regional Research Centre, St. Augustine, Trinidad.

—— (1965*a*). Cherelle (fruit) wilt of cocoa. *Cocoa Growers' Bull.* **4,** 10–13.

—— (1965*b*). Studies of fruit development of cacao (*Theobroma cacao*) in relation to cherelle wilt II. Auxins and development of the seeds. *Ann. Bot. N.S.* **29,** 181–96.

—— (1965*c*). Studies of fruit development of cacao (*Theobroma cacao*) in relation to cherelle wilt. III. Effects of fruit-thinning. *Ann. Bot. N.S.* **29,** 197–203.

—— and WALMSLEY, D. (1965). Translocation of phosphorus-32 into wilting and healthy fruits of cacao (*Theobroma cacao*). *Pl. Soil* **23,** 149–60.

NICOL, J. (1953*a*). Progress of research on systemic insecticides at W.A.C.R.I. *Rep. Cocoa Conf. Grosvenor House, London, W.1, 15th–17th Sept. 1953,* pp.. 98–104. Cocoa, Chocolate and Confectionery Alliance; London.

—— (1953*b*). The control of mealybug vectors of cacao swollen-shoot virus. *Proc. W. Afr. intl Cacao Res. Conf. W. Afr. Cacao Res. Inst., Tafo, Gold Coast, 12th–16th Dec. 1953,* pp. 18–20.

——, OWEN, H. and STRICKLAND, A. H. (1950). Biological control of the mealybug vectors of swollen-shoot virus of cacao. *Nature, Lond.* **165,** 490.

NIXON, G. E. J. (1951). *The association of ants with aphids and coccids,* pp. 1–36. Commonwealth Institute of Entomology; London.

NIXON, H. L. and GIBBS, A. J. (1960). Electron microscope observations on the structure of turnip yellow mosaic virus. *J. molec. Biol.* **2,** 197–200.

—— and —— (1963). Cocoa yellow mosaic virus. *Rothamsted exp. Stn Rep. 1962,* p. 113.

NORRIS, D. M., BISHOP, W. O., KNOKE, J. K. and SAUNDERS, J. L. (1968). Further studies of factors which influence *Xyleborus* spp. Emergence and attack of *Theobroma cacao. Ann. ent. Soc. Am.* **61,** 852–6.

NORRIS, J. R. and CHAPMAN, Heather M. (1968). Classification of Azotobacters. In: *Identification methods for microbiologists,* ed. B. M. Gibbs and D. A. Shapton.

Part *B*, pp. 19–27. The Society for Applied Bacteriology technical Series 2. Academic Press Inc.; London.

Nosti, J. (1943). La utilización de Heveas empleadas como árboles de sombra. *Bol. agric. Terr. esp. Golfo do Guinea*, Part 1, pp. 7–25. (abstract in *Rev. appl. Mycol.* **24**, 140 (1945)).

—— (1953). *Cacao, Cafe y Te*. Salvat Editores, S.A.; Barcelona.

Nowell, W. (1923). *Diseases of crop-plants in the Lesser Antilles*, London; Published on behalf of the Imperial Department of Agriculture by the West India Committee.

Ocfemia, G. O. and Celino, M. S. (1933). A brown bark rot of cacao trunk. *Philipp. Agric.*, Ser. A **21**, 665–73.

Oechsli, L. P. (1957). Recent developments in the control of cocoa pests and diseases in Latin America. *Rep. Cocoa Conf. Grosvenor House, London, W.1, 10th–12th Sept. 1957*, pp. 71–7. Cocoa, Chocolate and Confectionery Alliance; London.

Okaisabor, E. K. (1965). Preliminary studies on the epidemiology of *Phytophthora palmivora* I. Outbreak of black pod disease of cocoa. *Nigerian agric. J.* **2**, 67–70.

—— (1968). An active fungal parasite of *Phytophthora palmivora*. *Pest Artic. & News Summ. (PANS)* Sec. *B*, **14**, 353–60.

—— (1969a). The influence of leaf litter on outbreaks of *Phytophthora* pod rot disease. *C.R.I.N. half-yearly Prog. Rep. (April-Sept. 1969)* **9**, 15–16.

—— (1969b). The incidence of primary inoculum of *Phytophthora* in splash-borne soil particles. *C.R.I.N. half-yearly Prog. Rep. (April–Sept. 1969)* **9**, 16–17.

—— (1970). Control of *Phytophthora* pod rot disease by soil treatment I. Assay of some soil fungicides. *Phytopath. Z.* **69**, 125–30.

Okusanya, B. A. M. (1965). Serology. *Ann. Rep. W. Afr. Cocoa Res. Inst. (Nigeria) 1963–4*, pp. 25–6.

—— (1968). Serology. *Ann. Rep. C.R.I.N. 1966–7*, pp. 69–70.

—— (1969). Cocoa swollen-shoot virus. *Ann. Rep. C.R.I.N. 1967–8*, pp. 88–94.

Olivieri, F. E. (1897). *Cacao planting and its cultivation (Theobroma cacao)*, pp. 1–28. Fair Play Typ; Port of Spain, Trinidad.

Onesirosan, P. T. (1971). The survival of *Phytophthora palmivora* in a cacao plantation during the dry season. *Phytopathology* **61**, 975–7.

Orejuela, C. G. (1939). Preliminares al estudio del chancro y la fusariosis del cacao. *Revta Fac. nac. Agron., Medellín* **1**, 64–118.

Orellana, R. G. (1955). Cacao diseases in Mexico, Nicaragua, Costa Rica and Jamaica. *Pl. Prot. Bull. F.A.O.* **4**, 35–7.

—— (1956a). Cocoa diseases in Haiti. *Pl. Prot. Bull. F.A.O.* **4**, 148–51.

—— (1956b). Occurrence of Monilia pod rot and other cacao diseases in Eastern Panama. *Pl. Prot. Bull. F.A.O.* **4**, 168–9.

—— (1959a). Variation in *Phytophthora palmivora* isolated from cacao and rubber. *Phytopathology* **49**, 210–13.

—— (1959b). Cushion gall of cacao in Ceylon. *Pl. Prot. Bull. F.A.O.* **7**, 53–4.

—— and Peiris, J. W. L. (1957). The swollen-shoot phase of the virus disease of cacao in Ceylon. *Pl. Prot. Bull. F.A.O.* **5**, 165–71.

—— and Som, R. K. (1957). Correlation between low temperature and incidence of *Phytophthora* pod rot of cacao in Ceylon. *Pl. Prot. Bull. F.A.O.* **6**, 6–8.

ORIAN, G. (1954). Fiji disease of sugar cane in Madagascar—Report on a mission by G. Orian, Plant Pathologist, Department of Agriculture, Mauritius, pp. 1–17 (mimeograph) (abstract in *Rev. appl. Mycol.* **34**, 107–8 (1955)).

ORTON WILLIAMS, K. J. (1972). *Meloidogyne javanica. Descriptions of plant-parasitic Nematodes* Set 1, **3**. St. Albans; Commonwealth Institute of Helminthology.

—— (1973*a*). *Meloidogyne incognita. Descriptions of plant-parasitic nematodes* Set 2, **18**. St. Albans; Commonwealth Institute of Helminthology.

—— (1973*b*). *Hoplolaimus galeatus. Descriptions of plant-parasitic Nematodes* Set 2, **24**. St. Albans; Commonwealth Institute of Helminthology.

—— and SIDDIQI, M. R. (1973). *Radopholus similis. Descriptions of plant-parasitic Nematodes* Set 2, **27**. St. Albans; Commonwealth Institute of Helminthology.

OWEN, H. (1951). Cacao pod diseases in West Africa. *Ann. appl. Biol.* **38**, 715–18.

—— (1956). Further observations on the pathogenicity of *Calonectria rigidiuscula* (Berk. & Br.) Sacc. to *Theobroma cacao* L. *Ann. appl. Biol.* **44**, 307–21.

OWUSU, G. K. (1969). Mechanical transmission studies. *Ann. Rep. C.R.I.G. 1967–8*, pp. 25–7,

—— (1971*a*). Availability of cocoa swollen-shoot virus to mealybugs from tolerant and sensitive cocoa. III *intl Cocoa Res. Conf. Accra, Ghana 23–9 Nov. 1969*, pp. 512–17.

—— (1971*b*). Cocoa necrosis virus in Ghana. *Trop. Agric., Trin.* **48**, 133–9.

PADWICK, G. W. (1956). Losses caused by plant diseases in the Colonies. *Phytopath. Pap.* **1**, 1–60.

PALM, B. (1932). Pflanzenkrankheiten aus Guatemala. *Z. Pflkrankh.* **42**, 11–17.

PARK, M. (1953). Discussion. The effect of temperature. *Rep. Cocoa Conf. Grosvenor House, London, W.1, 15th–17th Sept. 1953*, p. 122. Cocoa, Chocolate and Confectionery Alliance; London.

PARSONS, J. J. (1949). *Antioqueño colonization in western Colombia.* Ibero-American Ser., 32, University of California Press; Berkeley.

—— (1968). *Antioqueño colonization in Western Colombia.* Rev. ed., University of California Press (Regents of the University of California); Berkeley.

—— and DENEVAN, W. M. (1967). Pre-Columbian ridged fields. *Scient. Am.* **217**, 92–100.

PARSONS, L. A. (1969). *Bilbao, Guatemala; an archaeological study of the Pacific coast Cotzumalhualpa region.* Milwaukee Public Museum Publication in Anthropology **11**, vol. 2.

PATOUILLARD, N. (1918). Sur deux formes conidiennes de Poro-hydnés. *Bull. Soc. mycol. Fr.* **34**, 198–201.

—— (1921). Liste des champignons recueillis à San Thomé communiqués par M. de Seabra. *Bull. Soc. port. Sci. nat.* **9**, 35–9.

—— (1922*a*). Quelques champignons saprophytes des arbres à S. Thomé. In: Études sur les maladies et les parasites du cacaoyer et d'autres plantes cultivées à S. Thomé. *Mém. Soc. port. Sci. nat. Sér. zool.* **2**, 70–116.

—— (1922*b*). Quelques parasites du cacaoyer à San Thomé. In: Études sur les maladies et les parasites du cacaoyer et d'autres plantes cultivées à S. Thomé, by A. F. de Seabra. *Mém. Soc. port. Sci. Nat. Sér. zool.* **2**, 89–94.

PEARCE, S. C. and THOM, Jean M. S. (1951). A study of plot-size with Nigerian estate cacao. *J. hort. Sci.* **26**, 261–7.

PEGLER, D. N. and GIBSON, I. A. S. (1972a). Armillariella mellea. *C.M.I. Descriptions of pathogenic Fungi and Bacteria* **321**.

—— and —— (1972b). Poria hypobrunnea. *C.M.I. Descriptions of pathogenic Fungi and Bacteria* **322**.

—— and WATERSTON, J. M. (1968a). Phellinus noxius. *C.M.I. Descriptions of pathogenic Fungi and Bacteria* **195**.

—— and —— (1968b). Rigidoporus lignosus. *C.M.I. Descriptions of pathogenic Fungi and Bacteria* **198**.

PEIRIS, J. W. L. (1953). Departmental Notes, a virus disease of cacao in Ceylon. *Trop. Agric. Mag. Ceylon agric. Soc.* **109**, 135–8.

PEREGRINE, W. T. H. (1971). *Dept Agric. Brunei, ann. Rep. Plant Pathologist June–Dec., 1970*), pp. 1–15. (Mimeograph). Plant Pathology Laboratory; Bandar Seri Begawan.

—— (1972). *Dept Agric. Brunei, ann. Rep. Plant Pathologist 1971*, pp. 1–18. (Mimeograph.) Plant Pathology Laboratory; Bandar Seri Begawan.

PEREZ ARBELAEZ, E. (1937). *Manual del cacaotero Venezolano. Biblioteca del Agricultor Venezolano* Tomo I. Ministerio de Agricultura y Cria, Dirección Técnica; Caracas.

PERIES, O. S. and IRUGALBANDARA, Z. E. (1973). Histology of *Hevea* roots infected by *Fomes lignosus. Ann. appl. Biol.* **73**, 1–7.

PETCH, T. (1906). Descriptions of new Ceylon fungi. *Ann. R. bot. Gdns Peradeniya* **3**, 1–10.

—— (1909). New Ceylon fungi. *Ann. R. bot. Gdns Peradeniya* **4**, 299–307.

—— (1910a). A list of the Mycetozoa of Ceylon. *Ann. R. bot. Gdns Peradeniya* **4**, 309–71.

—— (1910b). Cacao and Hevea canker. Circ. agric. *J. R. bot. Gdns Peradeniya* **5** Part I, 143–62; Part II, 162–80.

—— (1915). Horse-hair blights. *Ann. R. bot. Gdns Peradeniya* **6**, 1–26.

—— (1917). Summary report on the work of the Botanical and Mycological Division, pp. 6–7. *Ceylon Administration Reports, 1916.* Part IV. *Education, Science and Art.*

—— (1918). Report on the work of the Botanical and Mycological Division, pp. 9–10. *Ceylon Administration Reports, 1917.* Part IV. *Education, Science and Art.*

—— (1920). Hypocreaceae Zeylanicae. *Ann. R. bot. Gdns, Peradeniya* **7**, 85–138.

—— (1922). Report on the work of the Division of Botany and Mycology, pp. 21–3. *Ceylon Administration Reports of 1921, Department of Agriculture, Report of the Director of Agriculture 1921. Annexures I.*

—— (1923). *The diseases of the tea bush.* Macmillan and Co. Ltd.; London.

—— (1924). Meristic variation in Loranthus. *Ann. R. bot. Gdns Peradeniya* **9**, 239–41.

—— (1925a). Additions to Ceylon fungi III. *Ann. R. bot. Gdns Peradeniya* **9**, 313–28.

—— (1925b). Epipogon nutans. *Ann. R. bot. Gdns Peradeniya* **9**, 339–47.

—— (1928a). Tropical root disease fungi. *Trans. Br. mycol. Soc.* **13**, 238–53.

—— (1928b). Fomes lignosus. *Tea Q.* **1**, 64–6 (abstract in *Rev. appl. Mycol.* **8**, 72 (1929)).

—— and BISBY, G. R. (1950). The fungi of Ceylon. *Peradeniya Manual* **6**, 1–111. Colombo; Government Publications Bureau.

PETERSON, D. G. and BOND, E. F. (1964). The control of cocoa mirids (Hemiptera: Miridae) in Ghana with low-volume applications of Carbaryl and Sumithion. *Proc. Conf. on Mirids and other Pests of Cacao, W.A.C.R.I. (N) 24th–27th March 1964*, pp. 18–25.

PETRAK, F. and DEIGHTON, F. C. (1952). Beiträge zur pilzflora von Sierra Leone. *Sydowia, Ser. II*, 6, 309–22.

PHAFF, H. J. (1970). Genus 3. *Sporobolomyces* Kluyver & van Niel. In: *The yeasts. A taxonomic study*. 2nd rev. enl. ed., ed. J. Lodder, pp. 831–62. North-Holland Publishing Co.; Amsterdam.

—— and AHEARN, D. G. (1970). Genus 7. *Rhodotorula* Harrison. In: *The yeasts. A taxonomic study*. 2nd rev. enl. ed., ed. J. Lodder, pp. 1187–223. North-Holland Publishing Co.; Amsterdam.

—— and FELL, J. W. (1970). Genus 3. *Cryptococcus* Kützing emend. Phaff & Spencer. In: *The yeasts. A taxonomic study*. 2nd rev. enl. ed., ed. J. Lodder, pp. 1088–145. North-Holland Publishing Co.; Amsterdam.

PIENING, L. J. (1962). A check list of fungi recorded from Ghana. *Ghana Ministr. Agric. Bull.* 2. Government Printer; Accra.

PIERRE-LOUIS, F. and DADAILLE, B. (1956). Les maladies du cacaoyer en Haiti. *Bull. agricole, Port-au-Prince, Haiti* 5, 1–7.

PIRES, J. M. and KOURY, Humberto M. (1959). Estudo de um trecho de mata de várzea próximo de Belém. *Bolm téc. Inst. agron. N.* 36, 3–44.

PITTENDRIGH, C. S. (1948). The Bromeliad–Anopheles–Malaria Complex in Trinidad. I The Bromeliad Flora. *Evolution, Lancaster, Pa.* 2, 58–89.

—— (1950a). The ecoclimatic divergence of *Anopheles bellator* and *A. homunculus. Evolution Lancaster, Pa.* 4, 43–63.

—— (1950b). The ecotopic specialization of *Anopheles homunculus*; and its relation to competition with *A. bellator. Evolution, Lancaster, Pa.* 4, 64–78.

—— (1950c). The quantitative evaluation of *Kerteszia* breeding grounds. *Amer. J. trop. Med. Hyg.* 30, 457–68.

POLANIA, R. (1957). Enfermedades del cacao (*Theobroma cacao* L.) en Colombia. *Acta agron., Palmira* 7, 1–70.

POPENOE, W. (1919). Batido and other Guatemalan beverages prepared from cacao. *Am. Anthrop., N.S.*, 21, 403–9.

PORTER, G. R. (1833). *The tropical agriculturist: a practical treatise on the cultivation and management of various productions suitable to tropical climates*. London.

POSNETTE, A. F. (1938). Incompatibility and pollination in cacao. Summary of dissertation submitted. *7th ann. Rep. Cacao Res. 1937*, pp. 19–20. Imperial College of Tropical Agriculture, St. Augustine; Trinidad.

—— (1940). Transmission of 'swollen-shoot' disease of cacao. *Trop. Agric., Trin.* 17, 98.

—— (1941). Swollen-shoot virus disease of cacao (Review of research work to November 1940). *Trop. Agric., Trin.* 18, 87–90.

—— (1942). Note on twinning cacao seedlings. *Trop. Agric., Trin.* 19, 146.

—— (1943a). Control measures against swollen-shoot virus disease of cacao. *Trop. Agric., Trin.* 20, 116–23.

—— (1943b). Cacao selection on the Gold Coast. *Trop. Agric., Trin.* 20, 149–55.

—— (1943c). The diagnosis of swollen-shoot disease of cacao. *Trop. Agric., Trin.* 21, 156–8. (Repr. from *Farm and Forest* 4 (1943)).

—— (1943*d*). Botany. *Rep. Cent. Cocoa Res. Stn, Tafo, [Gold Coast] 1938–42*, pp. 56–62.

—— (1943*e*). Resistance of *Theobroma cacao* to *Sahlbergella* spp. on the Gold Coast. *Bull. ent. Res.* **34**, 159–62.

—— (1944*a*). Virus diseases of cacao in Trinidad. *Trop. Agric., Trin.* **21**, 105–6.

—— (1944*b*). Pollination of cacao in Trinidad. *Trop. Agric., Trin.* **21**, 115–18.

—— (1945). Cacao virus research in West Africa. *Rep. Proc. Cocoa Res. Conf. Colonial Office May–June, 1945. Colonial* **192**, 114–17. H.M.S.O.; London.

—— (1947*a*). Use of seeds in the insect transmission of some plant viruses. *Nature, Lond.* **159**, 500–1.

—— (1947*b*). Virus diseases of cacao in West Africa. I. Cacao viruses 1A, 1B, 1C and 1D. *Ann. appl. Biol.* **34**, 388–402.

—— (1950*a*). The pollination of cacao in the Gold Coast. *J. hort. Sci.* **25**, 155–63.

—— (1950*b*). Virus diseases of cacao. *Ann. appl. Biol.* **37**, 131–2.

—— (1950*c*). Virus diseases of cacao in West Africa. VII. Virus transmission by different vector species. *Ann. appl. Biol.* **37**, 378–84.

—— (1951). Progeny trials with cacao in the Gold Coast. *Emp. J. exp. Agric.* **19**, 242–52.

—— (1953). Virus diseases of cacao in West Africa: The present position. *Rep. 13th intl hort. Cong., 1952*, pp. 1224–30. Royal Horticultural Society; London.

—— (1960). Some aspects of virus spread among plants by vectors. *Rep. 7th Commonwealth ent. Conf., 6th–15th July, 1960*, pp. 162–5. Commonwealth Institute of Entomology; London.

—— (1969). Tolerance of virus infection in crop plants. *Rev. appl. Mycol.* **48**, 113–18.

—— and ENTWISTLE, Helen M. (1957). The pollination of cocoa flowers. *Rep. Cocoa Conf. Grosvenor House, London, W.1, 10th–12th Sept. 1957*, pp. 66–9. Cocoa, Chocolate and Confectionery Alliance; London.

—— and PALMA, M. (1944). Observations on cacao on the Paria Peninsula, Venezuela. *Trop. Agric., Trin.* **21**, 130–2.

—— and ROBERTSON, N. F. (1950). Virus diseases of cacao in West Africa. VI. Vector investigations. *Ann. appl. Biol.* **37**, 363–77.

——, —— and TODD, J. McA. (1950). Virus diseases of cacao in West Africa. V. Alternative host plants. *Ann. appl. Biol.* **37**, 229–40.

—— and STRICKLAND, A. H. (1948). Virus diseases of cacao in West Africa. III. Technique of insect transmission. *Ann. appl. Biol.* **35**, 53–63.

—— and —— (1949). Parasitism of the mealybug vectors of swollen-shoot of cacao. *Nature, Lond.* **163**, 105.

—— and TODD, J. McA. (1951). Virus diseases of cacao in West Africa. VIII. The search for virus-resistant cacao. *Ann. appl. Biol.* **38**, 785–800.

POTTER, T. I. (1894). Report of Club Meeting, on March 2nd, 1894. *J. Trin. Fld Nat. Club* **2**, 2–3.

—— (1895). Report of Club Meeting, on 9th November, 1894. *J. Trin. Fld Nat. Club* **2**, 139–42.

POUND, F. J. (1932*a*). The genetic constitution of the cacao crop. *1st ann. Rep. Cacao Res. 1931*, pp. 10–24. Imperial College of Tropical Agriculture; St. Augustine, Trinidad.

—— (1932b). Studies of fruitfulness in cacao. I. A note on the abscission of the flower. *1st ann. Rep. Cacao Res. 1931*, pp. 24–5. Imperial College of Tropical Agriculture; St. Augustine, Trinidad.

—— (1932c). Studies of fruitfulness in cacao. II. Evidence for partial sterility. *1st ann. Rep. Cacao Res. 1931*, pp. 26–8. Imperial College of Tropical Agriculture; St. Augustine, Trinidad.

—— (1933a). The genetic constitution of the cacao crop. *2nd ann. Rep. Cacao Res. 1932*, pp. 9–25. Imperial College of Tropical Agriculture; St. Augustine, Trinidad.

—— (1933b). Note on the progeny of a single cacao tree. *2nd ann. Rep. Cacao Res. 1932*, pp. 25–6. Imperial College of Tropical Agriculture; St. Augustine, Trinidad.

—— (1933c). Criteria and methods of selection in cacao. *2nd ann. Rep. Cacao Res. 1932*, pp. 27–9. Imperial College of Tropical Agriculture; St. Augustine, Trinidad.

—— (1933d). Studies of fruitfulness in cacao. III. Factors affecting fruit setting. *2nd ann. Rep. Cacao Res. 1932*, pp. 29–36. Imperial College of Tropical Agriculture; St. Augustine, Trinidad.

—— (1934). The progress of selection, 1933. *3rd ann. Rep. Cacao Res. 1933*, pp. 25–8. Imperial College of Tropical Agriculture; St. Augustine, Trinidad.

—— (1935a). The progress of selection, 1934. *4th ann. Rep. Cacao Res. 1934*, pp. 7–11. Imperial College of Tropical Agriculture; St. Augustine, Trinidad.

—— (1935b). Certain barren types of cacao. *4th ann. Rep. Cacao Res. 1934*, pp. 11–15. Imperial College of Tropical Agriculture; St. Augustine, Trinidad.

—— (1936). The completion of selection, 1935. *5th ann. Rep. Cacao Res. 1935*, pp. 7–16. Imperial College of Tropical Agriculture; St. Augustine, Trinidad.

—— (1938). Cacao and witchbroom disease (*Marasmius perniciosus*) of South America. With notes on other species of *Theobroma*. *Rep. on visit to Ecuador, the Amazon Valley and Colombia, April 1937–April 1938*, pp. 1–58. Yuille's Printerie; Port of Spain, Trinidad.

—— (1943a). Cacao and witches' broom disease (*Marasmius perniciosus*). *Rep. on recent visit to Amazon territory of Peru, Sept. 1942–Feb. 1943*, pp. 1–14. Government Printer; Trinidad and Tobago.

—— (1943b). The quest for witches' broom resistant trees. *Proc. agric. Soc. Trin.* **43**, 55–63.

PRENDERGAST, W. N. E. (1965). *Studies in the resistance of Theobroma cacao L. to Phytophthora palmivora (Butl.) Butl.* M. Sc. Thesis, University of the West Indies, Trinidad (*fide* Spence and Bartley 1966).

—— and SPENCE, J. A. (1965). A contribution to the study of the resistance of *Theobroma cacao* L. to *Phytophthora palmivora* (Butl.) Butl. *Conf. Intle Rech. agron. cacoyères. Abidjan 15–20 nov. 1965*, pp. 212–16.

PRESCOTT, G. W. (1969). *The algae: a review.* Thomas Nelson and Sons Ltd; London.

PRESCOTT, W. H. (1855). *History of the conquest of Mexico, with a preliminary view of the ancient Mexican civilisation, and the life of the Conqueror, Hernando Cortés.* 7th ed. Vol. I. Richard Bentley; London.

—— (1862). *History of the conquest of Peru with a preliminary view of the civilisation of the Incas.* Vol. I. Richard Bentley; London.

298 REFERENCES

PRILLIEUX, E. and DELACROIX, G. (1894). Sur quelques champignons nouveaux ou peu connus parasites sur les plantes cultivées. *Bull. Soc. mycol. Fr.* **10**, 161–9.

PRINTZ, H. (1939). Vorarbeiten zu einer Monographie der Trentepohliaceen. *Nytt Mag. Naturvid.* **80**, 137–210.

PROCTER, J. H. and PIRES, J. A. (1958). *Crop Pests and Diseases of British Guiana*, pp. 1–88 (mimeograph).

PURSEGLOVE, J. W. (1968a). *Tropical crops dicotyledons 1*. Longmans, Green, and Co. Ltd.; London.

—— (1968b). *Tropical crops dicotyledons 2*. Longmans, Green, and Co. Ltd.; London.

PYKE, E. E. (1932). The vegetative propagation of cacao. I. A survey of possibilities. *1st ann. Rep. Cacao Res. 1931*, pp. 4–9. Imperial College of Tropical Agriculture; St. Augustine, Trinidad.

—— (1933a). The vegetative propagation of cacao. II. Softwood cuttings. *2nd ann. Rep. Cacao Res. 1932*, pp. 3–9. Imperial College of Tropical Agriculture; St. Augustine, Trinidad.

—— (1933b). The physiology of cacao. I. General observations of growth, flowering and fruiting. *2nd ann. Rep. Cacao Res. 1932*, pp. 37–40. Imperial College of Tropical Agriculture; St. Augustine, Trinidad.

—— (1934a). The vegetative propagation of cacao. III. Observations on varietal differences in the rooting behaviour of cacao cuttings. *3rd annual Rep. Cacao Res. 1933*, pp. 4–7. Imperial College of Tropical Agriculture; St. Augustine, Trinidad.

—— (1934b). The vegetative propagation of cacao. V. Notes on the dimorphic branching habit of cacao. *3rd ann. Rep. Cacao Res. 1933*, pp. 8–11. Imperial College of Tropical Agriculture; St. Augustine, Trinidad.

—— (1935). Mycorrhiza in cacao. *4th ann. Rep. Cacao Res. 1934*, pp. 41–8. Imperial College of Tropical Agriculture; St. Augustine, Trinidad.

QUANSAH, S. T. (1964). Opening of Conference. *Proc. Cacao Mirid Control Conf., Cocoa Res. Inst. (Ghana Acad. Sci.), Tafo, Akim, Ghana, 6th–7th Aug., 1963*, pp. 1–2.

QUARTEY-PAPAFIO, E. (1961). Notes on the progress of swollen-shoot disease control in Ghana. *Rep. Cocoa Conf. Grosvenor House, London, W.1, 12th–14th Sept. 1961*, pp. 176–80. Cocoa, Chocolate and Confectionery Alliance; London.

—— and EDWARDS, D. F. (1961). The use of fertilisers on cocoa in Ghana. *Rep. Cocoa Conf. Grosvenor House, London, W.1, 12th–14th Sept. 1961*, pp. 123–5. Cocoa, Chocolate and Confectionery Alliance; London.

RAMAKRISHNAN, K. and THANKAPPAN, M. (1965). First report of black pod disease of cocoa in India. *S. Indian Hort.* **13**, 33–4.

RAPER, K. B. and FENNELL, D. I. (1965). *The genus Aspergillus*. The Williams and Wilkins Co.; Baltimore.

RAYNER, R. W. (1941). Notes on the larger fungi of Trinidad. *Dept Mycol. and Bact. Mem.* **6**, 1–11. Imperial College of Tropical Agriculture; St. Augustine, Trinidad.

REDDY, D. B. (1967). *F.A.O. Plant Prot. Committee for SE Asia and Pacific Reg., Q. Newsletter* **10**.

—— (1968). New records (A) in the region Malaysia-Sabah. *F.A.O. Plant Prot. Committee for SE Asia and Pacific Reg. Q. Newsletter* **11**, 6 (mimeograph).

—— (1969). New records of pests and diseases in South East Asia and Pacific region (1965–9). *F.A.O. Plant Prot. Committee for SE Asia and Pacific Reg. tech. Doc.* **69**, 1–10 (mimeograph).

—— (1970*a*). List of diseases of important economic crop plants of Indonesia. *F.A.O. Plant Prot. Committee for SE Asia and Pacific Reg. Tech. Doc.* **74**.

—— (1970*b*). A preliminary list of pests and diseases of plants of Western Samoa. *F.A.O. Plant Prot. Committee SE Asia and the Far East. Tech. Doc.* **77**, 1–15 (mimeograph).

REICHEL-DOLMATOFF, G. (1957). Momíl: a formative sequence from the Sinú Valley, Colombia. *Am. Antiq.* **22**, 226–34.

—— (1965). *Colombia.* In: Ancient Peoples and Places Series. Vol. 44, ed. Glyn Daniel. Thames and Hudson; London.

REICHLE, R. E. and SNYDER, W. C. (1964). Heterothallism and ascospore number in *Calonectria rigidiuscula. Phytopathology* **54**, 1297–9.

REID, D. A. (1966). Some new fungi from New Guinea. *Aust. J. Bot.* **14**, 31–4.

REINKING, O. A. (1919). *Phytophthora faberi* Maubl.: The cause of coconut bud rot in the Philippines. *Philipp. J. Sci.* **14**, 131–51.

—— (1920). Higher Basidiomycetes from the Philippines and their hosts, II. *Philipp. J. Sci.* **16**, 167–79.

—— (1921). Notes on diseases of economic plants in Indo-China and Siam. *Philipp. Agric.* **9**, 181–3.

—— and WOLLENWEBER, H. W. (1927). Tropical Fusaria. *Philipp. J. Sci.* **32**, 103–253.

REIS, A. B. (1938). 'Mata Cacau'. *Bahia rural* Núm. *53*, pp. 1976–7 [Brasil] (typewritten copy provided by Mr. F. D. Marquez, British Vice-Consul, Salvador, Bahia).

RENAUD, R. (1953). Observations sur les pourritures des cabosses de cacaoyer. *Bull. Cent. Rech. agron. Bingerville* **7**, 3–20.

—— (1957). The distribution of virus diseases of cocoa in the Ivory Coast. *Rep. Cocoa Conf. Grosvenor House, London, W.1, 10th–12th Sept. 1957*, pp. 79–80. Cocoa, Chocolate and Confectionery Alliance; London.

—— (1959). La première réunion technique de la F.A.O. sur le cacao et les problèmes phytosanitaires que pose actuellement cette production. *Agron. trop., Nogent* **14**, 601–11.

RESPLANDY, R., CHEVAUGEON, M. J., DELASSES, M. and LUC, M. (1954). Première liste annotée de champignons parasites de plantes cultivées en Côte d'Ivoire. *Annls Épiphyt.* **5**, 1–61.

REYES, E. H., DE REYES, Lilian C., and ARMAS, P. G. (1969). Observaciones sobre el marchitamiento de los chireles del cacao. *Agron. trop. Venezuela* **19**, 19–28.

REYNE, A. (1921). De Cacaothrips (*Heliothrips rubrocinctus* Giard). *Bull Dept van den Landbouw in Suriname* **44**, 1–214.

RIBEIRO, I. J. A. and CORAL, F. J. (1968). Estudo preliminar de ação do fungo *Ceratocystis fimbriata* Ell. & Halst., causador da seca da Mangueira (*Mangifera indica* L.), sobre cacaueiros (*Theobroma cacao* L.). *Bragantia* **27**, Note 20, lxxxvii–lxxxix (abstract in *Rev. Plant Path.* **49**, 483 (1970)).

RICHARDS, P. W. (1932). Ecology, In: *Manual of bryology,* ed. Fr. Verdoorn, pp. 367–95. Martinus Nijhoff; The Hague.

—— (1952). *The tropical rain forest. An ecological study.* University Press; Cambridge.

RIKER, A. J. (1961). Internationally dangerous tree diseases. *Unasylva* **15**, 88–90.

RILEY, E. A. (1960). A revised list of plant diseases in Tanganyika Territory. *Mycol. Pap.* **75**, 1–42.

RISBEC, J. (1949). Les parasites des *Pseudococcus* du cacaoyer, vecteurs du 'swollen-shoot' en Côte d'Ivoire. *Agron. trop., Nogent* **4**, 578–81.

RISHBETH, J. (1968). The growth rate of *Armillaria mellea. Trans. Br. mycol. Soc.* **51**, 575–86.

—— (1972). Resistance to fungal pathogens of tree roots. In: A Discussion on Disease Resistance in Plants, organized by P. W. Brian, F.R.S. and S. D. Garrett, F.R.S. *Proc. R. Soc. B. biol. Sci.* **181**, 211–351.

RITZEMA BOS, J. (1900*a*). Over krulloten en heksenbezems in de cacaoboomen in Suriname. *Tijdschr. PlZickt.* **6**, 65–90.

—— (1900*b*). Les nématodes parasites des plantes cultivées. *VI Cong. int. Agric. Paris II*, pp. 306–12.

RIZZINI, C. T. (1956). Pars specialis Prodromi Monographiae Loranthacearum Brasiliae terrarumque finitimarum. *Rodriguesia* **18** and **19**, 87–234.

ROCHA, H. M. (1965). Cacao varieties resistant to *Phytophthora palmivora* (Butl.) Butl. A literature review. *Cacao, Turrialba* **10**, 1–9.

—— (1966). A bibliographical survey of cocoa varieties resistant to black pod disease. *Papers pres. at 2nd Sess. tech. Working Party on Cocoa Production and Protection. Rome, 19–23 Sept. 1966*, pp. 1–9. F.A.O. of U.N. (mimeograph); Rome.

—— and JIMÉNEZ, S. E. (1966*a*). Mecanismo fisiologico de la resistencia del cacao (*Theobroma cacao* L.) a *Phytophthora palmivora* (Butl.) Butl. *Papers pres. at 2nd Sess. tech. Working Party on Cocoa Production and Protection. Rome, 19–23 Sept. 1966*, pp. 1–15. F.A.O. of U.N. (mimeograph); Rome.

—— and —— (1966*b*). Importancia de las sustancias polifenolicas en el mecanismo fisiológico de la resistencia de cacao (*Theobroma cacao* L.) a *Phytophthora palmivora* (Butl.) Butl. *Turrialba* **16**, 319–29.

—— and MEDEIROS, A. G. (1968). Bases para a selecão de cultivares de cacau resistentes a *Phytophthora palmivora* (Butl.) *Cacao, Turrialba* **13**, 10–17.

ROEPKE, W. (1917). *Cacao-Onze Koloniale Landbouw XI.* H.D. Tjeenk Willink and Zoon; Haarlem.

ROGER, L. (1934). Quelques champignons exotiques nouveaux ou peu connus. I. *Bull. Soc. mycol. Fr.* **50**, 325–7.

—— (1936). Quelques champignons exotiques nouveaux ou peu connus. II. *Bull. Soc. mycol. Fr.* **52**, 80–4.

—— (1951). *Phytopathologie des pays chauds.* Tome I. Paul Lechevalier; Paris.

—— (1953). *Phytopathologie des pays chauds.* Tome II. Paul Lechevalier; Paris.

—— (1954). *Phytopathologie des pays chauds.* Tome III. Paul Lechevalier; Paris.

—— (1960). *Les problemes phytopathologiques en Republique Malgache, dans l'Archipel des Comores, et a l'Ile de la Reunion. Organisation des recherches dans ces pays* (abstract in *Rev. appl. Mycol.* **40**, 272–3 (1961)). Office de la Recherche Scientifique et Technique Outre-Mer (mimeograph); Paris.

—— and MALLAMAIRE, A. (1937). Notes de phytopathologie africaine. *Annls agric. Afr. occid. fr.* **1**, 188–206.

ROGERS, H. H. and KNIGHT, R. (1955). Plant breeding and selection. *Ann. Rep. W. Afr. Cocoa Res. Inst. 1954–5*, pp. 78–81.

ROIVAINEN, O. (1968*a*). Insect transmission studies. *Ann. Rep. C.R.I.G. 1966–7*, 28–30.

—— (1968*b*). Control of mealybugs with systemic insecticides. *Ann. Rep. C.R.I.G. 1966–7*, p. 39.

—— (1969*a*). Effect of vector feeding on virus transmission. *Ann. Rep. C.R.I.G. 1967–8*, p. 40.

—— (1969*b*). Mealybug studies. *Ann. Rep. C.R.I.G. 1967–8*, 43–4.

—— (1971). Circulative transmission of cocoa swollen shoot virus by the mealybug *Planococcoides njalensis* (Laing) (Homoptera: Pseudococcidae). *III intl Cocoa Res. Conf. Accra, Ghana 23–9 Nov. 1969*, pp. 518–21.

ROJTER, S., BONNEY, J. K. and BOAFO, E. O. (1966). Mealybug studies, biological control. *C.R.I.G. Rep. for period 1st Oct. 1963–31st March 1965*, p. 29.

——, ——, —— and DAKWA, J. T. (1968). Mealybug studies, biological control. *Ann. Rep. C.R.I.G. 1965–6*, p. 31.

——, —— and LEGG, J. T. (1966). Investigations into the use of a pathogenic fungus (*Cephalosporium* sp.) as a means of controlling the mealybug (*Pseudococcidae*) vectors of swollen-shoot virus in Ghana. *Ghana J. Sci.* **6**, 110–14.

ROMBOUTS, J. E. (1937). Moléstias criptogámicas do cacaueiro. *Bolm Minist. Agric., Brasil* **26**, 33–57.

—— (1954). Some soil relations of the endotrophic mycorrhiza of cacao in Trinidad, B.W.I. *5th Intl Cong. Soil Sci.* **3**, 104–6.

ROOM, P. M. (1970). An introduction to cocoa mistletoes. C.M.B. Newsletter. *Q. Publ. of State Cocoa Marketing Board (Accra)* **45**, 26–7.

—— (1971*a*). The mistletoe *Tapinanthus bangwensis* and cocoa in West Africa. *III intl Cocoa Res. Conf. Accra, Ghana 23–9 Nov. 1969*, 522–7. Cocoa Research Institute; Tafo, Ghana.

—— (1971*b*). Some physiological aspects of the relationship between cocoa, *Theobroma cacao*, and the mistletoe *Tapinanthus bangwensis* (Engl. & K. Krause). *Ann. Bot.* **35**, 169–74.

RORER, J. B. (1910*a*). Pod-rot, canker, and chupon-wilt of cacao caused by *Phytophthora* sp. *Bull. Dept Agric. Trinidad* **9**, 79–120.

—— (1910*b*). Report of the mycologist for the year ending April 30, 1910. *Trinidad Dept Agric. Bull.* **9**, 154–9.

—— (1911). Report of the mycologist for year ending March 31, 1911 (Parts I and II). *Trinidad and Tobago Board of Agric. Circular* **4**, 1–70.

—— (1913). The Suriname witch-broom disease of cacao. *Trinidad and Tobago Board of Agric. Circular* **10**, 1–13.

—— (1916). The pink disease of cacao. *Bull. Dept Agric., Trin. Tobago* **15**, 86–9.

—— (1918*a*). Enfermedades y plagas de cacao en el Ecuador y metodos modernos apropriados al cultivo del cacao (Guayaquil: 1–80). Informe presentado al Presidente y Miembros de la Asociación de agricultores del Ecuador por James Birch Rorer, Micólogo, Junta de Agricultura Trinidad Antillas Británicas y Traducido del Inglés por Abelardo Pachano Profesor de Agronomía, Quinta Normal Ambato. Part in Stell, F. (1933). Rep. on visit to Ecuador to study witchbroom disease (*Marasmius perniciosus*) of cocoa. Council Paper No. 137 of 1933, Government Printer, Port of Spain.

—— (1918*b*). Algal disease of cacao. *Proc. agric. Soc. Trin. 1917*, **17**, 345–8.

—— (1925). Ecuador cacao succumbing to pests. *Tea and Coffee Trade J.* **49**, 919–21.

ROSEVEAR, D. R. (1969). *The rodents of West Africa*. British Museum (Natural History); London.

ROSS, S. D. and BROATCH, J. D. (1951). A review of the swollen-shoot control campaign in the Gold Coast. *Rep. Cocoa Conf. Grosvenor House, London, W.1, 11th–13th Sept. 1951*, pp. 92–100. Cocoa, Chocolate and Confectionery Alliance; London.

ROUSE, I. and CRUXENT, J. M. (1963). *Venezuelan archaeology*. Yale University Press; New Haven, U.S.A.

ROWE, F. P. (1966). Investigation of damage to cocoa by rats in the British Solomon Islands Protectorate. Mimeograph report, pp. 1–11.

RUDOLPH, B. A. (1931). *Verticillium hadromycosis. Hilgardia* **5**, 201–353.

RUINARD, J. (1963). A contribution to the technique of handpollination in cacao. *Trop. Agric., Trin.* **40**, 285–6.

RUINEN, Jakoba (1953). Epiphytosis. A second view on epiphytism. *Ann. bogor.* **1**, 101–58.

—— (1956). Occurrence of Beijerinckia species in the 'phyllosphere'. *Nature, Lond.* **177**, 220–21.

—— (1961). The phyllosphere I. An ecologically neglected milieu. *Pl. Soil* **15**, 81–109.

—— (1963*a*). The phyllosphere II. Yeasts from the phyllosphere of tropical foliage. *Antonie van Leeuwenhoek* **29**, 425–38.

—— (1963*b*). Cuticle decomposition by micro-organisms in the phyllosphere. *J. gen. Microbiol.* **32**, iv.

—— (1965). The phyllosphere III. Nitrogen fixation in the phyllosphere. *Pl. Soil* **22**, 375–94.

—— (1966). The phyllosphere IV. Cuticle decomposition by microorganisms in the phyllosphere. *Annls Inst. Pasteur* **111**, 342–6.

—— (1970). The phyllosphere V. The grass sheath, a habitat for nitrogen-fixing micro-organisms. *Pl. Soil* **33**, 661–71.

—— (1971). The grass sheath as a site for nitrogen fixation. In: Ecology of leaf surface micro-organisms. *Proc. intl Symp. Univ. Newcastle upon Tyne, Sept. 1970*, Ed. T. F. Preece and C. H. Dickinson, pp. 567–79. Academic Press Inc.; London.

RUIZ, M. Z. JIMÉNEZ, S. E. and SORIA, J. V. (1969*a*). Relación entre la destrucción de la clorofila y el grado de susceptibilidad del cacao al hongo *Ceratocystis fimbriata* (Ell. & Halst.) Hunt. *Mem. seg. Conf. Intl de Pesquisas em Cacau, 19–26 de Nov. de 1967, Bahia Brasil*, pp. 177–80. São Paulo, Brazil.

——, —— and —— (1969*b*). Método colorimétrico para evaluar la resistencia del cacao (*Theobroma cacao* L.) a *Ceratocystis fimbriata* (E. & H.) Elliot. *Turrialba* **19**, 518–21.

RUSSELL, T. A. (1952). The vigour of some cacao hybrids. *Trop. Agric., Trin.* **29**, 102–6.

—— (1953). The spacing of Nigerian cacao. *Emp. J. exp. Agric.* **21**, 145–53.

RUTGERS, A. A. L. (1913). The Fusariums from cankered cacao-bark and Nectria cancri nova species. *Annls Jard. bot. Buitenz. Sér.* 2, vol. **12** (vol. **27** old ser.), 59–64.

SABATER PÍ, J. and GROVES, C. (1972). The importance of higher primates in the diet of the Fang of Rio Muni. *Man* **7**, 239–43.

SACCARDO, P. A. (1916). Notae Mycologicae, II Fungi Philippinenses. *Nuovo G. bot. Ital., Nuova Ser.* **23**, 198–216.

SALE, P. J. M. (1968). Flushing and leaf growth of cacao under controlled temperature conditions. *J. hort. Sci.* **43**, 475–89.

—— (1969a). Flowering of cacao under controlled temperature conditions. *J. hort. Sci.* **44**, 163–73.

—— (1969b). Extension growth of cacao under controlled temperature conditions. *J. hort. Sci.* **44**, 189–93.

—— (1970). Growth and flowering of cacao under controlled atmospheric relative humidities. *J. hort. Sci,* **45**, 119–32.

SANDERS, W. T. and MARINO, J. (1970). *New World prehistory : archaeology of the American Indian.* Englewood Cliffs, Prentice-Hall, Inc.; New Jersey, U.S.A.

SANSOME, Eva (1966). Meiosis in the sex organs of the oömycetes. In: *Chromosomes today,* ed. C. D. Darlington and K. R. Lewis, vol. 1. *Proc. First Oxford Chromosome Conf., July 28–31, 1964,* pp. 77–83. Oliver and Boyd; London.

—— (1970). Selfing as a possible cause of disturbed ratios in *Phytophthora* crosses *Trans. Br. mycol. Soc.* **54**, 101–7.

—— and BRASIER, C. M. (1973). Diploidy and chromosomal structural hybridity in *Phytophthora infestans. Nature, Lond.* **241**, 344–5.

SANTESSON, R. (1952). Foliicolous lichens I. A revision of the taxonomy of the obligately foliicolous, lichenized fungi. *Sym. bot. Upsal.* **12**, 1–590.

SAUCHELLI, V. (1969). *Trace elements in agriculture.* Van Nostrand Reinhold Co.; New York.

SAUNDERS, J. L. (1964). *Scolytidae and platypodidae associated with Ceratocystis wilt of Theobroma cacao L. in Costa Rica,* pp. 1–67. University of Wisconsin Thesis (mimeograph).

—— (1965). The *Xyleborus–Ceratocystis* complex of cacao. *Cacao, Turrialba* **10**, 7–13.

—— and KNOKE, J. K. (1967). Diurnal emergence of *Xyleborus ferrugineus* (Coleoptera: Scolytidae) from cacao trunks in Ecuador and Costa Rica. *Ann. ent. Soc. Am.* **60**, 1094–6.

——, NORRIS, D. M. and KNOKE, J. K. (1967). Insect–host tissue interrelations between *Xyleborus ferrugineus* (Coleoptera: Scolytidae) and *Theobroma cacao* in Costa Rica. *Ann. ent. Soc. Am.* **60**, 419–23.

SAUNDERS, L. G. (1956). Revision of the genus Forcipomyia based on characters of all stages (Diptera, Ceratopogonidae). *Can. J. Zool.* **34**, 657–705.

—— (1959). Methods for studying *Forcipomyia* midges, with special reference to cacao-pollinating species (Diptera, Ceratopogonidae). *Can. J. Zool.* **37**, 33–51.

SAVAGE, E. J., CLAYTON, C. W., HUNTER, J. H., BRENNEMAN, J. A., LAVIOLA, C. and GALLEGLY, M. E. (1968). Homothallism, heterothallism, and interspecific hybridization in the genus Phytophthora. *Phytopathology* **58**, 1004–21.

SAWADA, K. (1928). *Descriptive catalogue of the Formosan fungi,* Part IV. Dept Agric. Gov. Res. Inst. Formosa, Rep. **35.**

SCHIEBER, E. (1969). Enfermedad del cacao 'mal de machete' provocada por *Ceratocystis fimbriata* en la Republica Dominicana. *Turrialba* **19**, 340–4.

—— and SOSA, O. N. (1960). Cacao canker in Guatemala incited by *Ceratocystis fimbriata*. *Pl. Dis. Reptr* **44**, 672.

SCHROEDER, C. A. (1958). Observations on the growth of cacao fruit. *Sépt. Conf. interamer. de Cacao, Palmira, Colombia 13–19 de julio de 1958*, 381–94.

SCHULTES, R. E. (1958). A synopsis of the genus Herrania. *J. Arnold Arbor.* **39**, 216–78.

SCHWEIZER, J. (1933). *Dictionary of the Asante and Fante language*. Evangelical Missionary Society; Basel.

SEAVER, F. J. (1928). Studies in tropical Ascomycetes. IV. Some Hypocreales from Trinidad. (Reference to '*North American Flora*' **3**, 27 (1910)). *Mycologia* **20**, 52–9.

SEESCHAAF, K. W. (1971). Changes in the amounts of total nitrogen, carbon, and reducing sugars in normal young cacao pods and those affected by physiological cherelle wilting. *Angew. Bot.* **45**, 285–97.

SELER, E. (1909). Die Tierbilder der mexikanischen und der Maya-Handschriften. *Z. Ethnol.* **3** and **4**, 381–457.

SEMANGUN, H. (1961). *Gedjala—gedjala mosaik pada daun tjoklat*. Univ. Gadjah Mada Jogjakarta, 2. (Abstracts: *Rev. appl. Mycol.* **42**, 533–4; *Hort. Abstr.* **33**, 809; as 'Mosaic symptoms on cocoa leaves in Java').

SEPÚLVEDA, R. L. (1955). Biologia del *Mecistorhinus tripterus* F. (Hem. Pentatomidae) y su posible influencia en la transmisión de la Moniliasis del cacao. *Cacao Colomb.* **4**, 15–42.

SEQUEIRA, L. (1958). The host range of *Mycena citricolor* (Berk. & Curt.) Sacc. *Turrialba* **8**, 136–47.

SEYMOUR, A. B. (1929). *Host index of the fungi of North America*. Harvard University Press; Cambridge, Massachusetts.

SHARPLES, A. (1922). A preliminary account of observations on the fungi causing 'brown root' disease. *Malay. agric. J.* **10**, 181–3.

SHAW, D. D., GEE, G. F. and DUNN, N. D. (1958). *Cocoa in Papua and New Guinea. I. An economy study of the cocoa growing industry in Papua and New Guinea. II. Long-term economic prospects for the cocoa industry of Papua and New Guinea*, pp. iv and 21. Department of Territories, Commonwealth of Australia; Canberra.

SHAW, Dorothy E. (1962). Diseases of cacao in Papua and New Guinea. *Papua New Guin. agric. J.* **15**, 79–90.

—— (1963). Plant pathogens and other microorganisms in Papua and New Guinea. *Bull. Port Moresby Dept Agric., Stock and Fisheries Res.* **1**, 1–82.

—— (1968). Traumatic vertical lysigenous canals in cacao in Papua and New Guinea. *Papua New Guin. agric. J.* **20**, 65–9.

—— and BURNETT, W. M. (1969). Galls of cacao in Papua and New Guinea. *Papua New Guin. agric. J.* **21**, 25–48.

SHEAR, C. L. and WOOD, Anna K. (1913). Studies of fungous parasites belonging to the genus Glomerella. *Bull. Bur. Pl. Ind. U.S. Dept Agric.* **252**, 1–110.

SHENEFELT, R. D., STELZER, M. J. and LARA, F. E. (1960). Results from preliminary studies of some aspects of the relationship of insects to cacao production in

Costa Rica. A second progress report. *VIII Inter-Amer. Cacao Conf. Trinidad and Tobago 15–25 June, 1960, proc.,* pp. 236–47.

SHEPHARD, C. Y. (1932a). *The cacao industry of Trinidad. Some economic aspects. Part III. History of the industry up to 1870,* pp. 1–8. Imperial College of Tropical Agriculture; St. Augustine, Trinidad.

—— (1932b). The cacao industry of Trinidad. Some economic aspects. Part IV. Historical 1870 to 1920. *Trop. Agric., Trin.* **9**, 1–8.

—— (1932c). *The cacao industry of Trinidad. Some economic aspects. Part V. Historical 1921 to 1932,* pp. 1–31. Imperial College of Tropical Agriculture; St. Augustine, Trinidad.

—— (1936). *The cacao industry of Trinidad. Some economic aspects. Series II. A financial survey of estates during the seven years 1923–24 to 1929–30.* Imperial College of Tropical Agriculture; St. Augustine, Trinidad.

—— (1937a). *The cacao industry of Trinidad. Some economic aspects. Series III. An examination of the effects of soil type and age on yield,* pp. 31–80. Imperial College of Tropical Agriculture; St. Augustine, Trinidad.

—— (1937b). *The cacao industry of Trinidad. Some economic aspects. Series IV. Recommendations for improving the efficiency of estates,* pp. 81–101. Imperial College of Tropical Agriculture; St. Augustine, Trinidad.

SIDDIQI, M. R. (1972a). *Rotylenchulus reniformis. Descriptions of plant-parasitic Nematodes Set 1,* **5**. St. Albans; Commonwealth Institute of Helminthology.

—— (1972b). *Pratylenchus coffeae. Descriptions of plant-parasitic Nematodes Set 1,* **6**. St. Albans; Commonwealth Institute of Helminthology.

—— (1972c). *Helicotylenchus dihystera. Descriptions of plant-parasitic Nematodes Set 1,* **9**. St. Albans; Commonwealth Institute of Helminthology.

—— (1973). *Trophurus imperialis. Descriptions of plant-parasitic Nematodes Set 2,* **22**. St. Albans; Commonwealth Institute of Helminthology.

SILLER, L. R. (1958). La *Ceratostomella fimbriata* en el cacao en Centro América. *Sépt. Conf. interamer. de Cacao, Palmira, Colombia, 13–19 de julio de 1958,* p. 95.

—— (1960). An attempt to transmit cushion gall of cacao by bud grafting and the effect of malathion on gall development. *VIII Inter-Amer. Cacao Conf. Trinidad and Tobago 15–25 June, 1960. Proc.,* pp. 263–6.

—— (1963). The influence of the cushion gall disease upon yields of cacao. *Phytopathology* **53**, 26.

SILVA, P. (1944). Insect pests of cacao in the State of Bahia, Brazil. *Trop. Agric., Trin.* **21**, 8–14.

—— and LELLIS, W. T. (1947). Cacao diseases in Brazil. *Trop. Agric., Trin.* **24**, 56.

SILVEIRA, V. D. (1954). Elementos de fitopatologia. *Rev. agron. Rio de J.* **13**, 99–148.

SIMMONDS, J. H. (1965). A study of the species of *Colletotrichum* causing ripe fruit rots in Queensland. *Queensl. J. agric. & Animal Sci.* **22**, 437–59. (Repr. *Bull. Div. Pl. Ind. Queensland Dept Primary Industries.* **329**, 437–59.)

—— (1966). *Host index of plant diseases in Queensland.* Queensland Department of Primary Industries; Brisbane.

SIMMONDS, N. W. (1949). Notes on the biology of the Araceae of Trinidad. *J. Ecol.* **38**, 277–91.

—— (1950). The Araceae of Trinidad and Tobago B.W.I. *Kew Bull.*, pp. 391–406.

SINGER, R. (1942). A monographic study of the genera 'Crinipellis' and 'Chaetocalathus'. *Lilloa* **8**, 441–534.

—— (1964). Monographic studies on South American Basidiomycetes, especially those of the east slope of the Andes and Brazil. 2. The genus Marasmius in South America. *Sydowia* **18**, 106–358.

SIVANESAN, A. and HOLLIDAY, P. (1972*a*). *Rosellinia bunodes*. C.M.I. *Descriptions of pathogenic Fungi and Bacteria* **351**.

—— and —— (1972*b*). *Rosellinia necatrix, C.M.I. Descriptions of pathogenic Fungi and Bacteria* **352**.

—— and —— (1972*c*). *Rosellinia arcuata. C.M.I. Descriptions of pathogenic Fungi and Bacteria* **353**.

SMALL, L. W. (1966). A technique for Ceratocystis screening. *Ann. Rep. Cacao Res. 1965*, pp. 51–4. Regional Research Centre, Imperial College of Tropical Agriculture, University of the West Indies; St. Augustine, Trinidad.

—— (1967*a*). Ceratocystis resistance test. *Ann. Rep. Cacao Res. 1966*, pp. 40–8. Regional Research Centre, Imperial College of Tropical Agriculture, University of the West Indies; St. Augustine, Trinidad.

—— (1967*b*). Chemical control of Ceratocystis–Xyleborus complex. *Ann. Rep. on Cacao Res. 1966*, p. 49. Regional Research Centre, Imperial College of Tropical Agriculture, University of the West Indies; St. Augustine, Trinidad.

SMALL, W. (1915). Annual report of the Government botanist for 1914–1915, pp. 57–70. In: *Uganda Protectorate ann. Rep. Dept Agric. for year ended 31st March, 1915*, pp. 1–89. Government Printer; Entebbe.

—— (1925). Annual report of the Government mycologist, pp. 18–20. In: *Uganda Protectorate ann. Rep. Dept Agric. for year ended 31st Dec. 1924*, pp. 1–54. Government Printer; Entebbe.

—— (1926*a*). On the identity of *Rhizoctonia lamellifera* and *Rhizoctonia bataticola. Trans. Br. mycol. Soc.* **10**, 287–302.

—— (1926*b*). Mycological notes—*Sclerotium bataticola* Taub. *Trop. Agric. Mag. Ceylon agric. Soc.* **67**, 94–5.

—— (1928). On *Rhizoctonia bataticola* (Taub.) Butler as a cause of root disease in the tropics. *Trans. Br. mycol. Soc.* **13**, 40–68.

SMITH, H. C. (1955). *Report on cocoa diseases in Samoa*, pp. 1–11. Department of Scientific and Industrial Research; New Zealand.

SMITH, L. B. (1953). Bromeliad malaria. In: *Smithsonian Rep. for 1952*, pp. 385–98. Smithsonian Institution; Washington, DC.

SMITH, R. (1969). *State of Sabah ann. Rep. of Dept Agric. for 1967*, pp. 1–157. Sabah Publishing House; Kota Kinabalu, Sabah, Malaysia.

SMITH, R. W. (1967). A new method of rat control in coconuts. *Trop. Agric., Trin.* **44**, 315–24 (abstract in *Hort. Abstr.* **38**, 552 (1968)).

SMYTH, A. J. (1966). The selection of soils for cocoa. *Soils Bull.* **5**. F.A.O. of U.N. Rome.

SNOWDEN, J. D. (1921). Report of the Government botanist for the period 1st April to 31st December, 1920. In: *Uganda Protectorate Dept Agric. Ann. Rep. for nine months ending Dec. 31, 1920*, pp. 43–6 (abstract in *Rev. appl. Mycol.* **1**, 205–7). Government Printer; Entebbe.

SNYDER, W. C. and HANSEN, H. N. (1945). The species concept in Fusarium with reference to Discolor and other Sections. *Am. J. Bot.* **32**, 657–66.

SOERJOBROTO WIDJANARKO (1967). Pollination of cocoa by *Forcipomyia* spp. in relation to endrin spraying. *Menara Perkebunan* **36**, 22–5 (abstract in *Cocoa Growers' Bull.* **14**, 41 (1970)).

SORIA, J. (1960*a*). The genetics and breeding of cacao. In: *Cacao manual* (English ed.) comp. and ed. F. Hardy, pp. 325–44. Inter-American Institute of Agricultural Sciences; Turrialba, Costa Rica.

—— (1960*b*). A note on the relationships between flowery cushion gall, self-incompatibility and flower development. *VIII Inter-Amer. Cacao Conf. Trinidad and Tobago 15–25 June, 1960.* Proc. 267–9.

—— (1970). The latest cocoa expeditions to the Amazon basin. *Cacao, Turrialba* **15**, 5–15.

—— (1971). A preliminary report on experiments of hand pollination and fertilizers in cacao. *III intl Cocoa Res. Conf. Accra, Ghana 23–9 Nov. 1969*, pp. 608–13.

—— and CERDAS, M. (1966). Pollination by flower movement with a small sorghum brush. In: Inter-American Cacao Center ann. Rep. 1965–6. *Cacao, Turrialba* **11**, 8–9.

—— and ESQUIVEL, O. (1969). Observaciones sobre resistencia del cacao a *Phytophthora, Ceratocystis,* buba floral y 'dieback', en Costa Rica. *Mem. seg. Conf. intl de Pesquisas em Cacau, 19–26 de Nov. de 1967, Bahia, Brasil*, pp. 174–6. São Paulo, Brazil.

SORIA, S. de J. (1971). La polinizacion del cacao por las mosquitas *Forcipomyia* spp. (Diptera, Ceratopogonidae) en Palmira, Colombia. *Acta agron., Palmira* **21**, 77–82.

SOUTH, F. W. (1912). Report on the prevalence of some pests and diseases in the West Indies for 1910 and 1911; Part II Fungus diseases. *W. Indian Bull.* **12**, 425–43.

SPAULDING, P. (1961). Foreign diseases of forest trees of the world. *U.S. Dept Agric., Agric. Handbook,* **197**, 1–361.

SPEGAZZINI, C. (1906*a*). Consulta sobre cacaoeiros doentes enviada pela Secretaria da Agricultura da Bahia, por intermedio da Sociedade Nacional de Agricultura. *Bolm Agric, S. Paulo* **5**, 522.

—— (1906*b*). Algunos micromicetas de los cacaoyeros. *Revta Fac. Agron. Univ. nac. La Plata* **2**, 303–9.

SPENCE, J. A. and BARTLEY, B. G. (1966). Testing of breeding material of *Theobroma cacao* for resistance to black pod disease (*Phytophthora palmivora*). *Papers pres. 2nd Sess. tech. Working Party on Cocoa Prod. and Prot., Rome, 19–23 Sept. 1966*, pp. 1–6. F.A.O. of U.N. (mimeograph); Rome.

—— and MOLL, E. R. (1958). Preliminary observations on a wilt condition of cocoa. *J. Agric. Soc. Trin.* **58**, 349–59.

SPEYER, E. R. (1923). Notes upon the habits of Ceylonese ambrosia-beetles. *Bull. ent. Res.* **14**, 11–23.

SQUIRE, F. A. (1947). On the economic importance of the Capsidae in the Guinean Region. *Revta Ent., Rio de J.* **18**, 219–47.

STAHEL, G. (1915). *Marasmius perniciosus* nov. spec. *Bull. van der Landbouw in Suriname* **33**, 1–26.

—— (1919). Bijdrage tot de kennis der krullotenziekte. *Bull. Dept van den Land-bouw in Suriname* **39**, 1–34.

—— (1923) (the name *Marasmius perniciosus* var. *ecuadoriensis* proposed). *Dept van Landbouw, Nijverheid en Handel in Suriname; Verslag over het jaar 1923*, pp. 30–31. (Relevant extract and translation provided by Dr. F. W. Ostendorf, Koninklijk Instituut voor de Tropen, 1963 *in litt.*)

—— (1924). Plantenziekten. In: *Dept van Landbouw, Nijverheid en Handel in Suriname-Verslag over het jaar 1923*, pp. 30–2.

—— (1932). Contribution to the knowledge of witch-broom disease (translation of *Bull.* 39 (Stahel, 1919) by B. G. Montserin). *Trop. Agric., Trin.* **9**, 167–76.

—— (1935). De krullotenziekte in Brazilie. *De Indische Mercuur* **58**, 71.

—— (1945). The natural resources of Surinam. In: *Plants and plant science in Latin America*, ed. Frans Verdoorn. Chronica Botanica Co.; Waltham, Mass., U.S.A.

STANDEN, J. H. (1952). Host index of plant pathogens of Venezuela. Pl. Dis. Reptr **212**, 59–106.

STANER, P. (1928). Insectes et maladies. In: Bellefroid, V. de (1928). Notes sur la culture du cacao dans les terres rouges de Lukolela. *Bull. agric. Congo Belge* **19**, 3–58.

—— (1930). Quelques maladies de l'Hévéa. *Bull. agric. Congo Belge* **21**, 649–58 (abstract in *Rev. appl. Mycol.* **11**, 2 (1932)).

STEJSKAL, M. (1969). Nectar y aroma de las flores del cacao. *Oriente Agropecuario Venezuela* **1**, 75–92.

STELL, F. (1928). Witch-broom disease of cacao and its control. *Bull Dept Agric. Trin. Tobago* **21**.

—— (1929). Plant pathology. In: *Admin. Rep. Dept Agric. Trin. Tobago 1928*, pp. 49–51 (abstract in *Rev. appl. Mycol.* **9**, 20 (1930)).

—— (1933). Report on visit to Ecuador to study witch-broom disease (*Marasmius perniciosus*) of cocoa. *Council Pap. Trin.* **137**, 1–12.

STEVEN, W. F. (1936a). A new disease of cocoa in the Gold Coast. *Gold Cst Fmr* **5**, 122.

—— (1936b). Swollen-shoot and dieback—a new disease of cocoa. *Gold Cst Fmr* **5**, 144.

STEVENS, F. L. (1927). Fungi from Costa Rica and Panama. *Illinois biol. Monogr.* **11**, 1–102.

—— and DOWELL, Ruth I. (1923). A Meliola disease of cacao. *Phytopathology* **13**, 247–50.

STEVENSON, J. A. (1926). *Foreign plant diseases*, U.S. Dept of Agric., Office of the Secretary, Contribution from the Federal Horticultural Board. Government Printing Office; Washington.

STEYAERT, R. L. (1948). Contribution à l'étude des parasites des végétaux du Congo belge. *Bull. Soc. Bot. Belg.* **80**, 11–58.

—— (1953). New and old species of *Pestalotiopsis*. *Trans. Br. myc. Soc.* **36**, 81–9.

STILES, W. (1946). *Trace elements in plants and animals*, pp. xi and 189. University Press; Cambridge.

STOCKDALE, F. A. (1908). Fungus diseases of cacao and sanitation of cacao orchards. *Imp. Dept Agric. W. Indies, Pamphlet Ser.* **54**, 1–47. (Also publ. (1909) in:—*W. Indian Bull.* **9**, 166–89.)

STRECKER, R. L. and JACKSON, W. B. (1962). Cacao plantings, In: 'Pacific island rat ecology', by Strecker, R. L., Marshall, J. T., Jackson, W. B., Barbehenn, K. R. and Johnson, D. H. *Bull. Bernice P. Bishop Mus.* **225**, 208–13.

STRICKLAND, A. H. (1945). A survey of the Arthropod soil and litter fauna of some forest reserves and cacao estates in Trinidad. *J. Anim. Ecol.* **14**, 1–11.

—— (1947a). Coccids attacking cacao (*Theobroma cacao* L.) in West Africa, with descriptions of five new species. *Bull. ent. Res.* **38**, 497–523.

—— (1947b). Three new species of Coccoidea (Hemiptera Homoptera) from the Gold Coast, British West Africa. *Proc. R. ent. Soc. Lond., Ser. B, Taxonomy* **16** 149–56.

—— (1948). The vectors of some West African cacao viruses. *Rep. Cocoa Conf. Grosvenor House, London, W.1, 14th–16th Sept., 1948*, pp. 58–61. Cocoa, Chocolate and Confectionery Alliance; London.

—— (1951a). The entomology of swollen-shoot of cacao. I. The insect species involved, with notes on their biology. *Bull. ent. Res.* **41**, 726–48.

—— (1951b). The entomology of swollen-shoot of cacao. II. The bionomics and ecology of the species involved. *Bull. ent. Res.* **42**, 65–103.

STRONG, W. D. (1935). Archaeological investigations in the Bay Islands, Spanish Honduras. *Smithson. misc. Collns* **92** (14).

STUART, L. C. (1964). Fauna of Middle America. In: *Handbook of Middle American Indians*, ed. R. Wauchope. Vol. 1, pp. 316–62. University of Texas Press; Austin, U.S.A.

SUTHERLAND, J. R. G. (1953). Some observations on mealybugs infesting cacao in Western Region, Nigeria, 1950–53. *Proc. W. Afr. intl Cacao Res. Conf. Tafo, Gold Coast, 12th–16th Dec. 1953*, pp. 90–4.

SWARBRICK, J. T. (1964). The growth and root distribution of some temporary shade plants for cocoa. *Trop. Agric., Trin.* **41**, 311–23.

——, TOXOPEUS, H. and HISLOP, E. C. (1964). Estate cocoa in Fernando Po. *Wld Crops* **16**, 35–40.

SWENSON, K. G. (1967). Plant virus transmission by insects. In: *Methods in virology* ed. K. Maramorosch and Hilary Koprowski, Vol. I, pp. 267–307. Academic Press, New York.

SYDOW, H. and SYDOW, P. (1909). Fungi Paraënses. *Hedwigia* **49**, 78–87.

SZENT-IVANY, J. J. H. (1961). Insect pests of *Theobroma cacao* in the Territory of Papua and New Guinea. *Papua New Guin. agric. J.* **13**, 127–47.

—— (1963). Further records of insect pests of *Theobroma cacao* in the Territory of Papua and New Guinea. *Papua New Guin. agric. J.* **16**, 37–43.

TABOR, R. J. and BUNTING, R. H. (1923). On a disease of cocoa and coffee fruits caused by a fungus hitherto undescribed. *Ann. Bot.* **37**, 153–7.

TALBOT, P. H. B. (1965). Studies of 'Pellicularia' and associated genera of Hymenomycetes. *Persoonia* **3**, 371–406.

—— and KEANE, P. J. (1971). *Oncobasidium*: A new genus of Tulasnelloid Fungi. *Aust. J. Bot.* **19**, 203–6.

TARJAN, A. C. (1971). Some interesting associations of parasitic nematodes with cacao and coffee in Costa Rica. *Nematropica* **1**, 5.

——, JIMÉNEZ, M. F. and SORIA, J. (1971). Reactions of nematized cacao to chemical treatment. *Nematropica* **1**, 16.

TARJOT, M. (1965). Quelques données sur la biologie du *Phytophthora palmivora* agent de la pourriture brune des cabosses du cacaoyer. *Conf. intle Rech. agron. cacaoyères. Abidjan 15–20 nov. 1965*, pp. 178–83.

—— (1971a). Nouvelle contribution à l'étude de la pourriture des cabosses du cacaoyer due au *Phytophthora palmivora* (Butl.) Butl. en Côte d'Ivoire. *Café-Cacao-Thé* **15**, 31–48.

—— (1971b). Quelques précisions sur le role de l'environnement dans le comportement des cabosses de cacaoyer envers le *Phytophthora palmivora* (Butl.) Butl. en Côte d'Ivoire. *Café–Cacao–Thé* **15**, 235–40.

—— (1972). Ètude anatomique de la cabosse de cacaoyer en relation avec l'attaque du *Phytophthora palmivora*. *Café–Cacao–Thé* **16**, 123–34.

TARR, S. A. J. (1962). *Diseases of sorghum, sudan grass and broom corn.* Commonwealth Mycological Institute; Kew.

TAYLOR, D. J. (1954). A summary of the results of capsid research in the Gold Coast. *W.A.C.R.I. tech. Bull.* **1**, 4–20.

—— (1958). Effect of dieldrin on ant activity. *Ann. Rep. W. Afr. Cocoa Res. Inst. 1956–7*, pp. 37–9.

—— and WHARTON, A. L. (1954). Insecticide/Fungicide trials. *Ann. Rep. W. Afr. Cacao Res. Inst. April, 1953–March 1954*, p. 17.

—— and —— (1955). Simultaneous control of capsids and Calonectria. *Ann. Rep. W. Afr. Cocoa Res. Inst. 1954–5*, p. 61.

TAYLOR, K. D. (1961). *An investigation of damage to West African cocoa by vertebrate pests*; pp. 1–35. Mimeograph report.

TEIXEIRA, A. R. (1946). Himenomicetos Brasileiros. III (*Agaricaceae*). *Bragantia* **6**, 165–78.

TEODORO, N. G. (1937). An enumeration of Philippine fungi. *Tech. Bull. Dept Agric. Commerce, Philipp. Isl.* **4**, 1–585.

THET, Su. U. (1935). New diseases of crops during the year 1934–5 in Burma. *Int. Bull. Pl. Prot.*, p. 273.

THOMAS, A. S. (1932). The dry season in the Gold Coast and its relation to the cultivation of cacao. *J. Ecol.* **20**, 263–9.

THOMAS, Cyrus (1888). Aids to the study of the Maya codices. *6th ann. Rep. Bureau Ethn., Washington*, pp. 253–371.

THOMAS, K. M. and RAMAKRISHNAN, T. S. (1948). Studies in the genus *Phytophthora* II. *Proc. Indian Acad. Sci., B* **27**, 55–73.

THOMPSON, A. (1929). *Phytophthora* species in Malaya. *Malay. agric. J.* **17**, 53–100.

—— (1950). The introduction of amelonado cocoa from the Gold Coast to Malaya. *Malay agric. J.* **33**, 209–18.

—— and JOHNSTON, A. (1953). A host list of plant diseases in Malaya. *Mycol. Pap.*, **52**, 1–38.

THOMPSON, J. E. S. (1948). An archaeological reconnaissance in the Cotzumalhuapa region, Escuintla, Guatemala. Carnegie Institution of Washington Publication 574. *Contr. Am. Anthrop. Hist.* **9**, 1–56.

—— (1956). Notes on the use of cacao in Middle America. *Notes Middle Am. Archaeol. Ethnol.* **5**, 95–116.

—— (1962). *A catalog of Maya hieroglyphs.* University of Oklahoma Press; Norman, Oklahoma, U.S.A.

—— (1972a). *Maya hieroglyphics without tears.* British Museum; London.

—— (1972*b*). A commentary on the Dresden Codex. *Mem. Am. phil. Soc.* **93**, 1–156.

THOROLD, C. A. (1943*a*). Witches' broom disease investigations V. Large-scale experiments on direct control. *Trop. Agric., Trin.* **20**, 176–81.

—— (1943*b*). Witches' broom disease investigations VII. Observations on direct control. *Trop. Agric., Trin.* **20**, 239–41.

—— (1943*c*). Plant Diseases: Witches' broom disease of cacao. In: *Admin. Rep. Director of Agric. 1942 (Trinidad and Tobago)*, pp. 13–14. Government Printer; Trinidad and Tobago.

—— (1945*a*). Cacao virus disease. *Proc. agric. Soc. Trin.* **45**, 295, 297–9.

—— (1945*b*). Observations on a trial of trees as shade for cacao. *Trop. Agric., Trin.* **22**, 203–6.

—— (1948). Plant pathology. In: *Trinidad and Tobago Admin. Rep. Director of Agric. 1946*, pp. 22–4. Government Printer; Trinidad and Tobago.

—— (1952). The epiphytes of *Theobroma cacao* in Nigeria in relation to the incidence of black pod disease (*Phytophthora palmivora*). *J. Ecol.* **40**, 125–42.

—— (1953*a*). Observations on fungicide control of witches' broom, black pod, and pink disease of *Theobroma cacao*. *Ann. appl. Biol.* **40**, 362–76.

—— (1953*b*). The control of black pod disease of cocoa in the Western Region of Nigeria. *Rep. Cocoa Conf. Grosvenor House, London, W.1, 15th–17th Sept. 1953*, pp. 108–15. Cocoa, Chocolate and Confectionery Alliance; London.

—— (1954). Use of ultra-violet fluorescent substances for observations on dispersal of *Phytophthora palmivora* sporangia. *Nature, Lond.* **174**, 409.

—— (1955*a*). Observations on *Theobroma cacao* in Fernando Po. *J. Ecol.* **43**, 219–25.

—— (1955*b*). Observations on black pod disease (*Phytophthora palmivora*) of cacao in Nigeria. *Trans. Br. mycol. Soc.* **38**, 435–52.

—— (1956). Observations on cacao pod production in relation to the incidence of black pod disease, caused by *Phytophthora palmivora*. *J. hort. Sci.* **31**, 149–55.

—— (1957*a*). Spray techniques: black pod control in Nigeria cocoa farms. *Common. phytopath. News* **3**, 33–35 and 39.

—— (1957*b*). A chlorosis disease of cocoa in the Southern Cameroons. *Jl W. Afr. Sci. Ass.* **3**, 96–106.

—— (1959). Methods of controlling black pod disease (caused by *Phytophthora palmivora*) of *Theobroma cacao* in Nigeria. *Ann. appl. Biol.* **47**, 708–15.

—— (1967). Black pod disease of *Theobroma cacao*. *Rev. appl. Mycol.* **46**, 225–37.

THRESH, J. M. (1958*a*). The control of cacao swollen shoot disease in West Africa. A review of the present situation. *Tech. Bull. W. Afr. Cocoa Res. Inst.* **4**, 1–36.

—— (1958*b*). The spread of virus disease in cacao. *Tech. Bull. W. Afr. Cocoa Res. Inst.* **5**, 1–36.

—— (1958*c*). Virus research. *Ann. Rep. W. Afr. Cocoa Res. Inst. 1956–7*, pp. 71–88.

—— (1960). Capsids as a factor influencing the effect of swollen-shoot disease of cacao in Nigeria. *Emp. J. exp. Agric.* **28**, 193–200.

—— (1961). Some isolates of virus causing swollen-shoot disease of cacao in Nigeria and their interrelationships. *Ann. appl. Biol.* **49**, 340–6.

—— and LISTER, R. M. (1960). Coppicing experiments on the spread and control of cacao swollen-shoot disease in Nigeria. *Ann. appl. Biol.* **48**, 65–74.

—— and TINSLEY, T. W. (1959). The viruses of cacao. *Tech. Bull. W. Afr. Cocoa Res. Inst.* **7**, 1–32.

THROWER, L. B. (1956). The root diseases of cacao in Papua and New Guinea. *Papua New Guin. Agric. J.* **10**, 1–14.

—— (1958). Observations on the root-knot nematode in Papua–New Guinea. *Trop. Agric., Trin.* **35**, 213–17.

—— (1960a). Observations on the diseases of cacao pods in Papua–New Guinea. I. Fungi associated with mature pods. *Trop. Agric., Trin.* **37**, 111–20.

—— (1960b). Observations on the diseases of cacao pods in Papua–New Guinea. II. Cherelle wilt. *Trop. Agric., Trin.* **37**, 121–3.

—— (1965). Parasitism of cacao by *Fomes noxius* in Papua–New Guinea. *Trop. Agric., Trin.* **42**, 63–7.

TIMM, R. W. (1965). *A preliminary survey of the plant parasitic nematodes of Thailand and the Philippines*, pp. 1–71. SE Asia Treaty Organization Secretariat-General; Bangkok.

—— (1969). The genus *Isolaimium* Cobb, 1920 (Order Isolaimida, Isolaimiidae new family). *J. Nematol.* **1**, 97–106.

TINSLEY, T. W. (1953a). The strains of cacao swollen-shoot virus occurring in West Africa. *Proc. W Afr. intl Cacao Res. Conf., W. Afr. Cacao Res. Inst., Tafo, Gold Coast, 12th–16th Dec. 1953*, 20–1.

—— (1953b). Strains of the cacao swollen-shoot virus (CSSV). *Ann. Rep. W. Afr. Cacao Res. Inst. April 1952–March 1953*, p. 7.

—— (1955a). The host range of cacao viruses. *Ann. Rep. W. Afr. Cocoa Res. Inst. 1954–5*, pp. 30–5.

—— (1955b). Classification of viruses and virus strains. *Ann. Rep. W. Afr. Cocoa Res. Inst. 1954–5*, pp. 35–6.

—— (1959). World survey of cacao virus diseases. Abstract: *Proc. 1st F.A.O. tech. Cacao Meeting, Accra, Ghana, 8–15 Feb., 1959*, pp. 104–6.

—— (1960). Summary of discussion. *VIII Inter-Amer. Cacao Conf. Trinidad and Tobago 15–25 June, 1960. Proc.*, p. 301.

—— (1961). Parasitic plants. *Ann. Rep. W. Afr. Cocoa Res. Inst. 1959–60*, p. 69.

—— (1971). The ecology of cacao viruses I. The role of wild hosts in the incidence of swollen-shoot virus in West Africa. *J. appl. Ecol.* **8**, 491–5.

—— and USHER, G. (1954). A colour test for detecting swollen-shoot disease in Gold Coast cacao. *Nature, Lond.* **174**, 87.

—— and WHARTON, A. L. (1958). Studies on the host ranges of viruses from *Theobroma cacao* L. *Ann. appl. Biol.* **46**, 1–6.

TODD, J. McA. (1951). An indigenous source of swollen-shoot disease of cacao. *Nature, Lond.* **167**, 952.

TOLLENAAR, D. (1958). *Phytophthora palmivora* of cocoa and its control. *Netherlands J. agric. Sci.* **6**, 24–38.

—— (1966). Boron deficiency in cacao, bananas and other crops on volcanic soils in Ecuador. *Netherlands J. agric. Sci.* **14**, 138–51.

—— (1967). Field symptoms of boron deficiency in cocoa. *Cocoa Growers' Bull.* **8**, 15–18.

TOPPER, B. F. (1960). Cacao. In: *Investigations 1956–7, Bull. Minist. Agric. Lds, Jamaica* **57** (New Ser.), pp. 86–7.

TORTO, J. O. (1959). History of cocoa in Ghana. *Ghana Farmer* **3**, 88–108.

TOXOPEUS, H. (1964). F3 Amazon cocoa in Nigeria. *Ann. Rep. W. Afr. Cocoa Res. Inst. (Nigeria) 1963–4*, p. 13.

—— (1969). Commercial assessment of W.A.C.R.I. Series I and II varieties. *Ann. Rep. C.R.I.N. 1967–8*, 40–2.

—— and OKOLOKO, G. E. (1967). Cacao marcotting in Nigeria. I: Use, technique and monthly rooting success. *Nigerian Agric. J.* **4**, 45–8.

TRENCH, A. D. le P., GILLETT, S. and McCLELLAND, T. L. (1937). Cultural practice and factory treatment. In: *Coffee in Kenya*, ed. J. McDonald. Colony and Protectorate of Kenya Department of Agriculture. Government Printer; Nairobi.

TUCKER, C. M. (1931). Taxonomy of the genus *Phytophthora* de Bary. *Bull. Mo. agric. Exp. Stn* **153**, 1–208.

TUKEY, H. B., Jr. (1971). Leaching of substances from plants. In: Ecology of leaf surface micro-organisms. *Proc. intl Symp. Univ. of Newcastle upon Tyne, Sept. 1970*, pp. 67–80. Ed. T. F. Preece and C. H. Dickinson. Academic Press Inc.; London.

TURCONI, M. (1920). Sopra una nuova malattia del cacao (*Theobroma cacao* L.) *Atti Ist. Bot. Univ. Lab. crittogam Pavia* **17**, 1–8.

TURNER, G. J. (1964). Transmission by snails of the species of *Phytophthora* which causes Foot Rot of *Piper nigrum* L. in Sarawak. *Nature, Lond.* **202**, 1133.

—— (1969). Leaf lesions associated with foot rot of *Piper nigrum* and *Piper betle* caused by *Phytophthora palmivora*. *Trans. Br. mycol. Soc.* **53**, 407–15.

TURNER, P. D. (1960a). Variation in *Phytophthora palmivora* (Butl.) Butl. on *Theobroma cacao* L. in West Africa. *Nature, Lond.* **186**, 495–6.

—— (1960b). Strains of *Phytophthora palmivora* (Butl.) Butl. from *Theobroma cacao* L. I. Isolates from West Africa. *Trans. Br. mycol. Soc.* **43**, 665–72.

—— (1960c). Sources of infection by *Phytophthora palmivora*. *Ann. Rep. W. Afr. Cocoa Res. Inst. 1958–9*, pp. 22–5.

—— (1960d). Minor fungal diseases of cocoa. *Ann. Rep. W. Afr. Cocoa Res. Inst. 1958–9*, pp. 29–30.

—— (1961a). Complementary isolates of *Phytophthora palmivora* from cacao and from rubber and their taxonomy. *Phytopathology* **51**, 161–4.

—— (1961b). Strains of *Phytophthora palmivora* (Butl.) Butl. from *Theobroma cacao* L. II. Isolates from non-African countries. *Trans. Br. mycol. Soc.* **44**, 409–16.

—— (1962). Laboratory studies. *Ann. Rep. W. Afr. Cocoa Res. Inst. 1960–1*, pp. 29–32.

—— (1963). Laboratory studies. *Ann. Rep. W. Afr. Cocoa Res. Inst. 1961–2*, pp. 21–5.

—— (1965a). Behaviour of *Phytophthora palmivora* in soil. *Pl. Dis. Reptr* **49**, 135–7.

—— (1965b). Polyphenoloxidase activity in cacao selections showing variable resistance to *Phytophthora* pod rot. *Pl. Dis. Reptr* **49**, 319–21.

—— (1965c). Comparative sporulation as an indication of resistance by cacao to *Phytophthora* pod rot. *Trop. Agric., Trin.* **42**, 305–9.

—— (1967). Cocoa dieback—a review of present knowledge. *Pl. Prot. Bull. F.A.O.* **15**, 81–101.

—— (1968*a*). Pod rot of cacao in Malaysia caused by *Phytophthora heveae. Pl. Prot. Bull. F.A.O.* **16**, 33–4.

—— (1968*b*). Dieback and other diseases of cocoa in Malaya. In: Blencowe, J. W. and Turner, P. D.; 'Cocoa and coconuts in Malaya'. *Proc. Symp. Kuala Lumpur, Sept. 1967*, pp. 1–116. The Incorporated Society of Planters; Kuala Lumpur.

—— (1971*a*). Micro-organisms associated with oil palm (*Elaeis guineensis* Jacq.). *Phytopath. Pap* **14**, 1–58.

—— (1971*b*). *Cocoa dieback in West Malaysia. An appraisal of the present situation and future considerations.* pp. 1–14. Harrisons Fleming Advisory Services; Kuala Lumpur.

—— and ASOMANING, E. J. A. (1962). Root infection of *Theobroma cacao* by *Phytophthora palmivora. Trop. Agric., Trin.* **39**, 339–43.

—— and WHARTON, A. L. (1960). Leaf and stem infections of *Theobroma cacao* L. in West Africa, caused by *Phytophthora palmivora* (Butl.) Butl. *Trop. Agric., Trin.* **37**, 321–24.

URICH, F. W. (1911*a*). Notes on some cacao pests, with directions for collecting. *Proc. agric. Soc. Trin.* **11**, 242–50.

—— (1911*b*). Miscellaneous notes—rats and other mammals on cacao estates. *Circ. Bd Agric. Trin.* **3**, 19–24.

—— (1911*c*). Short notes—rat from Tobago. *Circ. Bd Agric. Trin.* **3**, 24.

—— (1928). San Thomé cacao industry. *Trop. Agric., Trin.* **5**, 275–8.

URQUHART, D. H. (1955). *Report on the cocoa industry in Sierra Leone and notes on the cocoa industry of the Gold Coast,* pp. 1–43. Cadbury Brothers Ltd; Bournville, Birmingham.

—— (1958). *Prospects for cocoa-growing in Uganda and Zanzibar,* pp. 1–28. Cadbury Brothers Ltd; Bournville, Birmingham.

—— (1961). *Cocoa.* Longmans, Green and Co. Ltd.; London.

USHER, G. (1957). Fungi associated with capsid lesions. *Ann. Rep. W. Afr. Cocoa Res. Inst. 1955–6,* pp. 56–9.

VAINIO, E. A. (1915). Additamenta ad Lichenographiam Antillarum illustrandam. *Ann. Acad. Sci. Fenn. ser. 2,* vol. **6**, 3–226.

VALDEZ, R. B. (1972). Transmission of raspberry ringspot virus by *Longidorus caespiticola, L. leptocephalus* and *Xiphinema diversicaudatum* and of arabis mosaic virus by *L. caespiticola* and *X. diversicaudatum. Ann. appl. Biol.* **71**, 229–34.

VAN BREDA DE HAAN, J. (1900). Vorläufige beschreibung von pilzen bei tropischen kulturpflanzen beobachtet. *Bull. Inst. bot. Buitenz.* **6**, 11–13.

VAN BUUREN, H. L. (1928). An examination of the type-forms of fruit present in the progeny of a single forastero cacao. *Trop. Agric. Mag. Ceylon agric. Sci.* **71**, 328–42.

VAN DER KNAAP, W. P. (1955). Observations on the pollination of cacao flowers. *14th intl hort. Cong.—1955, Vol. II,* pp. 1287–93. H. Veenman and Zonen; Wageningen, Netherlands.

—— (1956). *Theobroma cacao* L. cultivation and research in Indonesia. *6th Interamer. Cacao Conf. Proc.,* pp. 407–14.

VAN DER PLANK, J. E. (1947). A method for estimating the number of random groups of adjacent plants in a homogeneous field. *Trans. R. Soc. S. Afric.* **31**, 269–78.

—— (1948). The relation between the size of fields and the spread of plant-diseases into them. Part I. Crowd Diseases. *Emp. J. exp. Agric.* **16**, 134–42.

VAN HALL, A. E. (1909). Kanker of roodrot van den cacaoboom veroorzaakt door Spicaria colorans n. sp. *Bull. Dept van den Landbouw Suriname* **20**, 1–22.

—— and DROST, A. W. (1909). De instervingeziekte der cacaoboomen en het 'bruinrot' de cacaovruchten, veroorzaakt door *Diplodia cacaoicola. Bull. Dept van den Landbouw Suriname* **21**, 1–15.

VAN HALL, C. J. J. (1914). *Cocoa.* Macmillan and Co. Ltd.; London.

—— and DROST, A. W. (1907). Les balais de sorcière du cacaoyer provoques par *Colletotrichum luxificum* n. sp. *Recl Trav. bot. néerl.* **4**, 243–321.

—— and —— (1909). De krullotenziekte der cacaoboomen in Suriname—haar oorzaak en haar bestrijding. *Bull. Dept van den Landbouw Suriname* **16**, 1–71.

VAN SUCHTELEN, N. J. (1955a). Ziekten van de cacao in Suriname. *Surin. Landb.* **3**, 18–29.

—— (1955b). Topsterfte bij cacao in de kwekerij. *Surin. Landb.* **3**, 223–4.

VAN UDEN, N. and BUCKLEY, H. (1970). Genus 2. *Candida* Berkhout. In: *The yeasts. A taxonomic study.* 2nd rev. enl. ed., ed. J. Lodder, pp. 893–1087. North-Holland Publishing Co.; Amsterdam.

VAN YZERDOORN, P. (1815). *De Goudkust,* p. 1–56. Gebroeders van Cleef, Amsterdam. (I am unable to confirm the authorship of this publication, because what appears to be the title-page of my photocopy is anonymous. This copy was provided by Koninklijk Instituut voor de Tropen, who were unable to confirm that the author was P. van Ijzerdoorn (*sic*). In other respects this copy is apparently similar to an original copy of *De Goudkust* by P. von Yzerdoorn (see *Gold Coast Dept Agric. Mon. Newsletter* **7** (1st Nov. 1928)).

VASUDEVA, R. S. (1960). Revision of *The fungi of India* by E. J. Butler and G. R. Bisby. Government of India Press; Calcutta.

VELLO, F. and MAGALHÃES, W. S. (1971). Estudos sôbre a participação da formiga caçarema (Azteca chartifex spiriti Forel) na polinizaçao do cacaueiro na Bahia. *Rev. Theobroma* **1**, 29–42 (abstract in *Trop. Abstr.* **27**, 675 (1972)).

VENNING, F. D. and GERTSCH, M. E. (1958). Field trials of low-volume high-concentration fungicides in oil and water in Cuban cacao plantings. *Cacao, Turrialba* **3**, 6–7.

VENTOCILLA, J. A. (1969). Efeito do BHC sôbre as mosquinhas Ceratopogonideas polinizadoras do cacaueiro. *Mem. seg. Conf. intl de Pesquisas em Cacau 19–26 de Nov. 1967, Bahia, Brasil,* pp. 287–90. São Paulo, Brazil.

VERNON, A. J. (1961). Control of cocoa capsids in West Africa. *Chemy Ind.* **31**, 1219–20.

—— (1964). Cocoa yield increase by control of capsids (*Miridae*). *Chemy Ind.* **8**, 320–1.

—— (1969). The description of yield curves of multi-harvest crops. *J. hort. Sci.* **44**, 3–25.

—— (1971). *Phytophthora palmivora* disease of cocoa in Fiji. *III intl Cocoa Res. Conf., Accra, Ghana, 23–9 Nov. 1969,* pp. 375–86. Cocoa Research Institute; Tafo, Ghana.

316 REFERENCES

VERWOERD, L. and DU PLESSIS, S. J. (1933). Descriptions of some new species of South African fungi and of species not previously recorded from South Africa V. *S. Afr. J. Sci.* **30**, 222–33.

VINCENS, F. (1918). Quelques maladies des plantes cultivées au Parà (Brésil). *Bull. Soc. Path. vég. Fr.* **5**, 45–55.

VITON, A. (1955). Cacao. A review of current trends in production, price and consumption. *F.A.O. Commod. Rev.* **27**, 1–97.

VITORI, M. and DELGADO, J. C. (1969). Determinación de niveles de resistencia a *Ceratocystis fimbriata* en la coleccion de clones de cacao de la Estación Experimental Tropical de Pichilingue. *Mem. seg. Conf. intl de Pesquisas em Cacau 19 a 26 de Nov. 1967, Bahia : Brasil*, pp. 170–3. São Paulo, Brazil.

VOELCKER, O. J. (1938a). Self-incompatibility in cacao II. *7th ann. Rep. Cacao Res. 1937*, pp. 2–5. Imperial College of Tropical Agriculture; St. Augustine, Trinidad.

—— (1938b). Cacao. A summary of literature since 1931. *7th ann. Rep. Cacao Res. 1937*, pp. 20–30. Imperial College of Tropical Agriculture; St. Augustine, Trinidad.

—— (1946). *Ann. Rep. W. Afr. Cacao Res. Inst. April 1944–March, 1945*, pp. 1–36.

—— (1947). *Ann. Rep. W. Afr. Cacao Res. Inst. April 1945–March 1946*, pp. 1–61.

—— (1948a). West African Cacao Research Institute: Field experiments. *Emp. J. exp. Agric.* **16**, 241–8.

—— (1948b). *Ann. Rep. W. Afr. Cacao Res. Inst. April 1946–March 1947*, pp. 1–70.

—— (1948c). *Ann. Rep. W. Afr. Cacao Res. Inst. April 1947–March 1948*, pp. 1–85.

—— and WEST, J. (1940). Cacao dieback. *Trop. Agric., Trin.* **17**, 27–31.

VON BERNEGG, A. S. (1934). Kakao und Kola. *Tropische und subtropische Weltwirtschaftspflansen ihre Geschichte, Kultur und volkswirtechaftliche Bedeutung* **3**. Ferdinand Enke Verlag; Stuttgart.

VON FABER, F. C. (1907). Bericht über die pflanzenpathologische Expedition nach Kamerun. *Tropenpflanzer* **11**, 735–75.

—— (1909). Die krankheiten und parasiten des kakaobaumes. *Arb. Kaiserlichen Biol. Anst. Land-u. Forstw.* **7**, 193–351.

VOORHEES, R. K. (1942). Life history and taxonomy of the fungus *Physalospora rhodina*. *Bull. Fla agric. exp. St.* **371**, 1–91.

WAITE, B. H. and DÍAZ, F. (1969). The survival of *Phytophthora palmivora* in cacao plantations in the chlamydospore stage. *Mem. seg. Conf. intl de Pesquisas em Cacau 19 a 36 de Nov. Bahia, Brasil, 1967*, pp. 233–5. São Paulo, Brazil.

WAKEFIELD, E. M. (1914). Nigerian fungi II. *Kew Bull.*, pp. 253–61.

—— (1917). *Fungi Exotici*: XXIII. *Kew Bull.*, pp. 308–14.

—— (1918). *Fungi Exotici*: XXIV. *Kew Bull.*, pp. 207–10.

—— (1920). *Fungi Exotici*: XXV. Notes on Uganda fungi. II. Microfungi. *Kew Bull.*, pp. 289–300.

WALTERS, E. A. (1928). *Report on the Agricultural Department, St. Lucia, 1927*, pp. 1–31.

WANNER, G. A. (1962). *The first cocoa trees in Ghana 1858–68*, pp. 1–19. Basle Trading Co. Ltd.; Switzerland.

WARBURG, O. (1905). Die Kautschukmisteln. *Tropenpflanzer* **9**, 633–47.

WARDLAW, C. W. (1929). Witch-broom in Suriname. *Trop. Agric., Trin.* **6**, 348–9.

WARMKE, H. E. (1952). Studies on natural pollination of *Hevea brasiliensis* in Brazil. *Science* **116**, 474–5.

WATERHOUSE, Grace M. (1956). The genus *Phytophthora*. *Misc. Pubs Commonw. mycol. Inst.* **12**, 1–120.

—— (1963). Key to the species of *Phytophthora* De Bary. *Mycol. Pap.* **92**, 1–22.

—— (1968). The genus *Pythium* Pringsheim. *Mycol. Pap.* **110**, 1–71.

—— (1970). The genus *Phytophthora* De Bary. *Mycol. Pap.* **122**, 1–59 and plates 1–21.

—— and STAMPS, D. Jean (1969). Isolation of *Phytophthora* and *Pythium*. In: *Isolation methods for microbiologists*, ed. D. A. Shapton and G. W. Gould, pp. 99–102. The Society for Applied Bacteriology Technical Series 3. Academic Press Inc.; London.

WATERS, H. B. (1941). *Gold Coast Report on the Department of Agriculture for the year 1940–41*. Government Printer; Accra.

—— and HUNTER, T. (1929). Measurement of rate of development of cacao pods. *Dept Agric., Gold Coast, Year Book 1928. Bull.* **16**, 121–7.

WATERSTON, J. M. (1941). Observations on the parasitism of *Rosellinia pepo* Pat. *Trop. Agric., Trin.* **18**, 174–84.

—— (1954). Notes on plant diseases. *Ann. Rep. Agric. Dept Nigeria 1951–2*, pp. 55–8. Government Printer; Nigeria.

WATSON, A., DALGLEISH, A. and MURRAY, K. A. H. (1948). Report of the Commission of Enquiry into Disturbances in the Gold Coast 1948. *Colonial* **231**, pp. 1–103. H.M.S.O.; London.

WEAVER, Muriel Porter (1972). *The Aztecs, Maya, and their predecessors*. Seminar Press Ltd; London.

WEBSTER, R. K. and BUTLER, E. E. (1967). A morphological and biological concept of the species *Ceratocystis fimbriata*. *Can. J. Bot.* **45**, 1457–68.

WEIR, J. R. (1926). A pathological survey of the Para rubber tree (*Hevea brasiliensis*) in the Amazon valley. *Bull. U.S. Dept Agric.* **1380**, 1–129.

WELLMAN, F. L. (1961). *Coffee, botany cultivation and utilization*, pp. ix–xv and 488. Leonard Hill; London.

—— (1964). Parasitism among Neotropical Phanerogams. *Annual Review of Phytopathology* **2**, 43–56. Annual Reviews Inc.; Palo Alto, California.

—— and ORELLANA, R. G. (1955). Buba or cushion gall of cacao in Nicaragua. *Pl. Prot. Bull. F.A.O.* **3**, 71–3.

WENT, F. A. F. C. (1904). Krulloten en versteende vruchten van de cacao in Suriname. *Verh. K. Akad. Wet. Amsterdam 2 Sect.* **10**, 1–40.

WESSEL, M. (1971). Fertilizer requirements of cacao (*Theobroma cacao* L.) in South-Western Nigeria. *Dept Agric. Res. Comm.* **61**. Koninklijk Instituut voor de Tropen; Amsterdam.

WESSEL-RIEMENS, P. C. and OKUSANYA, B. A. (1965). Mechanical transmission of cocoa viruses. The effect of alkaloids. *Ann. Rep. W. Afr. Cocoa Res. Inst. (Nigeria) 1963–4*, pp. 23–4.

WEST, J. (1936). Black pod of cacao. Experimental control on native farms. Repr. from the *11th Bull. Agric. Dept*, pp., 1–11. Government Printer; Lagos.

—— (1938). Preliminary list of plant diseases in Nigeria. *Kew Bull.*, pp. 1–7.

—— (1951). Progress of work at W.A.C.R.I. on systemic insecticides carried out with Pest Control, Ltd. *Rep. Cocoa Conf. Grosvenor House, London, W.1, 11th–13th Sept. 1951*, pp. 86–92. Cocoa, Chocolate and Confectionery Alliance; London.

—— and VOELCKER, O. J. (1942). Plantation cacao in the British Cameroons. *Trop. Agric., Trin.* **19**, 4–11.

WESTSTEIJN, G. (1966a). Susceptibility of *Theobroma cacao* L. to *Phytophthora* pod-rot disease I. Field observations on clonal cocoa. *Papers pres. 2nd Sess. tech. Working Party on Cocoa Prod. and Prot., Rome, 19–23 Sept. 1966*, pp. 1–20. F.A.O. of U.N. (mimeograph); Rome.

—— (1966b). Root diseases of cocoa. *Ann. Rep. C.R.I.N. 1964–5*, pp. 71–3.

—— (1967). Symptomatology and incidence of some root diseases of cacao (*Theobroma cacao* L.) in Nigeria. *Nigerian agric. J.* **4**, 60–3.

—— (1969a). Methods of screening *Theobroma cacao* L. for resistance to *Phytophthora* pod-rot disease. *Mem. seg. Conf. intl de Pesquisas em Cacau, Bahie Brasil, 19–26 de Nov. de 1967*, pp. 157–60. São Paulo, Brazil.

—— (1969b). Incidence of *Phytophthora* pod-rot disease of cacao at different heights in the tree. *Neth. J. Pl. Path.* **75**, 133–6.

WHARTON, A. L. (1955). Spraying and harvesting trials. *Ann. Rep. W. Afr. Cocoa Res. Inst. 1954–5*, pp. 49–55.

—— (1957). Cushion infection. *Ann. Rep. W. Afr. Cocoa Res. Inst. 1955–6*, pp. 47–8.

—— (1958). Cushion infection. *Ann. Rep. W. Afr. Cocoa Res. Inst. 1956–7*, pp. 34–5.

—— (1959). Effect of age and size of pod on susceptibility. *Ann. Rep. W. Afr. Cocoa Res. Inst. 1957–8*, pp. 25–8.

—— (1962). Black pod and minor diseases. In: *Agriculture and land use in Ghana*, ed. J. Brian Wills, pp. 333–42. Oxford University Press; London.

—— and ADAMS, S. N. (1955). Effect of host plant nutrition. *Ann. Rep. W. Afr. Cocoa Res. Inst. 1954–5*, pp. 36–8.

—— and BRUNT, A. A. (1959). Galls of cacao in Ghana. *Common. phytopath. News* **5**, 61–2.

WHEELER, W. M. (1922). Ants of the American Museum Congo Expedition. A contribution to the myrmecology of Africa. *Bull. Am. Mus. nat. Hist.* **45**.

WHETZEL, H. H. and OLIVE, E. W. (1920). A list of the Pyrenomycetes of Porto Rico. *Mycologia* **12**, 316–21.

WHITEHEAD, A. G. (1969). Nematodes attacking coffee, tea, and cocoa, and their control. In: Nematodes of tropical crops, ed. J. Peachey. *Tech. Commun. Common. Bur. Helminth.* **40**, 238–50.

WHITELEY, P. (1966). The occurrence and prevention of mould and algal growths on paint films. In: *Microbiological deterioration in the tropics*, pp. 161–9. Society of Chemical Industry Monograph **23**; London.

WICKENS, R. (1955). Frequency of picking experiments. *Ann. Rep. W. Afr. Cocoa Res. Inst. 1954–5*, p. 55.

WIDLAKE, Brian as 'Mammon' (1963). Bean of contention. *The Observer*, Sept. 22, p. 7.

WIEHE, P. O. (1948). The plant diseases and fungi recorded from Mauritius. *Mycol. Pap.* **24**, 1–39.

WILLEY, G. R. (1971). *An introduction to American archaeology: Vol. 2, South America.* Prentice-Hall, Inc.; Englewood Cliffs, New Jersey, U.S.A.

WILLIAMS, C. B. (1964). *Patterns in the balance of nature and related problems in quantitative ecology.* Academic Press Inc.; London.

WILLIAMS, D. J. (1958*a*). The mealybugs (Pseudococcidae: Homoptera) described by W. M. Maskell, R. Newstead, T. D. A. Cockerell and E. E. Green from the Ethiopian Region. *Bull. Br. Mus. nat. Hist. Ent.* 6, 204–36.

—— (1958*b*). The mealybugs (Pseudococcidae: Homoptera) described by W. J. Hall, F. Laing and A. H. Strickland from the Ethiopian Region. *Bull. Br. Mus. nat. Hist. Ent.* 7, 1–37.

—— (1962). The British Pseudococcidae (Homoptera: Coccoidea). *Bull. Br. Mus. nat. Hist. Ent.* 12, 1–79.

WILLIAMS, G. (1953). Field observations on the cacao mirids, *Sahlbergella singularis* Hagl. and *Distantiella theobroma* (Dist.) in the Gold Coast. Part I. Mirid damage. *Bull. ent. Res.* 44, 101–19.

—— (1954). Field observations on the cacao mirids, *Sahlbergella singularis* Hagl. and *Distantiella theobroma* (Dist.) in the Gold Coast. Part III. Population fluctuations. *Bull. ent. Res.* 45, 723–44.

WILLIAMS, R. O. (1943). In: Pound (1943*a*).

—— and WILLIAMS, R. O. Jnr. (1951). *The useful and ornamental plants in Trinidad and Tobago.* Rev. 4th ed. Guardian Commercial Printery; Port of Spain, Trinidad.

WILLIAMS, T. H. (1965*a*). In: Johnston, A. (1965*a*). New country records in the region. *F.A.O. Plant Prot. Committee SE Asia and Pacific Reg. 4th Q. Rep. Oct.–Dec. 1964,* p. 7 (mimeograph).

—— (1965*b*). In: Johnston, A. (1965*c*). New country records in the region. *F.A.O. Plant Prot. Committee SE Asia and Pacific Reg. Q. Newsletter* 8, 8. (Mimeograph.)

—— (1967). New records in the region, Sabah-Malaysia. In: Reddy, D. B. (1967) *F.A.O. Plant Prot. Committee for SE Asia and Pacific Reg. Q. Newsletter* 10, 7–9.

—— (1968). New records, Sabah-Malaysia, ed. D. B. Reddy. *F.A.O. Plant Prot. Committee for SE Asia and Pacific Reg. Q. Newsletter* 11, 7–9.

WILLIS, J. C. (1948). *A dictionary of the flowering plants and ferns.* 6th ed. rev. University Press; Cambridge.

WILSON, G. W. (1914). Studies in North American Peronosporales. V. A review of the genus Phytophthora. *Mycologia* 6, 54–83.

WOLLENWEBER, H. W. (1931). Fusarium Monographie, fungi parasitici et saprophytici. *Z. Parasitkde* 3, 269–516.

—— and REINKING, O. A. (1925). Aliquot Fusaria tropicalia nova vel revisa. *Phytopathology* 15, 155–69.

WOOD, D. L. and SILVERSTEIN, R. M. (1970). Bark beetle pheromones. *Nature, Lond.,* 225, 557–8.

WOOD, G. A. R. (1957). *Report on cocoa growing in the Dominican Republic, Mexico, Guatemala, and Costa Rica,* pp. 1–40. Cadbury Brothers Ltd.: Bournville, Birmingham.

—— (1959). *Cocoa growing in Venezuela, Colombia and Ecuador,* pp. 1–57. Cadbury Brothers Ltd.; Bournville, Birmingham.

320 REFERENCES

—— (1971). Editor's footnote. In: Underplanting coconuts with cocoa in West Malaysia. Part 2. Maintenance, by J. R. Leach, R. Shepherd, and P. D. Turner. *Cocoa Growers' Bull.* **17**, 7.

WOOD, R. K. S. (1972). Introduction: disease resistance in plants. A discussion on disease resistance in plants organized by P. W. Brian and S. D. Garrett. *Proc. R. Soc. Ser. B.* **181**, 213–32.

WRIGHT, H. (1903). A report by the Controller of the Experiment Station, Peradeniya. *Circ. agric. J. R. bot. Gdns Peradeniya* **2**, 49–93.

—— (1907). *Theobroma cacao or Cocoa, its botany, cultivation, chemistry and diseases.* Messrs A. M. and J. Ferguson; Colombo.

YATES, F. (1949). *Sampling methods for censuses and surveys.* Charles Griffin and Co. Ltd; London.

ZAIGER, D. and ZENTMYER, G. A. (1965). *Phytophthora* canker of cacao in the Caroline Islands. *Pl. Dis. Reptr* **49**, 565–7.

ZENTMYER, G. A., MIRCETICH, S. M. and MITCHELL, D. M. (1968). Tests for resistance of cacao to *Phytophthora palmivora. Pl. Dis. Reptr* **52**, 790–1.

—— and MITCHELL, D. M. (1971). Mating types in *Phytophthora palmivora. III intl Cocoa Res. Conf., Accra, Ghana, 23–29 Nov., 1969,* pp. 494–7. Cocoa Research Institute; Tafo, Ghana.

ZEVADA, Martha Z., YERKES, W. D. and NIEDERHAUSER, J. S. (1955). Primera Lista de Hongos de Mexico-Arreglada por Huespedes. *Folleto téc. of. Estud. esp. Secr. Agric. Ganad. México* **14**.

ZIMMERMANN, A. (1901*a*). Ueber an tropischen Kulturpflanzen beobachtete Pilze. I. *Zentbl. Bakt. Parasitkde Abt. 2,* Bd. **7**, 101–6 and 139–47.

—— (1901*b*). Sammelreferate über die tierischen und pflanzlichen parasiten der tropischen Kulturpflanzen. II. Die Parasiten des Kakaos. *Zentbl. Bakt. Parasitkde Abt. 2,* Bd. **7**, 914–24.

—— (1902). Ueber einige an tropischen Kulturpflanzen beobachtete Pilze II. *Zentbl. Bakt. Parasitkde Abt. 2, Bd.* **8**, 216–21.

MOULDINESS AND SOME OTHER DEFECTS OF RAW COCOA

Introduction

This book is mainly concerned with disorders affecting live cocoa plants. It is expedient to consider also certain defects of processed cocoa beans. The objective of increased productivity (p. vii) is not satisfactorily achieved unless the produce is marketable. An important criterion is mouldiness, but this is not a 'disease', which was defined by Ainsworth (1961) as 'a condition in which the use or structure of any part of a living organism is not normal'. Nevertheless, consideration of this and some other defects may be appended advantageously to the main topic.

Terminology

This appendix is mainly concerned with the 'bulk cocoa' which constitutes about 90 per cent of the world production of raw cocoa (Minifie 1970). It will be generally applicable to most of the remaining 10 per cent, comprising the 'fine cocoa' of commerce (Williamson 1973), although not necessarily relevant to the kind of fine cocoa referred to as 'criollo cocoa', discussed by Campbell (1947) and by Vyle (1949), when its production was declining (*ca.* 1 per cent of total production in 1947–9).

Fresh cocoa beans must be satisfactorily processed if destined for the manufacture of chocolate having the characteristic flavour which is lacking when the fresh beans are treated unsatisfactorily. Criteria of satisfactory processing, comprehensively referred to as 'curing', are the achievement of certain chemical changes which produce the 'flavour precursors' (Thaysen 1949), and certain physical changes giving the colour and texture characters of the bean which manufacturers require (Wadsworth 1955; Anon. 1968). These chemical and physical modifications occur contemporaneously, but they are not fermentation processes. Nevertheless, the term 'fermentation' is in general use, and preferable to the term 'curing', which includes the wet and dry stages of cocoa processing (Briton-Jones 1934; Hardy 1960; Forsyth and Quesnel 1963; Rohan 1963).

The mucilaginous pulp surrounding the fresh beans, is a suitable substrate for various micro-organisms, particularly yeasts and acetic acid bacteria. Through their activity at tropical ambient temperature, heat is generated and a 'hot spot' occurs when beans are heaped together in sufficient number for gradients in oxygen and temperature to develop. Loosely held liquid flows promptly from the pulp of bulked beans, which are said to 'sweat', and cognate terms are 'sweat-box' for the receptacle and 'sweatings' for the effluent from it. Loss of pulp through enzymic and microbial activities, facilitates later handling and drying (Kenten and Powell 1960). Although the quality of the beans is affected by fermentation, this process may have been used originally merely to remove the pulp surrounding the beans, and to prevent germination, as appears from a 1775 account of Guyana cocoa fermentation (Johnson 1912).

When a large quantity of beans is allowed to sweat, heating occurs unevenly throughout the mass, so that some beans may be unaffected ('unfermented'), or affected less than is considered desirable ('under-fermented'). The process of sweating is generally referred to as fermentation because characteristic odours indicate that alcohol is produced and acetified. When the fermentation procedure is unduly prolonged, putrefactive micro-organisms may develop to the detriment of the cocoa which is then said to be 'over-fermented'. Occurrences of off-flavours and offensive odours are associated with deamination and decarboxylation of amino acids (de Witt and Cope 1951; Lopez and Quesnel 1973).

Certain abnormal fermentations have been referred to as 'slimy fermentation' (Quesnel 1970, 1972). Affected beans were under-fermented. The cause of slimy fermentation was not understood.

In the 'International standards for cocoa beans' (Anon. 1969c), it is stated that 'merchantable quality beans must be fermented . . .'. However, cocoa beans are used in the unfermented state in some countries (Murray 1968; Anon. 1972a).

For the manufacture of chocolate or cocoa, the beans are roasted to develop flavour and to reduce the moisture content before winnowing, the object of which is the separation of the cotyledon (ca. 87 per cent) now referred to as the 'nib', from the testa (ca. 12 per cent) now termed 'shell' and 'germ' (ca. 1 per cent), the last being the unemerged radicle and plumule.

Cocoa beans from healthy and mature pods, which have been satisfactorily processed and maintained subsequently, should give 'sound raw cocoa', in contrast with 'defective raw cocoa' which may occur through default at one or more of the production stages from field to factory. When cocoa is faulty to the extent of being regarded as 'sub-standard', such bagged cocoa is marked accordingly (S.S.), and its marketing is restricted (Anon. 1969a,b,d).

An international grading-system by which points were to be given or subtracted for dimensions of beans, colour, odour, and absence of imperfect beans, was recommended but has not been adopted (Chatt 1953; Rohan 1963). Instead, grading is based on limits for objective defects, because of inherent difficulties in preparing samples and assessing them for subjective qualities (Anon. 1963; Rohan and Neirinck 1963). Some countries have adopted the 'International Cocoa Standards' which comprise the 'Model Ordinance and Code of Practice' (Wood 1972). These standards were framed to regularize through either prevention, deterrence, or limitation, the possible content of particular faults in accord with the extent to which they can be tolerated. Cocoa of merchantable quality is required to be *free from* smoky beans (having a smoky smell or taste, or showing signs of contamination by smoke), and abnormal or foreign odours. Further, it is required to be *reasonably free from* living insects, broken beans, fragments of beans and pieces of shell. In addition, cocoa is graded on the basis of *limits* to its content of particular defects. When a bean has several defects, it is classified in one category only, which is the most objectionable one. The accepted order of decreasing gravity is as follows: mouldy beans, slaty beans, insect-damaged beans, germinated beans, flat beans.

A 'mouldy bean' is defined as a cocoa bean on the internal parts of which mould is visible to the naked eye. This defect is sought through the procedure of the 'cut test', by which the maximum cut surface of the cotyledon (nib) is exposed. This defect will be interpreted here as including both external and internal invasions of the bean. Dade (1929) explained that for all cases of mouldiness, except when the shell was perforated mechanically or by the radicle through unwanted germination, moulds must first develop on the shell before internal mouldiness can ensue. Although mouldiness is determined from cut tests for grading purposes, some mycological reports of moulds associated with cocoa beans, were based on examination of the exterior of the bean, without indicating whether there was also internal invasion. A 'mould' was defined as 'a microfungus having well-marked mycelium or spore mass, especially an economically important saprobe [saprophyte]' (Ainsworth 1971). Here it is convenient to base the concept of a mould on the second part, rather than on the first part of this definition. The term mouldiness will be employed to include occurrences of other microfungi (e.g. yeasts), and bacteria (including actinomycetes) which may lack mycelium and/or spore masses.

A 'slaty bean' is a cocoa bean which shows a slaty colour on half or more of the surface exposed in the cut test. An allied defect is referred to as a 'purple bean'. Knapp (1937) tabulated the different interior colours and textures of beans when dried without fermentation, when 'half fermented', and when 'fully fermented'. Because the cut test was considered unreliable for assessing the degree of fermentation, Quesnel (1958) studied the changes in the cotyledons, and the means for judging the completion of fermentation. Maravalhas (1966b, 1970) used the principles of the present international method for colorimetric determination (Rohan and Neirinckx 1963) to quantify the intermediate stages. An objective procedure for specifying the colour of cocoa beans has been described (Hahn and Vincent 1972).

An 'insect-damaged bean' is one, the internal parts of which contain insects at any stage of development, or show signs of damage caused thereby.

A 'germinated bean' is one, the shell of which has been pierced by the growth of the radicle.

A 'flat bean' is one, the two cotyledons of which are atrophied to such a degree that it is not possible to obtain a cotyledon surface by cutting for the conventional cut test.

Economic importance

It seems that the first scientific approach to mouldiness of fermented cocoa beans, under the term 'maladie du vice propre', was made by Delacroix (1897). Affected beans had an 'off flavour' (mauvais goût), and depreciated commercial value.

The object of experiments considered by Smith (1913) was to avoid the unevenness and defectiveness of the commercial cocoa on offer at that time. Culham and Scott (1928) studied the procedure of cocoa sampling in Ghana which began in January 1927. One consignment had a large proportion of defective beans (42 per cent) in relation to sound beans (58 per cent). For some time, the improvement of cocoa quality was not commensurate with increased knowledge concerning its processing. When normal cocoa trading was resumed after the Second World War, there were price fluctuations, with 'peak' prices in 1954 (more than 60 cents per lb in U.S.A., more than £500 per ton in U.K.). High prices were prejudicial to quality but economic policies differed from one territory to another (Balleyguier 1949). The tendency was to penalize poor quality rather than to use price premium to make better quality a worthwhile objective. Another result of penalties was to make produce-inspection unpopular, its abandonment in French West Africa was associated with a decline in the percentage of 'superieur' grade from about 70 per cent of total production in 1948–9 to 3 per cent in 1954–5 (Anon. 1956). No price premium for quality was then paid in Ghana, except in 1953 (Cadbury 1956). A system of differential prices in Nigeria (Gibberd 1953) was associated with increased percentage of Grade I from 47 per cent in 1947–8, to 98 per cent in 1953–4 (Anon. 1956). There appears to have been a world-wide improvement in the proportions of sound beans exported. Occurrences of defects (expressed as percentages) in samples of cocoa exported from twenty-five different countries in 1961–2 (Dieckman 1962), showed that the range for mouldy beans was 0–6 per cent (mean 1·4 per cent), and for slaty beans the range was 0–33 per cent (mean 5·2 per cent). According to information provided by Wood, G. A. R. (1973 in litt.), cut tests applied in the period 1964–9 to imported cocoa, showed that the mean percentages of mouldy beans in samples from Ghana (1·1 per cent), and from Nigeria (1·2 per cent) were similar, despite annual variation (range 0·6–1·6 per cent).

There is little statistical information to indicate how much cocoa may be produced but withheld from export through failing to meet grading standards. Information provided by Messrs. Gill and Duffus Ltd., London (Gill and Duffus Cocoa Market Report 250, dated 5 April 1973), showed that annual subgrade bean purchases in Ghana, in the period 1964–71, ranged from 106 to 1,460 long tons (average 608 tons per year).

The economic importance of mouldiness arises in different ways. Obnoxious by any standard was the peculiarly disagreeable odour of beans due to actinomycetes, which Ciferri (1931) found in the Dominican Republic, associated with excessively wet beans (14–21 per cent moisture content). Bunting (1932) examined a sample of beans which were exported from Nigeria, with a musty odour. He isolated three actinomycete 'strains' which were not visibly obvious on the beans. He noted reports that cocoa exported from 'certain ports of South America' had been affected by a musty odour, which may have been due to actinomycetes, but there is no other evidence to support this possibility.

Samples of chocolate have been prepared which demonstrated the objectionable flavour imparted by mouldy beans (Campbell 1947). Such defective beans may also have insidious effects. Species of *Aspergillus* are harmful through various enzymatic activities. The degradation of fats in the bean by lipase may be serious. In association with the lipolytic activity of some moulds isolated from stored beans (Eyre 1932), the free fatty acid content of mouldy beans exceeds that of sound beans (Kavanagh, Reineccius, Keeney, and Weissberger 1970). Since it may be useful to have an objective chemical procedure to take the place of the subjective cut test for the assessment of mouldiness in raw cocoa, it is worth noting that the methyl ketone content of cocoa beans was related to mould activity (Boyd, Keeney, and Patton 1965; Hansen and Keeney 1970).

Moulds affecting raw cocoa may be clinically important through the reaction of the tissues of man, and other vertebrates, to contact with propagules and metabolites of these micro-organisms (Austwick 1966). Feuell (1966) gave details of assayed amounts of aflatoxin in cocoa beans from New Guinea and the West Indies. He discussed difficulties due to substances in cocoa which interfered with measurement of the fluorescence exhibited by aflatoxin under long-wave ultraviolet illumination (Pons and Goldblatt 1969), whilst the duckling test (Legator 1969) was vitiated by theobromine toxicity to poultry. Maravalhas (1965) reported failure to find any member of the *Aspergillus flavus* group as either external or internal mould of Bahia cocoa in 1964. There is no evidence that aflatoxin or other mycotoxins occur in cocoa in toxicologically important amounts.

Theimer (1958) discussed the hazards associated with the dust emanating from cocoa beans when handled in bulk. This dust comprises particles of shell and other debris, probably including bacteria and fungi. Cocoa-dust 'air spora' has not been sampled and analysed under industrial conditions. Some indication of its likely components is available from studies under laboratory conditions, made in relation to the air-sampling of other mouldy materials (Lacey 1970). The number of spores obtained per unit weight of substrate was smaller from cocoa beans than from bagasse or mouldy hay. Lacey, J. (1971 *in litt.*) pointed out that the procedure by which this data was obtained did not take into account the large difference in surface area between cocoa beans and similar weights of hay or bagasse. There is no evidence that workers handling raw cocoa in bulk have suffered from any allergy or infection through possible inhalation of airborne micro-organisms from the beans. Nevertheless, there is a potential hazard because the microflora of some cocoa beans may comprise species associated with the allergic pulmonary diseases referred to as 'farmer's lung' (Pepys, Jenkins, Festenstein, Gregory, Lacey, and Skinner 1963), and 'bagassosis' (Hearn 1968; Hearn and Holford-Strevens 1968; Lacey 1971; Lacey and Pepys 1971).

Fries (1966) used an extract from 'minimally altered cocoa beans' for an intracutaneous test and reported sensitivity in allergic patients. Headache was not reported as a reaction to chocolate by these allergic subjects. Attention has been given to the frequency with which an attack of migraine followed the eating of chocolate (Hanington 1967, 1968; Hanington and Harper 1968; Dunlop 1969). Hanington (1969) reported that chocolate and cocoa contained small amounts of tyramine. Subsequently, Hanington, Horn, and Wilkinson (1970) reported that chocolate contained little or no tyramine. Smith, Kellow, and Hanington (1970) confirmed that chocolate did not contain sufficient tyramine to produce the known dietary effects. These discordant results from determinations of tyramine in cocoa would accord with an extrinsic occurrence through the activity of micro-organisms. Tyramine is the amine derivative of an amino acid (tyrosine) which may be synthesized by moulds (Raper, Thom, and Fennell 1968), and has been recognized in fermented beans (Seiki 1973).

Factors affecting infection of beans before fermentation

The number and health of pods harvested in a particular period depend largely on environmental conditions about 5 months previously, when pollination and early critical developmental stages occur. Alvim (1965) reported that the mean length of the period from pollination to maturity in Bahia was $167 \cdot 84 \pm 0 \cdot 78$ days, which is in accord with experience in West Africa (Waters and Hunter 1929). Irregularities in the cropping cycle reflected moisture stress in Bahia (Alvim 1965), in Costa Rica, and in Trinidad (Murray 1955).

From information provided by Dieckmann (1962), it appears that for most northern hemisphere cocoa-producing countries, the main-crop months are in the period October/February, and likewise for Congo and Bahia, but with March/June and July/September as important cropping months in some countries south of the equator. However, in absence of clear evidence to the contrary, it seems that phases of the cropping cycle are inherent and unrelated to geographical position, but subject to local and annual variation (Maidment 1928). In West Africa, intervals between harvests should not exceed 3 weeks (Gibberd 1953; Hammond 1953). A certain degree of over-ripeness is not detrimental, but under-ripeness is undesirable (Rohan 1963). Harvesting tends to be infrequent when there are fewer pods available before and after the main-crop period. Consequently, produce from out-of-season harvests tends to be of poorer quality than that derived from main-crop harvests (Hammond 1953). Data relating to Ghana cocoa production in the period 1963–71 (Anon. 1972b), showed that main-crops graded better (average percentages: 98·1 per cent Grade I, 1·9 per cent Grade II) than mid-crops (average percentages: 93·5 per cent Grade I, 6·5 per cent Grade II).

The commonest cause of damage to beans is infection by *Phytophthora palmivora*. Such losses through incidence of black pod disease were greater when the interval between 'harvesting rounds' was unduly prolonged (West 1936). A special grade termed 'black cocoa' was produced in Cameroon from pods affected by black pod disease (West and Voelcker 1942). Such beans do not ferment properly (Urquhart 1961), so they were subjected to a particular heat treatment which apparently gave a marketable product (Knapp 1937). Although *P. palmivora* does not apparently persist in damaged beans, other fungi associated with it do. The observation by Bunting (1929a) in Ghana that defective beans were infected by *Botryodiplodia theobromae* before fermentation, was confirmed by Maclean (1953), and in Nigeria by Broadbent (1967) and by Broadbent and Oyeniran (1967, 1968).

Maturity is normally judged by the appearance of the pod but superficial discoloration following thrips (*Selenothrips rubrocinctus*) attack may be misleading, with the result that an affected pod may be harvested too soon or too late (Cotterell 1928). The use of beans from over-ripe or damaged pods should be avoided because there is likelihood of premature germination. Beans normally germinate in about a week, but this procedure was considered to be under the control of a 'germination inhibitor' (Holden 1959), which was apparently lost when there was injury to pulp and/or testa (Forsyth and Quesnel 1958). A consequence of emergence of the radicle through the testa is the likelihood of the cotyledons being invaded by moulds (e.g. species of *Aspergillus* and *Penicillium*), as shown by Bunting (1929a,b) and by Dade (1929).

Factors affecting invasion of beans during fermentation

An unfortunate result of cocoa fermentation is the tendency for the fermented product to have mouldy beans to a greater extent than unfermented cocoa. Several factors operate to make the fermented bean a more favourable milieu for moulds than the unfermented bean. Through fermentation, the testa is altered physically, and made capable of absorbing more liquid and retaining it longer (Laycock 1928). By diffusion of substance from the cotyledons through the shell (testa), the latter is altered chemically, as discussed by Knapp (1937). He reported the greater acidity (pH 3·4) of the shell from unfermented beans, in comparison with the shell of beans after a 7-day fermentation (pH 5·8). Through liquefaction of the pulp and diffusion from the cotyledons, $1\frac{1}{2}$–2 gals. of liquid were produced for every hundredweight (112 lb.) of dry cocoa produced (Birch 1941). Knapp and Wadsworth (1924) found that with a relatively short period of fermentation in Sri Lanka (36 hours), there was little change in the theobromine content of the beans, but with a longer period of fermentation in Trinidad (several days), theobromine entered the shell from the cotyledons. From data provided by Lockard and Burridge (1965*a,b*) and by Deschreider and Van Coillie (1956), concerning contents of copper in leaves (7–15 p.p.m.), cotyledons of unfermented beans (17–20 p.p.m.), cotyledons of fermented beans (33–68 p.p.m.), it seems that this element may be translocated ultimately to shells from leaves. Probably the most important factor determining the proneness of fermented beans to develop mouldiness, is a mainly biological one. In Trinidad, Rombouts (1952) confirmed that beans were contaminated (*ca.* 0·24 million micro-organisms/bean) before they were put into sweat-boxes. When the fermentation process is avoided, development of this microflora is arrested by immediate drying. Otherwise, within a period of about 12 hours, fermentative and non-fermentative yeasts together comprised over 90 per cent of the total microflora. In Jamaica, Bainbridge and Davies (1912) found 5 per cent alcohol (by weight) in the first sweatings.

Most of the heat generated in the course of the cocoa fermentation process comes from aerobic conversion of ethanol to acetic acid, carbon dioxide and water. Hence the need to regulate air supply to achieve a desirable balance between production and destruction of acetic acid (Quesnel 1969).

In the commercial practice of cocoa fermentation (Forsyth and Quesnel 1956, 1963; Rohan 1963), there is wide variation in temperature (range 36–55 °C (97–131 °F.)), aeration ('heap' versus 'box' fermentation), and duration (range $1\frac{1}{2}$–12 days). Various permutations and combinations of these conditions operate selectively with respect to a range of potential inhabitants of the fermented bean as substrate. In this connection, it is worth noting the selectivity of different media for studying (including enumerating) various groups of micro-organisms associated with fermented cocoa beans (Hansen and Welty 1971). There are inherent difficulties in sampling for determination of taxonomic groups and for estimating number of micro-organisms in the course of fermentation. Numbers ranged from 0·0005 millions per bean to 4,000 millions per bean (Rombouts 1952). When the fermenting mass was not stirred, there was on the surface prolific growth of moulds, as illustrated by Rohan (1963), and by Dade (1929).

The latter specified these fungi as *Aspergillus fumigatus* and *Mucor* sp. (subsequently identified as *M. pusillus*), and he commented that *A. fumigatus* actually raised the temperature of the fermenting mass of beans. Both species are thermophilic fungi, as defined by Cooney and Emerson (1964) (having a maximum temperature for growth at or above 50 °C. (122 °F.) and a minimum temperature for growth at or above 20 °C. (68 °F.)). *Pichia kudriavzevii*, also reported in the imperfect state (*Candida krusei*), is a thermotolerant yeast (maximum temperature for growth in range 43–50 °C. (109–122 °F.)) which occurred frequently in fermentations (Rombouts 1953; Roelofsen 1958; de Camargo, Leme, and Filho Martinelli 1963; van Uden and Buckley 1970). In Bahia (Maravalhas 1966d), this yeast was associated with a disfigurement of cocoa beans termed 'white spot' (Knowles 1925), but there and elsewhere this phenomenon was also due to chemical substances (Bunting and Coull 1925; Coull 1925; Knapp 1937; Spoon 1958), and sometimes associated with low air-humidity (Bunting 1929a; Laycock 1931).

Factors affecting invasion of beans after fermentation

There may be opportunity for germination during fermentation since Archibald (1954) reported that germination of uninfected beans was delayed compared with beans having testae infected by fungi. There have been differences of opinion as to whether an 'incipient germination' was necessary (Wadsworth and Howat 1954), or not (Rohan 1963) to initiate subsequent changes for the achievement of satisfactory bean quality (Roesch, Schubiger, and Egli 1961). It is uncertain whether killing of the bean at some stage in the course of fermentation is due to high temperature, alcohol, acetic acid, or carbon dioxide (Knapp 1937; Bridgland and Friend 1957). When germination was arrested so that the testa (shell) was not pierced, there might nevertheless be biodeterioration of the shell, since it is a suitable substrate for species of the genera *Aspergillus* and *Penicillium*. The shell contains tannins (*ca.* 5 per cent), which are used by several species of *Aspergillus* which occur as moulds of beans (Boidin and Prévost 1957).

An oxidation process starts during fermentation, continues enzymically afterwards whilst moisture is being lost (Quesnel and Jugmohunsingh 1970), and ceases when moisture content of the bean is insufficient for enzyme activity. One manifestation of oxidation is the development of the desirable 'chocolate brown' colour of the nib.

The drying process

The main purposes of drying cocoa beans are to avoid uneconomic transport and sale of unnecessary water and to prevent deterioration. Drying may be done expensively through the agency of artificially generated heat, or less expensively by natural 'sun drying'. The choice is not simply an economic one, because available sun heat may be limited. Some cocoa is generally harvested during wet periods when atmospheric humidity may be continuously high. Dade (1930) found that in Ghana sun drying cocoa sometimes extended over 14 days through frequent rain, with the consequence that 30 per cent of this cocoa became mouldy. In contrast to sun drying which generally occupies about 1 week, with use of an oil-fired dryer, Howat, Powell, and Wood (1957) dried cocoa in 1 day or less (14 hours). They discussed several kinds of dryer (Urquhart 1961; Rohan 1963; Wood 1964; Salz 1972).

Moisture content of beans must not exceed 7·5 per cent for purposes of trade outside the producing country (Wood 1972). The procedure for the determination of moisture content of beans is internationally standardized (Anon. 1967). The general theory of moisture in stored produce and its measurement were discussed by Mackay (1967a,b). Whilst a limiting standard of dryness is convenient for statutory purposes, for the study of mouldiness information is required on the condition of water in the beans; particularly important is the limit beyond which biodeterioration will not occur. In general terms, this limit may be considered as analogous to the state of dryness in soil referred to as the 'wilting point'. Moisture-content values do not necessarily indicate the availability of the water because this differs for various substrates having similar moisture contents, through their respective capacities to hold water. All cocoa beans are hygroscopic but some may be more hygroscopic than others (Wood 1965).

Scott (1956) used the term 'water activity' to describe the state of water in a substrate. He regarded a solid substrate of low water content (e.g. raw cocoa bean) as offering a highly concentrated solution for the growth of micro-organisms. When solutes are dissolved in water, the solution has a lower vapour pressure than the pure solvent (water). The term 'water activity' (a_w) is the ratio of the vapour pressure of the solution to the vapour pressure of the solvent. However, for present purposes, it is convenient to use the equivalence of 'water activity' values (o·xx a_w) to 'relative humidity' values (xx per cent R.H.). Snow (1949) and Ayerst (1969) studied the moisture limits (values expressed here as xx) for spore germination of some fungi which occur as moulds of cocoa beans. Two species (*Botrytis cinerea* and *Rhizopus nigricans*) required much moisture (93). Four species (*Aspergillus nidulans, A. niger, Cladosporium herbarum*, and *Trichothecium roseum*) required less moisture (80–90). Least moisture (70–78) was required by the following *Aspergillus* species: *A. candidus, A. glaucus* group (*A. amstelodami, A. chevalieri, A. repens, A. ruber*), *A. restrictus, A. sydowii, A. versicolor*.

Since cocoa beans are hygroscopic their moisture content is unstable until it is in equilibrium with ambient temperature and humidity conditions. Both cocoa bean and an associated fungus may gain or lose water from or to the surrounding atmosphere. To appreciate the conditions under which mould invasion may or may not occur, it is desirable to relate moisture content of the bean to relative humidity at specified temperature. The desideratum is a 'water sorption isotherm', as discussed by Ayerst (1965a,b), which might be used to predict water activity from moisture content, or the reverse. Attempts to establish such relationships for cocoa beans have given discordant results (Scott 1929; Dade 1929; Theimer 1958; Hall 1960; Riley 1961; Davey and Elcoate 1967).

The relations between whole cocoa beans and their environment are complicated because each bean comprises separate tissues (testa (shell) and cotyledons (nib)) which differ in hygroscopicity and consequently in moisture content. That cocoa beans are a 'composite commodity' is evident from the two 'families of curves' given by Mackay (1967a). The shell may be considered as analogous to certain cereal seeds, with equilibrium moisture contents in the range 11–18 per cent, while the nib alone may be considered as analogous to other shelled oil-seeds, with moisture contents in the range 4–10 per cent. The evaluation of bean moisture contents is rendered especially difficult through variations in the proportionalities of shell, nib, and the butterfat content of the latter (Toxopeus 1970). Determinations of moisture content by using either whole intact beans, or whole beans after grinding, are likely to give equivocal information in connection with liability to mouldiness.

Dade (1929) demonstrated the greater hygroscopicity of the shell compared with the nib. When dry cocoa was exposed to a damp atmosphere, water was rapidly taken up by the shell and external mould was likely to occur. Accidental wetting of raw cocoa by rain or sea water probably occurred more often when bulk handling was less efficient (Scott and Hudson 1928). Formerly in Ghana, bags were stacked on the beach and awaited transport in surf boats before shipment (Auchinleck 1930; Urquhart 1961). Such hazards to which cocoa was formerly subjected are epitomized in the name of a species of *Aspergillus* (*A. halophilus*) which was isolated and described from a bean in a bag of cocoa which had been wetted by sea water and then stored near the ship's boilers (Sartory, Sartory, and Meyer 1930).

Washing

Beans were washed to remove the pulp after a short fermentation in Sri Lanka (Knapp 1937), and after normal fermentation in a few countries which were not major producers of cocoa (Forsyth and Quesnel 1956). Any improvement in general appearance of the raw cocoa, including a reduced shell content through washing, was outweighed by the brittleness of the shell which it caused, with consequent susceptibility to mould and insect attack (Rohan 1963). Couprie (1970) considered that washing after fermentation in Uganda was advantageous because it lowered the acidity which tended to be too great when fermented beans there were not washed.

Polishing

The practice of 'working' the cocoa after fermentation comprised two processes termed 'claying' and 'dancing' which were intended to improve the external appearance of the cocoa. According to Rohan (1963), claying increased the weight of beans by 1–2 per cent. Hart (1911) stated a belief that 'cacao prepared by this method keeps better owing to the clay and mucilage forming a thin protective covering which prevents the attack of micro-fungi . . .'. If it has not already ceased everywhere, it is to be expected that the practice of claying will be universally discontinued as a result of regulations against adulteration (Wood 1972). In Bahia after 3 months storage, the mean percentage of mouldy beans was greater in a batch of cocoa which had been 'danced' (1·8 per cent), than in the lot which had not been danced (0·9 per cent), but the difference between these means was not statistically significant (Maravalhas 1966a).

Storage

Willbaux (1965) considered that in tropical ports, cocoa can be safely stored in bags only if its moisture content is below 8 per cent and when the humidity is in the range 66–70 per cent R.H. There is reason to believe that at shipping ports in cocoa-producing countries, atmospheric-humidity conditions (range ca. 72–90 per cent R.H.) are prejudicial to the maintenance of cocoa beans at a satisfactory degree of dryness (Meteorological Office, Tables of temperature, relative humidity and precipitation for the world, Parts I, II, IV, V, VI. London; H.M.S.O.).

Maravalhas (1966c) found that the mouldiness of bagged cocoa increased progressively from June to November in Bahia, where the mean minimum monthly humidity ranged from 71–76 per cent R.H., and the mean maximum monthly humidity ranged from 88–95 per cent R.H. The contents of bags averaged less than 1 per cent beans with internal mould initially, but after 3 months storage, the contents averaged 4 per cent beans with internal mould, with further increase of this average to 28 per cent beans with internal mould after 6 months storage.

In Ghana, for the period January 1970 to December 1971, there was greater incidence of mouldy beans in cocoa shipped from Takoradi than from Tema (Anon. 1972b). From relevant meteorological data (Anon. 1949), it seems likely that this difference was associated with the production and/or shipment of the cocoa from a wetter area (Takoradi), in comparison with a drier area (Tema).

The temperature and humidity conditions for survival and multiplication of some cocoa storage pests were studied by Howe (1956a,b; 1957). These insects will survive low water activity below the limit for spore germination and growth of moulds affecting cocoa (0·7 a_w). Despite the likelihood that insect-damaged beans will be more liable to mouldiness than undamaged beans, there is conflict of opinion as to whether there is such an association (Dade 1929; Forsyth 1962), or not (Passmore 1932). Cranham (1960) referred to 'mould-feeding beetles' (*Carpophilus* spp., Coleoptera, Nitidulidae), but it is not known to what extent insect attack may follow mouldiness.

It should be noted that information from the cut test for grading purposes, gives percentages of a single (prior) defect (e.g. mouldy beans, as either with or without insect damage, or insect-damaged beans without mouldiness) as explained on p. 323.

Sources and dispersal of moulds

The micro-organisms causing mouldiness of cocoa beans are mostly cosmopolitan with many habitats (Skinner, Emmons, and Tsuchiya 1945). Moulds are common constituents of the air-spora and likely to be deposited anywhere, as exemplified by the finding of *Aspergillus glaucus* and *A. niger* in rain samples collected on board ship in the North Atlantic (Gregory 1961).

In England, Passmore (1932) examined samples taken from bags of cocoa originating in Ghana and Nigeria, for a survey of mouldiness and other defects. Among the moulds observed were two species not otherwise reported on West African cocoa (*Aspergillus terreus* and *Penicillium citrinum*). They may have invaded the beans after export. Among twenty-four different species of *Bacillus* and *Micrococcus* isolated from cocoa powders obtained from different manufacturers, were three species also found in fermented beans (*B. cereus, B. megaterium,* and *B. subtilis*). These three species together comprised 38 per cent of the bacterial flora of the cocoa powders (Gabis, Langlois, and Rudnick 1970). It seems likely that some of this bacterial contamination may have occurred in the beans used to produce the powders. The duration (15–70 minutes) and temperature (116–21 °C. (240–50 °F.)) of roast for cocoa powder production (Minifie 1970), may not be lethal for bacteria present in beans. Further contamination may have occurred after the imported beans were roasted.

Ashby (1925) supposed that yeasts associated with fermentation came from pod surfaces. This supposition was supported by the isolation of *Kloeckera africana* from a rotting pod as well as from fermenting beans (Ciferri 1961). Three species were reported from cocoa leaves as well as from beans (*Candida parapsilosis, Rhodotorula rubra,* and *Scopulariopsis fusca*).

In general, the bacteria, yeasts, and other fungi associated with fermentations and mouldiness, probably exist independently of the living cocoa plant. In Nigeria, many cocoa moulds occurred at sites outside the main cocoa areas (MacNulty 1966; McDonald 1969).

Infections of beans presumably occur in the course of opening the pods and accumulating the beans for fermentation, through handling and from soil. The hands of workers are a potential source of infection (Kleinert 1971). It has been shown that the micro-organisms of cocoa fermentations are spread by 'fruit-flies' (probably *Drosophila melanogaster* Meigen, Diptera) in Trinidad (Smith 1913; Knapp 1937; Rombouts 1952). The absence of acetic acid bacteria from certain experimental fermentations (Hoynack, Polansky, and Stone 1941), may have been due to absence of *Drosophila* species (Rombouts 1952). The role of *Drosophila* spp. elsewhere in relation to transport of yeasts has been discussed (Spencer 1950; do Carmo-Sousa 1969; Last and Price 1969).

Control

Chemical methods

Methyl bromide is widely used as a fumigant against storage pests in store and in the holds of ships. Mould (1964) reported an observation that methyl bromide suppressed the rate of development of fungi, and Entwistle (1972) noted some evidence of fungistatic activity.

High moisture content is undesirable in relation to fumigation with methyl bromide (Kisiedu 1966). Because moist beans absorb more fumigant than drier ones, insect survival is greater through reduced concentration of the chemical, due to retention by the fatty tissues of the bean, and thereby the tolerance limit for bromide residue in beans may be exceeded.

In general, preventive chemicals are likely to be inadmissible for cocoa beans intended for food manufacture.

Technical methods

The empirical nature of most cocoa fermentations (Forsyth and Quesnel 1956) suggests that there should be some rationalization of this process. Quesnel (1969) mentioned indications that auxiliary flavours might arise through activities of micro-organisms and he discussed practical ways in which control of conventional fermentation procedures could be improved.

Wadsworth and Howat (1954) claimed that aseptically extracted beans could be made into chocolate having good 'chocolate flavour' either with or without inoculation (mixed culture of *Hansenula anomala* and *Bacterium orleanense*), provided that certain conditions were fulfilled, which included some postponement of the killing of the bean. To avoid the practical difficulty associated with the maintenance of aseptic conditions, Quesnel (1957) tried non-microbial 'fermentations'. The beans were freed from pulp in a washing machine and killed without a 'pre-fermentation' stage (a previous period at about 35 °C. (95 °F.) for about 84 hours, considered important by Wadsworth and Howat 1954). The washed beans were cured by immersion in acetic acid at a range of concentrations for different periods. The optimum condition was immersion in 1 per cent acetic acid at 45 °C. (113 °F.) for about 36 hours. Within the limits of these small-scale experiments, it seemed that a non-microbial procedure could give satis-factory chocolate flavour on roasting, but its possible utility would have to be tested on a larger scale.

A procedure described as 'tray fermentation' (Allison and Rohan 1958) has been used with success in Ghana (Allison and Kenten 1963), and in Costa Rica (Helfenberger 1964). Rohan (1963) discussed this procedure, which saved time and labour, and gave cocoa having a better appearance than the commercial Ghana product.

Rohan (1963) explained that the common criterion of dryness was the crackling sound associated with dried beans when a handful was com-pressed. This test may be misleading if applied in the course of sun drying, when the effects of insolation may be merely superficial. Brittleness of the shells should be tested after the beans have stood in the shade for a few hours.

In connection with use of artificially generated heat, if beans are dried at too high a temperature, there may be loss of fat from the nibs (Spoon 1956). Drying to an excessively low moisture content is undesirable because the protective shells become fragile.

There is need to exercise better control of the attainment of an appro-priate degree of dryness, and its maintenance. A number of devices for estimating surface moisture of cocoa beans is available (Rohan 1963; Mackay 1967b), but it is necessary to have standards against which they can be tested, for a proper appreciation of their imperfections and limita-tions. Scott (1956) advocated direct determination of water activity of foodstuffs in relation to biodeterioration. A method for rapid determination of equilibrium relative humidity of solid substances was adapted by Mossel and van Kuijk (1955) from the lithium chloride cell ('Dewcel') devised by Hickes (1947) for measuring the dew point of air. Ayerst (1965a) described a dew-point apparatus which had the advantage of quite rapid attainment of equilibrium with either whole or ground plant products.

If a sufficiently simple method can be developed for the estimation of moisture content of beans in relation to liability to mouldiness, the appro-priate 'safe' degree of atmospheric humidity may be conveniently checked by using humidity-sensitive impregnated paper (Solomon 1945).

In West Africa, and probably elsewhere under tropical conditions with fairly constant absolute humidity, and rather large diurnal temperature changes, it is generally practicable to achieve and maintain a sufficiently low moisture content of the beans through exposure to a high temperature in combination with sealing against moisture gain at lower temperatures (Powell and Wood 1959a). When the exposed cocoa is judged to have reached a sufficient degree of dryness, it should be bagged and stacked without delay, to limit uptake of moisture (Powell and Wood 1959b).

Powell and Wood (1959b) and Renaud (1960) found that moisture gain can be virtually prevented by containing the dry cocoa beans in a 'polythene liner' within the conventional jute-fibre bag (Coveney 1969). During the test periods (1–4 months duration), the gain of moisture was negligible (less than 1 per cent). Davey and Amos (1961) found that polyethylene film material was penetrated by various insects, including some cocoa storage pests. It is uncertain whether the possible occurrence of such penetration might limit the use of polythene-lined bags for protecting dry cocoa from uptake of moisture.

Bacteria associated with processed cocoa beans

Acetobacter aceti (Pasteur) Beijerinck
　　ASIA: Indonesia (Java) (Roelofsen and Giesberger 1947, as *Acetobacter rancens*). UNLOCALIZED: (Knapp 1935b, as *Bacterium aceti*).
Acetobacter ascendens (Henneberg) Bergey, Breed, Murray and Hitchens
　　UNLOCALIZED: (Knapp 1935b, as *Bacterium ascendens*).
Acetobacter melanogenum Beijerinck
see *Acetomonas oxydans* (Henneberg) Shimwell and Carr
Acetobacter rancens (Beijerinck) Kelly
see *Acetobacter aceti* (Pasteur) Beijerinck
Acetobacter xylinum (Brown) Holland
　　UNLOCALIZED: (Knapp 1935b, as *Bacterium xylinum*).
Acetomonas oxydans (Henneberg) Shimwell and Carr
　　ASIA: Indonesia (Java) (Roelofsen and Giesberger 1947, as *Acetobacter melanogenum*).
Actinomyces albus Krainsky
see *Streptomyces albus* (Rossi-Doria emend. Krainsky) Waksman and Henrici
Actinomyces cacaoi Waksman
see *Streptomyces cacaoi* (Waksman) Waksman and Henrici
Actinomyces griseus Krainsky emend. Waksman
see *Streptomyces griseus* (Krainsky) Waksman and Henrici
Aerobacter aerogenes (Kruse) Beijerinck
　　UNLOCALIZED: (Knapp 1935b, as *Coli aerogenes*; Rombouts 1952).
Bacillus cereus Frankland and Frankland
　　AFRICA: Ghana (Dade 1940, as *Bacillus undulatus*). WEST INDIES: Trinidad (Lopez and Quesnel 1973).
Bacillus cereus var. *mycoides* (Flügge) Smith, Gordon, and Clark
　　WEST INDIES: Trinidad (Lopez and Quesnel 1973).
Bacillus megaterium de Bary
　　AFRICA: Ghana (Dade 1940). WEST INDIES: Trinidad (Lopez and Quesnel 1973).
Bacillus subtilis Cohn
　　WEST INDIES: Jamaica (Bainbridge and Davies 1912); Trinidad (Lopez and Quesnel 1973).
Bacillus undulatus den Dooren de Jong
see *Bacillus cereus* Frankland and Frankland
Bacterium aceti (Pasteur) Lanzi
see *Acetobacter aceti* (Pasteur) Beijerinck

Bacterium ascendens Henneberg
see *Acetobacter ascendens* (Hennenberg) Bergey, Breed, Murray, and Hitchens
Bacterium orleanense Henneberg
UNLOCALIZED: (Knapp 1935*b*).
Bacterium xylinoides Henneberg
UNLOCALIZED: (Knapp 1935*b*).
Bacterium xylinum Brown
see *Acetobacter xylinum* (Brown) Holland
Coli aerogenes auct.
see *Aerobacter aerogenes* (Kruse) Beijerinck
Flavobacterium synxanthum (Ehrenberg) Holland
see *Pseudomonas synxantha* (Ehrenberg) Holland
Lactobacillus fermenti Beijerinck
ASIA: Indonesia (Java) (Roelofsen and Giesberger 1947).
Micropolyspora faeni Cross, Maciver and Lacey
WEST INDIES: Trinidad (Lacey, J. 1969 *in litt.*).
Pseudomonas synxantha (Ehrenberg) Holland
NORTH AMERICA: U.S.A. (Hoynack, Polansky, and Stone 1941, uncertain determination as *Flavobacterium synxanthum*).
Streptomyces albus (Rossi-Doria emend. Krainsky) Waksman and Henrici
AFRICA: Nigeria (Lacey, J., 1969 *in litt.*). WEST INDIES: Dominican Republic (Ciferri 1931, as *Actinomyces albus*); Trinidad (Lacey, J. 1969 *in litt.*).
Streptomyces cacaoi (Waksman) Waksman and Henrici
AFRICA: Nigeria (Bunting 1932, as *Actinomyces cacaoi*).
Streptomyces griseus (Krainsky) Waksman and Henrici
AFRICA: Nigeria (Lacey, J. 1969 *in litt.*). WEST INDIES: Dominican Republic (Ciferri 1931, as *Actinomyces griseus*); Trinidad (Lacey, J. 1969 *in litt.*).
Thermoactinomyces vulgaris Tsiklinsky
AFRICA: Nigeria (Lacey, J. 1969 *in litt.*). WEST INDIES: Trinidad (Lacey, J. 1969 *in litt.*).
Thermomonospora viridis (Schuurmans, Olson and San Clements) Küster and Locci
WEST INDIES: Trinidad (Lacey, J. 1969 *in litt.*).

Fungi associated with processed cocoa beans

Absidia blakesleeana Lendner
AFRICA: Ghana (Dade 1940, as *Absidia cristata*).
Absidia capillata van Tiegh.
AFRICA: Ghana (Dade 1940, uncertain taxon (Zycha, Siepmann and Linnemann 1969)).
Absidia corymbifera (Cohn) Sacc. and Trott.
AFRICA: Ghana (Dade 1940, as *Absidia regnieri*); Nigeria (Oyeniran 1973).
Absidia cristata Dade
see *Absidia blakesleeana* Lendner
Absidia ramosa (Lindt) Lendner
AFRICA: Ghana (Dade 1940, as *Absidia truchisi*).

Absidia regnieri (Lucet and Cost.) Lendner
see *Absidia corymbifera* (Cohn) Sacc. and Trott.

Absidia truchisi (Lucet and Cost.) Lender
see *Absidia ramosa* (Lindt) Lendner

Acrostalagmus vilmorinii Guéguen forma *thomensis* Guéguen
AFRICA: S. Tomé (Guéguen 1910, associated with damage by *Xyleborus perforans* (Wollaston)).

Alternaria alternata (Fr.) Keissler
WEST INDIES: Dominican Republic (Ciferri 1931, as *Alternaria tenuis*).

Alternaria tenuis Nees ex Pers.
see *Alternaria alternata* (Fr.) Keissler

Arthrinium phaeospermum (Corda) M. B. Ellis
WEST INDIES: Dominican Republic (Ciferri 1927*b*, as *Coniosporium phaeospermum*).

Aspergillus aculeatus Iizuka
AFRICA: Nigeria (Oyeniran 1973).

Aspergillus amstelodami (Mangin) Thom and Church
WEST INDIES: Trinidad (Lacey, J. 1969 *in litt.*).

Aspergillus candidus Link ex Fr.
AFRICA: Ghana (Dade 1940). WEST INDIES: Trinidad (Lacey, J. 1969 *in litt.*).

Aspergillus carbonarius (Bain.) Thom
AFRICA: Ghana (Dade 1940); Nigeria (Oyeniran 1973). SOUTH AMERICA: Venezuela (Ferdinandsen and Winge 1910, as *Aspergillus dipus*). WEST INDIES: Haiti (Busse, Henneberg and Zeller 1929).

Aspergillus chevalieri (Mangin) Thom and Church
AFRICA: Ghana (Dade 1940); Nigeria (Broadbent and Oyeniran 1968) WEST INDIES: Trinidad (Lacey, J. 1969 *in litt.*).

Aspergillus clavatus Desm.
AFRICA: Malagasy (Madagascar) (Wilbaux 1963).

Aspergillus delacroixii Sacc. and Syd.
see *Aspergillus olivaceus* Delacr.

Aspergillus dipus Ferd. and Winge
see *Aspergillus carbonarius* (Bain.) Thom

Aspergillus fischeri Wehmer
AFRICA: Ghana (Dade 1940).

Aspergillus flavipes (Bain. and Sart.) Thom and Church
AFRICA: Ghana (Dade 1940).

Aspergillus flavus Link ex Fr.
AFRICA: Cameroon (S.W.) Busse *et al.* 1929); Ghana (Dade 1940); Ivory Coast (Renaud 1953); Nigeria (West 1938); Sierra Leone (Deighton 1956); S. Tomé (Goveia and Sousa 1968). WEST INDIES: Dominican Republic (Ciferri 1927*b*); Haiti (Busse *et al.* 1929).

Aspergillus flavus Link ex Fr. var. *columnaris* Raper and Fennell
AFRICA: Nigeria (Lacey, J. 1969 *in litt.*). WEST INDIES: Trinidad (Lacey, J. 1969 *in litt.*).

Aspergillus flavus mut. *rufus* Blochwitz
see *Aspergillus tamarii* Kita
Aspergillus fumigatus Fres.
  AFRICA: Ghana (Dade 1940); Ivory Coast (Renaud 1953); Nigera (West 1938). SOUTH AMERICA: Brazil (Maravalhas 1966c). WEST INDIES: Dominican Republic (Ciferri 1931); Trinidad (Lacey, J. 1969 *in litt.*).
Aspergillus giganteus Wehmer
  AFRICA: Cameroon (S.W.) (Busse *et al.* 1929).
Aspergillus glaucus (group)
  AFRICA: Fernando Po (Nosti and Alvarez N.D.); Ghana (Bunting 1929b); Ivory Coast (Renaud 1953); Nigeria (Laycock 1931); S. Tomé (Lutz 1906). SOUTH AMERICA: Brazil (Maravalhas 1965). WEST INDIES: Dominican Republic (Ciferri 1931); Trinidad (Lacey, J. 1969 *in litt.*). ASIA: Indonesia (Java) (Knapp 1935a). EUROPE England (Bunting 1931).
Aspergillus gracilis Bain.
  AFRICA: Ghana (Dade 1940, as *Aspergillus gracilis* Saito). EUROPE: England (Passmore 1932).
Aspergillus halophilus A. and R. Sartory and Meyer
  EUROPE: France (Sartory, A., Sartory, R., and Meyer 1930).
Aspergillus insuetus (Bain.) Thom and Church
see *Aspergillus ustus* (Bain.) Thom and Church
Aspergillus japonicus Saito
  AFRICA: Ghana (Piening 1962).
Aspergillus nidulans (Eidam) Wint.
  AFRICA: Nigeria (Oyeniran 1973). WEST INDIES: Dominican Republic (Ciferri 1931); Trinidad (Lacey, J. 1969 *in litt.*).
Aspergillus niger van Tiegh.
  AFRICA: Cameroon (S.W.) (Busse *et al.* 1929); Fernando Po (Nosti and Alvarez N.D.); Ghana (Hughes 1952); Ivory Coast (Renaud 1953); Nigeria (Oyeniran 1973); S. Tomé (Lutz 1906, as *Sterigmatocystis nigra*). SOUTH AMERICA: Brazil (Bahia) (Maravalhas 1966e). WEST INDIES: Dominican Republic (Ciferri 1931); Haiti (Busse *et al.* 1929); Trinidad (Lacey, J. 1969 *in litt.*).
Aspergillus ochraceus Wilhelm
  AFRICA: Ghana (Dade 1940); Nigeria (Lacey, J. 1969 *in litt.*); S. Tomé (Goveia and Sousa 1968). WEST INDIES: Trinidad (Lacey, J. 1969 *in litt.*).
Aspergillus olivaceus Delacr.
  SOUTH AMERICA: Colombia (Delacroix 1897). ASIA: Philippines (Teodoro 1937, as *Aspergillus delacroixii*).
Aspergillus penicilloides Speg.
  AFRICA: Nigeria (Oyeniran 1973).
Aspergillus pseudoglaucus Blochwitz
  AFRICA: Nigeria (Broadbent 1967).
Aspergillus repens de Bary
  AFRICA: Cameroon (S.W.) (Busse *et al.* 1929); S. Tomé (Busse *et al.*, 1929). WEST INDIES: Trinidad (Lacey, J. 1969 *in litt.*). EUROPE: England (Passmore 1932).

Aspergillus restrictus G. Smith
  AFRICA: Nigeria (Broadbent and Oyeniran 1968). WEST INDIES:
  Trinidad (Lacey, J. 1969 *in litt.*).
Aspergillus ruber (Konig, Spieckermann and Bremer) Thom and Church
  AFRICA: Nigeria (Broadbent and Oyeniran 1968). EUROPE: England
  (Passmore 1932).
Aspergillus sydowii (Bain. and Sart.) Thom and Church
  AFRICA: Ghana (Dade 1940); Nigeria (West 1938). EUROPE: England
  (Passmore 1932).
Aspergillus tamarii Kita
  AFRICA: Ghana (Dade 1940, as *A. tamarii*, and as *A. flavus* var. *rufus* (Raper
  and Fennell 1965)); Ivory Coast (Renaud 1953); Nigeria (Laycock 1931); S.
  Tomé (Goveia and Sousa 1968). WEST INDIES: Dominican Republic
  (Ciferri 1931); Haiti (Busse *et al.* 1929); Trinidad (Lacey, J. 1969 *in litt.*).
Aspergillus tamarii var. *castus* Dade
  see *Aspergillus wentii* Wehmer
Aspergillus terreus Thom
  SOUTH AMERICA: Brazil (Busse *et al.* 1929). WEST INDIES: Trinidad
  (Lacey, J. 1969 *in litt.*). EUROPE: England (Passmore 1932).
Aspergillus umbrosus Bain. and Sart.
  EUROPE: England (Anon. 1973).
Aspergillus ustus (Bain.) Thom and Church
  AFRICA: Ghana (Dade 1940, as *A. insuetus*).
Aspergillus versicolor (Vuill.) Tirab.
  AFRICA: Cameroon (S.W.) (Busse *et al.* 1929); Nigeria (Oyeniran 1973).
  WEST INDIES: Dominican Republic (Ciferri 1931).
Aspergillus wentii Wehmer
  AFRICA: Ghana (Dade 1940; Piening 1962, as *A. tamarii* var. *castus* (Raper
  and Fennell 1965)).
Aureobasidium pullulans (de Bary) Arn.
  WEST INDIES: Dominican Republic (Ciferri 1931, as *Pullularia* (*Dema-
  tium*) *pullulans*).
Blastoconium tropicum Cif.
  WEST INDIES: Dominican Republic (Ciferri 1931).
Botryodiplodia theobromae Pat.
  AFRICA: Ghana (Bunting 1929*a*); Nigeria (Broadbent 1967).
Botrytis cinerea Pers. ex Pers.
  WEST INDIES: Dominican Republic (Ciferri 1931, as *Botrytis vulgaris*).
Botrytis vulgaris (Link) Fr.
  see *Botrytis cinerea* Pers. ex Pers.
Calonectria rigidiuscula (Berk. and Br.) Sacc.
  AFRICA: S. Tomé (Lutz 1906, as *Fusarium theobromae* Lutz (syn. *Fusarium
  decemcellulare* Brick, not *Fusarium theobromae* App. and Strunk).
Candida cacaoi Buckley and van Uden
  WEST INDIES: Trinidad (Buckley and van Uden 1968).
Candida catenulata Diddens and Lodder
  WEST INDIES: Trinidad (Roelofsen 1958).

Candida krusei (Castell.) Berkhout
see *Pichia kudriavzevii* Boidin, Pignal, and Besson
Candida krusei var. *vanlaeriana* (Lindner and Genoud) Diddens and Lodder
see *Pichia membranaefaciens* (Hansen) Hansen
Candida mycoderma (Reess) Lodder and Kreger-van Rij
  SOUTH AMERICA: Brazil (de Camargo *et al.* 1963; this taxon has been subdivided (van Uden and Buckley 1970)).
Candida parapsilosis (Ashford) Langeron and Talice
  SOUTH AMERICA: Brazil (de Camargo *et al.* 1963).
Catenularia fuliginea Saito
see *Sporendonema sebi* Fr.
Cephaliophora irregularis Thaxter
  EUROPE: England (Goos 1964).
Cephaliophora tropica Thaxter
  AFRICA: Ghana (Dade 1940).
Cephalosporium acremonium Corda
  WEST INDIES: Dominican Republic (Ciferri 1931).
Chrysosporium pruinosum (Gilman and Abbott) Carmichael
  WEST INDIES: Trinidad (Lacey, J. 1969 *in litt.*, as *Sporotrichum pruinosum*).
Circinella muscae (Sorokine) Berlese and de Toni
  AFRICA: Ghana (Dade 1940, as *C. spinosa*).
Circinella spinosa van Tiegh. and Le Monnier
see *Circinella muscae* (Sorokine) Berlese and de Toni
Cladosporium herbarum (Pers.) Link ex S. F. Gray
  WEST INDIES: Dominican Republic (Ciferri 1927*b*).
Coniosporium phaeospermum (Corda) Sacc.
see *Arthrinium phaeospermum* (Corda) M. B. Ellis
Curvularia lunata (Walker) Boedijn
  AFRICA: Nigeria (Oyeniran 1973).
Cylindrocarpon tonkinense Bugn.
  AFRICA: Nigeria (Oyeniran 1973).
Dactylomyces crustaceus Apinis and Chesters
see *Thermoascus crustaceus* (Apinis and Chesters) Stolk
Dendryphion congestum Cif.
  WEST INDIES: Dominican Republic (Ciferri 1931).
Endomycopsis javanensis (Klöcker) Dekker
  SOUTH AMERICA: Brazil (Bahia) (Maravalhas 1966*e*).
Eutorulopsis theobromae Cif.
see *Torulopsis candida* (Saito) Lodder
Fusarium equiseti (Corda) Sacc.
  AFRICA: Nigeria (Oyeniran 1973).
Fusarium oxysporum Schlecht.
  AFRICA: Nigeria (Oyeniran 1973). WEST INDIES: Dominican Republic (Ciferri 1931, uncertain determination as *F. zonatum*).
Fusarium sambucinum Fuckel
  WEST INDIES: Dominican Republic (Ciferri 1931, uncertain determination as *F. sarcochroum*).

Fusarium sarcochroum (Desm.) Sacc.
see *Fusarium sambucinum* Fuckel
Fusarium solani (Mart.) Sacc.
 AFRICA: Cameroon (S.W.) (Appel and Strunk 1904, as *F. theobromae*);
 Nigeria (Broadbent and Oyeniran 1967); Sierra Leone (Herb. I.M.I.).
Fusarium theobromae App. and Strunk
see *Fusarium solani* (Mart.) Sacc.
Fusarium theobromae Lutz
see *Calonectria rigidiuscula* (Berk. and Br.) Sacc.
Fusarium zonatum Wollenw.
see *Fusarium oxysporum* Schlecht.
Geotrichum byssinum Cif.
see *Geotrichum candidum* Link ex Pers.
Geotrichum byssinum var. *rigidum* Cif.
see *Geotrichum candidum* Link ex Pers.
Geotrichum candidum Link ex Pers.
 AFRICA: Nigeria (Oyeniran 1973). SOUTH AMERICA: Brazil (Bahia) (de
 Camargo *et al.* 1963). WEST INDIES: Dominican Republic (Fragoso and
 Ciferri 1927, as *Polyscytalum saccardianum*; Ciferri 1931, as *G. byssinum*,
 G. byssinum var. *rigidum, G. cerebrinum, G. flexuosum*; Ciferri 1961, as *G.
 candidum*, associated with pod damage by *Melanerpes striatus* (see Chapter 5));
 Trinidad (Butler 1960). ASIA: Indonesia (Java) (Knapp 1935*a*, as *Oidium
 lactis*).
Geotrichum cerebrinum Cif.
see *Geotrichum candidum* Link ex Pers.
Geotrichum flexuosum Cif.
see *Geotrichum candidum* Link ex Pers.
Gliocladium roseum Bain.
 WEST INDIES: Dominican Republic (Ciferri 1961, as *Penicillium roseum*).
Hansenula anomala (Hansen) H. and P. Sydow var. *anomala* Wickerham
 WEST INDIES: Dominican Republic (Ciferri 1931, as *Saccharomyces ano-
 malus*; 1961); Jamaica (Knapp 1935*a, b*); Trinidad (Roelofsen 1958).
Helicostylum piriforme Bain.
 EUROPE: England (Anon. 1973).
Helminthosporium cacaophilum Cif.
 WEST INDIES: Dominican Republic (Ciferri 1931).
Hemispora stellata Vuill.
 AFRICA: S. Tomé (Goveia and Sousa 1968).
Hormodendrum pallidum Oudem.
 WEST INDIES: Dominican Republic (Ciferri 1931, uncertain determination
 as *Hormodendron pallidum*).
Humicola lanuginosa (Griffon and Maublanc) Bunce
see *Thermomyces lanuginosus* Tsiklinsky
Isaria cretacea van Beyma
 AFRICA: Ghana (Anon. 1973).
Kloeckera africana (Klöcker) Janke
 WEST INDIES: Dominican Republic (Ciferri 1930, as *K. domingensis*; 1931,
 as *K. cacaoicola*; 1961, as *K. africana*).

Kloeckera apiculata (Reess emend. Klöcker) Janke
AFRICA: Cameroon (Knapp 1935*a*, *b* as *Saccharomyces apiculatus*); Ghana (Lodder and Kreger-van Rij 1952). SOUTH AMERICA: Brazil (de Camargo *et al.* 1963). WEST INDIES: Dominican Republic (Knapp 1935*a*, *b*); Jamaica (Knapp 1935*a*, *b*); Puerto Rico (Smith 1913); Trinidad (Roelofsen 1958).

Kloeckera cacaoicola Cif.
see *Kloeckera africana* (Klöcker) Janke

Kloeckera domingensis Cif.
see *Kloeckera africana* (Klöcker) Janke

Macrosporium commune Rabenh.
see *Macrosporium sarcinula* Berk.

Macrosporium sarcinula Berk.
WEST INDIES: Dominican Republic (Ciferri 1927*a*, as *M. commune*).

Monascus purpureus Went
AFRICA: Ghana (Manandhar and Apinis 1971).

Monilia sitophila (Mont.) Sacc.
see *Neurospora sitophila* Shear and Dodge

Mortierella spinosa Linnemann
SOUTH AMERICA: Brazil (Maravalhas 1966*d*).

Mucor arrhizus (Fischer) Hagem
see *Rhizopus arrhizus* Fischer

Mucor buntingii Lendner
see *Mucor pusillus* Lindt

Mucor circinelloides van Tiegh.
WEST INDIES: Dominican Republic (Ciferri 1927*b*, uncertain determination).

Mucor mucedo (L.) Fres.
AFRICA: S. Tomé (Henriques 1917). WEST INDIES: Dominican Republic (Ciferri 1927*b*).

Mucor pusillus Lindt
AFRICA: Ghana (Lendner 1930, as *M. buntingii*); Nigeria (Broadbent and Oyeniran 1967). SOUTH AMERICA: Brazil (Maravalhas 1966*e*). WEST INDIES: Trinidad (Baker and Dale 1951).

Mucor racemosus Fres.
WEST INDIES: Dominican Republic (Ciferri 1931, uncertain determination)

Mycotorula ramosa (Saito) Cif. var. *dominicana* Cif.
see *Rhodotorula aurantiaca* (Saito) Lodder.

Neurospora sitophila Shear and Dodge
AFRICA: Ghana (Bunting 1929*a*, *b*, as *Monilia sitophila*); Nigeria (Broadbent and Oyeniran 1967). WEST INDIES: Dominican Republic (Ciferri 1927*a*, *b*, as *Spicaria lateritia*).

Nigrospora sacchari (Speg.) Mason
AFRICA: Ghana (Dade 1940).

Oidium lactis Fres.
see *Geotrichum candidum* Link ex Pers.

Oospora nivea (Fuckel) Sacc. and Vogl.
WEST INDIES: Dominican Republic (Ciferri 1927*b*).

Paecilomyces variotii Bain.
  AFRICA: Ghana (Herb. I.M.I.); Nigeria (Broadbent and Oyeniran 1967).
  SOUTH AMERICA: Brazil (Bahia) (Maravalhas 1966e). WEST INDIES:
  Trinidad (Lacey, J. 1969 *in litt.*).
Penicillium candidum Link
  see *Penicillium expansum* Link (series)
Pencillium citrinum Thom
  AFRICA: Nigeria (Oyreniran 1973). SOUTH AMERICA: Brazil (Bahia)
  (Maravalhas 1966e). EUROPE: England (Passmore 1932).
Pencillium crustaceum Fr.
  see *Pencillium expansum* Link (series)
Pencillium expansum Link (series)
  AFRICA: S. Tomé (Lutz 1906, as *P. glaucum*). WEST INDIES: Dominican
  Republic (Fragoso and Ciferri 1927, as *P. candidum*; Ciferri 1931, as *P.
  leucopus*; Ciferri 1961, as *P. crustaceum*). ASIA: Indonesia (Java) (Knapp 1937,
  as *P. glaucum*).
Penicillium glaucum Link
  see *Penicillium expansum* Link (series)
Penicillium leucopus (Pers.) Biourge
  see *Pencillium expansum* Link (series)
Penicillium luteum Zukal (series)
  WEST INDIES: Dominican Republic (Ciferri 1961).
Penicillium multicolor Grigorieva-Manoilova and Poradielova
  UNLOCALIZED: (Hill and Lacey 1971).
Penicillium notatum Westling
  WEST INDIES: Dominican Republic (Ciferri 1931).
Penicillium piceum Raper and Fennell
  AFRICA: Nigeria (Lacey, J. 1969 *in litt.*). WEST INDIES; Trinidad (Lacey,
  J. 1969 *in litt.*).
Pencillium roseum Link
  see *Gliocladium roseum* Bain.
Penicillium steckii Zaleski
  AFRICA: Nigeria (Oyeniran 1973).
Pichia farinosa (Lindner) Hansen
  WEST INDIES: Trinidad (Roelofsen 1958).
Pichia fermentans Lodder
  SOUTH AMERICA: Brazil (Bahia) (de Camargo *et al.* 1963). WEST
  INDIES: Trinidad (Roelofsen 1958). ASIA: Indonesia (Java) (Roelofsen
  1953).
Pichia kluyveri Bedford
  WEST INDIES: Trinidad (Kreger-van Rij 1970). ASIA: Indonesia (Java)
  (Kreger-van Rij 1970).
Pichia kudriavzevii Boidin, Pignal and Besson
  AFRICA: Ghana (Lodder and Kreger-van Rij 1952, as *Candida krusei*).
  SOUTH AMERICA: Brazil (Bahia) (de Camargo *et al.* 1963). WEST IN-
  DIES: Trinidad (Roelofsen 1958).
Pichia membranaefaciens (Hansen) Hansen
  AFRICA: Ghana (Lodder and Kreger-van Rij 1952, as *Candida krusei* var.

vanlaeriana, isolated by Dade from fermentation (? cocoa or palm wine))
SOUTH AMERICA: Brazil (Bahia) (de Camargo *et al.* 1963). WEST
INDIES: Trinidad (Roelofsen 1958). ASIA: Sri Lanka (Knapp 1935*a*, as
Saccharomyces membranaefaciens).

Pichia pijperi van der Walt and Tscheuschner
 AFRICA: Ghana (Kreger-van Rij 1970).
Polyscytalum saccardianum Brizi
 see *Geotrichum candidum* Link ex Pers.
Pseudoabsidia vulgaris Bain.
 AFRICA: S. Tomé (Lutz 1906, uncertain taxon (not considered by Zycha,
 Siepmann and Linnemann 1969)).
Pullularia pullulans (de Bary) Berkhout
 see *Aureobasidium pullulans* (de Bary) Arn.
Rhizopus arrhizus Fischer
 AFRICA: Nigeria (Oyeniran 1973). WEST INDIES: Dominican Republic
 (Ciferri 1927*b*, as *Mucor arrhizus*). UNLOCALIZED: (Lendner 1908, as
 Rhizopus nodosus, on cocoa, probably in comestible form).
Rhizopus nigricans Ehrenb.
 AFRICA: S. Tomé (Goveia and Sousa 1968). WEST INDIES: Dominican
 Republic (Ciferri 1927*a*).
Rhizopus nodosus Namysl.
 see *Rhizopus arrhizus* Fischer
Rhodotorula aurantiaca (Saito) Lodder
 WEST INDIES: Dominican Republic (Ciferri 1931, as *Mycotorula ramosa*
 var. *dominicana*, and as *Torulopsis aurantiaca*).
Rhodotorula graminis di Menna
 ASIA: Indonesia (Java) (Phaff and Ahearn 1970).
Rhodotorula rubra (Demme) Lodder
 WEST INDIES: Dominican Republic (Ciferri 1931, as *Torulopsis mucila-
 ginosa*).
Saccharomyces anomalus Hansen
 see *Hansenula anomala* (Hansen) H. and P. Sydow var. *anomala* Wickerham
Saccharomyces apiculatus Reess
 see *Kloeckera apiculata* (Reess emend. Klöcker) Janke
Saccharomyces carlsbergensis Hansen
 see *Saccharomyces uvarum* Beijerinck
Saccharomyces cerevisiae Hansen
 AFRICA: Cameroon (von Lilienfeld-Toal 1927, as *S. ellipsoideus* var. *tropicus*);
 Ghana (Dade 1940). SOUTH AMERICA: Brazil (Ciferri 1931, as *S. ellip-
 soideus* var. *brasiliensis*). WEST INDIES: Dominican Republic (Ciferri
 1931, as *S. ellipsoideus* var. *tropicus*; 1961, as *S. cerevisiae* var *ellipsoideus*);
 Puerto Rico (Smith 1913, as *S. ellipsoideus*); Trinidad (Knapp 1935*a, b*;
 Roelofsen 1958). ASIA: Indonesia (Java) (Roelofsen 1953); Sri Lanka (Knapp
 1935*a, b*)
Saccharomyces cerevisiae Hansen var. *ellipsoideus* (Hansen) Dekker
 see *Saccharomyces cerevisiae* Hansen
Saccharomyces chevalieri Guillier.
 ASIA: Indonesia (Java) (Roelofsen 1953).

Saccharomyces ellipsoideus Hansen
see *Saccharomyces cerevisiae* Hansen
Saccharomyces ellipsoideus Hansen var. *brasiliensis* Cif.
see *Saccharomyces cerevisiae* Hansen
Saccharomyces ellipsoideus Hansen var. *domingensis* Cif.
see *Saccharomyces fermentati* (Saito) Lodder and Kreger-van Rij
Saccharomyces ellipsoideus Hansen var. *tropicus* Lilienfeld-Toal and Henneberg
see *Saccharomyces cerevisiae* Hansen
Saccharomyces fermentati (Saito) Lodder and Kreger-van Rij
   WEST INDIES: Dominican Republic (Ciferri 1931, as *S. ellipsoideus* var. *domingensis*).
Saccharomyces membranaefaciens Hansen
see *Pichia membranaefaciens* (Hansen) Hansen
Saccharomyces rosei (Guillier.) Lodder and Kreger-van Rij
   WEST INDIES: Trinidad (Roelofsen 1958, incorrectly as *Torulopsis rosei* (Roelofsen, P. A. 1962 *in litt.*))
Saccharomyces theobromae Preyer
see *Torulopsis candida* (Saito) Lodder
Saccharomyces theobromae-fermentans Cif.
   WEST INDIES: Trinidad (Ciferri 1931).
Saccharomyces uvarum Beijerinck
   SOUTH AMERICA: Brazil (de Camargo *et al.* 1963, as *S. carlsbergensis*).
Schizoblastosporion domingensis Cif.
see *Schizoblastosporion starkeyi-henricii* Cif.
Schizoblastosporion santhomensis Cif.
   AFRICA: S. Tomé (Ciferri 1931).
Schizoblastosporion starkeyi-henricii Cif.
   WEST INDIES: Dominican Republic (Ciferri 1931, as *S. domingensis*).
Schizosaccharomyces bussei Lilienfeld-Toal and Henneberg
see *Schizosaccharomyces pombe* Lindner
Schizosaccharomyces pombe Lindner
   AFRICA: Cameroon (von Lilienfeld-Toal 1927, as *S. bussei*).
   WEST INDIES: Dominican Republic (Ciferri 1931, as *Schizotorulopsis bussei*); Trinidad (Roelofsen 1958).
Schizotorulopsis bussei Cif.
see *Schizosaccharomyces pombe* Lindner
Scopulariopsis brevicaulis (Sacc.) Bain.
   AFRICA: Ghana (Dade 1940). WEST INDIES: Trinidad (Lacey, J. 1969 *in litt.*).
Scopulariopsis fusca Zach
   AFRICA: Ghana (Morton and Smith 1963).
Spicaria lateritia Cif.
see *Neurospora sitophila* Shear and Dodge
Sporendonema epizoum (Corda) Cif. and Red.
see *Sporendonema sebi* Fr.
Sporendonema sebi Fr.
   WEST INDIES: Dominican Republic (Ciferri 1931, as *Catenularia fuliginea*; Ciferri 1961, as *S. epizoum*).

Sporotrichum flavicans Fr.
  EUROPE: England (Passmore 1932).
Sporotrichum pruinosum Gilman and Abbott
see *Chrysosporium pruinosum* (Gilman and Abbott) Carmichael
Sterigmatocystis luteonigra Lutz
  AFRICA: S. Tomé (Lutz 1906).
Sterigmatocystis nigra van Tiegh.
see *Aspergillus niger* van Tiegh.
Syncephalastrum cinereum Bain.
see *Syncephalastrum racemosum* Cohn ex Schroet.
Syncephalastrum racemosum Cohn ex Schroet.
  AFRICA: Congo (Burle 1962, as *S. cinereum*); Ghana (Dade 1940); Nigeria
  (Oyeniran 1973). EUROPE: England (Passmore 1932).
Syncephalis nana Dade
  AFRICA: Ghana (Dade 1940, as hyperparasite, on *Absidia corymbifera*).
Thermoascus aurantiacus Miehe
  WEST INDIES: Trinidad (Lacey, J. 1969 *in litt.*).
Thermoascus crustaceus (Apinis and Chesters) Stolk
  AFRICA: Nigeria (Lacey, J. 1969 *in litt.*, as *Dactylomyces crustaceus*). WEST
  INDIES: Trinidad (Lacey, J. 1969 *in litt.*).
Thermomyces lanuginosus Tsiklinsky
  AFRICA: Nigeria (Lacey, J. 1969 *in litt.*, as *Humicola lanuginosa*). WEST
  INDIES: Trinidad (Lacey, J. 1969 *in litt.*).
Thielavia setosa Dade
  AFRICA: Ghana (Dade 1940).
Torula conglutinata Corda
  WEST INDIES: Dominican Republic (Ciferri 1927*b*).
Torula herbarum (Pers.) Link ex Fr.
  WEST INDIES: Dominican Republic (Fragoso and Ciferri 1927).
Torulopsis aurantiaca (Saito) Cif. and Red.
see *Rhodotorula aurantiaca* (Saito) Lodder
Torulopsis candida (Saito) Lodder
  SOUTH AMERICA: Brazil (Maravalhas 1966*e*). WEST INDIES: Domini-
  can Republic (Ciferri 1931, as *Eutorulopsis theobromae, T. hamel-smithii*,
  and *T. lilienfeld-toalii*; 1961, as *T. famata*); Jamaica (Knapp 1935*a, b*, as
  Saccharomyces theobromae); St. Lucia (Knapp 1935*a, b*). ASIA: Sri Lanka
  (Preyer 1901, as *S. theobromae*).
Torulopsis famata (Harrison) Lodder and Krefer-van Rij
see *Torulopsis candida* (Saito) Lodder
Torulopsis hamel-smithii Cif.
see *Torulopsis candida* (Saito) Lodder
Torulopsis lilienfeld-toalii Cif.
see *Torulopsis candida* (Saito) Lodder
Torulopsis mucilaginosa (Jörgensen) Cif. and Red.
see *Rhodotorula rubra* (Demme) Lodder
Torulopsis neotropica Cif.
  CENTRAL AMERICA: Costa Rica (Ciferri 1931). WEST INDIES:
  Trinidad (Ciferri 1931).

Torulopsis rosei auct.

see *Saccharomyces rosei* (Guillier.) Lodder and Kreger-van Rij

Trichosporon pullulans (Lindner) Diddens and Lodder
   WEST INDIES: Trinidad (Roelofsen 1958).

Trichothecium roseum (Pers.) Link ex S. F. Gray
   AFRICA: S. Tomé (Goveia and Sousa 1968). WEST INDIES: Dominican
   Republic (Ciferri 1931).

APPENDIX REFERENCES

AINSWORTH, G. C. (1961). *Ainsworth and Bisby's Dictionary of the fungi.* 5th ed. Commonwealth Mycological Institute; Kew.

—— (1971). *Ainsworth and Bisby's dictionary of the fungi.* 6th ed. Commonwealth Mycological Institute; Kew.

ALLISON, H. W. S. and KENTEN, R. H. (1963). Tray fermentation of cocoa. *Trop. Agric., Trin.* **40**, 15–24.

—— and ROHAN, T. A. (1958). A new approach to the fermentation of West African amelonado cocoa. *Trop. Agric., Trin.* **35**, 279–88.

ALVIM, P. de T. (1965). Eco-physiology of the cacao tree. *Conf. Intle Rech. agron. cacaoyères. Abidjan, 15–20 nov. 1965,* pp. 23–35. Imprimerie Jouve; Paris.

ANONYMOUS (1949). Weather on the West Coast of tropical Africa. *M.O.* **492**, 1–281. H.M.S.O.; London.

—— (1956). *The main products of the overseas territories. Cocoa.* The Organization for European Economic Co-operation; Paris.

—— (1963). Organoleptic examination. Present International Method. *Analytical methods of the Office International du Cacao et du Chocolat,* p. 2—E/1963. Zürich; Verlag Max Glättli.

—— (1967). Determination of moisture. Present International method. *Analytical methods of the Office International du Cacao et du Chocolat,* p. 3—E/1952. Zürich; Verlag Max Glättli.

—— (1968). *Raw Cocoa. Manufacturers' quality requirements.* 2nd ed., pp. 1–12. Cocoa, Chocolate, and Confectionery Alliance; London.

—— (1969a). Committee on commodity problems Study Group on cocoa, Working Party on cocoa grading. Summary of the comments of Governments on the Draft Model Ordinance of 1963: FAO of UN CCP. CC/GWP 69/6 (28 February 1969) (mimeograph).

—— (1969b). Committee on commodity problems Study Group on cocoa, Working Party on cocoa grading. Third session, Paris, 27–31 May 1969. Review of developments since the last session of the Working Party and outline of outstanding issues. FAO of UN CCP; CC/GWP 69/5 (17 March 1969); (mimeograph).

—— (1969c). Committee on commodity problems Study Group on cocoa. Working Party on cocoa grading. Third Session, Paris, 27–31 May 1969. International Standards for cocoa beans: an annotated comparison of texts. FAO of UN CCP; CC/GWP 69/7 (21 March 1969); (mimeograph).

—— (1969d). Committee on commodity problems Study Group on cocoa. Working Party on cocoa grading. Report of the third session, Paris 27–31 May 1969. FAO of UN CCP; CC/GWP 69/8 (12 September 1969); (mimeograph).

—— (1972a). Joint FAO/WHO Food Standards Programme Codex Alimentarius Commission Ninth Session, Rome, 1972. *Rep. of 9th Sess. Committee on Cocoa*

Products and Chocolate. Neuchâtel, Switzerland (mimeograph). (ALINORM 72/10 November 1971).

—— (1972*b*). Appendix II. National Standards of Cocoa Quality 1963 mid-crop to date. Appendix III. Tema Port Classification of mould percentage in cocoa shipments—Jan. 1970—Dec. 1971. Appendix IV. Takoradi Port Classification of mould percentages in cocoa shipments—Jan. 1970–Dec. 1971. *Intl Sem. Cocoa Grading Lagos 2nd–6th Oct., 1972* (mimeograph) (see note p. 360).

—— (1973). *Catalogue of the culture collection of the Commonwealth Mycological Institute.* 6th ed. Commonwealth Mycological Institute; Kew.

APPEL, O. and STRUNK, H. F. (1904). Ueber einige in Kamerun auf Theobroma cacao beobachtete pilze. *Zentbl. Bakt. Parasitkde,* **11**, 632–7.

ARCHIBALD, J. F. (1954). Germination of cacao beans. *Ann. Rep. W. Afr. Cacao Res. Inst. April 1953 –March 1954*, p. 23.

ASHBY, S. F. (1925). Mycological Notes. The sweating of cacao. *Trop. Agric., Trin.* **2**, 99–101.

AUCHINLECK, G. G. (1930). Problems concerning storage of cacao on the Gold Coast. *Dept Agric., Gold Coast Year Book 1929.* Bull. **22**, 5–18.

AUSTWICK, P. K. C. (1966). The role of the spores in the allergies and mycoses of man and animals. In: The fungus spore, ed. M. F. Madelin. *Colston Pap.* **18**, 321–38.

AYERST, G. (1965*a*). Determination of the water activity of some hygroscopic food materials by a dew-point method. *J. Sci Fd Agric.* **16**, 71–8.

—— (1965*b*). Water activity, its measurement and significance in biology. *Int. Biodeterior. Bull.* **1**, 13–26.

—— (1969). The effects of moisture and temperature on growth and spore germination in some fungi. *J. stored Prod. Res.* **5**, 127–41.

BAINBRIDGE, J. S. and DAVIES, S. A. (1912). The essential oil of cocoa. *J. chem. Soc. Trans.* Part II, **101**, 2209–21.

BAKER, R. E. D. and DALE, W. T. (1951). Fungi of Trinidad and Tobago. *Mycol. Pap.* **33**, 1–123.

BALLEYGUIER, A. (1949). French West African cocoa. *Rep. Cocoa Conf. Grosvenor House, London, W.1, 30th August–1st Sept. 1949*, pp. 8–9. Cocoa, Chocolate, and Confectionery Alliance; London.

BIRCH, H. F. (1941). Changes in the nitrogenous components of forastero cacao during fermentation. Proteins and protein-decomposition products. *10th ann. Rep. Cacao Res. 1940*, pp. 22–33. Imperial College of Tropical Agriculture, St. Augustine, Trinidad.

BOIDIN, J. and PRÉVOT, J. (1957). Les Aspergillus rencontrés en tannerie. Leurs actions. *Bull. Ass. fr. Chim. Ind. Cuir,* **18**, 47–72; (abstract in *Rev. appl. Mycol.* **36**, 488–9 (1957)).

BOYD, E. N., KEENEY, P. G. and PATTON, S. (1965). The measurement of monocarbonyl classes in cocoa beans and chocolate liquor with special reference to flavor. *J. Fd Res.* **30**, 854–9.

BRIDGLAND, L. A. and FRIEND, R. J. (1957). Experiments and observations on cocoa fermentation in New Guinea. *Rep. Cocoa Conf. Grosvenor House, London, W.1, 10th–12th Sept. 1957*, pp. 177–90. Cocoa, Chocolate, and Confectionery Alliance; London.

BRITON-JONES, H. R. (1934). *The diseases and curing of cacao*. Macmillan and Co. Ltd; London.

BROADBENT, J. A. (1967). The importance of different moulds in causing internal mouldiness of Nigerian cocoa. *Ann. Rep. Nig. stored Prod. Res. Inst., 1967; tech. Rep.* **5**, 53–7. Federal Ministry of Information, Printing Division; Lagos.

—— and OYENIRAN, J. O. (1967). The penetration of cocoa beans by filamentous moulds during fermentation and drying. *Ann. Rep. Nig. stored Prod. Res. Inst., 1967; tech. Rep.* **6**, 59–65. Federal Ministry of Information, Printing Division; Lagos.

—— and —— (1968). A new look at mouldy cocoa. In: Biodeterioration of materials, microbiological and allied aspects, edited by A. H. Walters and J. J. Elphick. Proc. *1st intl Biodetn Symp., Southampton 9th–14th Sept., 1968*, pp. 693–702. Elsevier Publishing Co. Ltd; London.

BUCKLEY, Helen, R. and VAN UDEN, N. (1968). Five new Candida species. *Mycopath. Mycol. appl.* **36**, 257–66.

BUNTING, R. H. (1929a). Defective cacao. *Dept Agric., Gold Coast. Year Book 1928. Bull.* **16**, 37–43.

—— (1929b). Fungi occurring in cacao beans. *Dept Agric., Gold Coast. Year Book 1928, Bull.* **16**, 44–57.

—— (1931). Deterioration of cacao-beans by internal moulds. *Bull. offi. Off. int. Fabr. Choc. Cacao* **1**, 295–304.

—— (1932). Actinomycetes in cacao-beans. *Ann. appl. Biol.* **19**, 515–17.

—— and COULL, R. (1925). In correspondence. Minutes by the Government Mycologist and Agricultural Chemist to the Director of Agriculture, dated 2nd January, 1925. *J. Gold Coast agric. and comml Soc.* **4**, 77–8.

BURLE, L. (1962). *Le cacaoyer*, II. G.–P. Maisonneuve et Larose; Paris.

BUSSE, W., HENNEBERG, W. and ZELLER, T. (1929). Neue Untersuchungen und Versuche über die Fermentation des Kakaos. *Tropenpflanzer* **32**, 1–87.

BUTLER, E. E. (1960). Pathogenicity and taxonomy of Geotrichum candidum. *Phytopathology* **50**, 665–72.

CADBURY, P. S. (1956). *Report on a visit to the Gold Coast, January 1956*, Buckler and Webb Ltd; Birmingham.

CAMPBELL, L. E. (1947). The aims of plant breeding and the preparation and quality of cocoa. Appendix Memorandum I, II and III. *Rep. Cocoa Conf. Grosvenor House, London W.1, 4th–5th Sept. 1947*, pp. 13–17. Cocoa, Chocolate and Confectionery Alliance. London.

CHATT, Eileen M. (1953). *Cocoa. Cultivation, processing, analysis*. Interscience Publishers, Inc.; New York.

CIFERRI, R. (1927a). Studien über Kakao. I. Untersuchunge über den mussigen Gerüch der Kakaobohnen. *Zentbl. Bakt. Parasitkde* **71**, 80–93.

—— (1927b). Notae mycologicae et phytopathologicae (Serie II, N. 1–15). *Revta Patologia vegetale, Pavia* **17**, 209–89.

—— (1930). Contribuzioni alla sistematica della Torulopsidaceae II–XIV. *Arch. Protistenk.* **71**, 404–52.

—— (1931). Studies on cacao. I. Actinomycetes on cacao beans. *J. Dept Agric. P. Rico* **15**, 223–86.

—— (1961). Mycoflora Domingensis integrata. *Quad. Lab. crittogam., Pavia* **19**, 1–539.

COONEY, D. G. and EMERSON, R. (1964). *Thermophilic fungi. An account of their biology, activities, and classification.* W. H. Freeman and Co.; San Francisco.

COTTERELL, G. S. (1928). The red banded cacao thrips, *Heliothrips rubrocinctus,* Giard. *Dept Agric., Gold Coast.* Year Book 1927. *Bull.* **13**, 94–9.

COULL, R. (1925). Preliminary attempts to reproduce the conditions causing white spot on cocoa. *J. Gold Coast agric. comml Soc.* **4**, 143.

COUPRIE, F. (1970). Traitement du cacao après fermentation. Essais de séchage et de stockage en Ouganda. *Café-Cacao-Thé* **14**, 39–46.

COVENEY, R. D. (1969). Sacks for the storage of food grains. *Trop. stored Prod. Inf.* **17**, 3–22.

CRANHAM, J. E. (1960). Insect infestation of stored raw cocoa in Ghana. *Bull. ent. Res.* **51**, 203–22.

CULHAM, A. B. and SCOTT, J. L. (1928). Determination of the accuracy of certain methods of sampling cacao-beans. *Dept Agric., Gold Coast, Year Book 1927. Bull.* **13**, 45–57.

DADE, H. A. (1929). Internal moulding of prepared cacao. *Dept Agric., Gold Coast. Year Book 1928, Bull.* **16**, 74–100.

—— (1930). A note on the sun-drying of cacao. *Dept Agric., Gold Coast. Year Book 1930. Bull.* **23**, 107–8.

—— (1940). A revised list of Gold Coast fungi and plant diseases. *Kew Bull.,* pp. 205–247.

DAVEY, Pauline M. and AMOS, T. G. (1961). Testing of paper and other sack materials for penetration by insects which infest stored products. *J. Sci. Fd Agric.* **12**, 177–87.

—— and ELCOATE, S. (1967). Moisture content/relative humidity equilibria of tropical stored produce (Part 3 Legumes, spices and beverages). *Trop. stored Prod. Inf.* **13**, 15–34.

DE CAMARGO, R., LEME, J. and FILHO, A. Martinelli (1963). General observations on the microflora of fermenting beans (*Theobroma cacao*) in Bahia (Brazil). *Food Tech.* (*J. Inst. Food Tech., Chicago, Ill.*) **17**, 116–18.

DEIGHTON, F. C. (1956). *Diseases of cultivated and other economic plants in Sierra Leone.* Government Printing Department; Sierra Leone.

DELACROIX, G. (1897). Quelques espèces nouvelles. *Bull. Soc. mycol. Fr.* **13**, 114–27.

DESCHREIDER, A. R. and VAN COILLIE, L. (1956). Les oligoélements dans les fèves de cacao. *Intl Choc. Rev.* **11**, 374–84.

DE WITT, K. W. and COPE, F. W. (1951). Notes on the quality factor in Trinidad cocoa. *Rep. Cocoa Conf. Grosvenor House, London, W.1, 11th–13th Sept. 1951,* pp. 64–8. Cocoa, Chocolate, and Confectionery Alliance; London.

DIECKMANN, D. (1962). *Cocoa bean tests 1961/62.* Gordian-Publishing House; Hamburg.

DO CARMO-SOUSA, Lídia (1969). Distribution of yeasts in nature. In: *The yeasts. Vol, 1. Biology of yeasrs,* ed. A. H. Rose and J. S. Harrison, pp. 79–105. Academic Press Inc.; London.

DUNLOP, D. (1969). The therapeutics of migraine. In: Background to migraine, ed. R. Smith. *2nd Migraine Symp. 24th Nov. 1967,* pp. 72–85. William Heinemann Medical Books Ltd.; London.

ENTWISTLE, P. F. (1972). *Pests of cocoa.* Longman Group Ltd; London.

EYRE, J. C. (1932). Cultural studies on the *Aspergilli*, with special reference to lipase production of strains isolated from stored copra and cacao. *Ann. appl. Biol.* **19**, 351–69.

FERDINANDSEN, C. C. F. and WINGE, O. (1910). Fungi from Prof. Warming's expedition to Venezuela and the West Indies. *Bot. Tidsskr.* **30**, 208–22.

FEUELL, A. J. (1966). Contribution to discussion. In: Microbiological deterioration in the tropics. 129–30. *Soc. chem. Ind. Monogr.* **23**, London.

FORSYTH, J. (1962). Major food storage problems. In: *Agriculture and land use in Ghana*, ed. J. B. Wills, pp. 394–401. Oxford University Press; London.

FORSYTH, W. G. C. and QUESNEL, V. C. (1956). Variations in cacao preparation (An interim report). *VIth Meeting Salvador-Bahia, Brazil, Inter-Amer. tech. Cacao Committee* (Colonial microbiol. Res. Inst. Questionnaire on Cacao Preparation) reprint, pp. 1–15 (mimeograph).

—— and —— (1958). Studies on cacao curing 1956–8. A review. *Sépt. Conf. inter-ameri. Cacao. Palmira, Colombia 13–19 de julio 1958*, pp. 479–85.

—— and —— (1963). The mechanism of cacao curing. In: *Adv. Enzymol. and rel. Subj. of Biochem.*, ed. F. F. Nord, **25**, 457–91. Interscience Publishers; London.

FRAGOSO, R. G. and CIFERRI, R. (1927). Hongos parasitos y saprofitos de la Republica Dominicana. *Boln R. Soc. Esp. Hist. nat., 9a Sér.* **27**, 68–81.

FRIES, J. H. (1966). The cocoa bean and the allergic child. *Ann. Allergy* **24**, 484–91.

GABIS, D. A., LANGLOIS, B. E. and RUDNICK, A. W. (1970). Microbiological examination of cocoa powder. *Appl. Microbiol.* **20**, 644–5.

GIBBERD, A. V. (1953). The improvement of quality of Nigerian cocoa with reference to purple beans. *Rep. Cocoa Conf. Grosvenor House, London, W.1, 15th–17th Sept. 1953*, pp. 26–9. Cocoa, Chocolate, and Confectionery Alliance; London.

GOOS, R. D. (1964). A new record of *Cephaliophora irregularis*. *Mycologia* **56**, 133–6.

GOVEIA, A. J. S. and SOUSA, M. E. S. (1968). Aspectos de defesa fitossanitária do cacau amarzenado em S. Tomé. *Garcia de Orto* **16**, 309–66.

GREGORY, P. H. (1961). *The microbiology of the atmosphere*. Leonard Hill (Books) Ltd; London.

GUÉGUEN, F. (1910). Sur une 'fumagine' ou 'noir' des grains de cacaoyer de San-Thomé, produit par un Acrostalagmus. *Bull. Soc. mycol. Fr.* **26**, 287–97.

HAHN, D. and VINCENT, J.-C. (1972). Essais de mesures spectroréflectométriques sur cafés vert et torréfié et sur cacao. *Café-Cacao-Thé* **16**, 149–60.

HALL, C. W. (1960). Equilibrium moisture content of cacao beans. *Acta Agron. Palmira*, **10**, 53–6.

HAMMOND, P. S. (1953). A discussion of some factors affecting the quality of cocoa produced by Gold Coast farmers. *Rep. Cocoa Conf. Grosvenor House, London, W.1, 15th–17th Sept. 1953*, pp. 29–32. Cocoa, Chocolate, and Confectionery Alliance; London.

HANINGTON, Edda (1967). Preliminary report on tyramine headache. *Br. med. J.* **1**, 550–1.

—— (1968). Address to the Annual General Meeting October 1968. *Migraine*

Newsletter Dec. 1968, pp. 4–10. The British Migraine Association; Bournemouth.

—— (1969). The effect of tyramine in inducing migrainous headache. In: 'Background to migraine', ed. R. Smith. *2nd Migraine Symp. 24th Nov. 1967*, pp. 10–18. William Heinemann Medical Books Ltd; London.

—— and HARPER, A. M. (1968). The role of tyramine in the aetiology of migraine, and related studies on the cerebral and extracerebral circulations. *Headache* **8**, 84–97.

——, HORN, M. and WILKINSON, M. (1970). Further observations on the effects of tyramine. In: 'Background to migraine', ed. A. L. Cochrane. *3rd Migraine Symp. 24th–25th April 1969*, pp. 113–19. William Heinemann Medical Books Ltd; London.

HANSEN, A. P. and KEENEY, P. G. (1970). Comparison of carbonyl compounds in moldy and non-moldy cocoa beans. *J. Fd Sci.* **35**, 37–40.

—— and WELTY, R. E. (1971). Microflora of raw cacao beans. *Mycopath. Mycol. appl.* **44**, 309–16.

HARDY, F. (1960). Cacao manual (English ed.) comp. and ed. F. Hardy, Inter-American Institute of Agricultural Sciences; Turrialba, Costa Rica.

HART, J. H. (1911). *Cacao. A manual on the cultivation and curing of cacao.* Duckworth and Co.; London.

HEARN, C. E. D. (1968). Bagassosis: An epidemiological, environmental, and clinical survey. *Br. J. ind. Med.* **25**, 267–82.

—— and HOLFORD-STREVENS, Valerie (1968). Immunological aspects of bagassosis. *Br. J. ind. Med.* **25**, 283–92.

HELFENBERGER, A. (1964). A series of experiments on small scale curing of cacao. *Cacao, Turrialba* **9**, 1–8.

HENRIQUES, J. A. (1917). Ilha de S. Tomé, sob o ponto de vista historico-natural e agricola. *Bolm Soc. broteriana* **27**, 1–216.

HICKES, W. F. (1947). Humidity measurement by a new system. *Refrigng Engng* **54**, 351–4 and 388.

HILL, R. A. and LACEY, J. (1971). Biodeterioration. Identification of *Penicillium* spp. and *Talaromyces* spp. from stored products. *Rep. Rothamsted exp. Stn 1970, Pt 1*, p. 143.

HOLDEN, E. Margaret (1959). Germination inhibitor, *Ann. Rep. W. Afr. Cocoa Res. Inst. 1957–8*, p. 66.

HOWAT, G. R., POWELL, B. D. and WOOD, G. A. R. (1957). Experiments on cocoa drying and fermentation in West Africa. *Trop. Agric., Trin.* **34**, 249–59.

HOWE, R. W. (1956a). The biology of two common storage species of *Oryzaephilus* (Coleoptera, Cucujidae). *Ann. appl. Biol.* **44**, 341–55.

—— (1956b). The effect of temperature and humidity on the rate of development and mortality of *Tribolium castaneum* (Herbst) Coleoptera, Tenebrionidae). *Ann. appl. Biol.* **44**, 356–68.

—— (1957). A laboratory study of the cigarette beetle *Lasioderma serricorne* (F.) (Col., Anobiidae) with a critical review of the literature on its biology. *Bull. ent. Res.* **44**, 9–56.

HOYNACK, S., POLANSKY, T. S. and STONE, R. W. (1941). Microbiological studies of cacao fermentation. *Fd Res.* **6**, 471–9.

HUGHES, S. J. (1952). Fungi from the Gold Coast. I. *Mycol. Pap.* **48**, 1–91.

JOHNSON, W. H. (1912). *Cocoa, its cultivation and preparation.* Imperial Institute Handbooks. John Murray; London.

KAVANAGH, T. E., REINECCIUS, G. A., KEENEY, P. G. and WEISSBERGER, W. (1970) Mold induced changes in cacao lipids. *J. Am. Oil Chem. Soc.* **47**, 344–6.

KENTEN, R. H. and POWELL, B. D. (1960). Production of heat during fermentation of cacao beans. *J. Sci. Fd Agric.* **11**, 396–400.

KISIEDU, E. W. (1966). Fumigation of cocoa storage silos with methyl bromide at Tema in Ghana. *Papers pres. 2nd Sess. tech. Working Party on Cocoa Prod. and Prot., Rome, 19–23 Sept. 1966,* Rome; F.A.O. of U.N.

KLEINERT, J. (1971). Microbiology and food spoilage. The importance of washing your hands. *Int. Choc. Rev.* **26**, 130–2, 134–6 and 138–9.

KNAPP, A. W. (1935*a*). Scientific aspects of cacao fermentation. Part I. A field for research. *Bull. Imp. Inst., Lond.* **33**, 31–49.

—— (1935*b*). Scientific aspects of cacao fermentation. Part II. Succession of organisms and explanation of high temperatures. *Bull. Imp. Inst., Lond.* **33**, 147–61.

—— (1937). *Cacao fermentation. A critical survey of its scientific aspects.* John Bale, Sons and Curnow, Ltd; London.

—— and WADSWORTH, R. V. (1924). The distribution of theobromine during the fermentation of cacao. *J. Soc. chem. Ind. Lond.* **43**, 124–6.

KNOWLES, C. H. (1925). In correspondence. *J. Gold Coast agric. comml Soc.* **4**, 77.

KREGER-VAN RIJ, N. J. W. (1970). Genus 15. *Pichia* Hansen. In: *The yeasts. A taxonomic study,* ed. J. Lodder, pp. 455–554. North-Holland Publishing Co.; Amsterdam.

LACEY, J. (1970). Deterioration of tropical products. *Rep. Rothamsted exp. Stn 1969, Part 1,* pp. 172–3.

—— (1971). *Thermoactinomyces sacchari* sp. nov., a thermophilic actinomycete causing bagassosis. *J. gen. Microbiol.* **66**, 327–38.

—— and PEPYS, J. (1971). Biodeterioration. Bagassosis. *Rep. Rothamsted exp. Stn 1970, Part 1,* pp. 142–3.

LAST, F. T. and PRICE, D. (1969). Yeasts associated with living plants and their environs. In: *The yeasts. Vol. 1. Biology of yeasts,* ed. A. H. Rose and J. S. Harrison, pp. 183–218. Academic Press Inc.; London.

LAYCOCK, T. (1928). An investigation of the causes of mouldiness of cured cacao. *7th ann. Bull. Dept of Agric., Nig.,* pp. 1–12 (as reprinted). Government Printer; Lagos.

—— (1931). Experiments on the fermentation and moulding of cacao. *9th ann. Bull. Dept Agric., Nig.,* pp. 1–22 (as reprinted). Government Printer; Lagos.

LEGATOR, M. S. (1969). Biological assay for aflatoxins. In: *Aflatoxin. Scientific background, control and implications,* ed. L. A. Goldblatt, pp. 107–49. Academic Press, Inc.; London.

LENDNER, A. (1908). Les Mucorinées de la Suisse. In: *Matériaux pour la flore cryptogamique Suisse,* pp. 1–180. K.-J. Wyss; Berne.

—— (1930). Détermination de Mucorinées (Deux Mucors nouveaux). *Bull. Soc. bot. Genève, Sér. 2,* **21**, 256–63.

LOCKARD, R. G. and BURRIDGE, J. C. (1965*a*). The levels of manganese, sodium, aluminium, iron, boron, zinc, and copper in the leaves of cacao (*Theobroma* *cacao* L.) as affected by shade, fertilizer, irrigation, and season. *Ann. Bot. N.S.* **29**, 283–92.

—— and —— (1965*b*). The levels of macro- and micro-nutrients in the beans of cacao (*Theobroma cacao* L.) in relation to shade, fertilizer, irrigation, and season. *Ann. Bot. N.S.* **29**, 377–82.

LODDER, J. and KREGER-VAN RIJ, Nelly J. W. (1952). *The yeasts, a taxonomic study*. North-Holland Publishing Co.; Amsterdam.

LOPEZ, A. and QUESNEL, V. C. (1973). Volatile fatty acid production in cacao fermentation and the effect on chocolate flavour. *J. Sci. Fd Agric.* **24**, 319–26.

LUTZ, L. (1906). Trois champignons nouveaux de l'Afrique Occidentale. *Bull. Soc. bot. Fr.* **53**, 48–52 (as xlviii–lii).

MACKAY, P. J. (1967*a*). Theory of moisture in stored produce. *Trop. stored Prod. Inf.* **13**, 9–14.

—— (1967*b*). The measurement of moisture content. *Trop. stored Prod. Inf.* **14**, 21–30.

MACLEAN, J A. R. (1953). Some chemical aspects of 'black pod' disease in West African amelonado cacao. *Emp. J. exp. Agric.* **21**, 340–9.

MACNULTY, B. J. (1966). The testing of materials against fungi and termites in the tropics. In: Microbiological deterioration in the tropics. 135–60. *Soc. chem. Ind. Monog.* **23**, London.

MAIDMENT, W. T. O. (1928). Correlation between rainfall and cacao yields in the Gold Coast, with special reference to effect of April rains on the following cacao crop. *Dept Agric., Gold Coast. Year Book 1927. Bull.* **13**, 83–4.

MANANDHAR, Keshari L. and APINIS, A. E. (1971). Temperature relations in *Monascus. Trans. Br. mycol. Soc.* **57**, 465–72.

MARAVALHAS, N. (1965). Aflatoxina, agente de intoxicação dos animais. O cacau está isento desta susstància. *Cacau Atual.* **2**, 38–9.

—— (1966*a*). The effect of 'dancing' on the quality of fermented cocoa. *Trop. Agric., Trin.* **43**, 351–3.

—— (1966*b*). Origin of the slaty and 'compact violet' beans in raw cocoa. *Papers pres. 2nd Sess. tech. Working Party on Cocoa Prod. and Prot., Rome, 19–23 Sept. 1966*, pp. 1–6 (mimeograph). Rome; F.A.O. of U.N.

—— (1966*c*). Mycological deterioration of cocoa beans during fermentation and storage. In: Microbiological deterioration in the tropics. 98–104. *Soc. chem. Ind. Monograph* **23**, London.

—— (1966*d*). The 'white spot' in fermented cocoa bean. *Int. Biodeterior. Bull.* **2** 147–8.

—— (1966*e*). Micological deterioration of cocoa beans during fermentation and storage in Bahia. *Int. Choc. Rev.* **21**, 375–8.

—— (1970). Origin of the slaty and compact violet beans on raw cocoa. *Int. Choc. Rev.* **25**, 242–3.

McDONALD, D. M. (1969). The influence of the developing groundnut fruit on soil mycoflora. *Trans. Br. mycol. Soc.* **53**, 393–406.

MINIFIE, B. W. (1970). *Chocolate, Cocoa and Confectionary: Science and Technology*. J. and A. Churchill; London.

MORTON, F. J. and SMITH, G. (1963). The genera *Scopulariopsis* Bainier, *Microascus* Zukal, and *Doratomyces* Corda. *Mycol. Pap.* **86**: 1–96.

MOSSEL, D. A. A. and VAN KUIJK, H. J. L. (1955). A new and simple technique for the direct determination of the equilibrium relative humidity of foods. *Fd Res.* **20**; 415–422.

MOULD, H. A. (1964). Cocoa storage and shipment. *Papers pres. 1st Sess. F.A.O. Techl Working Party on Cocoa Prod. Rome, 7–11 September 1964.* pp. 1–6. F.A.O. of U.N.; Rome.

MURRAY, D. B. (1955). Climatic requirements of cocoa with particular reference to shade. Report of the Cocoa Conference held at Grosvenor House, London, W.1, 13th to 15th September 1955: 17–22. Cocoa, Chocolate, and Confectionery Alliance; London.

—— (1968). Report on a visit to Bolivia in April–May 1968; mimeograph, pp. 1–21.

NOSTI, J. and ALVAREZ, J. (N.D.). Classificacion y caracteristicas de los cacaos de Fernando Poo. *Dirección de Agric. de los Territorios Españoles del Golfo de Guinea, Publ.* **4**, 1–78.

OYENIRAN, J. C. (1973). Internal mouldiness of commercial cocoa in Ibadan, Western State, Nigeria. *Nigerian Stored Products Research Institute Federal Ministry of Trade Annual Report for 1970 (January 1973)*, 19–27. Federal Ministry of Information Printing Division Lagos.

PASSMORE, F. R. (1932). A survey of damage by insects and moulds to West African cacao before storage in Europe. Season 1930–31. *Bull. Imp. Inst.* **30**, 296–305.

PEPYS, J., JENKINS, P. A., FESTENSTEIN, G. N., GREGORY, P. H., LACEY, M. E. and Skinner, F. A. (1963). Farmer's Lung. Thermophilic actinomycetes as a source of 'farmer's lung hay' antigen. *Lancet*, 607–11.

PHAFF, H. J. and AHEARN, D. G. (1970). Genus 7. *Rhodotorula* Harrison. In: *The yeasts. A taxonomic study.* 2nd rev. enl. ed., ed. J. Lodder, pp. 1187–223. North-Holland Publishing Company; Amsterdam.

PIENING, L. J. (1962). A check-list of fungi recorded from Ghana. *Bull. Ghana Minist. Agric.* **2**. Government Printer; Accra.

PONS, W. A. and GOLDBLATT, L. A. (1969). Physicochemical assay of aflatoxins. In: *Aflatoxin. Scientific background, control and implications,* ed. L. A. Goldblatt, pp. 77–105. Academic Press, Inc.; London.

POWELL, B. D. and WOOD, G. A. R. (1959a). Storage, transport and shipment of cocoa. 1. Prevention of moulding in storage. *Wld Crops* **11**, 314–16.

—— and —— (1959b). Storage, transport and shipment of cocoa. 2. Protection during handling and shipment. *Wld Crops* **11**, 367–8.

PREYER, A. (1901). Über kakaofermentation. *Tropenpflanzer* **5**, 157–73.

QUESNEL, V. C. (1957). Curing cocoa in the laboratory. Rep. *Cocoa Conf., Grosvenor House, London, W.1, 10th–12th Sept. 1957*, pp. 150–5. Cocoa, Chocolate, and Confectionery Alliance; London.

—— (1958). An index of completion of the fermentation stage in cacao curing. *Sépt. Conf. interamer. de Cacao. Palmira, Colombia 13–19 de julio 1958*, pp. 512–16.

—— (1969). Aeration and the technology of cacao fermentation. *Mem. segunda Conf. de Pesquisas em Cacau 19 a 26 de Nov. 1967, Bahia, Brasil*, pp. 503–9. São Paulo, Brazil.

—— (1970). Slimy fermentation. *Ann. Rep. Cacao Res. 1970*, pp. 47–8.

358 REFERENCES

Regional Research Centre, Imperial College of Tropical Agriculture, University of the West Indies; St. Augustine, Trinidad.

—— (1972). Slimy fermentations. *Cocoa Growers' Bull.* **18**, 19–24.

—— and JUGMOHUNSINGH, K. (1970). Browning reaction in drying cacao. *J. Sci. Fd Agric.* **21**, 537–41.

RAPER, K. B. and FENNELL, Dorothy I. (1965). *The genus Aspergillus.* The Williams and Wilkins Co.; Baltimore.

——, THOM, C. and FENNELL, Dorothy I. (1968). *A manual of the Penicillia.* Hafner Publishing Co., Inc.; New York.

RENAUD, R. (1953). Les moisissures du cacao marchand. *Bull. Cent. Rech. agron. Bingerville* **7**, 45–64.

—— (1960). La lutte contre les moisissures du cacao marchand dans l'Ouest Africain. *VIII Inter-Amer. Cacao Conf. Trinidad and Tobago 15–25 June 1960,* pp. 71–80 (mimeograph).

RILEY, J. (1961). The moisture content of cocoa beans in relation to the relative humidity of the atmosphere. In: *W. Afr. stored Prod. Res. Unit ann. Rep. 1961,* pp. 42–4. Federal Ministry of Commerce and Industry; Nigeria.

ROELOFSEN, P. A. (1953). Polygalacturonase activity in yeast, Neurospora and tomato extract. *Biochim. biophys. Acta* **10**, 410–13.

—— (1958). Fermentation, drying and storage of cacao beans. *Adv. Fd Res.* **8**, 225–96.

—— and GIESBERGER, G. (1947). Onderzoekingen over cacaobereiding (Investigations on the curing of cacao). *Archief Koffiecult. Indonesië* **16**, 1–159.

ROESCH, E., SCHUBIGER, G. F. and EGLI, R. H. (1961). Biochemical changes in cocoa beans during germination and growth. In: 'The chemistry of cocoa' (Papers presented at a Symposium arranged by the Plant Phenolics Group at Bournville, September, 1960). *Scient. tech. Survs Br. Fd mfg Ind. Res. Ass.* **38**, 3–12.

ROHAN, T. A. (1963). Processing of raw cocoa for the market. *F.A.O. agric. Stud.* **60**.

—— and NEIRINCKX, G. (1963). Colorimetric determination of the cocoa pigments (According to T. A. Rohan and G. Neirinckx) Present International Method. *Analytical methods of the Office International du Cacao et du Chocolat,* p. 11–E/1963. Verlag Max Glättli; Zurich.

ROMBOUTS, J. E. (1952). Observations on the microflora of fermenting cacao beans in Trinidad. *Proc. Soc. appl. Bact.* **15**, 103–111.

—— (1953). Contribution to the knowledge of the yeast flora of fermenting cacao (1. A critical review of the yeast species previously described from cacao.) *Trop. Agric., Trin.* **30**, 34–41.

SALZ, A. G. (1972). Cocoa processing—a practical approach to fermenting and drying. Cocoa and Coconuts in Malaysia. *Proc. Conf. Kuala Lumpur 25–7 Nov. 1971,* ed. R. L. Wastie and D. A. Earp, pp. 181–218. The Incorporated Society of Planters; Kuala Lumpur, Malaysia.

SARTORY, A., SARTORY, R. and MEYER, J. (1930). Étude d'une nouvelle espèce d'Aspergillus: Aspergillus halophilus. *Annls mycol.* **28**, 362–3.

SCOTT, J. L. (1929). Preliminary observations on the moisture content and hygroscopicity of cacao beans. *Dept Agric., Gold Coast. Year Book 1928. Bull.* **16**, 58–73.

—— and HUDSON, W. R. (1928). Effect of sea water on mould in cacao beans. *Dept Agric., Gold Coast, Year Book 1927. Bull.* **13**, 62–6.

SCOTT, W. J. (1956). Water relations of food spoilage microorganisms. *Adv. Fd Res.* **7**, 83–127. Academic Press Inc.; New York.

SEIKI, K. (1973). Chemical changes during cocoa bean fermentation using the tray method in Nigeria. *Int. Choc. Rev.* **28**, 38–42.

SKINNER, C. E., EMMONS, C. W. and TSUCHIYA, H. M. (1945). *Henrici's molds, yeasts, and actinomycetes. A handbook for students of bacteriology.* 2nd ed. John Wiley and Sons, Inc.; New York.

SMITH, H. H. (1913). *The fermentation of cacao*, John Bale, Sons and Danielsson, Ltd.; London.

SMITH, J., KELLOW, A. H. and HANINGTON, Edda (1970). Tyramine metabolism in dietary migraine. In: 'Background to Migraine', ed. A. L. Cochrane. *3rd Migraine Symp. 24th–25th April 1969*, pp. 120–4. William Heinemann Medical Books Ltd.; London.

SNOW, D. (1949). The germination of mould spores at controlled humidities. *Ann. appl. Biol.* **36**, 1–13.

SOLOMON, M. E. (1945). The use of cobalt salts as indicators of humidity and moisture. *Ann. appl. Biol.* **32**, 75–85.

SPENCER, W. P. (1950). Collection and laboratory culture. In: *Biology of Drosophila*, ed. M. Demerec, pp. 535–90. John Wiley and Sons, Inc.; New York.

SPOON, W. (1956). Onderzoek van Surinaamse cacao in het laboratorium. *Berichten afdeling tropische Producten van het koninklijk Inst voor de Tropen* **258**, 1–6.

—— (1958). White spot in Ghana-cacao. *Ber. Afd. trop. Prod. K. Inst. Trop.* **263**, 1–5.

TEODORO, N. G. (1937). An enumeration of Philippine fungi. *Tech. Bull. Dept Agric. Commerce Philipp. Isl.* **4**, 1–585.

THAYSEN, A. C. (1949). In discussion. *Rep. Cocoa Conf. Grosvenor House, London, W.1, 30th Aug.–1st Sept. 1949*, pp. 88–9. Cocoa, Chocolate, and Confectionery Alliance; London.

THEIMER, O. F. (1958). On the storage of raw cocoa beans in silo compartments. *Int. Choc. Rev.* **13**, 162–7.

TOXOPEUS, H. (1970). Mean cured bean weight (open pollinated) of progenies in the 1963 Ogbere Establishment Ability Trial. *Ann. Rep. C.R.I.N. 1968–9*, 103–4.

URQUHART, D. H. (1961). *Cocoa.* Longmans, Green and Co. Ltd.; London.

VAN UDEN, N. and BUCKLEY, H. (1970). Genus 2. *Candida* Berkhout. In: *The yeasts. A taxonomic study.* 2nd rev. enl. ed., ed. J. Lodder, pp. 893–1087. North-Holland Publishing Co.; Amsterdam.

VON LILIENFELD-TOAL, O. A. (1927). Über Kakaohefen. Ein Beitrag zur Kenntnis der Biologie der Kakaofermentation. *Tropenpflanzer* **30**.

VYLE, L. R. (1949). Criollo cocoa. *Rep. Cocoa Conf. Grosvenor House, Lond., W.1, 30th Aug.–1st Sept. 1949*, pp. 83–6. Cocoa, Chocolate, and Confectionery Alliance; London.

WADSWORTH, R. V. (1955). The quality of raw cocoa as it affects the manufacturer. *Trop. Agric., Trin.* **32**, 1–9.

—— and HOWAT, G. R. (1954). Cocoa fermentation. *Nature, Lond.* **174**, 392.

WATERS, H. B. and HUNTER, T. (1929). Measurement of rate of development of cacao pods. *Dept Agric., Gold Coast, Year Book 1928, Bull.* **16**, 121–7.

WEST, J. (1936). Black pod of cacao. Experimental control on native farms. *11th Bull. agric. Dept*, pp. 1–11. Government Printer; Lagos.

—— (1938). Preliminary list of plant diseases in Nigeria. *Kew Bull.*, pp. 1–7.

—— and VOELCKER, O. J. (1942). Plantation cacao in the British Cameroons. *Trop. Agric., Trin.* **19**, 4–11.

WILBAUX, R. (1963). Observations sur la Préparation du cacao criollo à Madagascar et à l'archipel des Comores. *Café–Cacao–Thé* **7**, 119–30.

—— (1965). Les problèmes que pose le stockage du cacao. *Café–Cacao–Thé* **9**, 24–36; (abstract in *Hort. Abstr.* **36**, 417 (1966)).

WILLIAMSON, A. P. (1973). International cocoa agreement. *Cocoa Growers' Bull.* **20**, 5–9.

WOOD, G. A. R. (1964). Quality improvement. *Papers pres. 1st Sess. tech. Working Party on Cocoa Prod. Rome, 7–11 Sept. 1964*, pp. 1–9. Rome; F.A.O. of U.N.

—— (1965). Storage of raw cocoa. *Cocoa Growers' Bull.* **5**, 21–4.

—— (1972). Manufacturers' quality requirements. In: Cocoa and Coconuts in Malaysia. *Proc. Conf. Kuala Lumpur 25–7 Nov. 1971*, ed. R. L. Wastie and D. A. Earp, pp. 233–40. The Incorporated Society of Planters; Kuala Lumpur, Malaysia.

ZYCHA, H., SIEPMANN, R. and LINNEMANN, G. (1969). *Mucorales. Eine beschreibung aller gattungen und arten dieser pilzgruppe*; Verlag von J. Cramer; Lehre, Germany.

Note added in proof

Data discussed on pages 327 and 332 (Anon. 1972*b*) have now been published (seen August 1974) in 'standards of cocoa quality applied in Ghana: review of developments from 1952 to 1972 and national legislation on cocoa quality' pp. 71–9, by T. M. Bannerman-Martin. In: *Report of the Training Seminar on Cocoa Grading Lagos, Nigeria, 2–6 October 1972*. United Nations Development Programme, FAO No. TA 3195; 1973 F.A.O.; Rome,

MAPS

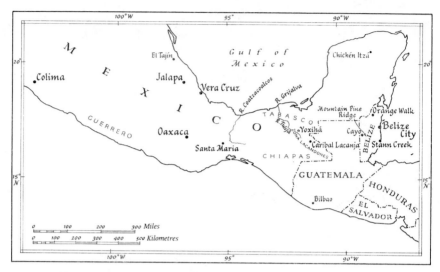

MAP 1. North-western part of Central America.

MAP 2. Costa Rica and adjacent parts of Nicaragua and Panama.

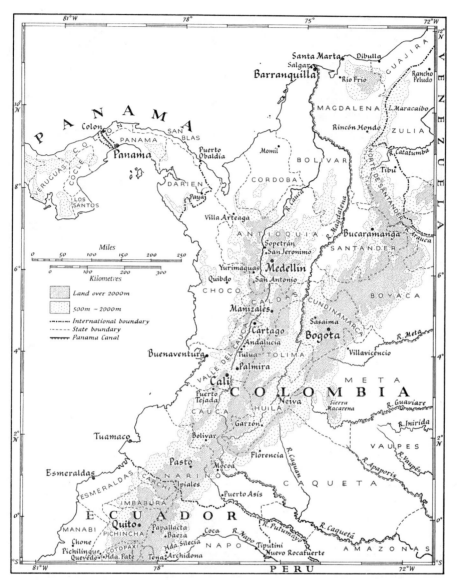

MAP 3.   Parts of Colombia, Ecuador, Panama, Peru, and Venezuela.

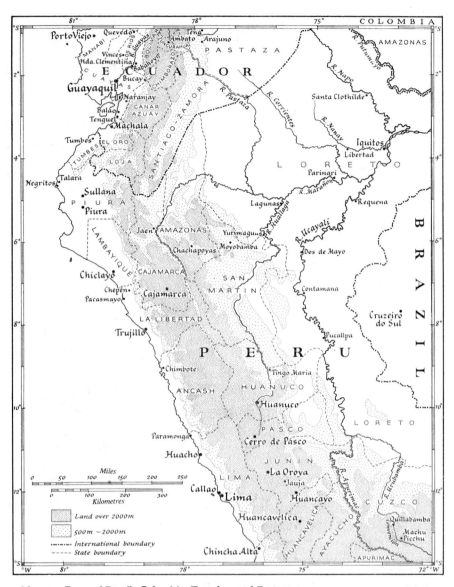

MAP 4. Parts of Brazil, Colombia, Ecuador, and Peru.

[364]

MAP 5. Guyana and Surinam, with adjacent parts of Brazil, French Guiana, and Venezuela.

MAP 6.   Part of Brazil (Bahia, Espírito Santo, and Rio de Janeiro).

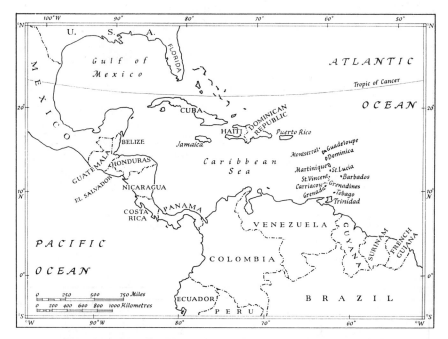

MAP 7.   Central America, the West Indies, and the northern part of South America.

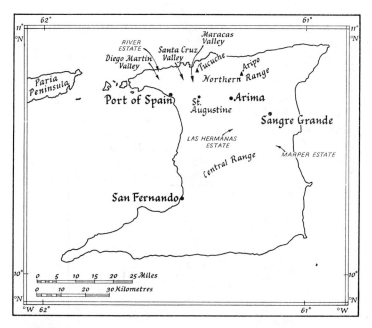

MAP 8.   Trinidad.

[367]

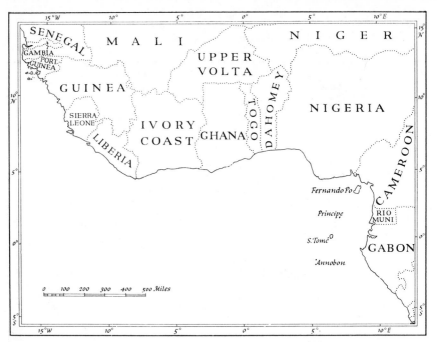

MAP 9. Part of West Africa.

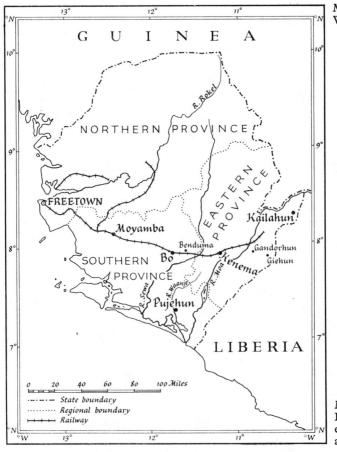

MAP 10. Sierra Leone, with adjacent parts of Guinea and Liberia.

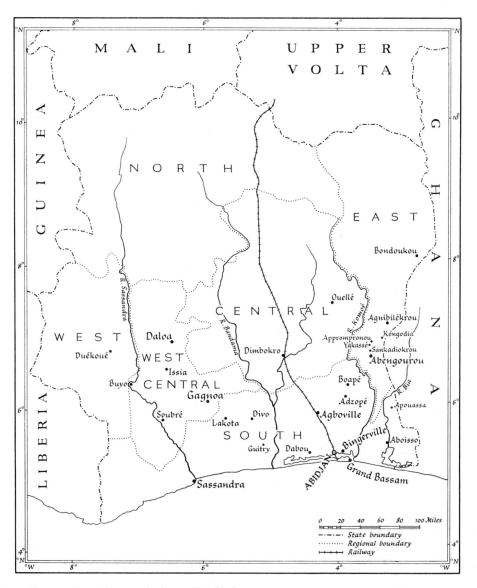

MAP 11. Ivory Coast and adjacent Territories.

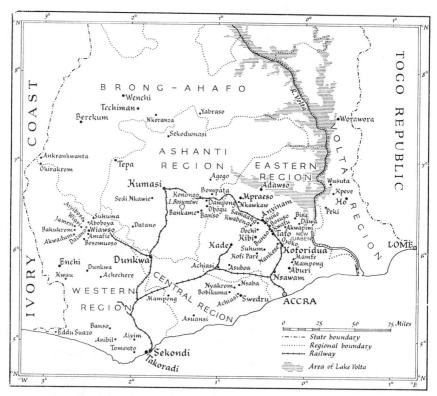

MAP 12. Southern part of Ghana, and adjacent parts of Ivory Coast and Togo Republic.

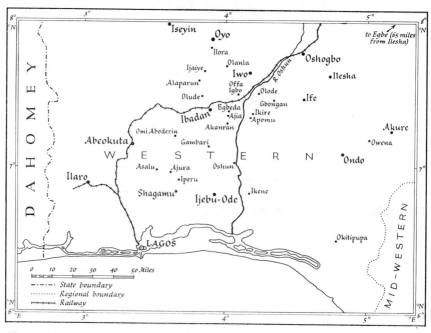

MAP 13. South-western part of Nigeria, and adjacent part of Dahomey.

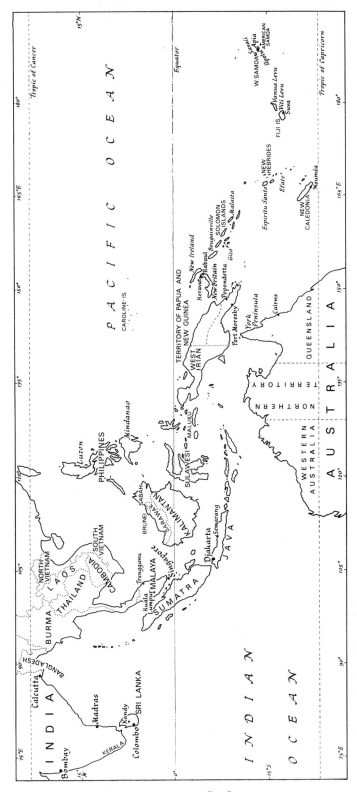

MAP 14. Parts of Asia and Australasia.

AUTHOR INDEX

Numbers in *italic type* indicate pages where names occur in the two lists of references

SUBJECT INDEX

Numbers in **bold type** indicate pages for geographical distributions of plant and animal associations with cocoa

virus—*continued*
 importance, 70–1: geographical distri-
 bution, virus diseases and suspected
 virus diseases, 70
Viscum album, 171
Vittaria guineensis, 220
Volta River, 70, Map 12
Vriesia procera, **227**
Vriesia splendens var. *longibracteatea*, **227**

Wallace's Line, 5
Wallrothiella subiculosa, **205**
warty pod disease, 162
Wasmannia auropunctata, 132
water spot pod rot, 197
watery pod rot (Monilia disease), 27
whitefly (Aleyrodidae), association with
 Verticillium cinnamomeum, 205
white root disease, 147, 151
white spot, 329
white thread disease, 163
Wiasi, 74, Map 12
Wiawso, 74, Map 12
wilt disease, 113–22: control; chemical
 methods, 120–1; cultural methods,
 harvesting, 121, sanitation, 121; resistance testing, 121–2: economic importance, 113–4: factor affecting, climate,
 120: geographical distribution, 113:
 symptoms, 114–5
witches' broom disease, 7, 11–26, 28–9, 113,
 144, 239; control; prevention of spore
 production, 24, 194; protection against
 infection, 24; resistance, 24–6; sanitary methods, 22–3: disease escape,
 22: economic importance, 11, 13:
 geographical distribution, 11: host
 range, 13: symptoms, fruits, 16–17,
 inflorescence tissue, 16, vegetative
 tissue, 14–16
Worawora, 76, Map 11
Woroma, 77

Xanthochrous korthalsii, 199, 205
Xanthomonas spp., association with cushion
 gall disease, 138
Xerotus nigritus, **205**
Xerus erythropus, 55, 58
Xiphinema
 attorodorum, **232**

 ebriense, **232**
 elongatum, **232**
 ifacolum, 229, **232**
 insigne, **232**
 longicaudatum, **232**
 nigeriense, **232**
 setariae, **232**
 spp., 229, 233: association with virus-
 infected cocoa, 229
Xylaria
 anisopleura, **205**
 fastigiata, **205**
 feejeensis, 206
 ianthino-velutina, 206
Xyleborus–Ceratocystis complex, 114, 117
Xyleborus
 confusus, association with *Ceratocystis*
 fimbriata, 177
 corniculatus, 119
 ferrugineus, 119
 fornicatus, association with *Ceratocystis*
 fimbriata, 177
 hirtellus, 119
 perforans, association with *Acrostalagmus*
 vilmorinii forma *thomensis*, 338
 posticus, 119
 theobromae, 119
 spp., 116, 117–20
Xylocladium clautriavii, **206**
Xylosandrus
 compactus, 120
 morstatti, 120
Xylosphaera
 feejeensis, **206**
 fockei, 194, **206**
 ianthino-velutina, **206**
xylostromata, 148

Yakassé, 76, Map 11
yeasts, 159–61; lipolytic activity, 160
Yoxihá, 2, Map 1

Zignoella büttneri, **206**
Zona Lacandonense, 2, Map 1
zone lines, 154, 166
Zulia Province (State), 27, Map 3
Zygodontomys brevicauda brevicauda, 54,
 56, **58**
Zygosporium echinosporum, **206**
Zygosporium oscheoides, **206**

Alphabetical list of species,
subspecies, variety and form epithets

abbreviata, Archilejeunea
abengouroui, Neodiscodes
abietina, Trentepohlia
abortiva, Lopholejeunea
aburiense, Sporidesmium
accedens, Lemmaphyllum
acerinus, Aleurodiscus
aceti, Acetobacter
aceti, Bacterium
acremonium, Cephalosporium
acrita see incognita
aculeatus, Aspergillus
acuminata, Cola
acuta, Lejeunea
acuta, Lockhartia
adansoniae, Polystachya
adonidum, Pseudococcus
adunca, Phthirusa
aegyptiacus, Achrysopophagus
aequinoctialis, Lecanora
aeria see lunata
aerogenes, Aerobacter
aerogenes, Coli
aestuans hoffmanni, Sciurus
affine, Gloeosporium
affinis, Physalospora
affinis, Ratufa
africana, Archilejeunea
africana, Beltrania
africana, Cheilolejeunea
africana, Kloeckera
africana, Leptocolea
africana, Microlejeunea
africana see also lagenifera
africanum, Asplenium
africanum, Tremotylium
africanum, Trichomanes
africanus, Homalotylus
agilis, Azotobacter
alba, Phyllophiale
albescens, Polystachya
albiflora, Herrania
albiflora form titanica, Herrania
albiseda, Nectria
alboatrum, Trichothelium
albo-atrum, Verticillium
albonotata, Graphina

album, Cylindrocarpon
album, Fusarium
album, Viscum
albus, Actinomyces
albus, Corymbomyces
albus, Streptomyces
alexandrinus, Mus
allescherianum, Fusarium
allescherianum, Gloeosporium
alneum, Schizophyllum
alternata, Alternaria
amaranticolor, Chenopodium
amazonica tobagensis, Amazona
ambavillaria, Sticta
ambavillaria, Stictina
ambrizensis, Graphina
americana, Cuscuta
ampullaceum, Exosporium
ampullaceum, Helminthosporium
amstelodami, Aspergillus
anceps, Tillandsia
anerythrus, Funisciurus
anfractuosum, Eriodendron
angelicus, Pseudaphycus
angolensis, Graphis
angustifolium, Theobroma
angustissima, Vaginularia
anisopleura, Xylaria
annuus, Helianthus
anomala variety anomala, Hansenula
anomala, Phlyctaena
anomalus anomalus, Heteroymys
anomalus, Paraputo
anomalus, Saccharomyces
anthophilum, Fusarium
anthophilum see also moniliforme
anthracodes variety gliricidiae, Nummularia
antillarum see elegans
antonii, Helopeltis
apiahica, Bacidia
apiculata, Kloeckera
apiculatus, Saccharomyces
apiformis, Platyngomiriodes
applanatum, Ganoderma
aquaeductum, Fusarium
aquaeductum variety elongatum, Fusarium
aquatica, Pestalotiopsis

cingulata variety minor, Glomerella
cinnabarina, Nectria
cinnabarinum, Stilbum
cinnabarinus, Acrostalagmus
cinnabarinus, Polyporus
cinnabarinus, Polystictus
cinnamomeum, Verticillium
cinnamomi, Phytophthora
circinelloides, Mucor
cirmolinae, Theobroma
citri, Melanographium
citri, Planococcus
citricolor, Mycena
citrina, Asbolisia
citrinum, Penicillium
citrophthora, Phytophthora
cladosporioides, Cladosporium
cladosporioides, Hormodendrum
clathricaudatum, Scutellonema
claudelii variety clemensiae, Parmelia
clautriavii, Xylocladium
clavata, Solenangis
clavatus, Aspergillus
clavifer, Helopeltis
clematidis, Phaeoisaria
clemensiae see claudelii
coccineus, Chroodiscus
coccoes, Pyxine
coccophila, Microcera
coccophila, Sphaerostilbe
coccophila variety platyspora, Microcera
cococarpa, Diplodia
cocophillus, Hemicriconemoides
coenopus, Rhopalopsis
coffeae, Geococcus
coffeae, Pratylenchus
coffeae, Tylenchus
coffeanum, Colletotrichum
coffeicola, Nectria
coleoptrata, Kerrichiella
collatinensis, Graphina
colocasiae, Phytophthora
colorans, Spicaria
columnaris see flavus
commune, Macrosporium
commune, Schizophyllum
communis, Pilotrichella
communis, Ricinus
compacta, Rodriguezia
compactus, Xylosandrus
complanata, Strigula
complectens, Pythium
compressum, Physarum
comstocki, Pseudococcus
concavocerarii, Pseudococcus
concavus, Helicotylenchus
conferta, Maxillaria
confusus, Xyleborus
congestum, Dendryphion

conglutinata, Torula
consortiale, Alternaria
consortiale, Ulocladium
convexa, Pyrenula
copelandii, Pyxine
cordifolia, Cola
cordifolius, Oryctanthus
cornea, Auricularia
cornea, Hirneola
corniculatus, Xyleborus
cornui, Phaeoisaria
corrugata, Trametes
corticola, Diplodina
corymbifera, Absidia
costaricensis, Beloglottis
coucha, Mastomys
couesi, Rhipidomys
cradwickii, Colletotrichum
crassisporum, Sporidesmium
cremea, Calonectria
cremea, Nectria
cretacea, Isaria
cristata, Absidia
cristifera, Parmelia
crucipila, Niesslia
crustaceum, Penicillium
crustaceus, Dactylomyces
crustaceus, Thermoascus
cryptomeriae, Polystictus
cuatrecasana, Herrania
cubensis, Trametes
cucurbitarum, Choanephora
cuneata, Scaphyglottis
cuneatum, Asplenium
currori, Asplenium
curvatum, Cylindrocarpon
curvitatus, Paratylenchus
cyanogenys see morio
cyphella, Marasmius

dactylopii, Achrysopophagus
dactylopii, Leptomastix
dactylosporifera, Trichosphaeria
dahliae, Verticillium
dealbata, Nectria
dealbata, Penzigia
debaryanum, Pythium
decemcellulare, Fusarium
decretus, Necator
decumanus, Mus
deducta, Phaeographina
defua, Dephomys
defua, Rattus
deightoni, Pseudopyrenula
deightonii, Sarcoxylon
delacroixii, Aspergillus
delicata, Auricularia
delicatus, Oryzomys
demidovii, Galago

filiformis, Anthromycopsis
filiformis, Cassytha
filiformis, Panagrolaimus
fimbriata, Ceratocystis
fimbriata, Ceratostomella
fimbriatum, Ophiostoma
fimbriatum, Sphaeronaema
fischeri, Aspergillus
flabelligera, Phycopeltis
flammea, Nectria
flavicans, Sporotrichum
flavida, Calonectria
flavida, Heterochaete
flavipes, Aspergillus
flavissimum, Sporotrichum
flavolanata, Nectria
flavus, Aspergillus
flavus, Potos
flavus mutation rufus, Aspergillus
flavus variety columnaris, Aspergillus
flexuosa, Tillandsia
flexuosum, Geotrichum
florea, Mastigolejeunea
floribunda, Catopsis
floribunda, Floribundaria
florulentus, Oryctanthus
fockei, Xylosphaera
foliicola, Lopadium
foliolosa see tremelloides
foliosa, Polystachya
foratum, Thelotrema
formosus, Macrosolen
fornicatus, Xyleborus
fragilis, Lopholejeunea
fragilis, Pseudococcus
fragrans, Epidendrum
fructiflexa, Polystachya
fructigena, Trachysphaera
fructi-theobromae, Colletotrichum
frustrator, Akodon
fugiens, Aspidothelium
fujikuroi variety subglutinans, Gibberella
fulgens, Temnospora
fulica, Achatina
fuliginea, Catenularia
fuliginosa, Catenularia
fuliginosa, Forcipomyia
fulvellum, Ganoderma
fumigatus, Aspergillus
fumosa, Ocellularia
funerea, Pestalotia
fungicola, Rhizophidium
funicola, Chaetomium
fusca, Scopulariopsis
fuscolurida, Pyrenula
fuscosuccinea, Auricularia
fuscum, Lopadium
fusiformis, Scaphyglottis

gabonensis Englerina
gahani Pseudococcus
galeatus, Hoplolaimus
gambianus, Cricetomys
gambianus, Epomophorus
gambianus, Heliosciurus
gambianus punctatus, Heliosciurus
gelatinosa, Ciliospora
geniculata, Curvularia
geniculatus, Cochliobolus
gibbosa, Trametes
gigantea, Cola
gigantea variety glabrescens, Cola
giganteus, Aspergillus
gigaspora, Calonectria
gigaspora, Fenestella
gileri, Theobroma
gilletii, Calymperes
glabrescens see gigantea
glabriflorum, Canthium
glabrum see vermisporum
gladiatus, Ornithocephalus
glauca, Erythrina
glauca, Leucaena
glaucum, Penicillium
glaucum, Theobroma
glaucus, Aspergillus
gliricidiae see anthracodes
globulosa, Cuscuta
gloeosporioides, Colletotrichum
gloeosporioides variety minus, Colletotrichum
glutinis, Rhodotorula
golungensis, Bacidia
goniosporus, Marasmiellus
goodeyi, Criconemella
goodeyi, Criconemoides
gossweileri, Parmelia
gossypii, Aphis
gracile, Anthurium
gracile, Cylindrocarpon
graciliformis, Mesorhabditis
gracilis, Aspergillus
gracilis, Rhabditis
graminis, Rhodotorula
granatensis chapmani, Sciurus
grandiflora, Stanhopea
grandiflorum, Theobroma
granifera, Lecidea
graphidea, Calenia
gratum, Thuidium
grisea, Chaetodiplodia
griseus, Actinomyces
griseus, Streptomyces
guepini, Pestalotia
guianae, Loncheres
guianense, Helminthosporium
guianensis, Irenopsis
guianensis, Meliola
guineensis, Anthracothecium

minimus, Cephaleuros
minor see cingulata
minor see theae
minus see gloeosporioides
minus see solani
minuscula, Botryosphaeria
minutum, Collema
minutum see also nigrescens
minutus, Chroococcus
mirabile, Lophophytum
mirabile, Sphaeronaema
mirabilis, Lopharia
mirabilis, Usingeria
mocino, Pharomachrus
modesta, Scaphyglottis
moenkemeyeri, Plagiochila
molleri, Tapellaria
molliceps, Selaginella
moloch, Hylobates
moluccana, Albizzia
moluccense, Calymperes
molybditis, Bacidia
momota bahamensis, Momotus
mona, Cercopithecus
moniliforme, Fusarium
moniliforme variety anthophilum, Fusarium
moniliforme variety subglutinans, Fusarium
moniliforme form theobromae, Ophiostoma
moniliformis, Ceratocystis
moniliformis form theobromae, Ceratocystis
monilioides, Epochnium
monocarpa, Arthropteris
monosporum, Asterothyrium
monostachia, Guzmania
monostachyus, Solenostemon
montagnei, Apiospora
morio, Praomys
morio, Psilorhinus
morio, Rattus
morio cyanogenys, Psilorhinus
morstatii, Xylosandrus
mortuifolii, Forcipomyia
moyobambae, Epidendrum
mucedo, Mucor
mucilaginosa, Rhodotorula
mucilaginosa, Torulopsis
mucronata, Belvisia
mülleri, Rattus
multicinctus, Heliocotylenchus
multicolor, Penicillium
multispinosa, Paraputo
murina, Marmosa
murorum variety polychroma, Gliomastix
musarum, Sphaerostilbe
muscae, Circinella
mutabilis, Hibiscus
mycoderma, Candida
mycoidea, Cephaleuros
mycoides see cereus

nana, Forcipomyia
nana, Syncephalis
nannus, Helicotylenchus
nanum, Stilbum
natalensis, Diplodia
natalensis, Mastomys
navicularis, Phaeographis
necator, Ramularia
necatrix, Rosellinia
neelgherrensis, Dendropthoë
neelgherrensis, Loranthus
neglecta, Pestalotiopsis
nemathora, Strigula
nemestrina, Macaca
nemoralis, Theobroma
neoformans, Cryptococcus
neotropica, Torulopsis
nicotianae, Phytophthora
nicotianae variety parasitica, Phytophthora
nidulans, Aspergillus
niger, Aspergillus
niger, Paradoxurus
nigerica, Leptocolea
nigeriense, Isolaimium
nigeriense, Leptogium
nigeriense, Xiphinema
nigeriensis, Bacidia
nigeriensis, Bombyliospora
nigeriensis, Cryptothecia
nigeriensis, Graphis
nigeriensis, Laurera
nigeriensis, Lecidea
nigeriensis, Melanotheca
nigeriensis, Opegrapha
nigeriensis, Physcia
nigra, Lasiodiplodia
nigra, Sterigmatocystis
nigrescens, Collema
nigrescens, Megalonectria
nigrescens variety minutum, Collema
nigricans, Rhizopus
nigritana, Phragmanthera
nigritum, Anthracophyllum
nigritus, Xerotus
nigrum, Piper
nipae, Nipaeccocus
nitens, Stereophyllum
nitida, Cola
nitida, Herrania
nitida form sphenophylla, Herrania
nitidula, Porina
nitidula, Strigula
nivea, Oospora
njalensis, Planococcoides
nkoemvonensis, Nectria
nocturnum, Epidendrum
nodosa, Brassavola
nodosus, Rhizopus
nodulosa, Frullania

phyllocarpum, Leptogium
phyllocarpus variety macrocarpa, Leptogium
phyllogenum, Lopadium
phyllophila, Tapellaria
piceum, Penicillium
picnospora, Periconia
picta, Dichaea
pijperi, Pichia
pinnatum, Epipremnum
pinniflora, Plagiochila
piperis see palmivora
piperoides, Phoradendron
piriforme, Helicostylum
pittieri, Asterothyrium
pityrodes variety saccharina, Nectria
platyspora see coccophila
plicatula, Phaeobotryosphaeria
poensis, Aethiosciurus
poeppigiana, Erythrina
polycarpa see aurea
polycarpon, Polypodium
polychroma see murorum
polygonoides, Begonia
polykomos polykomos, Colobus
polyphragmospora, Cesatiella
polytricha, Auricularia
polytrichum, Mystrosporium
pombe, Schizosaccharomyces
poncinsii, Physcia
porosa, Melanotheca
porteoides, Aechmea
portoricensis, Nectria
posticus, Xyleborus
praelonga, Orthezia
praemorsa, Plagiochila
prevostii, Callosciurus
principensis, Cheilolejeunea
prismatocarpa, Begonia
procera, Carapa
procera, Vriesia
proliferans, Stilbella
proporicus, Hoplolaimus
prosodea, Opegrapha
proteae, Pseudococcus
pruinosa, Pleurothallis
pruinosum, Chrysosporium
pruinosum, Sporotrichum
pseudofarinacea see denticulata
pseudoferreum, Ganoderma
pseudoglaucus, Aspergillus
pseudotinctorum, Parmelia
pseudotrichia, Megalonectria
pseudotrichia, Thyronectria
puiggarii, Lopadium
pulcher, Marasmius
pulcherrima, Herrania
pulcherrima variety pacifica, Herrania
pulcherrima, Perichaena
pulchra, Cyphella

pullulans, Aureobasidium
pullulans, Dematium
pullulans, Pullularia
pullulans, Trichosporon
punctatum, Microsorium
punctatus see gambianus
purpurea, Herrania
purpureus, Monascus
pusillum, Oncidium
pusillus, Mucor
putumayonis see mariae
pycnospora, Periconia
pyrifolia, Phthirusa
pyrrhopus, Funisciurus

quadrangula, Aulaxina
quasi-ingrami, Forcipomyia
quinquenervis, Gongora

racemosum, Syncephalastrum
racemosus, Mucor
radicicola, Heterodera
ramosa, Absidia
ramosa variety dominicana, Mycotorula
ramosum, Epidendrum
rancens, Acetobacter
rattus, Mus
rattus, Rattus
recurvata, Tillandsia
reflexa, Hexisea
regnieri, Absidia
reniformis, Rotylenchulus
repanda, Lenzites
repens, Aspergillus
repens, Sphaerostilbe
restrictus, Aspergillus
retzii, Phormidium
rhapidophylli, Bacidia
rhinopetala, Sterculia
rhipsalisocia, Rangaëris
rhodina, Physalospora
rhodophaeum, Graphium
ridleyi, Polystachya
rigidiuscula, Calonectria
rigidiuscula, Nectria
rigidiuscula forma specialis theobromae,
   Calonectria
rigidiusculum, Fusarium
rigidiusculum forma specialis theobromae,
   Fusarium
rigidula, Trentepohlia
rigidum, Epidendrum
rigidum see also byssinum
ritchiei, Paraputo
rolfsii, Corticium
rolfsii, Sclerotium
roreri, Monilia
roridum, Myrothecium
rosei, Saccharomyces

vanlaeriana see *krusei*
variabilis, Maxillaria
variolosa, Cyphella
variotii, Paecilomyces
veluntina, Erythina
velutinum, Theobroma
velutinus see *capito*
vermisporum variety *glabrum, Chaetothyrium*
verpiforme, Leptogium
verrucosum, Macrosporium
versicolor, Aspergillus
versicolor, Pestalotiopsis
versicolor, Selaginella
verus, Colobus
vesicata, Chamaeangis
vesiculosa, Glaziella
vesiculosum, Leptogium
vestita, Macrophoma
victoriae, Cylindrocarpon
vilmorinii form *thomensis, Acrostalagmus*
vinelandii, Azotobacter
virescens, Cephaleuros
virgata, Ferrisia

viride, Trichoderma
viridis, Thermomonospora
volkensii, Drynaria
vulgaris, Botrytis
vulgaris, Knyaria
vulgaris, Phaseolus
vulgaris, Pseudoabsidia
vulgaris, Thermoactinomyces

wainioi, Trentepohlia
wentii, Aspergillus
werckleri, Eriopsis
westwoodi, Tylococcus
womersleyi, Chaetothyrium

xylinoides, Bacterium
xylinum, Acetobacter
xylinum, Bacterium

zamiae, Melanospora
zenkeri, Ceratolejeunea
zonalis, Polyporus
zonata, Ustulina
zonatum, Fusarium